the man-made world

TEACHER'S MANUAL

the man-made world

TEACHER'S MANUAL

Engineering Concepts Curriculum Project
Polytechnic Institute of Brooklyn

McGRAW-HILL BOOK COMPANY

New York · St. Louis · San Francisco · Düsseldorf · Johannesburg
Kuala Lumpur · London · Mexico · Montreal · New Delhi · Panama
Rio de Janeiro · Singapore · Sydney · Toronto

EDITORS:

MR. JOHN S. BARSS
ANDOVER, MASS.

DR. THOMAS T. LIAO
POLYTECHNIC INSTITUTE
 OF BROOKLYN

DR. E. J. PIEL
POLYTECHNIC INSTITUTE
 OF BROOKLYN

CONTRIBUTORS:

Dr. Thomas Earnshaw
Episcopal Academy, Philadelphia

Professor J. Richard Goldgraben
Polytechnic Institute of Brooklyn

Dr. D. W. Hagelbarger
Bell Telephone Laboratories

Mr. Lester Hollinger
Glen Rock High School, New Jersey

Professor D. A. Huffman
University of California at Santa Cruz

Mr. Benjamin Katz
West Side High School, Newark, New
 Jersey

Mr. Richard King
Staples High School, Connecticut

Mr. A. E. Korn
James Caldwell High School, New Jersey

Mr. James J. McNeary
University of Wisconsin

Mr. Rolla Rissler
Aurora Schools, Colorado

Mr. M. Simpson
West Essex High School, New Jersey

Mr. R. A. Went
West Essex High School, New Jersey

ECCP has been supported primarily by grants from the National Science Foundation.

ISBN 07-019506-4

TABLE OF CONTENTS

INTRODUCTION

THE MAN-MADE WORLD TEACHER'S MANUAL is a part of the teacher's total instructional package. The other parts of the package include a set of approximately 300 transparency masters. These are packaged separately but accompany this manual. A list of other instructional materials follows; sources are footnoted.

Five Unit Tests (Feedback Instruments) and one Final Test*

Tape Cassettes and Workbooks for individualized and small group study**

Equipment Maintenance Details**

Observation Check Lists†

Student Attitude Survey†

The concept of this teacher's manual has been developed over a test-period of six years. The authors' vision of the teacher as the primary decision-maker in the dynamic system that is *The Man-Made World* requires a variety of materials, equipment, student-centered activities, audio-visual materials, and teaching strategies.

This manual has suggestions for a wide range of approaches to teaching *The Man-Made World*. It is not a book to be followed without deviation, but rather a guide for alternative strategies for introducing students to the choices and opportunities they have for effective living in a highly technological society.

* McGraw-Hill Book Company
Distribution Center
Western Region
8171 Redwood Highway
Novato, California 94947

Mid-Continent Region
Manchester Road
Manchester, Missouri 63011

Eastern Region
Princeton Road
Hightstown, New Jersey 08520

** AMF Electrical Products Development Division
1025 N. Royal Street
Alexandria, Virginia 22314

† Engineering Concepts Curriculum Project
Polytechnic Institute of Brooklyn
333 Jay Street
Brooklyn, New York 11201

ORGANIZATION OF THE TEACHER'S MANUAL

The organization of chapters parallels the text. Each chapter is then organized into the following sections:

A Approach including objectives

B Black and white transparency masters

C Cues (answers to discussion questions and problems)

D Demonstrations and laboratory hints for the teacher

E Evaluation (keyed to objectives and performance levels)

F Film references

G General, including Bibliography

Check List

The first left-hand page of each chapter contains a check list which should be studied prior to teaching the chapter. This check list indicates not only how much time most teachers spend on each section of the chapter, but also which transparencies, demonstrations, films, discussion questions, problems, and quiz questions apply to each section.

Approach

The approach to each section is described in some detail. This is an important section, since the ECCP approach is often quite different from that of conventional science, mathematics, or social-science teaching. It is this approach that gives *The Man-Made World* its distinct flavor as an interdisciplinary course, which is particularly effective with nonscience students. One vital facet of the approach throughout the course is the emphasis on student laboratory, group discussion rather than lecture, and the presentation of problems as motivation prior to the development of concepts. The cognitive objectives for the chapter are listed at the beginning of this section.

B Black and White Transparency Masters

Much of the development of the course content relies on discussions that involve diagrams of some sort. Rather than having you laboriously drawing these diagrams on the chalkboard, the teacher's manual package furnishes black and white masters from which transparencies can be made on copying machines in your school. Some of these diagrams are quite useful as student worksheets (e.g., routing police cars). This constitutes a saving of some $300 compared to other courses using the same number of transparencies. The manual has small reproductions of these transparencies which are reproduced full size in the Transparency Packet.

C Cues

This section has cues to the use of discussion questions and problems. Suggestions as to the timing and the difficulty of these questions and problems are made in the check list. Emphasis is on the approach to the answer rather than on having each student give the same answer to a given question.

D Demonstrations and Laboratory

This section explains the use of existing laboratory experiments and demonstrations, and suggests additional activities with the normal equipment of the course as well as with supplementary equipment usually found in high school laboratories.

Typical but not all-inclusive answers to the marked laboratory questions are given; these are guides and are keyed with asterisks. There are additional answers students may give which are also appropriate and which must be considered in the light of your own experience during the laboratory period.

E Evaluation

The items in these sections are samples that may be copied, modified, or discarded as you wish. They are neither mandatory nor all-inclusive.

F Film References

While the ECCP has not made films specifically for the course, the staff has reviewed many commercially available films and has written film notes for those which are most relevant, in approach and content, to the objectives of the course.

Sources for Films

Many of the films recommended for use with ECCP classes are available at local film libraries. However, if they are not available locally then contact the following sources. The numbers here correspond to "Sources" in the F sections.

1. Pennsylvania State University
   Audio-Visual Services
   University Park, Pennsylvania 16802
2. Modern Talking Picture Service (Headquarters)
   1212 Avenue of the Americas
   New York, New York 10036. (Look in your local telephone book for addresses of branch offices.)
3. International Film Bureau, Inc.
   322 N. Michigan Ave.
   Chicago, Illinois 60604
4. Contemporary Films/McGraw-Hill
   330 West 42nd Street
   New York, New York 10036
5. Indiana University
   Audio-Visual Center
   Bloomington, Indiana 47401
6. Bell Telephone Laboratories
   Film Librarian
   Murray Hill, New Jersey
7. Modern Learning Aids
   Division of Modern Talking Picture Service
   1212 Avenue of the Americas
   New York, New York 10036

8. Film libraries at Yeshiva, Syracuse, and Indiana Universities have it for rental ($5.40 from Indiana) as does Association Film, Inc. Write to 600 Madison Avenue, New York, New York 10022, for address of Association center nearest you. If unable to locate film, write Indiana University (at address given in number 5) for a closer source.

9. Division Engineer
U.S. Army Engineer Division, Ohio River
Federal Building
P.O. Box 1159
Cincinnati, Ohio 45202

10. U.S. Army Engineer Waterways Experiment Station
P.O. Box 631
Vicksburg, Mississippi 39180

11. If unable to locate, write:
Educational Testing Service
20 Nassau Street
Princeton, New Jersey 08540. Ask for a list of film libraries which have "Horizons of Science" series. Rental fees vary.

12. Tektronix, Inc.
P.O. Box 500
Beaverton, Oregon 97005

13. Available for purchase only. No. 80-3858/1 in Super 8mm cartridge is $21.50; No. 80-3858/2 in regular 8mm cartridge is $18.50. Order from:
Ealing Film Loops
2225 Massachusetts Avenue
Cambridge, Massachusetts 02140

14. Address requests for loan to Commandant of your local Naval District, Attention of Film Librarian. (No charge.) Plan this one well in advance to allow for delay in processing your request.

15. If unable to locate a closer source, you might write to producers:
National Film Board of Canada
680 Fifth Avenue
New York, New York 10019. Unfortunately, Part I does not seem to be available without Part II.

16. Local Bell Telephone business office. (No charge.)

17. Film Library
General Motors Corporation
Public Relations Staff
3044 W. Grand Blvd.
Detroit, Michigan 48101 (No charge.)

18. Local film libraries or directly from:
Coronet Instructional Films
65 E. South Water Street
Chicago, Illinois 60601

19. Available for purchase only. No. 80-218/1 in Super 8mm cartridge is $15.50; No. 80-218/2 in regular 8mm cartridge is $12.50. Order from:
Ealing Film Loops
2225 Massachusetts Avenue
Cambridge, Massachusetts 02140

20. National Medical Audio-Visual Center (Annex)
   Station K
   Atlanta, Georgia   30324. (Films from this source are free.)

G   General, including Bibliography

Much of the revision of *The Man-Made World* course during its six-year trial period included the elimination of some material as well as the expansion of other material. Some of the material was eliminated because it was considered too difficult for most students. Many teachers felt that this material was excellent background enrichment material for teachers and it is therefore included in this section.

While outside readings are vital to the complete presentation of the approach and content of the course, the inclusion of detailed bibliographies in the text is found by many teachers to be unnecessary. The detailed bibliographies are therefore listed in this section.

Time Schedule

It is the firm conviction of the authors that no two teachers should use the same time schedule to teach *The Man-Made World*. Local societal-technological situations should be used to emphasize concepts whenever they occur. On the other hand, teachers have requested at least a suggested time schedule for the entire course as well as for the sections of each chapter. The times which most teaching situations have required for the course range as follows:

Chapter	Class Periods	Laboratory Periods	Total
1	8 — 10	3 — 4	11 — 14
2	10 — 12	3 — 4	13 — 16
3	10 — 12	3 — 4	13 — 16
4	12 — 14	5 — 6	17 — 20
5	10 — 12	4 — 6	14 — 18
6	10 — 12	5 — 7	15 — 19
7	11 — 12	4 — 6	15 — 18
8	8 — 10	1 — 2	9 — 12
9	7 — 8	1 — 2	8 — 10
10	5 — 6	1 — 2	6 — 8
11	5 — 6	During Class	5 — 6
12	6 — 8	3 — 4	9 — 12
13	6 — 8	3 — 4	9 — 12
14	8 — 10	3 — 4	11 — 14
15	4 — 5	1 — 1	5 — 6
Total	120 — 145	40 — 56	165 — 206

Laboratory Notebook

A Laboratory Notebook is not supplied, but any wire bound notebook will do. Much of the value of *The Man-Made World* course is in the laboratory. In the words of an ancient Chinese proverb: "I hear and I forget, I see and I remember, I do and I understand"; most of the doing is in the laboratory, some is in the involvement in discussions, and some is in the doing of problems at the end of each chapter.

One value of a laboratory notebook is in its use as a reference book some time in the future. Another value is that of attempting to answer the questions in each laboratory exercise. These questions focus on the more important phases of the laboratory experience. Many students go beyond these preliminary questions. They should be encouraged to describe their excursions beyond the suggested activities and report them fully in the notebook. Many of the present laboratory experiences are the result of student excursions of prior years.

Depending on time, class interest, and amount of equipment, you might want to have groups of students do some of the laboratory exercises as class demonstrations. In such cases it is helpful to discuss the answers to the laboratory questions during the demonstration. This will help the students who sometimes have trouble in arriving at conclusions based on their observations during laboratory.

FEEDBACK AND THE EDUCATIONAL PROCESSES

One of the concepts with which *The Man-Made World* deals is that of feedback. As you know, various demonstrations and experiments show that delayed or improperly filtered feedback can result in an unstable system.

The educational feedback instruments used in working with students can also result in instability. We have tried to develop systems that will have a minimum of delay and a minimum of noise in the filtering process.

Feedback Instruments

There are cognitive objectives stated at the beginning of each chapter of this manual. Test items for measuring student achievement of the chapter objectives make up the Evaluation sections (E). Other instruments, not a part of this manual, but available to interested teachers from the sources listed at the beginning of this introduction are:

Unit and Final Feedback Instruments (tests): These are paper and pencil instruments which include both multiple choice and essay items. They are divided as follows:

Instrument	Chapters
1	1 — 3
2	4 — 6
3	7 — 9
4	10 — 11
5	12 — 15
Final	1 — 15

Check Lists: These have been developed for teachers to use as they observe students during laboratory and discussion sessions. The check lists are organized around the behavioral objectives and are divided into the same sections as the feedback instruments.

Performance Levels of Understanding

Achievement of cognitive objectives takes place at different levels. There are three major levels into which most student performance falls. We have indicated on each of the feedback instruments the levels at which a particular item was designed to measure. The levels are as follows:

Level 1. This level ranges from *imitating, duplicating* and *following immediate instructions* to *recalling* the essential features of the activity when encountered later.

Level 2. Level 1 plus *discriminating, reformulating, interpreting,* and *predicting.* Here the student can discriminate among a mass of data to form a model from which he can make justifiable predictions. This represents a rather high level of performance.

Level 3. Levels 1 and 2 plus *creating, formulating new hypotheses, new questions,* and *problems.* At this level a student demonstrates that he can make discoveries that are new to him and can restructure and reorganize his knowledge on the basis of these discoveries and insights. Very few students are expected to attain this level consistently.

MEASURING OBJECTIVES IN THE AFFECTIVE DOMAIN

The Man-Made World course is designed to develop technological literacy among all students in this age of technology. Put differently, future citizens, in order to control the growth and use of technology, need to develop some understanding of the characteristics, capabilities, and limitations of modern technology. Technological literacy involves the development of attitudes toward the use of technology for individuals and society, as well as the learning of cognitive ideas (concepts, techniques, and skills). There are approximately 150 cognitive behavioral objectives stated in the Approach sections (A). The following statements, however, describe the major course objectives of *The Man-Made World* in the *affective* domain. After taking this course, a technologically literate student should:

1. Recognize that technology will create entirely new possibilities for people and society. As a result, the world will be a different place to live in the future, and that only knowledge of both technology and society can insure that it will be a better place in which to live.

2. Recognize that we live in an age of rapid technological change and our ability to adapt to and control modern technology depends on our understanding of its characteristics, capabilities, and limitations.

3. Develop the awareness that society, its culture and values, are constantly being influenced by advances in science and technology, and that culture and the values of society should affect the direction of changes in science and technology.

4. Understand that modern technology is related to both "pure" sciences and social sciences, and that solution of societal-technological problems requires a multi-disciplinary approach.

5. Recognize that when using the products of technology, it is important to match machines to people and technological systems to society.

6. Weigh the benefits and possible side effects of technological "improvements" on the environment.

7. Consider the need for governmental support of research related to the matching of technology to individuals, society, and the environment.

8. Consider the idea that survival of the human race requires that we look upon the earth as a closed system (i.e., space ship) in which resources must eventually be recycled.

9. Attempt systematic (rational) approaches to decision-making and avoid emotional reactions to complex problems.

10. Recognize the need to look for multiple answers to complex problems, particularly in the area of science-technology-society interaction.

11. Realize that decision-making in a complex world usually involves trade-offs among alternative courses of action.

12. Investigate the possibility of utilizing the tools and techniques of technology for analyzing and solving problems outside the area of technology.

13. Recognize that machines, including computers, have limitations as well as capabilities.

14. Recognize that the development of criteria and the stating of constraints in a decision problem are usually subjective activities.

15. Recognize that when analyzing complex systems it might be just as illogical to attempt to use too much information as it is to use too little.

16. Realize that many complex machines, such as digital computers, are made up of systems composed of simple, understandable parts.

The objectives stated above can be divided in three major categories as follows:

(a) Interaction of science, technology, and society (1 — 4).

(b) Matching technology to people, society, and the environment (5 — 8).

(c) Use of technological concepts (i.e., systems analysis) and tools (i.e., digital computer) for analyzing and making decisions about complex problems (9 — 16).

An attitude survey for measuring the above objectives has been developed. This survey consists of thirty statements which the student can rate on a scale of five, from agree strongly to disagree strongly. This survey is available from project headquarters.

the man-made world

TEACHER'S MANUAL

CHECK LIST FOR CHAPTER 1

TECHNOLOGY AND MAN

APPROX. TIME:
Text: 11 days
Lab: 4 days

A. APPROACH	CLASS PERIODS	B. BLACK & WHITE TRANSPARENCIES	C. CUES (k = key problem) Discussion Questions	Problems Easy	Problems Medium	Problems Hard	D. DEMONSTRATIONS, LABS & PROJECTS	E. EVALUATION	F. FILMS	G. GENERAL
1. The Man-Made World	2	0115, 0116 (See Section G)	1,2,3,4,5				I	1a	0101 0102 0103	3, 8, 9 The Game of Future (Experts' Opinion) T-0115 T-0116
2. Matching Technology to the Human User	2	0101 0102 0103	6			3	II, III	1b, 5a	0104	
3. A Quantitative Look at the Problem	3	0104 0105 0106 0107 0110 0111	7, 9	4	1k	2k	IV	1d, e, f, g, 2, 3, 4, 5b, c, d, e, f, h, 6, 8		
4. Matching Technology to Society	1	0112 0113 0114							0105 0106	
5. An MHT Center	1	0108 0109						1h, i, j, k, l, 5g, i, j		
6. Problems with the MHT Center			8							
7. Problems Which Appear in Most Social Systems	2							1c, 7		
8. Final Comment										

Technology and Man

1

A | APPROACH

I. Organization of the Chapter

After defining the term "man-made world" and explaining the basic objectives of the course, this chapter moves on to an example of a seemingly simple technological device, a traffic light, and discusses how it should be operated to serve people best. In the process, it gives a preview of the chapters on decision making, optimization, and modeling, though without saying so explicitly. The rest of the chapter is taken up with a fairly detailed look at a technological system, a multiphasic health testing center, in which the results of recent developments are being applied specifically for the benefit of a significant fraction of society that has hitherto been neglected.

II. Objectives for Students

Upon completion of the study of this chapter a student should be able to:

1. Recognize and identify the following terms: *acceleration, amplifier, life expectancy, quantitative, reaction time,* and *technology.*

2. Demonstrate the use of graphs to determine stopping distance and stopping time of a car from a given speed, using knowledge of reaction time, minimum braking distance, and time.

3. Demonstrate the method of deriving data from a graphical display of a family of linear curves.

4. Calculate horsepower, given the formula for horsepower, force applied, distance force acts, and elapsed time (conversion factor—550 ft-lb/sec-H.P. —being provided). Or given any three of the four variables, calculate the fourth.

5. Describe and explain a rational way to set the timing of traffic light signals.

6. Apply critical judgment to the evaluation of automobile safety devices.

7. Recall the essential features of the multiphasic health testing center.

III. Suggestions for Teaching

It is very important at this time to stress the philosophy that underlies the approach to this course. This course is designed for the student who is "turned off" by mathematics and science. It is the opinion of the authors that students will be motivated to study the concepts if they understand the crucial issues which face them in a technological society.

The issues with which we are concerned center on the matching of technology to man and his society. New technology must be developed and then used to allow the continued transition into the age of technology without serious unfavorable effects on man, his social organization, and his environment.

No doubt the following remark will be repeated later, but it probably needs to be said several times. Students who study *The Man-Made World* are expected to develop certain attitudes and certain ways of viewing the world; facts, rules, and principles of technology have no special importance to us here except insofar as they help to produce the kinds of effects listed above. Therefore, you should be sure that you really do have freedom to tailor the course to suit your own circumstances and preferences. You can skip this, replace that, make insertions of fresh material to whatever extent is necessary.

In almost every case the material of the course can be made most effective if problems, situations, observations, and discussions are presented in class prior to the assignment of the same material in the text. For example, Questions 1, 2, and 3 at the end of the chapter might be discussed on the first day of class even before the students get a textbook. Transparency T-0110, "Joel Stuart is about . . . ," should be shown before any discussion of the yellow light takes place. Experience during the past five years indicates that when this pattern is followed, the students are more inclined to read the book as a means of amplifying and clarifying points made in class, rather than as preparation for the next day's class discussion.

More laboratory exercises than anyone might want to assign are listed at the end of this chapter (and the same is true for most of the other chapters). The reason is to give you a chance to select those exercises which are most appropriate for your particular class. Sometimes it is convenient to have extra ones to suggest to selected students as special projects.

In the first section of the chapter the students look at both a technology-society problem, traffic flow in an urban area, and a man-machine problem, the yellow light, stopping distance, and reaction time. In this way we attempt to tie the student personally to the larger societal problem.

Section 1. The Man-Made World. There are two or three particular observations to be made. We may wonder what happens to non-burnable rubbish. Of-

ten it goes into rivers. Where the local government is more enlightened, it is deposited in a dumping ground and burned, which adds to air pollution. Influenced by ecologists, some city governments use landfill techniques without burning. It is not easy to do this without polluting the ground water.

Students may not understand why the local electric company continues to use outdated generating equipment. Why not get something modern? The point is that it takes years to build a new power house, so steam generators and dynamos that have long been ready for retirement have had to be continued in use to carry the skyrocketing load. Frequently there is an outcry from people when nuclear power plants are proposed. The old power plants are not only polluters; they cost more to run than the latest models and the price of electric energy will start to increase sooner than would otherwise be the case.

The word "technology" makes its appearance without being explained. The Random House Dictionary calls it "the sum of the ways in which a social group provide themselves with the material objects of their civilization." One can quibble with the word "material," because many services should be included. The essence is that the methods developed by scientists for learning about the world, and the knowledge thus gained, are *used* to produce goods and services and not just left in textbooks.

Since this is your students' first look at this course, it will take at least a full period and probably longer to get all the juice out of Section 1. Part of the assignment for the next day should be preparation for the first lab: The Game of Future. This is good to get at as soon as possible. It gets debate started, and in this course the more debate the better, so long as it remains rational. Moreover, there are few "right answers," the game is open-ended; therefore, the application of reasoning and thought will immediately be found by your students to have more value than just being able to manipulate equipment or numbers or to regurgitate memorized facts.

Section 2. Matching Technology to the Human User. A good way to introduce this material is to discuss Fig. 1-5 (T-0102) before making any assignment. Students will recognize this real problem. We do it in precisely the manner to be described in detail in the next chapter. A model is established (T-0101) the criterion is described (allow the maximum number of cars in a given time with a minimum number of accidents to pass, by means of a light cycle acceptable to drivers), constraints are listed, and the conclusion is drawn that a compromise must be found between alternative solutions.

Section 3. A Quantitative Look at the Problem. This section illustrates both the sharpening up of both a model and a criterion, with more exact statements of the constraints. There is an example of optimization by means of what is, in effect, an algorithm (giving stopping times and distances). The claim that eight men, pumping with their feet, could defeat a racing shell with eight oarsmen is an exaggeration in order to make a point. Of course, the racing crew do pump with their legs, using sliding seats, and also using the muscles of arms and back.

Important by-products can be derived from this section. So many students now have access to cars, often without benefit of a driver education course, that you will want to emphasize the aspects of this section that deal with safety. Many "rules" for drivers are stated without giving a reason, but the clear-cut experimental data found in Fig. 1-13 (T-0106) can be used to show, for instance, why the good driver never tailgates, why leaving a gap of one car length for every 10 mph of speed is not a satisfactory safety measure at turnpike speeds, why "speed kills" and why a rather small increase in speed can make a crash a lot worse, and why you have to think about the other fellow's speed as well as your own.

In connection with the inflatable bag to protect motorists from injury during collisions, it is interesting that the General Motors Corporation released a progress report in May, 1970, claiming that the device with which they are experimenting requires only 0.060 sec to inflate. Compare with the textbook's statement that the passenger may be expected to hit the windshield in only 0.040 sec (we are not told the car speed). Have the students measure the distance from the passenger's forehead

to the windshield in a variety of cars. Using $v = t/d$, calculate the speed necessary to travel the distance in 0.040 sec and 0.060 sec.

By all means use the ruler-dropping experiment. Let the catcher sit with his forearm resting on a desk, so that he won't be able to follow the target down with his hand. This experiment may be followed up by Lab IIA and/or Demonstration IIB, as well as Lab III. Lab IV is really a project, either for small teams or for the whole class.

Section 4. Matching Technology to Society. To a people accustomed to boasting "we're the biggest, we're the best, we're the tops," some of the material in this section is sobering. One specific point you might want to discuss is the amazing dip in the curve of Fig. 1-15a (T-0108) which was caused by the disastrous influenza epidemic of 1918. In that year, so many people of all ages died that the averaging process that is used in computing life expectancy resulted in a low number that was really quite meaningless.

Section 5. An MHT Center. The optimum way to handle this section is again to mention the problems raised in the text prior to the assignment of the text material. Study the patient flow schedule (Fig. 1-16) with the class after they have individually listed the problems which they think might occur at each station. Discuss these again in terms of the need to match machines (audiometer for example) to the patient and to the system in which they are used. For example, at one MHT center there seemed to be erratic functioning of the audiometer for no apparent reason. An investigation of the entire system revealed that the audiometer room was adjacent to the men's room. The sudden flow of water next door drowned out the test sounds on the audiometer.

Section 6. Problems with the MHT Center. The problems of what data to measure, how to win acceptance by the public, and "how the MHT center affects the total health system" should be the basis for full class discussion prior to the assignment of these pages. After the class has discussed these questions, they should be encouraged to read this section and the one which follows.

Section 7. Problems Which Appear in Most Social Systems. The emphasis given here to the difficulties pointed out in the previous section is quite important. Many people tend to complain that "the scientists [meaning technologists] have got us into a terrible mess. The only way out is to pay no further attention to them." A little thought will make it clear to your pupils that the blame for the mess cannot be assigned to any one group of people; nearly all the public were happy enough to benefit, as it then seemed they did, from all the gifts showered on them by a technological fairy god-mother. It is doubtful that we can disentangle ourselves without help from those who really have some understanding of the causes and interrelationships. Fortunately, there are some, and here is the evidence.

Section 8. Final Comment. This section should be discussed briefly as a conclusion to the chapter and as an opportunity to preview the remainder of the course. Materials brought to class for Question 4 (text page 32) might be discussed as part of this preview.

B | BLACK AND WHITE TRANSPARENCIES

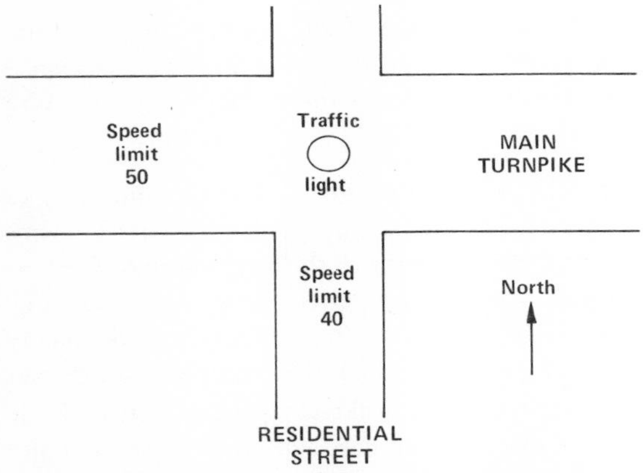

T-0101 RESIDENTIAL STREET AND MAIN TURNPIKE

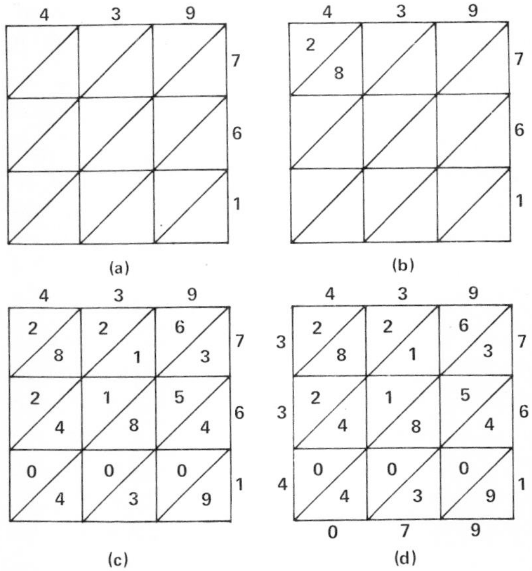

T-0103 ARABIC MULTIPLICATION

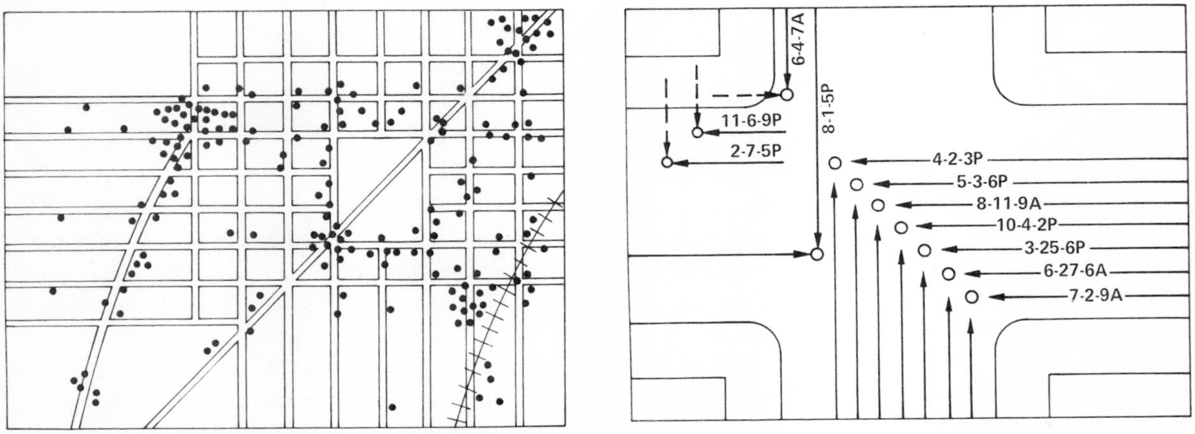

T-0102 ACCIDENT MAPS

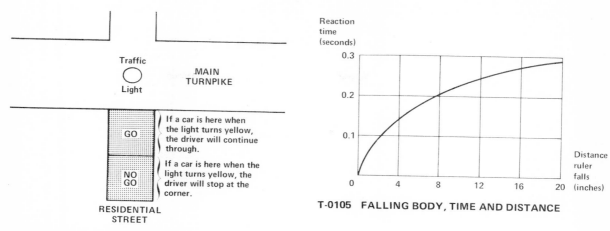

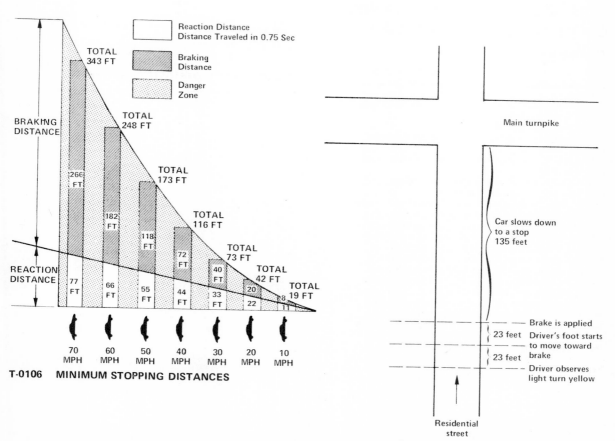

T-0104   GO AND NO-GO ZONES

T-0105   FALLING BODY, TIME AND DISTANCE

T-0106   MINIMUM STOPPING DISTANCES

T-0107   CAR-STOPPING DISTANCE SEGMENTS

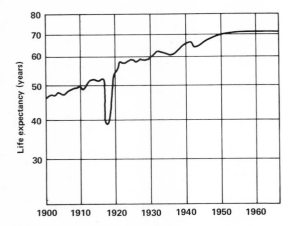

T-0108 LIFE EXPECTANCY AT BIRTH, UNITED STATES FEMALES

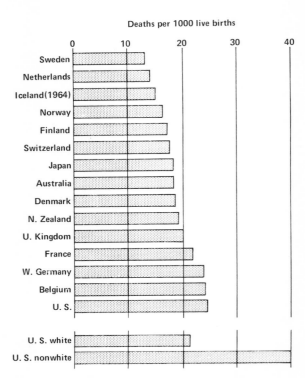

T-0109 INFANT MORTALITY RATES IN 1965

Joel Stuart is about to be killed obeying a Vermont traffic law in Kansas.

The signal light was yellow. So he stepped harder on the gas to try and drive through the intersection before the light turned red.

He never expected the truck to start crossing the intersection. Not until it was too late.

Because in Vermont, where he comes from (and in 31 other states), a driver can drive through an intersection before the yellow light turns red.

But in Kansas (as well as in 11 other states) a yellow signal light means stop.

And Joel Stuart is more than a thousand miles from being right. In fact, he's going to be dead wrong.

Five years ago about 94 million people drove from one state to another. This year that number will probably be a lot higher.

But nobody knows how many drivers are confused by basic rules of road and right-of-way that change from state to state.

We do have one statistic however: Last year 12 per cent (6,000) of all highway fatalities involved out-of-state drivers.

And experts claim that if there were uniform nationwide traffic laws, instead of so many laws that change from state to state, 2,000 lives a year would be saved.

That senseless loss frightens us. That's why we're asking you to write to the Director of the National Highway Safety Bureau in Washington, and to the governor of your state—to let them know you also want uniform nationwide traffic laws, as recommended in the National Highway Safety Standards.

Be frightened with us. Please.
It could save your life.

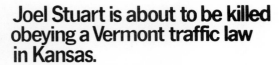

The Continental Insurance Companies, the dial-a-claim companies.
Continental Insurance · Firemen's of Newark · Fidelity & Casualty
Commercial Insurance · Seaboard · & M · Buckeye Union · American Title
National Ben Franklin · Cox · Boston Old Colony · Pacific Insurance
HOME OFFICES: 80 MAIDEN LANE, N.Y., N.Y. 10038.
80 PARK PLACE, NEWARK, N.J. 07101.

Reproduced with permission of
Continental Insurance Company

T-0110

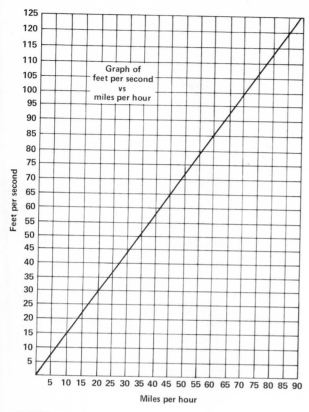

Graph of
feet per second
vs
miles per hour

Feet per second

Miles per hour

T-0111

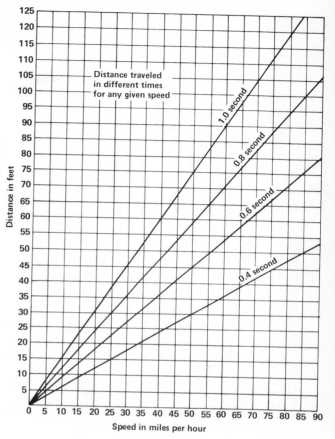

Distance traveled
in different times
for any given speed

1.0 second

0.8 second

0.6 second

0.4 second

Distance in feet

Speed in miles per hour

T-0112

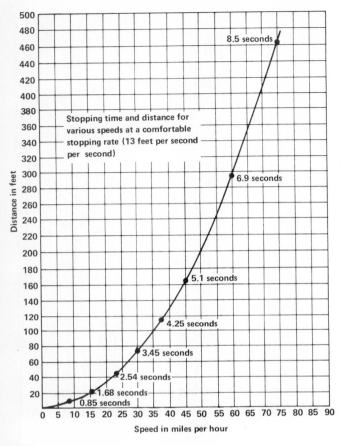

Stopping time and distance for various speeds at a comfortable stopping rate (13 feet per second per second)

8.5 seconds

6.9 seconds

5.1 seconds

4.25 seconds

3.45 seconds

2.54 seconds

1.68 seconds

0.85 seconds

Distance in feet

Speed in miles per hour

T-0113

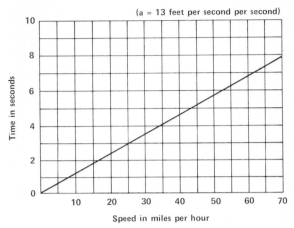

(a = 13 feet per second per second)

Time in seconds

Speed in miles per hour

T-0114 TIME TO SLOW DOWN COMFORTABLY FROM GIVEN SPEED

C | CUES TO QUESTIONS AND PROBLEMS

Questions for Study and Discussion

1. Garbage disposal unit (discomfort: noise pollution, and overload of sewage treatment plants)

Household telephone (noise, interruptions)

Automobile (air pollution, noise, accidents, and death)

Electronic amplifier (noise to the extent of permanent ear damage). Encourage students to continue to bring in additional examples from papers and magazines throughout the year.

2. Man-machine interaction is a measure of how the individual person gets on (or doesn't) with "machines" in the sense of technical gadgets, in-

cluding automobiles. Society-technology interaction tells how the social group, considered as a whole, is affected for better or worse by the whole set or system of technological gadgets and their side effects.

3. *Technology* and *science* are different in that they exist for different purposes. *Technology* tries to find applications for new ideas which *science* discovers. The above dichotomy is not always so clear-cut. Sometimes new ideas grow out of *technology* and *science* suggests applications for the new ideas.

4. It is important to make sure that the articles presented fulfill the stated conditions, and that the class discussion sticks to the point. Encourage this activity throughout the year by putting the relevant article on the bulletin board and setting aside specific days throughout the year for discussions of news articles.

5. It describes how far each person manages to avoid becoming merely a statistic, a number in a master computer. We live in a zip-coded place, answer a telephone number, carry and are increasingly identified by a Social Security number, may use numbered credit cards, perhaps have a numbered bank checking account and a numbered savings account and one or more numbered insurance policies, wear a numbered dog tag if the Draft gets us, are known more and more as 12 048 0412 2 rather than as Mr. or Mrs. Nemo Ouden Numquam.

6. (In Michigan this is actually the practice, though starting at 200 ft.) The driver must pull his wheel to counteract the tendency of the bank to turn his car, and then at the curve he must quickly pull the other way, perhaps oversteering in consequence. You should certainly point out what seems to be a little-known technique: that of alternately tugging gently at the wheel and then releasing it, thus preventing either under- or oversteering.

7. In contrast to seat belts, no action by the passenger is needed, and stopping force is spread over the passenger's whole front surface, a sort of "snowshoe effect," instead of being concentrated in a small area where internal organs may be damaged; a bag would protect a small child even if he were standing on the seat; under normal conditions it does not interfere with the driver's ability to reach all controls. Obviously, this matches the technology to the user, who does not have to take any positive action (such as fastening his seat belt) in order to benefit.

8. Data pollution: Many detailed questionnaires, such as those circulated by the admissions committees of some colleges, are probably never examined completely.

Bad match to the target public: When a computer issues an erroneous bill, it is nearly impossible to straighten things out, even by paying a visit in person to the giant's lair.

Side effects: The whole problem of air pollution by the automobile, of thermal pollution by electrical generating plants, of mass killing of fish and genocide of birds with DDT. The class will provide many. Examine them carefully to eliminate "fuzzy" thinking in their presentations.

9. The length of the GO zone will be greater if the speed limit is higher, because the cars can cover a longer space in a fixed time; if the street slopes down to the intersection, because this makes it harder to stop, if drivers are rash and take chances. The NO-GO has no sharp beginning, because cars at varying speeds will be at varying distances from the intersection when the light turns yellow; the NO-GO zone should end at the start of the GO zone. However, depending on the speed limit and the length of time the light is yellow, it might actually start beyond the GO zone and form a zone of dilemma in which the driver can neither get through the intersection before the light turns red nor stop comfortably in the time allowed by the yellow light.

Problems

1. a) At least 73 ft
   b) At least 2 x 73 = 146 ft
   c) At least 248 ft
   d) (Optional because this part requires experience with physics)

In both cases the total reaction distance is 66 ft, but the stopping distance of a car increases as the square of its speed, other things being equal (which they apparently are not in the case of this table). Doubling the speed means at least 4 times the stopping distance, or twice that of two half-speed cars approaching each other. Because most passenger car braking systems do not dissipate the heat rapidly enough, the braking ability at 60 mph diminishes slightly. This accounts for the 182 ft instead of 160 ft (4 x 40 ft).

2. a) The distances in Fig. 1-13 are minimum and involve a panic stop, while the text distance assumes reasonable comfort during the braking situation.

b)
$$40 \ \frac{mi}{hr} = \frac{40 \ \frac{mi}{hr} \times 5280 \ \frac{ft}{mi}}{60 \ \frac{min}{hr} \times 60 \ \frac{sec}{min}} = \frac{176}{3}$$

$$= 59 \ \frac{ft}{sec} \quad \text{(or refer to Transparency T-0111)}$$

$$\text{Light time} = \frac{116 \ ft}{59 \ \frac{ft}{sec}} = 2.0 \ sec$$

c) Reaction distance comes from multiplying reaction time by speed: $d = vt$. Since t is a constant (by assumption), this yields a straight-line graph. As explained in Problem 1d, the braking distance depends on the square of the speed: $d = kv^2$, which is the equation of a parabola.

3. Electric Motor: 0.1 H.P. costs $0.04/hr or $1.60 for a 40-hr week.

Man: 0.1 H.P. costs $1.50/hr or $60.00 for a 40-hr week.
Because laborers can be replaced by more efficient and inexpensive machines, it pays to finish one's education.

4. Shortest human delay: 0.2 sec

$$d = vt = 10\frac{yd}{sec} \times 0.2 \ sec = 2 \ yd$$

Longer human delay = 0.8 sec (assumed here)

$$d = 10 \times 0.8 = 8 \ yd$$

D | DEMONSTRATIONS, LABS, AND PROJECTS

I. The Game of Future

One of the objectives of *The Man-Made World* is to make students aware of some of the situations with which they will be living in the future. Another objective is to demonstrate that in a technological society seemingly unrelated events have a profound effect on each other.

The issue of *The Science Teacher* for January, 1969, is devoted to the consideration of the future. In one of the articles, "The Science Teacher as a Futurist," Edward Cornish (President of the World Future Society) makes the following statement:

> Since the accumulation of scientific and technical knowledge is the great force that is shaping tomorrow, a science teacher has a special role to play as young peoples' guide to the future. Certainly many young people will look to their science teachers for some hints about the mysterious future, because most of them know full well that tomorrow's world is being shaped by today's science. The science teacher may properly feel that he has enough to do without becoming a teacher of the future, but in many instances there will be no one else so well equipped to take on the task. The science teacher will be the faculty member who has, in Sir Charles Snow's words, "the future in his bones."

With these comments in mind, the authors prepared a series of Future games. A form of the game is presented on pages 36 and 37 of the student text. The opinion of experts using the Delphi Technique is presented in Section G.

The decision on when to play Future on later occasions is in the hands of each individual teacher. One of the most important things to remember about the game is that it is designed to provoke student discussion. It is important therefore that you refrain as much as possible from giving your opinions on either the likelihood of a "conse-quence" resulting from the stated development or the favorable or unfavorable effect of that consequence—at least until the class has had an opportunity to discuss it rather completely. The fact that there are differences even among the "experts" should be stressed as further evidence that many questions facing society today do not have definite "yes" or "no" answers. Their lack of information on these questions should motivate some students to find out more about them through outside readings suggested in the Bibliography in Section G at the end of this chapter.

II. Measuring Human Horsepower

PART A

The most interesting conclusion from this exercise is the inadequacy of the human being as a source of power. We investigate the power output, under several circumstances, of adolescents ("young adults" in their view, of course), but no arrangements are made to find out what happens to the power output when a comparatively large output is demanded over a long period of time. Your students are familiar with the need to "pace oneself" in this case, and need only to be reminded. An 8-oared crew in a 4-mi race rows itself out in about 20 min, and measurements suggest that the output is around 0.5 H.P. per oarsman. A dray horse, working continuously, actually develops only about 3/4 H.P. (James Watt wished to be conservative in rating his steam engines as replacements for horses to pump water out of coal mines.)

The flight of stairs called for may not be easy to find in a modern school (and the noise of its use may be disruptive to other classes, if one does exist). A convenient substitute may be a grandstand on the school's athletic field. Failing this, you might use the "step test." Find a good sturdy bench and measure its height. The subject steps up onto it (one foot first, then the other foot), then one foot down, then the other foot, and repeats for a predetermined count, say 12.

It will be a good self-protective measure, and protective to the class, too, if you can find out from the school's medical service whether any students should be excluded for health reasons from performing the exercise.

Some teachers have assigned the experiment as an activity to be performed at home, with parental help (thus giving them "a piece of the action" in the course). Comparison of results for boys and girls in the class has some interest. Record all results and calculate maximum, minimum, and group average for each way of climbing.

Equipment for Class:

Yardstick or footrule; measure the height of one step and multiply by the number of steps.

Set of bathroom spring scales (or preferably, lever-arm scales of adequate capacity)

Stopwatch

Answers to Questions:

*1. (Sample data)

Weight: 170 lb   165 lb
Vertical displacement: 13.3 ft
Time: a) 10.5 sec   14.0 sec
        b) 5.3   6.6
        c) 3.5   4.0

(Climbing stairs two steps at a time often slows down a girl.)

*2. (Sample data)

H.P.   a) 0.39   0.28
       b) 0.78   0.61
       c) 1.2   1.0

Note that since times (c) were measured only to 1 part in 35 or 40 (roughly 3%), the horsepowers (c) should not be reported in more precise detail than two significant figures.

If a department store with an escalator is accessible, an estimate of the horsepower expended by the motor on customers going up will be an interesting project. Count the number of people discharged at the upper level in one minute. Repeat several times and take an average. Assume an average weight per person of 150 lb. Measure (or estimate) the difference between levels. Then

$$\text{H.P.} = \frac{\dfrac{\text{no. of people}}{\text{minute}} \times \dfrac{150 \text{ lb}}{\text{person}} \times \text{no. ft vertically}}{550 \ \dfrac{\text{ft lb}}{\text{sec}} \times 60 \dfrac{\text{sec}}{\text{min}}}{\text{H.P.}}$$

*3. and 4. Questions for student research.

PART B (DEMONSTRATION EXPERIMENT)

This useful demonstration demands some physics for full understanding, but not very much. This kind of mechanical amplifier is called a windlass; small pile drivers and well diggers are often built on this pattern, and they are used on ships and yachts to raise the anchor and hoist the sails.

One end of the rope is connected to the load to be lifted; the middle part is wrapped around the drum which is rotated by a gasoline engine or electric motor, with the operator holding the free end. If the operator leaves this end slack, the drum spins freely inside the loose turns, and no power is delivered to the load. But when the operator pulls at the free end of the rope, the turns tighten on the drum; friction between the drum and the rope produces a tension in the rope which exerts a force on the load. Of course, the operator has to walk away or pull in on the rope just as fast as the load is raised.

Physicists among the teachers of this course will wish to measure forces in proper units, namely, newtons. However, to save lengthy discussion, confusing to the members of the class, we use the units marked on the spring balance that comes with the equipment. These show where the pointer of the balance would come to rest if it were used to support a mass of so many grams. Thus, 100 on the scale means that if a mass of 100 grams were supported by the spring balance, the latter would have to exert a force equal to the pull of gravity on that mass. We call the force 100 grams-weight. It happens that the pull of gravity varies from place to place, so this is not a definite force. But as long as one stays on the earth's surface, the pull of gravity varies less than 1/2%, so the inaccuracy is unimportant.

So that you won't have to walk across the room with the end of the string during the demonstration, the load is replaced by a spring. The more this spring is stretched, the greater the reaction force it exerts. It is necessary to find out, first, how the spring's force is related to its increase in length when stretched. To do this, lay the spring on the lab table and fasten one end to the edge of the table, using a hook, a clamp, or a screw in the table. Lay a meter stick alongside (easier than a yardstick because of the decimal divisions), and make a note of the position of the free end of the spring. Hook the spring balance to the end of the spring and by pulling gently on the ring of the balance extend the spring by a force of 50 grams-weight as measured on the scale of the spring balance. Record the displacement of the spring's end from its original position. Repeat with forces of 100, 150, and 200 grams-weight. Graph the measurements. The graph is a straight line, which means that the extension of the spring is directly proportional to the force used to stretch it, and also that the spring pulls back with a force which is equal to the stretching force and therefore also is proportional to the extension. We can express this by an equation, using the slope-intercept pattern: $y = mx + b$. Here y stands for the force f, m is the slope which we call k (the spring constant), and the y intercept b is 0. Hence we may translate to the equation:

$$f = kx$$

Properly speaking, there should be a minus sign, since the extension is one way and the resulting force is the other, but this has no bearing on the present experiment. We can easily determine k. If we take two values of f differing by Δf, and the two corresponding values of x, differing by Δx, then k equals "rise over run," or

$$k = \frac{\Delta f}{\Delta x}$$

The advantage of this is that for any extension Δx of the spring we can immediately calculate the force which the spring exerts. This relationship was discovered by Robert Hooke in about 1660. It is important to remember that Hooke's law loses its validity if a spring is stretched enough to distort it permanently, or "beyond the elastic limit."

It will be recalled that in Part A we measured the time (t) to raise the experimenter's own weight (F) from one floor to another (h) and then computed his horsepower.

At best this demonstration is not quick. Many teachers find it works best to carry out the experiment, having one of the class act as a recorder to put down the numbers in tabular form on the chalkboard. The class members copy these but do the arithmetic and the graphing as a homework assignment.

Many teachers prefer to skip the mathematics at this stage and concentrate on the difficulty of control as the amplification factor increases. Your handling of the mathematics will depend on your interests and the mathematics ability of your students.

Equipment for Demonstration:

    Windlass model
    Spring balance (0—2000 grams-weight)
    Meter stick

Answers to Questions:

1. It should be fairly evident even from the back of the room that the spring balance reading is greater when you try to pull the string against the reaction of the spring with no amplification than it is with a few turns around the amplifier drum. (The motor should be turned on for this preliminary observation.)

*2. (Sample data)

	Force in (gm-wt) Δf	Displacement (m) Δx	Force out (gm-wt) $k\,\Delta x$
1 turn	25	0.030	75
	50	0.060	150
	75	0.085	212
	100	0.130	262
	125	0.130	325
2 turns	20	0.080	200
	25	0.093	232
	30	0.105	262
	35	0.115	288
	40	0.130	325
	45	0.140	350
3 turns	10	0.120	300
	15	0.150	375
	20	0.200	500
	25	0.240	600
4 turns	1	0.045	112
	3	0.070	175
	5	0.110	275
	7	0.140	350
	9	0.180	450
	11	0.210	525

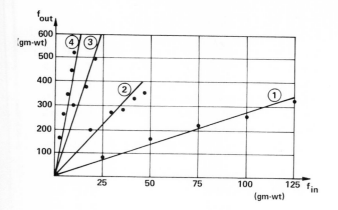

*3. (Sample data)

Average amplification factors:

1 turn	2 turns	3 turns	4 turns
3.0	10.0	30	112*
3.0	9.3	25	58
2.8	8.7	25	55
2.6	8.2	24	50
2.6	8.1		50
	7.8	av. 26	48
av. 2.8			
	av. 8.7		av. 52

*rejected value.

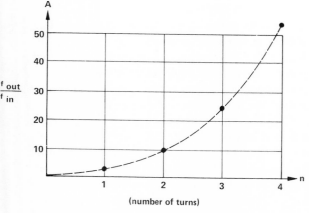

(number of turns)

The curve is drawn dashed because the data are discrete; there is no convenient way to use partial turns.

*4. Gain in power comes from the motor: in an amplifier the output power from another source is always larger than the input power.

III. Coordination of Human Systems

Equipment for Each Lab Team:

> 1 Tantalizer
> 3 sheets of white paper each marked in ink with one of the diagrams of Fig. 2 (Text page 39)
> 3 sheets of tracing paper, onion skin, or manifold paper for each student
> 4 bits of masking tape to hold assembly of diagrams and tracing paper in place

General Lab Supplies:

> Spare tracing paper
> Spare masking tape

Answers to Questions:

*1. Most people find (a) easiest, although some vote for (c). Nearly all find (b) hardest.

*2. Many find improvement after three tries, further improvement is less marked after five times.

*3. The fact that the hand tries to follow what the eye sees in the mirror shows that the muscular-nervous system which controls the hand is assisted by the system of which the eye is a part.

A different way to test eye-muscle coordination, fun and easily prepared, is shown in the following diagram.

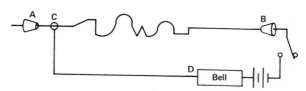

A piece of bare copper wire, stiff enough so it will not sag, is bent into a series of curves and angles. The bends should lie in various planes. The wire is supported by two corks, A and B, either hung from threads or supported by clamps. C is a 1-in loop of wire, the connection from C to D being flexible and long enough so that C can make contact with the bare wire anywhere, thus ringing the bell. C can be hung over A to start. Each student in turn is invited to see how far he can move from C to A before ringing the bell.

IV. The Yellow Light

Part A of this laboratory exercise can be done either as a class project or by smaller groups working as teams. The choice depends upon the number of street intersections in the neighborhood of the school that are protected by traffic lights, the time available, and, perhaps, special circumstances in your particular case. If you have to make the "other arrangements" mentioned in the text, you can pace off distances *a* and *b* and measure the time of the yellow light on your way home at night, without appreciable delay.

Parts B and C can be done in class or as assignments at home, whichever is more convenient.

If time permits, it might be interesting to make also a study of the traffic flow at the intersection by the method described on pp. 184 and 185.

Equipment for Each Lab Team:

Stopwatch

PART A

Copies of T-0112 and T-0113 made on your duplicator for all pupils will be easier to use than Figs. 5 and 6, being larger. Copies of T-0114 will eliminate the difficult interpolation in Fig. 6 to find the time to stop (*after* hitting the brakes) from other speeds than those marked.

Answers to Questions:

*1. Using Fig. 5, or by means of T-0111, find speed in feet per second. Then multiply by the duration of the yellow light.

*2. Figure 7 is correct; ignore the numerical misprints in the text.

PART B

Answers to Questions:

*1. Use T-0111; then length of GO zone = v ft/sec times t_{sec} minus width of street.

*2. See Fig. 6 or T-0113. Add 0.8 sec x $v_{ft/sec}$ to distance traveled while braking.

*3. Answer 2 minus Answer 1.

*4. To the minimum distance for a comfortable stop (found in Q.2) add the width of the cross street. Divide this sum by the speed limit in ft/sec to find the time the yellow light should be on.

*5. Use T-0114 to determine the time for comfortable braking. Adding 0.8 sec gives total time from start of yellow light to stopping of car. If yellow is on for less time than this, then the car continues to travel after the light turns red but still can stop before it gets to the intersection. This is due to the fact that the distance for the GO zone has a linear relationship ($d \alpha t$) with time while the stopping distance has a nonlinear relationship with time ($d \alpha t^2$).

*6. Your car must stop at least one car length from the intersection, so you must brake *before* entering the normal dilemma zone. Therefore, slow down as you approach an intersection before you think you must, if there is a car on the road between you and the intersection.

PART C

Answers to Questions:

*1. v = 45 mi/hr = 60 ft/sec
   w = 50 ft
   t = 3 sec
   a) 66 ft/sec x 3 sec = 198 ft;
      198 − 50 = 148 ft
   b) 168 + 0.8 x 66 = 221 ft
   c) 221 − 148 = 73 ft
   d) 221 + 50 = 271;
      271 ft/(66 ft/sec) = 4.1 sec
   e) This seems unduly long. If light is too long (extending GO zone unduly) people tend to run through the yellow when in fact there is not enough time (so they go through the red). People on the other street, if they see no one approaching, sneak through the red without waiting for the green.

*2. A visual device to show remaining time before change to red (a pointer moving across a scale, or a row of lights extinguished one by one). Or diminish the speed limit, thus making it practicable to shorten the yellow (use the customary system of preliminary signs warning of lowered limit, and perhaps change the limit down in stages). A sign indicating the end of the NO-GO zone and the beginning of the GO zone.

*3. v = 60 mi/hr = 88 ft/sec
   w = 50 ft
   t = 4.1 sec
   a) (88 x 4.1) − 50 = 311 ft, GO zone

b) $298 + 0.8 \times 88 = 368$ ft

c) $368 - 311 = 57$ ft, dilemma zone

d) $368 + 50 = 418$; $418/(88) = 4.75$ sec

This time is certainly too long. The light should not be set to cater to speed maniacs. But other drivers, about to enter an intersection when light has turned green, had better look both ways to see whether such a driver is coming.

V. Build a Reaction Timer

By now, most ECCP teachers are familiar with measuring human reaction time with a ruler. The time it takes to catch a falling ruler is a reaction to a very simple task. To provide students with an opportunity to measure reaction times for more complex tasks, you can build a reaction timer, using an analog computer and a logic circuit board (LCB).

Start by getting an output of one volt from the power supply of the analog computer. Then connect this one volt output to C1c of the LCB. Next, make the following connections: C1m to A1c, A1b to the input to one of the integrators of the analog computer (make sure that the initial condition is zero). The output of the integrator is then connected to the 1.5 volt scale of the meter (in this case 1 volt = 1 sec). Finally, make the following connections on the LCB: Neg. to C2c, C2m to A2c, A2b to L_1.

Notice that when you operate switch C, L_1 goes on and the voltmeter starts to register voltage. When switch A is operated, L_1 will go out and the meter will stop increasing. Next, place a barrier (notebook) between switch B and C and measure reaction times under varying conditions.

First have the student (subject) place his hand on switch A and operate it when L_1 comes on (the operator controls L_1 by operating switch C). Typical voltmeter readings will be about 0.2 volts which is equivalent to 0.2 sec. Next, have the student place his hand on switch B so that in reacting he has to move his hand before operating switch A. This situation will result in reaction times of about 0.3 to 0.5 sec.

To simulate more complex situations, an identical circuit can be wired using switches B, D, and L_2 of the LCB and the same one volt signal and integrator of the analog computer. Now a student can be asked to react to L_1 or L_2 and operate switch A if L_1 goes on and switch B if L_2 goes on. This task requires that the subject make a simple decision as well as react to the stimulus (light coming on).

This activity is designed to be used with the analysis of the "yellow light" problem. It allows students to measure reaction times which are quite analogous to reaction times which occur when driving a car.

E | EVALUATION

The questions in this section are rated according to the chapter objectives and the performance levels stated in the introduction to the teacher's manual. This group of questions is not intended to be all inclusive, but just as a guide to possible questions. Zeros in the chapter objective column indicate no chapter objective for this question.

Chapter Objective	Performance Level	
		Judged to be Relatively Easy:
2	II	1. In each of the following cases mark the statement *T* if it is true, *F* if it is false.
1	I	a) The minimum stopping distance for car running at 60 mph would be less for a driver with faster than normal reaction time than for an ordinary driver.
1	II	b) The life expectancy at birth for baby girls in the United States is shorter than it was fifty years ago.
		c) If businessmen understood about matching technology to its target, they would not send out reply envelopes too small for the bills they come with.
2	II	d) A sensible driver always stops when the traffic light turns yellow.
1	I	e) When we make a quantitative estimate of something, it is needless to make any measurements.

Chapter Objective	Performance Level
2	I
2	I
7	I
7	II
7	I
7	I
7	I
4	II
4	I
3 and 4	II
3 and 4	II
3 and 4	II
3 and 4	II
3 and 4	II

Judged to be Relatively Easy:

f) The end of the NO-GO zone on a street is always at the same place.

g) The shortest human reaction time is between 0.1 sec and 0.2 sec.

h) Trying to put large numbers of people through MHT centers is just a fad, so such centers are already diminishing in number.

i) MHT centers would be more practical only if there were enough chemists available to make all the laboratory tests.

j) Since all the results are sent out, there is no need to have a doctor at hand at an MHT center.

k) All the MHT center tests are very expensive. Therefore, only a few people can afford to go to such a center.

l) One danger with the MHT center is that the doctors will be victims of "data pollution."

In the following two questions, check the best answer:

2. A boy who weighs 100 lb climbs up a stairway 10 ft high:
   a) He will need 10 sec to make the climb.
   b) If the stairway were higher, he could climb faster.
   c) The length of time he takes depends on the horsepower he develops.
   d) If the stairs were half as high and he took twice as long, his horsepower would be the same.

3. The word "power"
   a) means the same as work.
   b) means the same as work multiplied by time.
   c) is another word for energy.
   d) is work per unit time.
   e) is force multiplied by time.

4. Using the following graph, fill in the blanks in the 5 statements below:

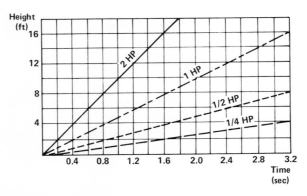

Load raised in each case = 110 lb.

a) To raise 110 lb 4 ft would take a $\frac{1}{4}$-H.P. motor _____ sec.

b) To raise 110 lb 4 ft would take a $\frac{1}{2}$-H.P. motor _____ sec.

c) To raise 110 lb 8 ft would take a 1-H.P. motor _____ sec.

d) To raise 110 lb 8 ft would take a 2-H.P. motor _____ sec.

e) In 1.6 sec a 2-H.P. motor could raise 110 lb. _____ times as high as a $\frac{1}{4}$ - H.P. motor could.

Chapter Objective	Performance Level
5	II
2	I
2	I
2	II
6	I
6	II
7	II
1 and 6	I
7	I
7	II
4	II
1	II
5	II

Judged to be More Difficult:

5. In each of the following cases, mark the statement *T* if it is true, but mark it *F* if it is false:

    a) The shorter the cycle of a traffic light, the more cars are apt to be held up by it.

    b) A small alcoholic drink relaxes a person and so makes him a better automobile driver.

    c) If it takes 60 ft to stop a car traveling at 25 mph, it will take 120 ft to stop a car traveling twice as fast.

    d) If the yellow traffic signal were made just as long as human reaction time uniformly throughout the country, people would soon learn to stop in time.

    e) The only reason that inflatable bags in front of riders in cars are not legally required safety devices is careless neglect of the problem by Congress.

    f) Even though there is a requirement of safety belts in all cars, the attempt to develop inflatable bags to be mounted in front of all riders is wise.

    g) Some states require all automobiles to be checked for condition at regular intervals. The garages where this is done might be said to be something like MHT centers.

    h) The "quantitative point of view" makes it seem that inflatable safety bags are both attractive and likely.

    i) If doctors could be assigned according to the need, there would be reason to believe that the number of doctors in the United States is large enough for all our needs.

    j) One danger of the MHT system is that hospitals may be swamped with new patients.

In the following three questions, check the best answer:

6. An outboard motor is rated at 2 H.P., and when its boat travels at full speed the water offers a resistance of 55 lb. One H.P. = 550 ft-lb/sec. The motor drives the boat against this resistance of 55 lb a distance of
    a) 10 ft in 1 sec.
    b) 20 ft in 1 sec.
    c) 20 ft in 2 sec.
    d) 1 ft in 10 sec.
    e) 2 ft in 10 sec.

7. "Technology doesn't create problems; it is just a convenient whipping boy that on-confused people use."

This quotation
    a) proves that the speaker was an engineer.
    b) could not have been made if the speaker had been aware of the facts.
    c) would not be true if there were no confused people.
    d) shows that the speaker believes we have no problems.
    e) is what any sensible person would say.

8. At any intersection between two streets that do not carry much traffic there is sometimes a light that is set green on the more important (Main) street except when a car approaches on the less important (Side) street. This car runs over a bar in the pavement which makes the light change. With such an arrangement, there is
    a) no need for a yellow light on Main Street.
    b) no need for a yellow light on either street.
    c) no way for a car on Main Street to turn legally into Side street.
    d) less interruption to traffic on Main Street than there would be with conventional lights.
    e) No need for a yellow light on Side Street.

Answers to Evaluation Questions:

1. a) T g) T
   b) F h) F
   c) T i) F
   d) F j) T
   e) F k) F
   f) F l) T

2. c

3. d

4. a) 3.2 c) 1.6 e) 8
   b) 1.6 d) 0.8

5. a) T f) T
   b) F g) T
   c) F h) F
   d) F i) T
   e) F j) T

6. b

7. b

8. d

F | FILMS

F-0101 BATS, BIRDS, AND BIONICS

Recommendation: Good film to illustrate a relatively new area of science.

Application: Enrichment. May be used either as an introduction or a summary to the course.

Length and Type: 30 min, color, sound.

Source: #4 (No longer available on free-loan basis from #2)

Summary: One of the CBS "21st Century" series. It shows how engineers are applying principles derived from living creatures to the solution of human problems.

F-0102 BEWARE THE WIND

Recommendation: Good introduction to a very current topic—air pollution.

Application: Development of a discussion topic important in this course.

Length and Type: 22 min, color, sound.

Source: #20 (No charge)

Summary: Principal sources of air pollution, and ways to apply technology to clean up the air.

F-0103 NOISE: THE NEW POLLUTANT

Recommendation: A good introduction to one of the more lately recognized forms of pollution in the man-made world.

Application: Enrichment and reinforcement of the text. (Can also be used with Chapter 5.)

Length and Type: 30 min, b & w, sound.

Source: #5

Summary: This is an NET TV film. Begins with the sensation of hearing, but is mostly on research into physiological damage caused by excessive noise.

F-0104 A TRIP FROM CHICAGO

Recommendation: Optional film for use as recommended below.

Application: Enrichment. Use only if the topic of future transportation is of special interest to teacher and class.

Length and Type: 30 min, color, sound.

Source: #2 (No charge)

Summary: One of the CBS "21st Century" series. It explores the possibilities for future transportation, including high-speed trains, supersonic transports, hovercraft, and rockets.

F-0105   MAN-MADE MAN

Recommendation: Optional film for use as indicated below.

Application: Enrichment. May be used to illustrate technological advances in the medical sciences. Some young people are sensitive about seeing pictures of "insides." You had better review the film yourself before showing it in class.

Length and Type: 30 min, color, sound.

Source: #4 (No longer available on free-loan basis from #2)

Summary: One of the CBS "21st Century" series. The major emphasis is on modern medical advances, particularly in the area of organ transplants and synthetic replacement parts.

F-0106   BIO-MEDICAL ENGINEERING

Recommendation: Good film to illustrate an interdisciplinary field not covered in detail in the text.

Application: Enrichment. Best used at the beginning of the course to stimulate interest. (This would also be a good film for the biology classes.)

Length and Type: 30 min, b & w, sound.

Source: #1

Summary: One of a series, "Science and Engineering Television Journal," produced by WNDT, New York. It is concerned with the artificial pacemaker for heart block patients. Both medical point of view —how it is used and implanted—and engineering, selection of materials, and power supply problems.

G | GENERAL

Bibliography

B. Commoner, *Science and Survival.* Viking Press, 1966 (A) (paper)

> A sober, factual, depressing report by a distinguished ecologist. "We already know the enormous benefits [modern technology] can bestow; we have begun to perceive its frightful threats. The political crisis generated by this knowledge is upon us."

Environmental Action (National Staff), *Earth Day —The Beginning: A Guide for Survival.* Bantam Extra, 1970 (A) (paper)

> By practically a publisher's miracle, this book followed the event (Earth Day) by only a few weeks. It presumably suffered from such speed, but not noticeably. At the price, you couldn't go wrong even if it were not up to scratch.

V. C. Ferkiss, *Technological Man: the Myth and the Reality.* George Braziller, 1969 (B)

> A cornucopia of ideas, facts, and forecasts, fine for background and orientation, but too much in too little space. The writing is fascinating, the author realistic (maybe cynically so), historically knowing, and persuasive. But hard to get one's teeth into the material.

P. T. Flawn, *Environmental Geology.* Harper & Row, 1970 (C)

> It is hard to believe that this was not written to complement *The Man-Made World.* You can skip the first three chapters on geology if time presses, but the next four are essential. It presents numerous useful examples of what we study. A casual count turned up more than a dozen examples, some of them detailed case histories. Firm grasp of what is economically and politically possible to the ecologist, a point often missed. Taking care of the environment is expensive, and it is not clear what consumers will stand for it in time to save everybody's life. This book is a *must.*

F. Graham Jr., *Since Silent Spring.* Houghton Mifflin, 1970 (B)

> *Facts and Figures,* written by a journalist who nearly counterbalances the essential dryness of such material by his passionate concern. Describes the writing of *Silent Spring,* the uproar at its publication and the controversy since.

P. Shepard and D. McKinley, eds., *The Subversive Science.* Houghton Mifflin, 1969 (C)

> 37 "Essays toward an Ecology of Man" by authors of such distinction that many are known even to this writer, a physics teacher by

trade. Not stiff reading, but full of facts and interesting points of view; will be enjoyed by both teachers and students.

J. H. Storer, *Man in the Web of Life.* Signet (New American Library), 1968 (A) (paper)

Runs all the way from human evolution, through many aspects (economic, ecological, biological) of the current scene, to look at what is perhaps in the cards for tomorrow. Too much material per page to digest, luckily we all know much of the contents. Excellent book for a bright, concerned youngster who has gone past the stage of pure emotion.

Sir George Thomson, *The Foreseeable Future.* Viking Press, 1960 (out of print. Maybe your library has a copy.)

First published in 1955 by the Nobel-winning physicist son of Nobel-winning Sir J. J. (discoverer of the electron). Much sensible and interesting comment as would be expected, but perfectly fascinating (a) for what has already come to pass in 15 years when he set his sights on 100; (b) for what he utterly missed (like the problem of disposing of radioactive "ash" from nuclear reactors). A wonderful way to readjust one's perspective.

"The Williamstown Study of Critical Environmental Problems." *Bulletin of Atomic Scientists,* October, 1970, pages 24-30.

This is a summary of major findings and recommendations of about 100 scientists and professionals who conducted a month-long study (July, 1970) of critical environmental problems. It is essentially an up-to-date assessment of the state of knowledge about these problems. The full text of this historic work is being published by the Massachusetts Institute of Technology Press.

Environment Magazine, 438 N. Skinker Boulevard, St. Louis, Missouri 63130

The members of the ECCP staff recommend that all ECCP teachers subscribe to this magazine individually or via their school librarian. It is the best source of up-to-date information concerning the impact of technology on our environment.

II. The Game of Future (Experts' Opinion)

The following information is adapted from "Forecasts of Some Technological and Scientific Developments and Their Societal Consequences" by T.J. Gordon and R.H. Ament, Report R6, The Institute for the Future, Middletown, Connecticut. Two types of information are presented: the method that was used to obtain expert opinion (the Delphi Technique) and some of the actual forecasts and their societal consequences.

THE DELPHI TECHNIQUE

Most decision-makers utilize expert advice in forming their judgment. Where the question being examined is so complex and involves such obscure inter-relationships that no single person could be expected to be expert in the many disciplines required, the traditional approach to the answer is to seek a consensus among experts through open discussion or a conference. However, joint committee activity often introduces certain undesirable psychological factors, "such as specious persuasion, unwillingness to abandon publicly expressed opinions, and the bandwagon effect of majority opinion."

The Delphi Technique, which was used in this study, makes it possible to avoid some of these difficulties because the experts involved exchange their opinions anonymously and through an intermediary, who controls the feedback of opinion in subsequent rounds of the inquiry. It has been found in previous studies of this type that the Delphi process—involving anonymity, iteration, and controlled feedback—tends to produce a converging group consensus.

In a typical Delphi investigation, the participants are sent a series of questionnaires through the mail. In the first questionnaire, they might be asked to provide their judgment as to likely dates of occurrence of a group of events and developments. The collated responses normally reveal a spread of opinions; these data are presented to the respondents in the second questionnaire. In this round, the respondents are given the opportunity to

NEW METHODS OF MODIFYING THE ENVIRONMENT			How likely is it that the result will be a consequence of the development?				What will the effect of the consequence be?				
If these developments were to occur	**During this decade**	**They might result in:**	Virtually certain	Probable	Possible	Almost impossible	Very favorable	Favorable	Little or no importance	Detrimental	Very detrimental
Limited weather control, predictably affecting regional weather at acceptable cost.	1990	**A.** Improvement in agricultural efficiency.									
		B. Disruption in ecological balance.									
		C. Weather being used as military, economic, or political weapon.									
		D. Civil suits alleging damage caused by weather.									
		E. Emergence of a power group of "weather makers."									
		F. Others—specify.									
Widespread use of automobile engines, fuels, or accessories which eliminate harmful exhaust.	1980	**A.** Increased traffic congestion since smog-free automobiles will be allowed to increase in numbers.									
		B. Delay in development of high-speed mass transit systems.									
		C. Continued economic domination by the automobile industry.									
		D. Higher efficiency of engine performance.									
		E. Relaxation of efforts to reduce industrial and municipal air pollution.									
		F. Other.									

Page 24

NEW METHODS OF MODIFYING THE ENVIRONMENT

If these developments were to occur	During this decade	They might result in:	How likely is it that the result will be a consequence of the development?				What will the effect of the consequence be?				
			Virtually certain	Probable	Possible	Almost impossible	Very favorable	Favorable	Little or no importance	Detrimental	Very detrimental
Widespread use of self-contained dwelling units using systems that recycle water and air to provide independence from the external environment.	2010	A. Further fragmentation of society.									
		B. Reduction in degree of dependence of suburban residents on municipal government.									
		C. Further development of units for living in space and underseas.									
		D. Rejection by most people.									
		E. Other.									
Establishment of a central data storage facility with wide public access for general and specialized information in the areas of library, medical, and legal data. (*Adapted from "Forecasts of Some Technological and Scientific Developments and Their Societal Consequences," T. J. Gordon and R. H. Ament, Report R6, The Institute for the Future.*)	1980	A. Use of home terminal for education.									
		B. Information storage becoming a salable service resulting in revision of business practices.									
		C. Improvement in social science research.									
		D. Individual citizens becoming "expert" in law and medicine.									
		E. Information overload problems will arise in decision making because people will not be able to handle all the data.									
		F. Invasion of privacy.									
		G. Other.									

revise their estimates in light of the group response, and those participants whose estimates have fallen earlier or later than those of the majority are asked to provide reasons for their position. These reasons, along with the new estimates for the group as a whole, are collated and fed back to the respondents on the third questionnaire, and they are again asked to reassess their earlier estimates in view of the new group response and reasons provided for early and late dates.

Even though this technique has been used with some success, it should not be interpreted as a device that produces "truth about the future." The Delphi method is designed to produce consensus judgments in inexact fields; it would be a mistake to consider such judgments as complete or precise descriptions about the future.

The future will contain events that are totally unanticipated today; perhaps this is the only thing that can be said about the future with absolute certainty. Furthermore, all techniques of forecasting that rely on judgment and opinion (rather than on the more rigid laws of causality of the natural sciences) depend on the imagination and technical adequacy of the forecasters. Nevertheless, forecasting the future seems to be a worthwhile enterprise despite the certainty of the unexpected and despite the limitations imposed by relying on human judgment, however well-informed. Forecasts, even hazy forecasts, based on careful judgment can provide a seemingly coherent structure for testing alternative contemplated actions, for warning that certain other actions may be needed or should be avoided, and for defining the scope of reasonable expectations in a world where expectations sometimes seem unbounded.

FORECASTS AND CONSEQUENCES

The summary of expert opinion concerning forecasts of technological breakthroughs and their societal consequences is depicted in the preceding tables. The polygons are used to show the final range of opinions generated by the group. The high point on the bar indicates the median of the responses. The shorter legs of the polygon define the limits of the upper and lower quartiles, and the bar itself the interquartile range.

The respondents developed an extensive list of prospective consequences which they felt might be expected as a result of the forecasted technological and scientific developments. Each of these consequences was judged as to its likelihood of being a result of the event, and assuming it should occur, whether it was favorable or unfavorable.

REFERENCES FOR "THE GAME OF FUTURE"

Victor C. Ferkiss, *Technological Man: The Myth and Reality*. Braziller, 1969. Also available in paperback—Mentor Books ($1.50).

Alvin Toffler, *Future Shock*. Random House, 1970. Also available in paperback ($1.95).

World Future Society, *The Futurist Magazine*. P. O. Box 19285, 20th Street Station, Washington, D. C. 20036.

Refer to "The Futurist" book service for many other appropriate references for extending discussions on the future impact of technology.

CHECK LIST FOR CHAPTER 2

DECISION MAKING

A. APPROACH	CLASS PERIODS	B. BLACK & WHITE TRANSPARENCIES	C. CUES (k = key problem) Discussion Questions	Easy	Problems Medium	Hard	D. DEMONSTRATIONS, LABS & PROJECTS	E. EVALUATION	F. FILMS	G. GENERAL
1. The Elements of Decision Making	3	0201a,b,c 0215	1,8		1,3k		I, II	1,2,3, 4,7,8		
2. Types of Decisions	1		18,19					9,10, 13,14		
3. Algorithms	3	0202 0203 0211	3,4 2,7,9, 10,12, 17		4,5		III	5,11	0201	
4. Criteria	2	0204 0205	5,6,11, 13,16			2,6,7	Demonstration	12		
5. Optimization with Few Alternatives	1	0206a,b 0207 0208a,b	15		8k,9	10,11,12	Competition	6	0202	
6. Dynamic Programming	2	0209 0210								
7. Problems Without Solutions	1	0212 0213 0214	14						0203	
8. Final Comment	1									

Decision Making 2

A | APPROACH

I. Purpose and Organization of the Chapter

The purpose of Chapter 2 is to present the fundamentals of rational decision making and to indicate how an engineer attempts to find solutions to problems. This is of basic importance as we try to orient our students in today's world.

The chapter begins with examples of decision problems that are familiar to high school students, then uses one of the examples to develop the four elements of decision making. We see decision problems ranging from the very easy to the very difficult. The nature of algorithms and their usefulness in optimization are explained. Further discussions of criteria and of optimization illustrate algorithmic solutions of several kinds. Finally, we have a problem that can only be solved by legislative action.

II. Objectives for Students

Upon completion of the activities, laboratory, discussions, and reading in this chapter, students should be able to:

1. Recognize and identify
   a) the following terms: *algorithm, binary choice, constraint, criterion, dynamic programming, model, optimization.*

   b) the symbols · and + as used in Boolean algebra to express the connectives AND and OR.

2. Draw distinctions between "common-sense" solutions and those based on reliable algorithms, or a systematic attack on a problem.

3. Discriminate between criteria and constraints which are based mainly on opinion (or are subjective) and those which are based on demonstrable facts (or are objective).

4. Construct and read nonlinear graphs as one technique of optimization.

5. Explain why it is legitimate for different people to attack a problem in different ways.

6. Interpret the difference between two optimization solutions to the same problem, when the criteria have developed during the solution.

7. Infer, when an accepted solution is not the one sought for, that the criteria first suggested proved to be too restrictive, so that a compromise had to be adopted.

III. Suggestions for Teaching

The importance of this chapter is that there is a *rational* method of making decisions. The method has four elements:

1. The model: this describes as accurately as possible what we know about the problem.

2. The constraints: these frame or limit the decision.

3. The criteria: the standards used to tell whether a decision is acceptable or not, or the statement of what we are trying to achieve.

4. Optimization: this involves maximizing the level of acceptability of the decision (a compromise).

Optimization can sometimes be accomplished by applying an algorithm, and then a computer can often be programmed to do the work. Unfortunately, algorithms are somewhat rare. However, in a complex problem like the route-planning problem of Section 6, breaking it into several partial problems may permit application of a simple algorithm.

Some of the examples shown in the text, in this and later chapters, have been chosen as examples of important problem-solving techniques; the use of Boolean algebra and dynamic programming. Their importance lies in the fact that each of these methods has many possible applications. The ideas which these principles illustrate are essential. The point is to teach the students not only how to solve new problems, but also that while in some cases methods exist for their solution, in others methods for solution are still being sought. It is to be hoped that students may come to feel that the concept of optimization has a place in their own lives.

Section 1. The Elements of Decision Making.
The questions which open the chapter as well as Discussion Questions 1 and 8 at the end of the chapter should be considered *before making any text assignments.* This technique should be followed as much as possible throughout the course. Experience throughout the testing period has indicated that students get much more out of the reading of the text if they have been exposed to some of the content prior to their reading assignment. Overhead transparencies T-0201a, b, and c should be shown in class prior to text assignment.

A familiar remark is that a problem is half solved if it is asked correctly. Similarly, constructing a proper model takes us part way to a correct decision. Make sure your students understand this unfamiliar use of the word "model." It has no direct connection with model trains (small replicas in appearance), nor with artists' models (to be copied in paint), nor with model behavior (ideal). A model in the present sense is simply a partial description of reality. It must contain all known *relevant* details, no irrelevant ones, and should be as quantitative as possible. See text, Chapter 4.

The criterion really states what is to be decided. Usually it includes the words "the largest" or "the smallest." For any problem, anyone may make a snap solution, but to be satisfactory the solution must be the best possible. Optimization is the name given to this process.

When a student's mother says that he really *must* straighten out his room, or his share of it, he has a decision problem. The model, not quantitative, is the current state of the room. The constraints are the available shelf and the drawer space; the criterion is to have everything put away. Optimization then means to arrange things so they will be easy to find if this was the major criterion. If the major criterion is that the room should look like a page out of one of the homemaking magazines, then optimization means to hide things in places where they cannot be seen, but from which they can readily be retrieved when needed.

Assignment of Labs I and II is recommended after studying Section 1. The order of assignment is not important. The latter is great fun, while the former is more obviously pertinent to the text. Lab I has a concealed purpose: to show that mathematics can be useful. A few students will relish the hint that there is still a quicker way to find the answer: the "magic" process of differentiation, giving

$$\frac{dA}{da} = 1000 - 4a$$

and for maximum

$$\frac{dA}{da} = 0$$

whence $a = 250$ ft

Section 2. Types of Decisions.
Here again class discussion of Questions 18 and 19 should occur *before the text reading is assigned.* Read aloud to the class the first two paragraphs of "Choosing a Road," but don't let talk get out of hand. The point to be drawn from the discussion here is that we don't

know the model, so our hands are tied. There has been quite a lot of discussion about computerizing traffic control, but not much on just how this will be done. The suggestions should be interesting.

Section 3. Algorithms. The 11-match game is part of Lab III. The solution is given in the lab notes. Another easy algorithm is that for tick-tack-toe, although of course it must allow for various strategies by the second player, and one of these is a spoiler. Bridge players use one or another algorithm, depending on the "system" used for bidding.

Students tend to find it exciting to try to solve the bridge problem themselves. Film F-0201 is short, delightful, and will reinforce the reading of the text description of the Königsberg bridge problem.

In studying T-0203, it may be better to work out a route for a letter carrier, a snowplow (in the north), or milk delivery than for police, if you feel that this would be more appropriate for your students. The most fruitful way to approach this problem is to reproduce enough copies of T-0203 for the entire class. Have each student at his desk try to route the vehicle from A through the pattern of streets. Allow about 10 to 15 min for this activity prior to the assignment of the text or the showing of the film. After the discussion of the Königsberg bridge, have the students return to the original problem and solve it. One thing which should be emphasized is that once they have the algorithm there will be many different paths, all of which are correct. This can then be tied in with newspaper routing in which certain customers insist on getting the paper early, or police car routing so that potential lawbreakers cannot predict when the patrol car will pass a given point, or letter carrier routing so that he arrives at the local diner at coffee-break time.

Section 4. Criteria. The point of this section is to introduce the notation and methods as well as some understanding of the power of Boolean algebra. Boolean algebra will be helpful later on in the work on contact networks. This is a good place to bring out the L.C.B.'s and have the series and shunt (AND and OR) switch arrangements shown. This should be a *demonstration*, not a *lab*.

A Boolean postulate allows a^2 or a^3 to be re-

duced to a simple a: "a man at a." Of course, few students will be able to handle anything but a very simple problem by this method. The important thing is that they understand what is being done and the resulting "evolution of the criterion." Classroom explanation is assisted by using colored ink on transparency T-0204, or colored chalk on the board. (An inexpensive set of 4-colored transparency pens is marketed as PENTEL PROJECTOR MARKER.)

T-0205 may be helpful now in giving an overall review of the decision-making process.

Section 5. Optimization with Few Alternatives. This course is almost exclusively about the real world; and the airport example gives a chance to contrast problem solutions that save money right now which are politically attractive and others that may be financially more attractive but only in the long run, and then only if things work out as expected. Another is that different criteria will, in general, lead to different optimum solutions. Criteria *are* important.

Some teachers prefer to omit the car-replacement problem, which can turn into busy work (T-0206a, b). It does carry a message to young people, however. Some of the motoring magazines give more up-to-date figures for specific car models. An interesting assignment for investigation outside class is finding the car-replacement program used by large businesses with many employees such as salesmen and service men on the road. Suggested businesses: power, gas, or telephone companies, supermarket chains. The crucial points are the questions: What are the criteria? How do they optimize? A report should be made to the class.

Section 6. Dynamic Programming. Begin the topic with T-0207, which looks deadly but turns out to be surprisingly easy if we start at the destination (dynamic-programming fashion) and work back. This can be presented as a separate work sheet, as suggested in Section 3 of this chapter. Use red ink to mark on the transparency each extension as it is agreed upon. Transparencies T-0212, T-0213, and T-0214 should be used.

The investigation of the number of possible routes will be made easier by using transparencies.

Notice that the dotted lines on T-0209 connect numbers which are the coefficients in a series of binomial expansions (Pascal's Triangle).

Section 7. Problems Without Solutions. The apartment house discussion will be an eye-opener to students in city high schools. They may wonder how the owner got so far into debt. It is standard business practice, of course, to borrow money in order to make money (just as a man might borrow money to buy a car needed in his business, or to take him to work). Still, you should be prepared for the young person who is ready to doubt the propriety of whatever "businessmen" do. The apparently excessive interest charges on the mortgages include installment payments on the principal.

Section 8. Final Comment. The work on the chapter might well conclude with F-0203, followed by class discussion.

B | BLACK AND WHITE TRANSPARENCIES

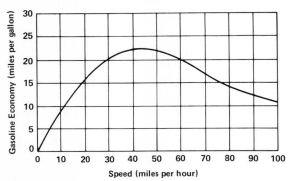

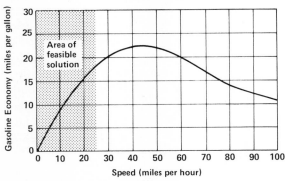

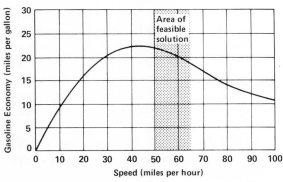

T-0201a *TOP:* **GASOLINE ECONOMY AS A FUNCTION OF SPEED**

T-0201b *MIDDLE:* **GASOLINE ECONOMY AS A FUNCTION OF SPEED (IMPOSITION OF SPEED-LIMIT CONSTRAINT)**

T-0201c *BOTTOM:* **GASOLINE ECONOMY AS A FUNCTION OF SPEED (CONSTRAINTS IMPOSED ON LIMITED-ACCESS ROADS)**

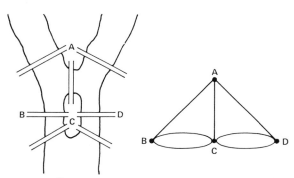

T-0202 KÖNIGSBERG BRIDGES WITH GRAPHICAL MODEL

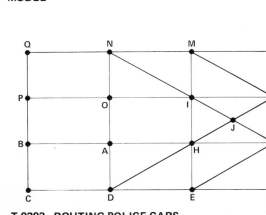

T-0203 ROUTING POLICE CARS

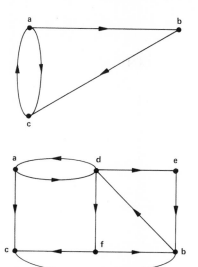

T-0204 TWO CORRIDOR PROBLEMS

	ESTIMATED DATA		COMPUTATIONS ("BRUTE FORCE" METHOD)			
1	2	3	4	5	6	7
Age of car in years	Sale Value	Oper. Cost.	Depreci-ation	Cumu. Oper. Cost	Total Cost	Av. Cost Per Year
0	$3000	—	—	—	—	—
1	2400	$ 800	$ 600	$ 800	$1400	$1400
2	1920	850	1080	1650	2730	1365
3	1540	900				
4	1230	950				
5	980	1000				
6	740	1050				
7	520	1100				
8	320	1150				
9	150	1200				
10	50	1250				

THE MODEL

	ESTIMATED DATA		COMPUTATIONS ("BRUTE FORCE" METHOD)			
1	2	3	4	5	6	7
Age of car in years	Sale Value	Oper. Cost	Depreci-ation	Cumu. Oper. Cost	Total Cost	Av. Cost Per Year
0	$300	—	—	—	—	—
1	2400	$ 800	$ 600	$ 800	$ 1400	$1400
2	1920	850	1080	1650	2730	1365
3	1540	900	1460	2550	4010	1337
4	1230	950	1770	3500	5270	1318
5	980	1000	2020	4500	6520	1304
6	740	1050	2260	5550	7810	1302
7	520	1100	2480	6650	9130	1304
8	320	1150	2680	7800	10480	1310
9	150	1200	2850	9000	11850	1317
10	50	1250	2950	10250	13200	1320

THE MODEL

T-0206a,b CAR REPLACEMENT PROBLEM

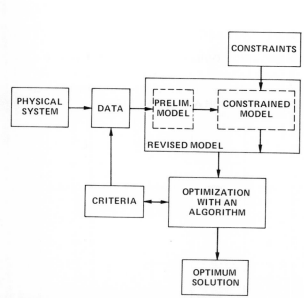

T-0205 FLOW CHART OF DECISION-MAKING

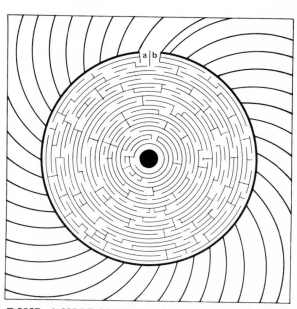

T-0207 A MORE COMPLEX ROUTE-PLANNING PROB-LEM (MAZE)

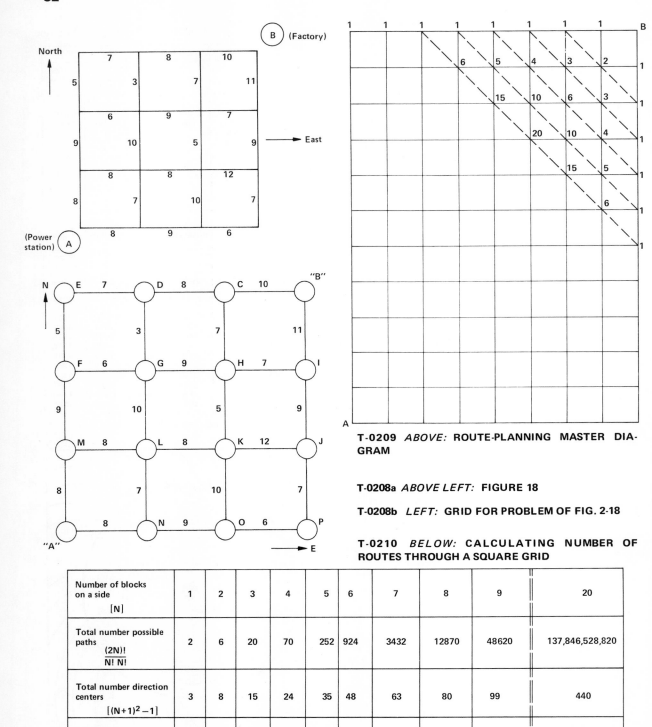

T-0209 *ABOVE:* **ROUTE-PLANNING MASTER DIA-GRAM**

T-0208a *ABOVE LEFT:* **FIGURE 18**

T-0208b *LEFT:* **GRID FOR PROBLEM OF FIG. 2-18**

T-0210 *BELOW:* **CALCULATING NUMBER OF ROUTES THROUGH A SQUARE GRID**

Number of blocks on a side [N]	1	2	3	4	5	6	7	8	9	20
Total number possible paths $\dfrac{(2N)!}{N!\,N!}$	2	6	20	70	252	924	3432	12870	48620	137,846,528,820
Total number direction centers $[(N+1)^2-1]$	3	8	15	24	35	48	63	80	99	440
Total number decision nodes $[N^2]$	1	4	9	16	25	36	49	64	81	400

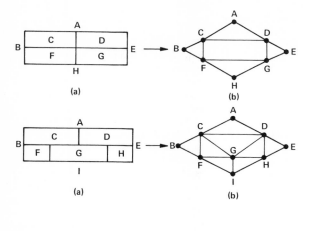

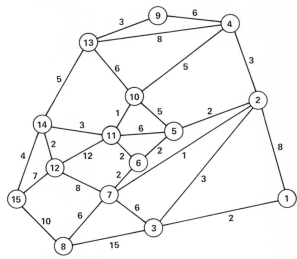

T-0214   PROBLEM 11

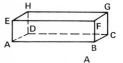

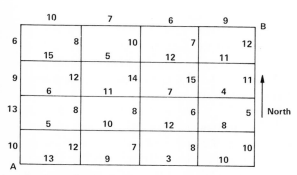

T-0211   QUESTIONS 9, 10, AND 15

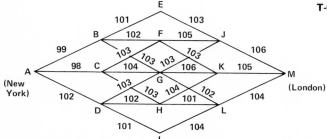

T-0212   PROBLEM 8

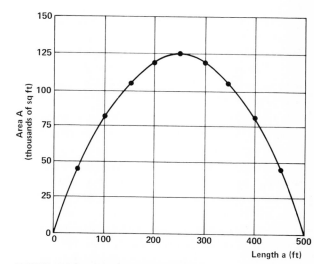

T-0215   LAB 1, PART B, QUESTION 1

T-0213   PROBLEM 10

C | CUES TO QUESTIONS AND PROBLEMS

Questions for Study and Discussion

1. A model is important to decision makers because it is a clear and concise description of a problem and very often can be made quantitative. It changes the problem from one of intuition or "common sense" to one of objective evaluation.

2. Detailed discussion can be found on pages 55-56 of the text. Basically, this type of problem has two phases. The first is to decide if a solution is possible. Once a solution is shown to be possible, the actual path can be found by Euler's solution.

3. Yes, for example, teaching a child the operations needed to dress himself can be classified as an algorithm and does not involve numbers.

4. a) Probably the most common algorithm is to make note of the purchase price and use pennies to get up to a 5¢ level and then use nickels, dimes, and quarters, in that order, to get up to a dollar. (The statement would be much longer if the possible 25¢, 50¢ and 75¢ way-stations were considered.)

b) When given a $5 bill, use the above procedure to get to the dollar level and then use dollar bills to get to $5.

Note that we do not tell her how to make change for the 22¢ , but rather the *general* system for making change.

5. Suggest that the students pick that piece of sporting equipment with which they are most familiar. For example ski equipment. The intended type of skiing offers some constraints, of course, but the criteria for the weekend recreational skier are safety, ease of control, and comfort. For a ski racer, on the other hand, the criteria might well be speed and balance, with the bindings and boots as tight as possible.

Generally speaking, the criteria fall into categories: (1) How serious are you about the sport? (2) What is your size?

To summarize, the following list contains specific criteria for each sport.

Equipment	Criteria
Skis & Ski Boots	Safety, weight and balance, ease of control, comfort, transportability.
Baseball Glove	Position played, size of hand, age and experience of ball player. Glove must be flexible but firm.
Surfboard	Will depend on weight and height of surfer and surf encountered, weight and balance. surf encountered, weight and balance.
Tennis Racket	Balance, weight, material used—wood or metal, age and experience of player, hand size.
4-Iron	Balance and weight, material used in shaft (wood, metal, glass), age and experience of player, type of hand grip.

6. As far as ski equipment is concerned, if one has to cut back on cost the place *not* to do it is in the purchase of boots and skis. Ski poles and clothing are items which allow for cutback. Skis and ski boots directly affect skiing fun and safety. In general, the "Luxury Look" and fancy material can be sacrificed, but the criteria which affect weight, balance, and safety must be retained.

7. One way to complete the path is

$$AHJGKIOPBPQNIMKGEHDA$$

Assuming that the four short blocks around J each take 1 min (they could be unpaved and muddy), the path shown takes 32 min, the other one takes 42 min, a saving of 10 min.

8. Extra-high density traffic on some cross streets at particular times, such as shift changes in factories; extra numbers of pedestrians for the same reason, or when schools let out. Need to allow fire engines, ambulances, police cars, and other emergency vehicles to pass. Traffic density going east on the same street.

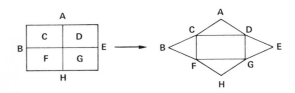

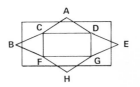

9. Each rectangular area, and each of the four outer regions, can be thought of as an "island," and each separating line is then a bridge. The number of bridges from each island is even. T-0211 can be used by showing 9a first, then 9b, then drawing 9b on the 9a transparency in a different color.

10. No solution is possible because 4 of the "Vertices" (C, D, G, J) have odd numbers of edges ("bridges").

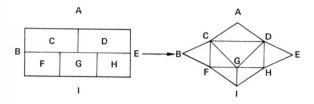

11. a) Maximum undistorted volume, perhaps dynamic range.

  b) Fidelity (he wants it to sound reasonably like the original, but has no use for loud sounds).

  c) All the above.

12. Yes, path BACBCDCAD: (You might want to assign starting point D to a portion of the class and compare paths.)

13. $(a+b+d)(b+e+f)(a+c+f)(a+d+e+f)$
  to light a · to light b · to light c · to light d

This assumes that the directional arrows in Fig. 2-14 do not apply to the light, and that a block is the distance from a to c. The problem can be further modified by stating that certain specific intersections must have a street light.

14. Example #1: immediate solution of problem of air pollution by automobiles by banning all cars. Results: chaos in public transportation, chaos in all activities which require numerous people to come together (business, educational, musical, theatrical, etc.). In consequence, the Gross National Product would drop catastrophically and so would tax income, leaving less money available for relief, Social Security, etc.

  Example #2: failure to solve air pollution by automobiles. Results: rising smog levels; physical damage to people's eyes, throats, and lungs; hospitals even more overcrowded; doctors, nurses, and aides more overworked; rising death tolls; rising medical costs. Airplane traffic interfered with, plans for business and for holidays interrupted, accidents increased.

15. The wires may be installed in many ways. AEHG, AEFG, ADHG, ADCG, ABFG, and ABCG would require a minimum of wire: ADCBFG, ABFEHG, ADHEFG, ABCDHG, and AEFBCG would require more wire. The AEHG and AEFG patterns are equally satisfactory since most of the wiring is at the ceiling with direct vertical access to A. No wiring changes would be required due to furniture shifts. If a student adds the constraint that the wire must be as inconspicuous as possible, he might run it on top of the baseboard ABCG or ADCG.

16. Model: to study X-rays from stars we need rockets to put satellites into orbit.

  Criteria:

  a) Satellite must be large enough to house scientific equipment and small enough to be launched.

  b) Satellite must be fairly stable, so that measurements can be taken.

  Constraints:

  a) X-rays from stars can only be studied from orbiting satellites because X-rays do not penetrate the atmosphere very far.

  b) Satellite must be able to communicate with earth.

17. Once a sketch for the footpaths of the park is drawn, the procedure for the solution of the problem is the same as in Question 2.

18. The constraints may be:

  a) Available money: capital is needed to buy a house (usually 10% of cost of house plus commission to the broker).

  b) Type of company: some companies ask employees to move frequently.

  Some of the criteria might be:

  a) Enough rooms (3 bedrooms) for a growing family.

  b) Need for flexibility: the young man may want to change jobs in the near future.

  c) Best use of money: buying a house represents an investment, while renting does not.

  d) Schools, churches, and stores should be nearby.

19. Probably money would not be as strong a constraint. Need for flexibility and number of rooms as criteria would not apply to the 55-year-old man, nor would schools, but an excess of rooms might; his wife won't want a big house to look after, if she can't hire help.

Problems

1. a)

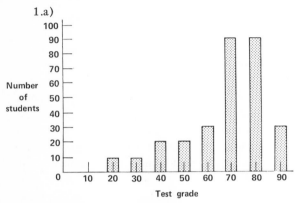

b) Passing grade would be 60%.

c) Grade for honor classes would be 90%.

2. a) This is a difficult problem. Class time should be set aside if the problem is assigned for homework. Although there is no definite algorithm for this problem, we can start by realizing that if we were *not* constrained by having only 5 coins, the optimum system for giving change would be the binary system. Since we are constrained, we can try the ternary system. It turns out that the binary system results in coins which are too small and the ternary system in coins whose values are too large.

	1st coin	2nd coin	3rd coin	4th coin	5th coin
binary	1	2	4	8	16
ternary	1	3	9	27	81

By using a number sequence roughly based on 2.5, the values which solve the coin problem are 1, 3, 8, 20, 50. Other values are also possible. Two such, generated by student-programmed computer:

$$1, 3, 7, 18, 48$$
$$1, 2, 5, 13, 34$$

b) Average number of coins required to make change using the current U.S. system is 4.24.

b) Average number of coins required to make change using the current U.S. system is 4.24.

c) Average number of coins required to make change for system developed in part(a) is 3.60.

3. For minimum fuel consumption, speed = 45 mph.

a) $\text{Fuel}_{max} = \frac{40}{16} + \frac{40}{15} = 5.2$ gal

$\text{Fuel}_{min} = \frac{40}{22} + \frac{40}{22} = 3.6$ gal

Fuel saved = 1.6 gal

b) $\text{Fuel}_{max \, speed} = \frac{40}{16} + \frac{40}{22} = 4.3$ gal

Fuel saved = 0.7 gal

c) $\text{Time}_{optimum} = \frac{40}{45} + \frac{40}{45} = 1.8$ hr

$\text{Time}_{fastest} = \frac{40}{70} + \frac{40}{45} = 1.5$ hr

Time wasted = 0.3 hr

With gasoline selling at \$.40 per gallon we save 0.7 gal x \$.40/gal or 28 ¢ by wasting 18 min.

4. To find the square root by this algorithm, it is quicker to estimate first to a whole number which looks about the right size (i.e., to find $\sqrt{46}$ to start with 7).

a) $\sqrt{72} = 8.50$

b) $\sqrt{6} = 2.45$

c) $\sqrt{948} = 30.8$

5. Use dynamic programming. A must have the last play where he picks up 1 or 2 matches; therefore he must have left B either 1 + 2 or 2 + 1 or 3. This indicates the algorithm: A and B *together* must pick up 3 matches during each "inning," so at the start of each inning there must be 3, 6, 9, 12, 15, and 18 matches. Hence A must play first and pick up 2.

6.

N	V_n	C_n	$V_o - V_n$	$C_1 + \ldots C_n$	C	C/N
1	\$2400	800	600	800	1400	1400
2	1920	850	1080	1650	2730	1365
3	1536	900	1464	2550	4014	1338
4	1229	950	1771	3500	5271	1318
5	983	1000	2017	4500	6517	1303
6	786	1050	2214	5550	7764	1294
7	629	1100	2371	6650	9021	1289
8	503	1150	2497	7800	10297	1287
9	402	1200	2598	9000	11598	1289

The average cost per year decreases until the 8th year, so best time to trade in is at the end of the 8th year.

7.

N	V_n	C_n	$V_o - V_n$	$C_1 + ..C_n$	C	C/N
1	2400	840	600	840	1440	1440
2	1920	935	1080	1775	2855	1427
3	1526	1035	1464	2810	4274	1424
4	1229	1140	1771	3950	5721	1430
5	983	1250	2017	5200	7217	1443
6	786	1365	2214	6565	8779	1463
7	629	1485	2371	8050	10421	1488

The optimum year to trade in is after 3 years.

8.

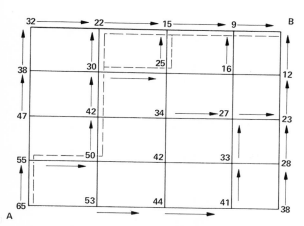

Note that there are two choices of path at one point

9.

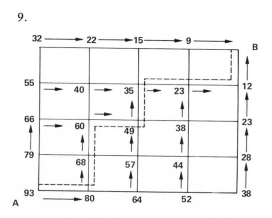

10.

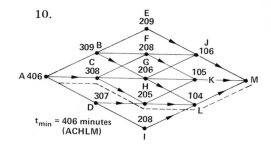

t_{min} = 406 minutes (ACHLM)

11.

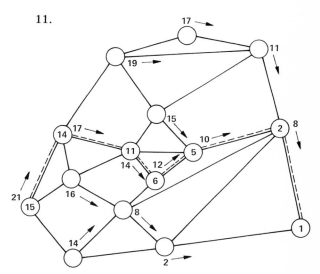

15, 14, 11, 6, 5, 2, 1 taking 21 units of time

12.

Junc.	Old esti-mate	Arrow to	New estimate #						Arrow to
			1	2	3	4	5	6	
2	8	1	5						3
3	2	1							1
4	11	2		8					2
5	10	2		7					2
6	12	5	10		8				7
7	8	3		6					2
8	14	7			12				7
9	17	4			14				4
10	15	5			12				5
11	14	6		12		10			6
12	16	7			14				7
13	19	4			16				4
14	17	11				15	13		11
15	21	14					19	17	14

Final route: 15, 14, 11, 6, 7, 2, 3, 1.

D | DEMONSTRATIONS, LABS, AND PROJECTS

I. Minimum Fence for Maximum Area

This experiment illustrates the fundamental elements of decision making.

Equipment for Each Lab Team:

3 sheets lab notebook graph paper, 4 (or 5) squares to the inch

2 10-in lengths of bare copper wire, #18 or heavier, without kinks or sharp bends. (This is much less trouble than using pipe cleaners.)

1 ruler with inch scale

General Lab Supplies:

1 pair pliers (more if available) for straightening kinks in wire.

Wire cutter

Extra graph paper and wire

Drawing compasses

The best way to manage the wire, before dispensing it, is to take a fresh spool, nip the end of the wire in a vise, unroll as long a piece as you have room to work with, grasp this end of the wire with pliers, and pull—hard enough to stretch the wire slightly. This will straighten it, and 10-in lengths can then be cut off easily.

For investigating Part B, Question 4, a fresh, unkinked length of wire is advisable.

Many students will quickly observe that they can work faster in the rectangular case if they merely sketch various fences on the squared paper. This is entirely proper. Care must be used to see that the "fence" is still "1000 feet."

Area determination is made by counting squares (looking forward to the integration procedure to be met later). Encourage intelligent shortcuts in the curved-fence cases (pencil outlines around rectangular blocks with areas easily calculated). The areas of partial squares outside these rectangles can be estimated as closely as the student thinks advisable. Remember that the precision of the exercise is low, and it is a good plan to pick two or more partial squares at a time which add up approximately to whole ones.

The compasses should be available in case someone wishes to improve on his crude fence shapes.

PART A

Answers to Questions:

*1. The criterion: to find the maximum area.

*2. The constraints: a) rectangular shape, b) 1000 ft of fencing.

*3. The maximum area would be about 125,000 ft^2 (250 x 500 ft). The perfect solution is a rectangle 2.5 x 5 in. With the measuring equipment supplied, an "error" (more exactly, an uncertainty) of half a square's edge or 1/8 (or 1/10 in) is quite likely, or about 5% and 3% in the two dimensions. "Error" percents add when their principals are multiplied, so the expected uncertainty is around 8% or 10,000 ft^2.

*4. The curved fence that results in maximum area is semicircular, and the area would be about 160,000 ft^2. This can be calculated as follows: For the whole circle the perimeter would be 2000 ft.

$$C = 2\pi R \quad \text{or} \quad 2000 = 2\pi R$$

$$R = \frac{1000}{\pi}$$

$$A_{semicircle} = \frac{\pi R^2}{2} = \frac{1,000,000\pi}{2\pi^2}$$

$$= 160,000 \text{ ft}^2$$

Here the uncertainty lies in a wandering radius, say 1/8 inch in 3¼ or 4%. R^2 raises the uncertainty to about 8%, so the expected area is 160,000 ± 8%, say between 145,000 and 175,000 sq ft.

PART B

The completed table follows:

Length a (ft)	Area A (ft^2)
0	0
50	45,000
100	80,000
150	105,000
200	120,000
250	125,000
300	120,000
350	105,000
400	80,000
450	45,000
500	0

Answers to Questions:

*1. Length (the independent variable) should be plotted on the horizontal axis (the abscissa).

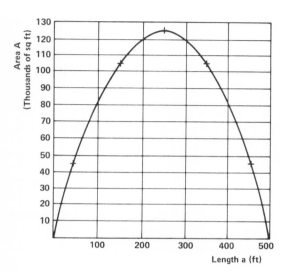

*2. $a = 250$ ft. Since $2a + b = 1000$, $b = 500$ ft.

*3. The study leading up to Part A, Question 4, makes it apparent that the fence should be an arc of a circle.

*4. For the 350-ft beach line, the area is about $128,000 \pm 8\%$.

For the 300-ft beach, it is about $102,000 \pm 8\%$.

The thing to notice is that as the chord of the circle shrinks from being a diameter, the area enclosed by an arc of constant length diminishes (and drops below 80,000 ft^2 when the chord disappears). Therefore *maximum* area bounded by a straight line and a given length of fence appears to be a semicircle. Of course this is because the straight line is part of the boundary, but not part of the fence, and its length is not a restriction.

It will be advisable to follow the exercise with a classroom discussion, insofar as possible involving students and helping them to become aware of the relative merits and drawbacks of scale models, mathematical models, and graphic models. Try such a question as: Which way of managing this investigation did you prefer? Why?

II. Optimization and the Paper Airplane

This experiment illustrates the fundamental elements of decision making, though not so obviously as the previous one. Note reference in Bibliography, Section G of this chapter.

Equipment for Each Student:

> 1 sheet of paper, typewriter stock or the like
> 1 single-edge razor blade (or double-edge with one edge protected by masking tape)
> 2 in of ½-in masking tape
> 2 "standardized" paper clips (i.e., out of the same package for all)
> 1 ruler with inch scale

General Lab Supplies:

> Spares of all the above
> Razor blades may be replaced with shears

A possible variant in the rules would allow a preliminary practice model to be built and then a final official entry in the competition. This should be decided by vote of the class after due consideration. It helps impress the elements of decision making, and the realization that the process is not always straightforward. For instance, no one is expected to devise an algorithm for optimizing his model plane. On the other hand, since the planes are load carriers, the optimum design is probably for a large plane, not a small one.

III. Games and Algorithms

PART A

Equipment for Each Lab Team (2 students):

> 11 matches or toothpicks

The solution (algorithm) can be determined by dynamic programming: work from the end toward the beginning, as follows:

The last (nth) move must be B's, so he must find 1 match on the table.

Move $(n-1)$ is A's, who can leave 1 for B if he finds 2, 3, or 4 matches.

Move $(n-2)$ is B's, who must find 5 matches if he is to leave 2, 3, or 4.

Move $(n-3)$ is A's, who can leave 5 if he finds 6, 7, or 8 matches.

Move $(n-4)$ is B's, who must therefore find 9 matches.

Move $(n-5)$ or first is A's, who must pick up 2 matches.

The algorithm: A's moves must leave, in succession, 9, 5, and 1 match.

PART B

Have three people, one who will lie every time (L), one who will tell the truth every time (T), and one who will vary from truth to lie (U), stand in front of the class and let the class in free discussion try to develop the algorithm under the rules stipulated in the text.

The possible arrangements are as follows:

LTU
UTL
ULT
TLU
LUT
TUL

Left   Right

1. Ask the person on the left the following question: Is the Liar to the immediate left of the Undecided person?

If the answer is "yes," the only possible arrangements of people are:

LTU
UTL
ULT   Group Y
TLU

If the answer is "no," the only possible arrangements of people are:

UTL
ULT
LUT   Group N
TUL

If the answer to Question 1 was "yes," ask the center person Question 2. Is white white?

If the answer is "yes," the arrangement can only be:
LTU or UTL Group YY

If the answer is "no," the arrangement can only be:
ULT or TLU Group YN

If, on the other hand, the answer to the first question was "no," ask the person on the right Question 2. Is white white?

If the answer is "yes," the arrangement can only be:
ULT or LUT Group NY

If the answer is "no," the arrangement can only be:
UTL or TUL Group NN

You now have only one of the four possible groups left to question YY or YN or NY or NN. Ask the center person in Group YY 3: Is L on the left? If he says "yes," the arrangement is LTU. If he says "no," it is UTL.

Ask the center person in Group YN: Is T on the left? If he says "yes," the arrangement is ULT. If "no," then TLU.

Ask the person on the right in group NY: Is L to the left of U? If the answer is "yes," then LUT. If the answer is "no," then ULT.

Ask the person on the right in group NN: Is T to the left of U? If the answer is "yes," then the arrangement is UTL. If the answer is "no," then the arrangement is TUL.

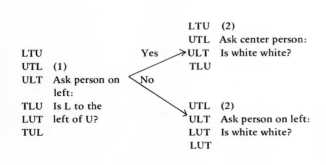

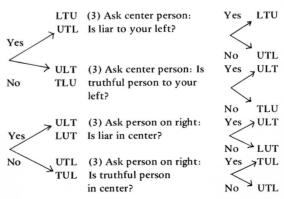

Demonstration Competition

A CONTEST IN BRIDGE DESIGN

Nearly all who have tried this contest have been impressed with its success and value. The set of rules printed below are merely suggestions, and can be changed as appropriate. You can alter the model and constraints to fit your own situation, with the assistance of your students.

Use the results for public relations: parents' night, school open house, bulletin board photographs, and school and local daily newspapers.

A similar contest in kite building and flying (time to reach a given altitude) would be interesting.

RULES OF THE CONTEST

1. *Model*: a balsa-wood bridge, free standing (not fastened to any base), not more than 16 inches in length and not more than 10 inches in height. The river to be spanned with no intermediate supports is 10 inches wide, and a 5-inch clearance is required in the center for ships to pass through.

2. *Constraints*: permitted building materials are balsa sticks, 3/32-in sq, held together with "Brand X" model-airplane glue; maximum length of balsa used: 30 ft.

3. *Criterion*: greatest load carried. The load can be applied by means of a drill press pushing on a loading block which rests on the bridge, while the latter in turn rests on a platform scale. If your drill press has insufficient clearance, use it to exert force on a lever which loads the bridge. Several ways to compare the bridges will occur to you, and the decision among these and any others thought of by the contestants should be agreed upon after preliminary discussion. For example, each bridge in turn could be tested to destruction, or to the first sign of it; or all bridges might be subjected to a given load, those which sustained it being passed into a higher classification; then these high-rated bridges could be tested with a heavier load. It would probably be well to photograph all bridges, either individually or as a group, before making any tests.

4. *Optimization*: no algorithm for balsa-wood bridge design is known to exist, so optimization will have to be done empirically. Contestants should be encouraged to make preliminary designs on paper. This will lead them to questions of dimensions, angles, and bracing, which they should resolve by actually building three or four varying examples of the bridge in question and subjecting them to their own crude tests. Gluing methods could also be studied. This brings up one other matter for preliminary discussion: whether (for reason of time saving or of money saving) there should be a limit on the amount of material allowed for testing, and if so, how great.

Reference: Bibliography, third item.

E | EVALUATION

The questions in this section are rated according to the chapter objectives and the performance levels stated in the introduction to the teacher's manual. This group of questions is not intended to be all inclusive, but just as a guide to possible questions. Zeros in the chapter objective column indicate no chapter objective for this question.

Chapter Objective	Performance Level	Judged to be Relatively Easy:
		In Questions 1 through 4, check the best answer:
3	I	1. The most economical speed at which a car might be driven a) is always the same. b) is faster in daytime than at night. c) depends upon who is driving. d) sometimes depends upon the legal restrictions at the time. e) depends upon how badly the driver wants to reach his destination.
1a	I	2. Nearly all human activity is necessarily based upon a) modeling. b) optimizing.

Chapter Objective	*Performance Level*	*Judged to be Relatively Easy:*

c) economizing.
d) dynamic programming.
e) decision making.

1a	I

3. The objectives of a problem are known as the
a) decisions.
b) criteria.
c) constraints.
d) models.
e) optimization.

1a	I

4. Which of the following is a list of instructions for the solution of a class of problems?

a) A production plan.
b) An algorithm.
c) A computation program.
d) An optimum solution.
e) An equation or formula.

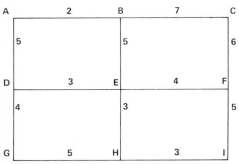

5. A high school principal visits a class in *The Man-Made World* and is so surprised to find what they are studying that he discusses his problems with them, using the above diagram, which stands for a pattern of corridors. Mark *each* of the following statements *T,* if it is true, or *F,* if it is false.

1b	I

a) If he writes on the chalkboard $(a + b)$, it means that he must station monitors at a and at b.

1b	I

b) If he writes $ab,$ it means that points a and b can be covered from either point but no others.

0	II

c) If the corridors can be traversed in either direction, it is evident that d can be covered from any of the other points.

0	II

d) If the corridors can be traversed in either direction, it is evident that a monitor at b can be assigned to cover all the other points.

0	I

e) If the principal writes a^2, it means that he must post two monitors at a.

0	I

6. Find the fastest route to follow in traveling from G to C, if the numbers represent the time per block in minutes.

7. Mark each of the following statements T, if it is true, or F, if it is false:

2	I

a) Unless he has an answer to every social problem, a mayor does not deserve to be reelected.

1a	I

b) Criteria are added factors that must be taken into account in the model of a decision problem.

Chapter Objective	Performance Level	

Judged to be Relatively Easy:

3 and 7	I	c) When two criteria conflict, it is reasonable to seek a compromise solution.
1a	I	d) A boy planning for a weekend has only $8 and nobody will lend him any more. These facts are constraints to be considered in making his plans.
1a	I	e) The Konigsberg-bridges problem was solved by use of an algebra.
2	I	f) When political decisions are to be made, their probable effects should be considered before they are made.
5	I	g) Many kinds of decision problems have no known definite method of solution.
5	I	h) Everybody ought to use the whole decision-making scheme before he makes up his mind about anything.
1	I	i) If only a *few* possible solutions to a problem exist, it is important to find an algorithmic solution.
0	II	j) If an airport were placed on an artificial island in the ocean, it could only be used at low tide.

Judged to be More Difficult:

In Questions 8 and 9, check the best answer:

1a	II	8. The model for a decision problem should always be a) an exact picture of the real world. b) valid for the particular situation. c) more complex than the real situation. d) an ideal situation. e) none of the above.
3	I	9. In everyday life we often make decisions on the basis of subjective criteria. This means that the criteria a) have been mathematically defined. b) certainly do not meet all the specifications of the problem. c) depend on the individual decision maker. d) need production-planning constraints. e) depend upon the constraints.
3	III	10. In a certain high school there was no marching band, but the School Committee voted to buy instruments if the Music Department would organize a aand. A debate then started in the school: Should there be a Boys' Band and a Girls' Band, or should there be a single band with boys and girls? From the point of view of the decision-making process, suggest a reason for this trivial argument.
2	II	11. A "match game" starts with 8 matches. The rules are that each person in turn may pick up either 1 or 2 matches. The loser is the player who picks up the last match. Give an algorithm by which the player who plays first can always win.
3	II	12. "It is common to find that one man's performance criterion is another man's constraint and vice versa." When would "top speed 70 mph" be a constraint on an automobile designer? When would it be a performance criterion?
4	I	13. A hunter has 100 ft of fencing with which to build a "run" for his dog. For convenience, he will build a rectangle, but wants to find out what dimensions will give the largest area. He carries out the following analysis:

Chapter Objective	Performance Level

Judged to be More Difficult:

$2x + 2y = 100$, or

$x + y = 50$

$A = xy$

$= x(50 - x)$

$= 50x - x^2$

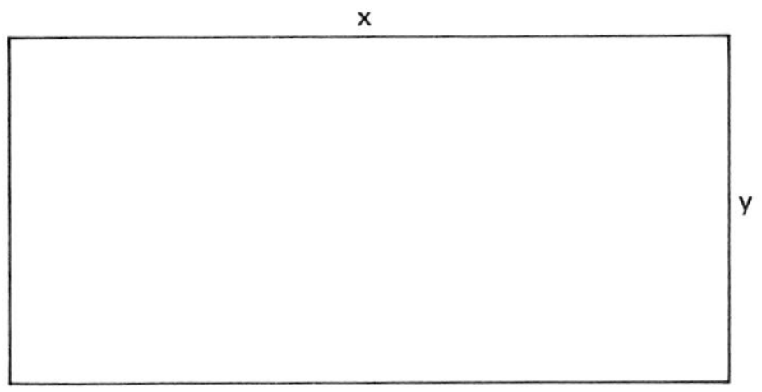

Fill out this table, and plot A against x on this graph chart. Connect the points with a smooth curve, and estimate

a) the best value of x.
b) the corresponding value of y.
c) the resulting largest area.

x	A
10	
20	
30	
40	

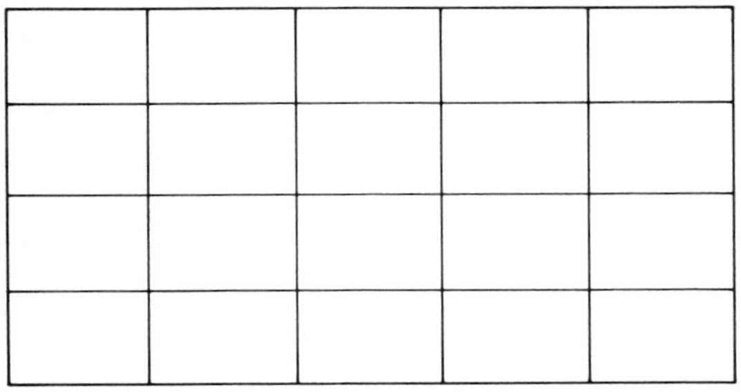

14. Mr. A builds a fence along the edge of his house lot. Mr. B then says that the fence is actually inside his boundary line and sues Mr. A for trespass. The case is heard by a judge alone, without a jury. Court cases are usually problems in decision making. The following statements are based on the example shown:

1. The criterion for the judge is the proper position of the boundary.
2. The judge's final decision can afterward be optimized by calling a surveyor as a witness.
3. Constraints provided by real estate laws must be considered by the judge.
4. Mr. A's testimony before the judge is also a constraint.
5. Proper decision can only be made by finding an algorithm.

Which of the above statements is correct?

a) All five statements
b) Statements 1, 2, 3, and 4
c) Statements 1, 3, and 4 only
d) Statements 3, 4, and 5 only
e) Statements 1 and 3 only

3   II

Solutions to Evaluation Questions:

1. d
2. e
3. b
4. b

5. a) F
   b) F
   C) T
   d) T
   e) F

6. 17 min; GDEFC

7. a) F f) T
   b) F g) T
   c) T h) F
   d) T i) F
   e) F j) F

8. b
9. c

10. Either the debaters had different models in mind, or they used different criteria.

11. A picks up his matches to leave 7, 4, and 1 after his three turns.

Solutions to Evaluation Questions:

12. It would be a constraint if, by law or for another reason, the car being designed was required not to be able to run faster than 70 mph. It would be a performance criterion if the car had a very small motor for the weight of the body but even so he was able to drive the car at a speed as high as 70 mph.

13.

x	A
10	400
20	600
30	600
40	400

a) 25 ft
b) 25 ft
c) 625 ft^2

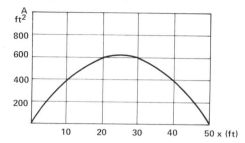

14. e

F | FILMS

F-0201   THE SEVEN BRIDGES OF KÖNIGSBERG

Recommendation: Highly recommended for illustration of this problem.

Application: Concept development. Use either as an introduction to the problem or after students have read the problem in the text.

Length and Type: 4 min, color, sound.

Source: #3

Summary: A delightful animated presentation of this classical problem, showing Euler's analysis.

F-0202   CRITICAL PATH

Recommendation: Good film to illustrate another type of optimization.

Application: Enrichment. Use after Chapter 2.

Length and Type: 15 min, color, sound.

Source: #3

Summary: This is a British film which shows, by animation, how the concept of "critical path" is used in establishing schedules in the construction industry.

F-0203   SCIENCE AND SOCIETY—A RACE AGAINST TIME

Recommendation: Good film for reinforcing technology-society interactions.

Application: To emphasize the difficulty of social problems that have resulted from the application of scientific knowledge.

Length and Type: 30 min, b & w, sound, TV film.

Source: #5

Summary: President Dubridge of Cal Tech and Vice Chairman of the Board of TRW, Inc., Simon Ramo, predict that our problems will be solved, but will become worse first.

G | GENERAL

Bibliography

R. S. Barnaby, *How to Make and Fly Paper Airplanes.* Bantam Books

M. Gardner, ed., *Scientific American Book of Mathematical Puzzles and Diversions.* Simon and Schuster, 1959 (1st book), 1961 (2nd book) (A) (paper)

> Some mazes and logic problems. Mostly off the point of this course, however.

T. R. Porter, compiler, *Teaching Tips from The Science Teacher,* 1960—1966. NSTA, 1967. Vol. 2, *Earth-Space Science;* Vol. 3, *Physical Science.* (B)

> All members of the NSTA know the quality and pertinence of these articles.

B. A. Trakhtenbrot, *Algorithms and Automatic Computing Machines,* D. C. Heath, 1963 (A) (paper)

> Some of the algorithms are familiar, some are new. Shows how an algorithm fits into a computer, discusses Turing machines and the question of solvable and unsolvable problems.

"Resale Prices and Depreciation of Automobiles." *Motor Trend Magazine,* June, 1967.

CHECK LIST FOR CHAPTER 3

OPTIMIZATION APPROX. TIME: Text: 11 days Lab: 2-3 days

A. APPROACH	CLASS PERIODS	B. BLACK & WHITE TRANSPARENCIES	C. CUES (k = key problem) Discussion Questions	Easy	Medium	Hard	D. DEMONSTRATIONS, LABS & PROJECTS	E. EVALUATION	F. FILMS	G. GENERAL
1. Introduction	1		1, 2, 3							III
2. Queueing Problems			9							
3. Probability	2	0301	8			1,19		3:5,6,9, 11,18; 4:7-5		
4. Queueing Studies	2	0302	10		2,6k	3,4k, 5,7	I	2;3:1-4, 8, 10, 12,13 7:2,3,6		
5. Games	1	0303,4					II	3:17;5; 7:4		
6. Linear-Programming Problems	1		4		10k					
7. Graphing Inequalities	1	0306, 11	5, 6, 7	9k	8k			1;3:7,14, 15;6:1,2; 7:7,8	0301	
8. A Transportation-Planning Problem	2	0305a, b c; 0307, 0308–10 0312–15		16k	12k, 13,14, 17,18	11,15	III	3:16; 6:3,4; 7:1	0302	II
9. Final Comment	1									

Optimization
3

A | APPROACH

I. Purpose and Organization of the Chapter

Chapter 3 is a direct continuation of Chapter 2. It is concerned with a further discussion of optimization methods. As time has passed, more and more cases have been recognized where a single method applies to several situations. By now so many exist that in such a book as *The Man-Made World* only a small sample can be presented. Those involved here are queueing, game theory, and linear programming. In queueing theory, methods are considered for mitigating an inherently annoying (and sometimes costly) condition: waiting in line. Game theory examines the situation where there are two or more competitors each intent on his own maximum advantage (in many cases at the other's expense). Recently, however, there has been emphasis on games in which everyone wins. These are called nonzero sum games. Buckminster Fuller's "World Game" is such an endeavor. Linear programming enables one to cope with two or more variables: what mix is most profitable or otherwise desirable? All of these have had their greatest development in quite recent years.

About half the chapter is concerned with queueing theory, including a necessary interpolation on probability. After a detour to look at game theory (a quite different kind of optimization), the chapter ends with a discussion of linear programming and the necessary technique of handling linear inequalities by means of graphs.

II. Objectives for Students

Upon completion of the activities, discussion, and reading involved in the study of this chapter, students should be able to:

1. Recognize and identify the following terms: *feasible region, game theory, linear programming, payoff matrix, probability, queue and queueing, random, strategy,* and *utilization factor.*

2. Calculate probabilities in very simple cases, such as the probability of drawing a face card from a shuffled pack.

3. Apply the concept of probability in the treatment of arrival time in a queue (random arrival).

4. Compare the application of queueing theory to people seeking service and to components in a production line.

5. Predict, with the aid of queueing theory, the outcome of efforts to improve service at such places as toll booths and supermarkets (a) by supplying more service channels, or (b) by diminishing average service time.

6. Explain the use of game theory as a serious effort to maximize one's benefits or at least to mini-

mize one's losses in spite of the worst one's rivals can do.

7. Demonstrate the method of graphing linear equalities and inequalities on Cartesian coordinates.

8. Use the skills involved in (7) in solving simple linear-programming problems with two independent variables.

III. Suggestions for Teaching

By the time this chapter is reached, you may feel that the calendar is pressing you. All the material here happens to be unusually interesting and you will be loath to omit any. Actually, many of the later chapters are quite a bit shorter as can be seen in the original timetable in the front of this book. One solution, if you feel pressed for time, is to reduce the emphasis on some sections such as the latter parts of Sections 3, 5, and 8 now and plan to pick them up later if time permits.

Section 1. Introduction.

Section 2. Queueing Problems.   Queues are so much a part of everybody's life that not much time need be spent on this descriptive section, except as a reading assignment after discussing Questions 9 and 10 in class. Since standing in queues is a bore, and few pay much attention to them, students may be fascinated to find out how much there is to know about them.

The mathematical theory of queues was founded with the use of certain simplifying assumptions, of which three are especially important:

a) The operation has reached a "steady state."

b) The pool of customers is not at all depleted as they arrive and are serviced (practically true in nearly all cases).

c) Arrivals are random. The need to define this term accounts for the detour into probability in the next section.

The concept of "steady state" is a statistical one, and in effect means that the averages no longer fluctuate measurably as more data are included. It takes a very long time indeed to reach this condition. In the case of the supermarket, the store will close for the night long before a "steady state" occurs.

This brings up a logical question: Since the steady state is so hard to reach, is queueing theory actually used in business? One of the best-known and most active developers of queueing theory is the telephone industry, which does use it in forecasting future needs for switching equipment. The quality of telephone service in many of our largest cities (notably New York) is so bad that one cannot help wondering about the value of queueing theory. While the theory is good, the model from which it was derived was built on incomplete data. The theory has nothing to offer toward predicting completely unexpected major local shifts in population, especially of business offices, which overload switchboards which were supposedly designed to be good for a decade. The control of queues in industry is certainly extremely important. Lack of one particular kind of component, because it has been blocked in a queue, can shut down an entire factory.

Section 3. Probability.   If you stand beside an interstate highway, you may see a car with the license MASS 215 072. What is the probability that this will happen? Obviously, so near 0 that one cannot tell the difference (something like 1 in 10^8 at present), and the same for any other license—including the ones you actually do see. Such an actual occurrence of an utterly improbable event has caused a good deal of philosophical dismay. Before your students lose themselves in this, point out that in this section we are dealing with a *limited set* of events, and the essential thing is that any one of the set is equally likely.

The principal question to be answered at present is the technical meaning of the word "random." It is worth a minute or two to distinguish between "random" and "irregular" arrivals. In the former, if time is broken into equal brief intervals, an arrival during any one is as probable as during any other. Contrast this with the irregular arrival of students at the principal's office: it is much more probable that they will turn up during time intervals near class-changing times than at others.

Experimental studies of probability (like coin tossing, or the wrong hats question, T-0301) are attractive to think about but quickly become extremely dull. A study of coin tossing would have to continue until a "steady state" is reached, as defined above. Life has too many important obligations. A different way to handle the wrong hats question might be to draw up a series of tables like those in T-0301 and determine the probabilities by actual count; but the number of entries for n men is $n!$ or 6, 24, 120, 720 for 3, 4, 5, 6 men respectively. This is already unmanageable, and an experimental study with real hats takes as long as it does to toss coins. Therefore you are advised to skip the idea.

Your pupils may be both fascinated and puzzled by the three-way "duel." This is in fact one of the problems that might be discussed in game theory (but with three "players" it gets a bit sticky). One ingredient missing from the argument is the question: Why are they shooting, and how mad at each other are they? Push the students on to the explanatory final paragraph, and suggest that we have a kind of model of the automobile industry. Here 1 takes pains not to kill off 3 lest it bring on regulation of the industry by the Federal government. The model also resembles the television broadcasting industry in which a few major networks had a weak sister for a long time.

Section 4. Queueing Studies.   Here it is easy to become lost in detail. Keep your students aware that the study of queues is a branch of the topic of optimization. The aim of queueing studies is to minimize the average queue length (and of course the time a person in the queue wastes while waiting in it).

"Exponential distribution of times between arrivals" means, in effect, that there is a most probable interarrival time; either shorter or longer intervals occur less often. The greater the difference between the length of the most probable interval and the length of some actual interval, the less likely the latter is.

Probably the best way to handle this section is to do the first lab exercise, Part A, in the classroom. One student can roll the die, five others keep the records (and the teams should be changed every "hour" or twenty rolls). The records needed are:

1. Arrival time (as in Fig. 3-8, T-0302).
2. Interarrival intervals, in terms either of an

arbitrary time length T or of actual minutes, whichever you prefer. These will be averaged at the end.

3. Servicing record; this will help in drawing up the queue-length record by showing when the barber is at liberty.

4. Queue-length graph (as in Fig. 3-9, T-0302).

5. Table of queue lengths, to be averaged at the end. Yard or meter sticks are needed for numbers 1, 3, and 4. Afterward the data can be reinterpreted. What would happen if the servicing time were reduced to 15 min (or lengthened to 20)? What would happen if there were two barbers (assuming that nobody in the queue insists on his special barber)? In the servicing record, use white chalk for one barber, yellow for the other, and chart one of them above the axis and the other below.

Students should not be expected to learn the formulas for queue length. Remind them as often as necessary that the q formulas are part of a mathematical model, no more. It would be worth asking them to try to put the formula $q = \beta/(1 - \beta)$ into comprehensible English, just to show that the language of algebra has certain advantages. (The formula might be expressed as "the average queue length is the quotient of the utilization factor divided by the nonutilization factor," but is this either comprehensible or English?) It will perhaps be more comprehensible to do a little algebraic simplification in this manner: let S = average servicing time and let I = average interval between arrivals of customers. Then $\beta = S/I$. Now substitute these letters into the q formula:

$$q = \frac{\frac{S}{I}}{1 - \frac{S}{I}}$$

Multiply by I/I on the right-hand side, giving

$$q = \frac{S}{I - S} = \frac{\text{average servicing time}}{\text{average idle time}}$$

It may seem intuitively reasonable to most students that the queue length should be inversely proportional to the idle time: the smaller the proportion of the time that the facility is unused, the longer the queue is likely to become. Unfortunately, it is not possible to make the formula for fixed service times equally easy to swallow.

Section 5. Games. Here again, as in the study of queues, it is easy to forget that the topic is optimization, that the point is not the games as such but the serious topic of business (or other) rivalry. Of course, most of the games presented seem (and are) trivial. The optimization algorithms are not. The games have been chosen because they show fairly clearly what is going on (granted that the mixed strategy algorithm is a bit complex).

For the teacher's benefit (not his students') we attempt an explanation. Consider the games presented under "Solution of Simple Games." In the first, the solution stated has the initial design of maximizing X's gain, then of minimizing Y's loss; in the second, the argument is reversed: first we minimize Y's loss, then maximize X's gain. These are evidently optimizations, and fairly clear.

There is another type of game, like the following:

		Y	
		y_1	y_2
X	x_1	6	5
	x_2	5	4

Here X will play x_1 because thus he will gain no less than 5 (his "maximin"). Y, on the other hand, reasons that he should play y_2, where at most he will lose (his "minimax") 5. The invariable payoff is, thus, 5, which is called a "saddle point."

Turning now to the game in this section of the text, we find no saddle point because X's maximin is 4 while Y's minimax is 6. This occasions the need for mixed strategies on both sides. Morganstern and von Neumann gave the algorithm quoted in our text, supported by a lot of algebra. Its essence is as follows. Suppose a whole set of many long series of games were played, in which each series was conducted according to a different strategy mix (on both sides). For instance, let Y first play nothing but y_1, while X varies his strategies between x_1 and x_2, first always x_1, then x_1 6 times to once for x_2, then 5 to 2, etc. (or any other series of values you wish); then let Y shift to (say) a 6 to 1 variation while X goes through the original plays again. Now, for each series, calculate the probable payoff. Finally, arrange the payoffs in a matrix. The matrix turns

out to have a saddle point, and it comes at the strategy-mix described in the text. This is all described on p. 1274 (Volume 2) of *World of Mathematics* (see Bibliography at end of this chapter).

The final comment of the section should be stated to the class prior to the assignment of the section, to explain why game theory was invented. The hope mentioned at the end assumes that the two competitors ignore the physical world at their peril, and that enlightened cooperation may be best for all concerned.

Lab II consists of a series of games involving strategy, but not game theory as discussed in this section. It can therefore be done at whatever time during the study of the chapter that is most convenient for the teacher.

Section 6. Linear-Programming Problems. Here we have the final example of an optimization method. A technique which was suggested earlier proves quite useful here; that is, to have the students work on Problems 11 and 18 in class before any discussion or assignment of the section. After they have been sufficiently discouraged by the difficulty of the problems (in about 5 min), assign the study of Sections 6 and 7 for home study.

Section 7. Graphing Inequalities. Inequalities are presumably studied at one time or another by most high school undergraduates, but because very little use is (or used to be) made of the concept, especially in connection with graphs, you should certainly spend plenty of time in this review work.

Section 8. A Transportation-Planning Problem. This is a difficult problem. Allow plenty of time, and plan to have F-0301 at hand for help. It may be worth remarking that the solution to such a problem as this may conceivably lie anywhere along one edge of the feasible area, if this happens to have the same slope as the cost equation; it is not *necessarily* at a vertex.

Good algebra students should be able to see that in the equation $y = -3x + (4596 - C)$ it is desired to make C a minimum. Then by rather simple reasoning, the smaller C grows, the larger $(4596 - C)$ becomes, and the *higher* on the y-axis the intercept comes. There are other problems, however, in which the intercept term becomes smaller as

C is optimized (usually minimized, of course, though not necessarily so). E. g., suppose the intercept term had been $(C - 4596)$, where of course $C \geq 4596$. Here, then, the intercept slides lower on the y-axis as C shrinks, and the vertex to select is at the lower left, provided the cost equation slopes downward to the right.

Another kind of optimization that is very important to builders and can probably be studied at the builder's or architect's office if a big structure is going up near you, is Critical Path Analysis (see F-0302). Several teachers have asked that the minimum-wire-length problem be retained. It will be found in Section G.

Section 9. Final Comment. This section reviews the chapter quite well. One new idea suggested is that occasional small bottlenecks might actually improve the total system involving queues. Students might want to challenge or support that statement based on their own experiences. During this type of discussion many of the less mathematical but more imaginative students sometimes shine.

B | BLACK AND WHITE TRANSPARENCIES

The 3 men are: A   B   C

The hat returns: v = no one gets his own hat

#			
1	A	B	C
2	A	C	B
3	B	A	C
4	B	C	A v
5	C	A	B v
6	C	B	A

2 v's out of 6

Probability $p = \dfrac{2}{6}$

$p = 33\%$

The 4 men are: A   B   C   D

The hat returns:

#				
1	A	B	C	D
2	A	B	D	C
3	A	C	B	D
4	A	C	D	B
5	A	D	B	C
6	A	D	C	B
7	B	A	C	D
8	B	A	D	C v
9	B	C	A	D
10	B	C	D	A v
11	B	D	A	C v
12	B	D	C	A
13	C	A	B	D
14	C	A	D	B v
15	C	B	A	D
16	C	B	D	A
17	C	D	A	B v
18	C	D	B	A v
19	D	A	B	C v
20	D	A	C	B
21	D	B	A	C
22	D	B	C	A
23	D	C	A	B v
24	D	C	B	A v

9 out of 24

$p = \dfrac{9}{24}$

$p = 38\%$

T-0301 THE HAT PROBLEM

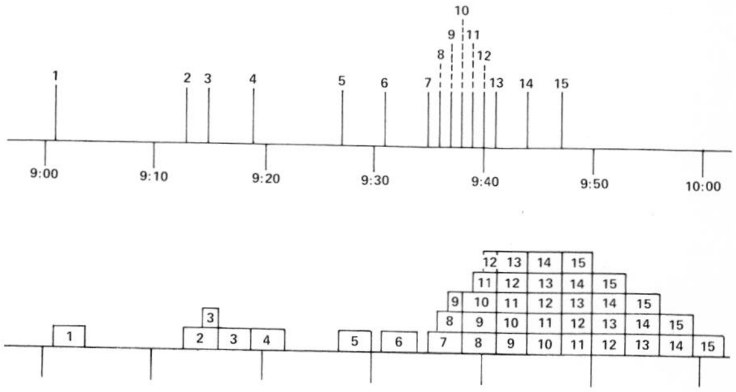

1	9:01	6	9:31	11	9:39
2	9:13	7	9:35	12	9:40
3	9:15	8	9:36	13	9:41
4	9:19	9	9:37	14	9:44
5	9:27	10	9:38	15	9:47

T-0302 QUEUEING PROBLEM

First Game

		JOE One	JOE Two
DICK	One	10	−10
	Two	−10	10

Second Game

		JOE One	JOE Two
DICK	One	10	−20
	Two	0	10

T-0303 JOE AND DICK GAMES

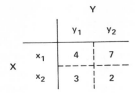

	Y	
	y_1	y_2
x_1	4	7
x_2	3	2

X always plays x_1
Y always plays y_1
Value of game = 4

	Y	
	y_1	y_2
x_1	6	2
x_2	5	3

Y always plays y_2
X always plays x_2
Value of game = 3

	Y		
	y_1	y_2	Diff.
x_1	4	7	3
x_2	6	2	4
Diff.	2	5	

x_1 4 times to x_2 3 times
y_1 5 times to y_2 2 times

T-0304 THREE MATRICES

WHEAT FREIGHT RATES ($/carload)

To \ From	Denver	Miami	New York
Grand Forks	42	55	60
Chicago	36	47	51

DATA ARRANGEMENT FOR SOLVING TRANSPORTATION PROBLEM

↓ Quantity in storage \ Quantity → to be delivered DEST. ORIGIN	⟨20⟩ Denver	⟨36⟩ Miami	⟨34⟩ New York
⟨50⟩ Grand Forks	42	55	60
⟨40⟩ Chicago	36	47	51

T-0305a TRANSPORTATION-PLANNING PROBLEM

DATA ARRANGEMENT FOR SOLVING TRANSPORTATION PROBLEM

QUANTITY IN STORAGE	QUANTITY TO BE DELIVERED \ DEST. ORIGIN	⟨20⟩ DENVER	⟨36⟩ MIAMI	⟨34⟩ NEW YORK
⟨50⟩	GRAND FORKS	42 \ x	55 \ y	60 \ 50 − x − y
⟨40⟩	CHICAGO	36 \ 20 − x	47 \ 36 − y	51 \ x + y − 16

Since amounts shipped cannot be negative:

$X \geqslant 0$
$Y \geqslant 0$
$50 - X - Y \geqslant 0$
$20 - X \geqslant 0$
$36 - Y \geqslant 0$
$X + Y - 16 \geqslant 0$

Inequalities to be satisfied (terms rearranged):

$X \geqslant 0$
$Y \geqslant 0$
$Y \leqslant - X + 50$
$X \leqslant 20$
$Y \leqslant 36$
$Y \geqslant - X + 16$

$$C = 42X + 55Y + 60(50 - X - Y) + 36(20 - X) + 47(36 - Y) + 51(X + Y - 16)$$
$$C = 4596 - 3X - Y$$

T-0305b TRANSPORTATION-PLANNING PROBLEM

FEASIBILITY GRAPH FOR TRANSPORTATION PLANNING PROBLEM

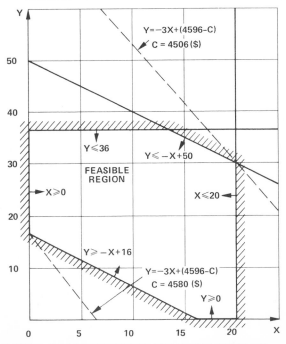

T-0305c TRANSPORTATION-PLANNING PROBLEM

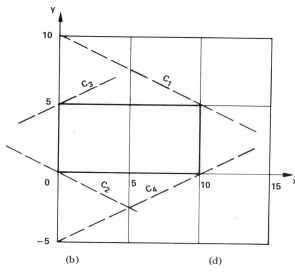

$C = 20 - X - 2y$ $C = 20 + X - 2y$

$y = \dfrac{x}{2} + (20 - C)$ $y = \dfrac{x}{2} + (20 - C)$

$C_1 = 20 - 10 - 10 = 0$ $C_3 = 20 + 0 - 10 = 10$

$C_2 = 20 - 0 - 0 = 20$ $C_4 = 20 + 10 - 0 = 30$

T-0306   GRAPH FOR PROBLEM 9

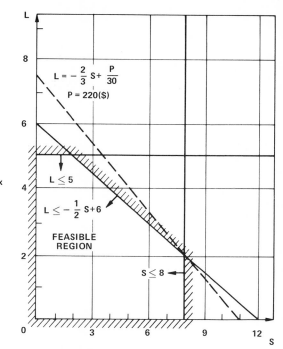

T-0307   SOLUTION TO PROBLEM 11

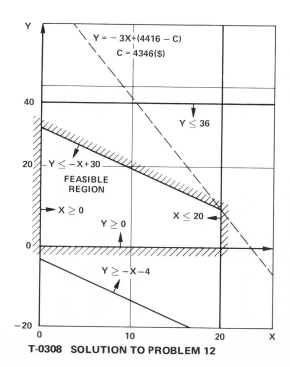

T-0308   SOLUTION TO PROBLEM 12

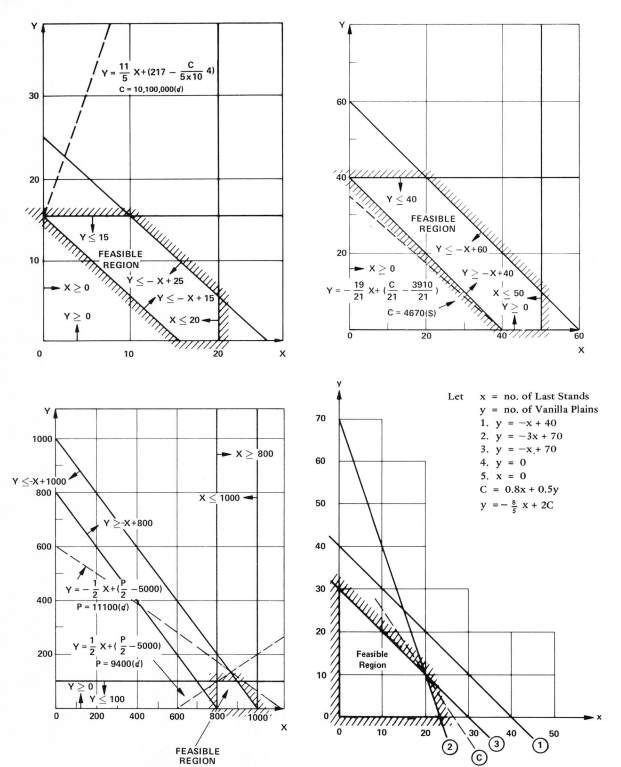

$$Y = \frac{11}{5}X + (217 - \frac{C}{5 \times 10}\,4)$$
C = 10,100,000(¢)

$Y \leq 15$

FEASIBLE REGION

$X \geq 0$

$Y \leq -X + 25$

$Y \geq 0$

$Y \leq -X + 15$

$X \leq 20$

$Y \leq 40$

FEASIBLE REGION

$Y \leq -X + 60$

$X \geq 0$

$Y \geq -X + 40$

$Y = -\frac{19}{21}X + (\frac{C}{21} - \frac{3910}{21})$

$X \leq 50$

C = 4670(S)

$Y \geq 0$

$X \geq 800$

$Y \leq -X + 1000$

$X \leq 1000$

$Y \geq -X + 800$

$Y = -\frac{1}{2}X + (\frac{P}{2} - 5000)$

P = 11100(¢)

$Y = \frac{1}{2}X + (\frac{P}{2} - 5000)$

P = 9400(¢)

$Y \geq 0$

$Y \leq 100$

FEASIBLE REGION

Let x = no. of Last Stands
     y = no. of Vanilla Plains
1. y = −x + 40
2. y = −3x + 70
3. y = −x + 70
4. y = 0
5. x = 0
C = 0.8x + 0.5y
$y = -\frac{8}{5}x + 2C$

Feasible Region

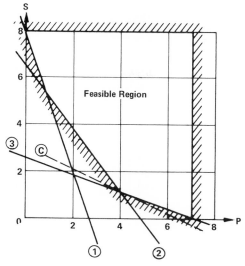

1. $S \geq -3P + 8$

2. $S \geq -\dfrac{4P}{3} + \dfrac{19}{3}$

3. $S \geq -\dfrac{P}{3} + \dfrac{7}{3}$

$C = 0.3P + 0.8S,$

or

$S = \dfrac{-3P}{8} + \dfrac{10C}{8}$

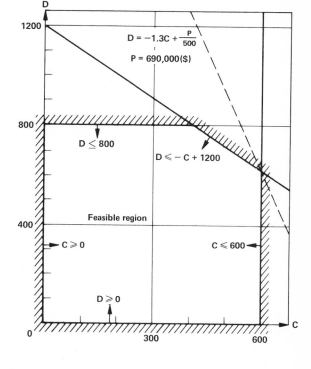

$D = -1.3C + \dfrac{P}{500}$

$P = 690,000(\$)$

$D \leq 800$

$D \leq -C + 1200$

$C \geq 0$

$C \leq 600$

Feasible region

$D \geq 0$

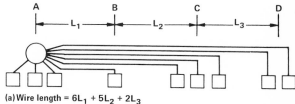

(a) Wire length = $6L_1 + 5L_2 + 2L_3$

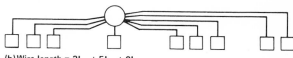

(b) Wire length = $3L_1 + 5L_2 + 2L_3$

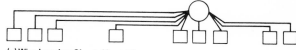

(c) Wire length = $3L_1 + 4L_2 + 2L_3$

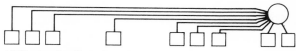

(d) Wire length = $3L_1 + 4L_2 + 7L_3$

OPPOSITE PAGE:

T-0309 *TOP LEFT:* **SOLUTION TO PROBLEM 13**

T-0310 *TOP RIGHT:* **SOLUTION TO PROBLEM 14**

T-0311 *BOTTOM LEFT:* **SOLUTION TO PROBLEM 15**

T-0312 *BOTTOM RIGHT:* **SOLUTION TO PROBLEM 16**

THIS PAGE:

T-0313 *ABOVE LEFT:* **SOLUTION TO PROBLEM 17**

T-0314 *ABOVE RIGHT:* **SOLUTION TO PROBLEM 18**

T-0315 *BELOW RIGHT:* **MINIMUM WIRE LENGTH PROBLEM**

C | CUES TO QUESTIONS AND PROBLEMS

Questions for Study and Discussion

1. Judgments concerning the purchase of manufactured goods are made with criteria which are subjective as well as objective. For example, when buying canned or frozen vegetables, the apparent size of the package, the picture on the label, memory of previous articles packed by the same firm, memory of advertisements, word-of-mouth recommendations—all these affect the decision. When buying electrical appliances, price, appearance, reputation (if known) of manufacturer, salesman's recommendation, and union label, guide and influence the purchaser. When buying a new automobile, a person might read automobile magazines, test-drive the car, and talk to people about the car to gather information about it. He will then use these more-or-less objective data and add his personal likes and dislikes (subjective criteria) to arrive at a decision. His decision might also be influenced by advertisements in newspapers and magazines as well as TV commercials. Recently enacted legislation requires more accurate labeling to reduce the amount of mathematics and/or guessing on the part of the consumer.

2. Objective criteria for canned tomatoes:
   Weight of contents (compared to label)
   Weight of strained-out solid, as percent of whole
   Are tomatoes essentially whole or in small pieces?
   Approximate size, if whole
   Cost of solid pieces, in ¢/oz

   Subjective criterion:
   Appearance and flavor (preferably judged by a representative group of people chosen at random)

   Objective criteria for hamburgers:
   Examination with magnifying glass for dirt of various kinds
   If this is passed, the analysis: beef, other meat, fat
   Cost of lean meat, in ¢/oz

Subjective criterion:
Flavor, judged as before

Objective criteria for hot dogs:
Essentially same as for hamburgers
Are they pure beef? (Some are now partly chicken)
Statement of contents on label

Subjective criterion:
Flavor, judged as before

3. The major criterion is maximum profit within accepted ethical standards (note that unless the business keeps going, such values as social usefulness cannot exist).

   Constraints:
   Small initial sales and profits
   Local bank charges for loans
   Available quarters, and their rent and location
   Available salespeople. Must they be trained?

   Market survey:
   List of present shops, assessment of appearance, convenience of situation, apparent volume of sales, stock in trade, appeal to younger people.
   Are there needed or useful services which are not provided, or badly provided?
   Growth potential

4. $xy = 5$ is not a linear equation because all linear equations must have the mathematical form $y = mx + b$ (where m is the slope and b is the y-intercept). Actually it is a hyperbola which has the mathematical form xy = constant.

5. The "feasible region" is the region on the graph which includes all the sets of values of the solution to the problem for which all the restrictions are met.

6. The graph of the feasible region would not change. The fact that the original inequality was changed to $x < 50 - y$ does not change the meaning of the inequality.

7. Many nonmathematical students will not be able to graph any equation until someone suggests that they substitute two or three different values for X in the equation in order to give them some points from which they can draw their graph.

a)

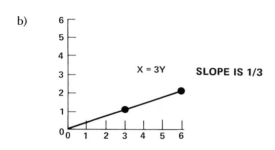

3X = Y   **SLOPE IS 3**

b)

X = 3Y   **SLOPE IS 1/3**

c)

X + Y = 3   **SLOPE IS −1**

d)

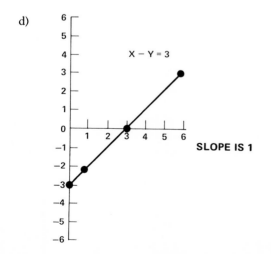

X − Y = 3

SLOPE IS 1

e) The "slope of a line" is defined mathematically as the change in y with respect to the change in x, $\Delta y/\Delta x$. It is given the symbol m.

8. 50%, or 1 in 2. For every question, T and F are equally probable.

9. Some examples of queue-formation in schools are:

　a) Cafeteria: usually multi-service queue

　b) Principal's office: single-service queue

　c) Gym: multi-service queue for shower and single-service queue for equipment

10. a) The average time between arrivals = 30 sec = 1/2 min = 1/120 hr

b) $\beta = \dfrac{\frac{1}{3}\ \text{min}}{\frac{1}{2}\ \text{min}} = \dfrac{2}{3} = .67$

c) $q = \dfrac{\beta\left(1-\frac{1}{2}\beta\right)}{1-\beta} = \dfrac{\frac{2}{3}\left(1-\frac{1}{2}\cdot\frac{2}{3}\right)}{1-\frac{2}{3}}$

$q = \dfrac{\frac{2}{3}\cdot\frac{2}{3}}{\frac{1}{3}} = \dfrac{4}{3} = 1.33$

d) No, β would not be affected. However, q would be affected.

$q = \dfrac{\beta}{1-\beta} = \dfrac{\frac{2}{3}}{1-\frac{2}{3}} = \dfrac{0.667}{0.333} = 2$

Problems

1. This problem exploits the device of multiplying the probability of a given result by the cost or value of that result.

　a) When driving his car the most likely outcome is arriving safely (0.85). When taking a bus the most likely outcome is arriving late (0.90).

　b) and c) In order to answer the two questions a priority of criteria must be set up. For example, if a man's office superior is very strict about his getting to his desk on time, he will take his car. But if his wife is very nervous about the small probability of his having an accident, and its resulting high cost, then he may regard the extra cost of the bus as worthwhile insurance to keep peace at home. If necessary, he can take an earlier bus to keep peace at the office, too. In the final analysis, the decision to be made is quite subjective. The answer to question (d) is an example of a decision based on objective analysis.

d) "Drive-car" expectation = (.850) (.00) +
(1.45) (1.00) +
(.005) (50.00) +
0.75 = $1.145

"Take-bus" expectation = (.100) (.00) +
(.9) (1) + .30 =
$1.20

On the basis of the above calculation, one would drive the car as this involves an expected cost of $1.145 versus an expected cost of taking the bus of $1.20. It should be pointed out that the various probabilities might be in error and that in certain cases one would want to look at what would happen if the various probabilities were shifted a certain percentage. This type of examination is called a sensitivity analysis.

2. a) $\dfrac{360}{4}$ = 90 pass./attend.

$\dfrac{\frac{1}{2} \text{ min}}{\text{pass.}}$ × 90 pass. = 45 min

b) $\dfrac{30 \text{ min/attend.}}{\frac{1}{2} \text{ min/pass.}}$ = 60 pass./attend.

$\dfrac{360}{60}$ = 6 attend.

c) In (a), each gate has 90 pass. arriving over 45 min. Therefore,

av. interarrival time = $\dfrac{45 \text{ min}}{90 \text{ pass.}}$ = $\dfrac{1}{2}$ min/pass.

$\beta = \dfrac{\frac{1}{2}}{\frac{1}{2}} = 1$. The same result is found in (b).

3. a) $\dfrac{360}{5}$ = 72 pass./gate; interarrival time =

$\dfrac{45 \text{ min}}{72 \text{ pass.}}$ or $\dfrac{5}{8}$ min/pass.

b) $\beta = \dfrac{\frac{1}{2} \text{ min/pass.}}{\frac{5}{8} \text{ min/pass.}} = 0.8$

$q = \dfrac{0.8}{0.2}$ (1 − 0.4) = 4 × 0.6 = 2.4 pass. (av.)

c) q = 4 pass. (random servicing time)

d) For first 10% (36 pass.):

Interarrival time = $\dfrac{15 \text{ min}}{36 \text{ pass.}}$ = $\dfrac{5}{12}$ min/pass.

Interarrival time at each gate = 5 × $\dfrac{5}{12}$ = $\dfrac{25 \text{ min}}{12 \text{ pass.}}$

$\beta = \dfrac{\frac{1}{2} \text{ min/pass.}}{\frac{25}{12} \text{ min/pass.}} = 0.24$

For remaining 90% (324 pass.):

Interarrival time = $\dfrac{30 \text{ min}}{324 \text{ pass.}}$ = $\dfrac{5}{54}$ min/pass.

Interarrival time at each gate = 5 × $\dfrac{5}{54}$ = $\dfrac{25 \text{ min}}{54 \text{ pass.}}$

$\beta = \dfrac{\frac{1}{2} \text{ min/pass.}}{\frac{25}{54} \text{ min/pass.}} = 1.08$

e) For first 10%, $q = \dfrac{0.24}{0.76}$ (0.88) = 0.28

For remaining 90%, q = "∞" (or 65 pass./gate)

f) Essentially the same answers as in (e).

g) In (c), β = 0.8 and the service was random. The line has two alternatives: more gates or faster service.

For more gates, 0.8 = $\dfrac{0.5}{I}$, I (interarrival time) = $\dfrac{5}{8}$ min/pass.

Then $\dfrac{30 \text{ min}}{P}$ = $\dfrac{5 \text{ min}}{8 \text{ pass.}}$; P = 48 pass./gate

$\dfrac{324}{48}$ = 7 gates needed

For shorter av. service time,

$$0.8 = \frac{t}{\frac{25}{54}}, \quad t = 0.37 \text{ min or } 22 \text{ sec}$$

(For the first 15 min, the service will be more than adequate with only 2 gates open.)

To work out the problem for fixed service, we have to solve a quadratic equation, which yields $\beta = 9\,1/8$ or $7/8$.

Choosing the second value, we find $7/8 = 0.5/I$, or $I = 4/7$, $30/P = 4/7$, $P = 52.5$ pass./gate; $324/52.5 = 6$ gates needed; or $7/8 = t/(25/54)$; $t = 0.405$ min = 24 sec.

4.a) $\dfrac{15}{20} \times 100 = 75\%$

b) $\beta = \dfrac{15}{20} = 0.75$

$$q = \frac{0.75}{(1 - 0.75)} \frac{(1 - 0.75)}{2} = 3 \times 0.625 = 1.88$$

c) 3 customers/hr = 24 customers/day, income/day = $2(24) = \$48$

d) $20/day means 10 more customers per day. The shop is 4 customers above the break-even point; therefore, if business increases by *6 more customers* the barber can afford a new man.

e) $\beta = \dfrac{15}{16} = .94$

$$q = .94\left[(1 - \frac{1}{2}(.94)\right] \Big/ 1 - .94 = 8.3 \text{ customers}$$

5.a) $\beta = .75$, $q = \beta/(1-\beta) = .75/(1 - .75)$
   $= 3$ customers
   $\beta = .94$, $q = \beta/(1-\beta) = .94/.06$
   $= 15.7$ customers

b) Random serving time is more realistic because each customer requires a different amount of time for a haircut.

c) By increasing the servicing time.

6. Using the data from text page 108, simply add the waiting times and divide by 15. Only 9 customers have waiting times, t_W. Thus average t_W =

$$\frac{1 + 2 + 4 + 6 + 8 + 10 + 12 + 12 + 12}{15}$$

$$= \frac{67}{15} = 4.5 \text{ min}$$

7. No, the average queue length and waiting time would not change. The only thing that would change is the person who is waiting.

8.a) y-intercept = 0. The inequality is satisfied 5 units above y-intercept and it is in the feasible region.

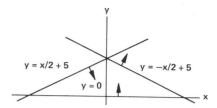

b) y-intercept = 5. The inequality is not satisfied 5 units above the y-intercept and it is not in the feasible region.

c) y-intercept = 5. The inequality is satisfied 5 units above the y-intercept and it is in the feasible region.

d) Rule for determining feasible region:

   1) Plot all the linear equations.

   2) Depending on the inequality ($>$ or $<$), draw appropriate arrows in the proper direction. E.g., the arrows trend *upward* if the graph derives from an inequality in which $y \geqslant$ some quantity.

9.a) $y \leqslant 5$, $x \leqslant 10$
   $y \geqslant 0$, $x \geqslant 0$

b) $C = 20 - x - 2y$
   $2y = -x + 20 - C$
   $y = -x/2 + (10 - C/2)$
   $\therefore m = -1/2$ and $b = 10 - C/2$

To minimize cost, the y-intercept should be as large as possible.

c) The graph of the cost equation can run across any part of the feasible region. However, for minimum cost the equation must run across point $(10,5)$.

d) $C = 20 + x - 2y$
   $y = x/2 + (10 - C/2)$
   $\therefore m = 1/2$, $b = 10 - C/2$

For minimum cost, the graph must run across point $(0,5)$.

10. The model: $0 \leqslant V \leqslant 800$
   $0 \leqslant C \leqslant 600$
   $V = 1000 - C$
   hence $0 \leqslant 1000 - C \leqslant 800$

Constraints on C:

$$C \geqslant 0$$
$$C \leqslant 600$$
$$1000 - C \geqslant 0 \qquad \text{or } C \leqslant 1000$$
$$1000 - C \leqslant 800 \qquad \text{or } C \geqslant 200$$

Profit equation: $P = 10V + 13C$
$$= 10(1000 - C) + 13C = 10,000 + 3C$$

P increases as C increases, C must be maximized (but not more than 600). Hence C = 600, V = 400, P = \$118.

11. Let r_s = number of standard radios produced per day. Let r_l = number of luxury radios produced per day.

$$r_s \leqslant 8$$
$$r_l \leqslant 5$$
$$r_s + 2r_l \leqslant 12$$
$$\therefore r_l \leqslant -\frac{1}{2} r_s + 6$$
$$P = 20 r_s + 30 r_l$$
$$\therefore r_l = -\frac{2\emptyset}{3\emptyset} r_s + \frac{P}{30}$$

For max. P we want max. y-intercept.

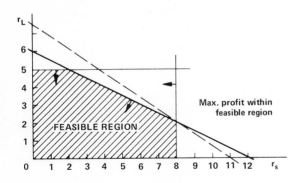

a) For max. profit make 8 r_s, 2r_l
b) $P = 20(8) + 30(2) = 160 + 60 = 220

	Denver		Miami		New York		
		42		55		60	
Grand Forks	x		y		30−x−y		30
		36		47		51	
Chicago	20−x		36−y		4 + x + y		60
	20		36		34		

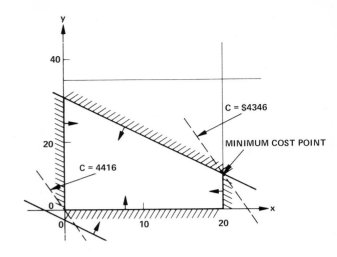

$$C = 42x + 55y + 60(30 - x - y) + 36(20 - x) +$$
$$47(36 - y) + 51(4 + x + y)$$
$$= -3x - y + 4416 = \$4346 \text{ at } x = 20, y = 10$$

	Denver	Miami	New York	
Grand Forks	20	10	0	30
Chicago	0	26	34	60
	20	36	34	

13.

	Kuwait	Galveston	Caracas	Total cost =
New York	0	150,000	100,000	\$101,000.
London	200,000	0	0	

	Kuwait		Galveston		Caracas		
		38		10		18	
New York	x		y		25−x−y		25
		34		22		25	
London	20 − x		15 − y		x + y − 15		20
	20		15		10		

$$C = 10,000 [38x + 10y + 18(25 - x - y) +$$
$$34(20 - x) + (22)(15 - y) + 25(x + y - 15)]$$
$$= 10,000 [11x - 5y + 1085]$$

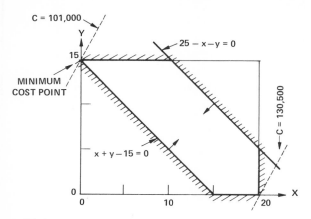

C = 101,000

25 − x − y = 0

15

MINIMUM
COST POINT

C = 130,500

x + y − 15 = 0

10   20

Minimum cost at $x = 0, y = 15$

$C_{min} = 10,000 \times 1010 = 10,100,000$ ¢ = \$101,000

	Kuwait	Galveston	Caracas
New York	0	15	10
London	20	0	0

14. Constraints

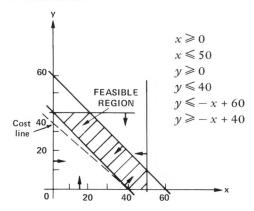

$x \geqslant 0$
$x \leqslant 50$
$y \geqslant 0$
$y \leqslant 40$
$y \leqslant -x + 60$
$y \geqslant -x + 40$

FEASIBLE
REGION

Cost
line

Cost Criteria

$C = 42x + 55(50 - x) + 36y + 47(40 - y)$
$\quad + 28(60 - x - y) + 60(x + y - 40)$
$C = 19x + 21y + 3910$

$y = \dfrac{-19}{21x} - \dfrac{3910}{21} + \dfrac{C}{21}$

$y = \dfrac{-19}{21x} - \dfrac{3910}{21} + \dfrac{C}{21}$

a)For minimum cost $x = 40, y = 0$
b) ∴ $C = 19(40) + 21(0) + 3910$
$\quad\quad = 760 + 3910 = \$4670$

15. a)Constraints
$\quad 800 \leqslant x \leqslant 1000$
$\quad 0 \leqslant y \leqslant 100$
$\quad x + y \leqslant 1000$
b)Let P = Profit
$\quad P = Tx + 12y + 10(1000 - x - y)$
c)If $T = 9$¢/lb
$\quad P = 9x + 12y + 10(1000 - x - y)$
$\quad P = 9x + 12y + 10,000 - 10x - 10y$
$\quad P = -x + 2y + 10,000$
$\quad y = \dfrac{x}{2} + \dfrac{P - 10,000}{2}$

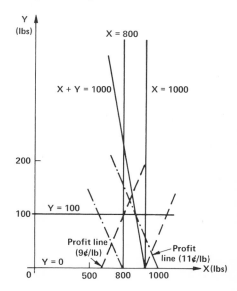

X = 800

X + Y = 1000   X = 1000

Y = 100

Profit line
(9¢/lb)

Profit
line (11¢/lb)

Y = 0

As P increases, the y-intercept increases.
For maximum P, $A = 800$ lbs, $B = 100$ lbs, $C = 100$ lbs

d)If $T = 11$¢/lb
$\quad P = 11x + 12y + 10(1000 - x - y)$
$\quad P = x + 2y + 10,000$
$\quad y = -x/2 + P/2 - 5000$

Since as P increases, the y-intercept increases, for maximum P, $A = 900$ lb, $B = 100$ lb, $C = 0$ lb.

16. Let x = no. of Last Stands sold
$\quad\quad y$ = no. of Vanilla Plains sold
From the milk constraint, $2x + 2y \leqslant 80$, or $x + y \leqslant 40$
ice cream $\quad 3x + y \leqslant 70$ (1)
syrup $\quad\quad x + y \leqslant 30$ (2), which is stronger
$\quad\quad\quad\quad\quad$ than the milk constraint

Also, the ice cream is only enough to make 70/3 Last Stands, so $70/3 \geqslant x \geqslant 0$.

By similar reasoning with the syrup, $30 \geqslant y \geqslant 0$.

The price equation is $P = 80x + 50y$.

Plotting these inequalities gives us:

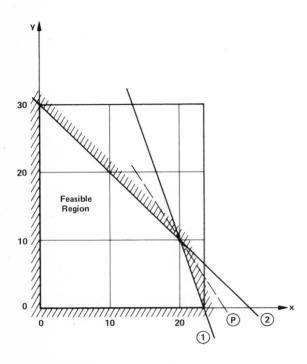

Higher values of P (the price paid for sodas) increase y. The intersection is at the vertex

$\qquad x = 20$ Last Stands

$\qquad y = 10$ Vanilla Plains

$\qquad P = 16 + 5 = 21$ (dollars income) for a profit of $1 or 5%.

17. Let P = no. of units of potatoes bought

$\qquad S$ = no. of units of steak bought

Then $\quad 3P + S \geqslant 8 \quad$ or $\quad S \geqslant -3p + 8 \qquad (1)$

$\qquad 4P + 3S \geqslant 19 \qquad S \geqslant -\dfrac{4P}{3} + \dfrac{19}{3} \qquad (2)$

$\qquad P + 3S \geqslant 7 \qquad S \geqslant -\dfrac{P}{3} + \dfrac{7}{3} \qquad (3)$

When plotted, these inequalities do not lead to a closed feasible area (because the statement puts no limit on the amount of food bought). However, we can tell how much of each food would be necessary,

if she bought only that, to supply all three nutriments. Thus, for carbohydrates, $S \leqslant 8$, $P = 2\ 2/3$; for vitamins, $S \leqslant 6\ 1/3$, $P \leqslant 4\ 3/4$; and for proteins, $S \leqslant 2\ 1/3$, $P \leqslant 7$. The weakest of these, $S \leqslant 8$, $P \leqslant 7$, have been used to define the outer boundaries.

The cost equation is $C = 0.3P + 0.8S$, or

$$S = -\frac{3P}{8} + \frac{10C}{8}$$

The cost is minimized as the S-intercept grows smaller.

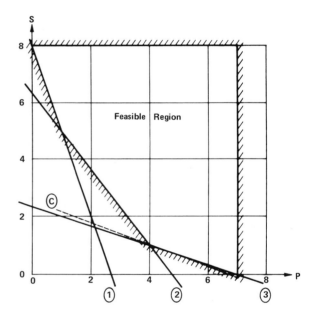

The solution lies at $P = 4$, $S = 1$, the cost then being $2. It is interesting to notice how clearly the cost equation coincides with equation 3. The buyer would have done as well nutritionally with 7 units of potatoes and no steak, for only 10¢ more; but she would have been less popular with her boarders. A final comment is that the "units" in which the various measurements are expressed are, fairly obviously, different in each case.

18. a) $C \geqslant 0$

$\qquad D \geqslant 0$

$\qquad C \leqslant 600$

$\qquad D \leqslant 800$

$\qquad D \leqslant -C + 1200$

b)

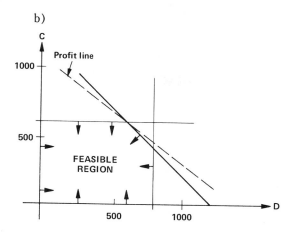

c) $P = 500D + 650C$

$D = -1.3C + P/500$

d) The profit line within the feasible region will be the line with the largest y-intercept.

e) For maximum $C = 600$ $D = 600$

$P = 500 (600) + 650 (600)$

$P = \$690,000$

D | DEMONSTRATIONS, LABS, AND PROJECTS

I. Queueing

Part A offers an experimental study of queue formation, while Part B requires observation of actual queues.

PART A

Equipment for Each Lab Team (2 to 4 students):

1 die
1 footrule or 30-cm scale
1 sheet of standard graph paper

General Lab Supplies:

Extra graph paper

It is much easier to use teams than to have individual experimentation, because the die roller does not have to keep track of a pencil at the same time, and running records can be kept of customer arrivals, interarrival times, and queue lengths by the rest of the team.

PART B

Equipment for Each Lab Team (2 students; if there are more, some will no doubt wander off to the candy counter):

For each team member, clipboard with ruled paper, or pad of ruled paper with backing intact
2 watches
Pencil and spare pencil for each member

One observer should specialize in arrival times and queue length, the other in actual service times. Remind both to keep alert for the answers to text questions 2, 3, and 4.

The queue in the school cafeteria for clearing and turning in plates has been used with success for this experiment, though it gives no insight into methods of managing a queue which gets too long.

II. Games

These games do not illustrate the matrices of game theory, but they do bring out the standard situation, namely, two intelligent opponents, each intent on maximizing his gains (in this case, winning the game).

Equipment for Each Lab Team (2 contestants):

For each player, 20 paper matches (1 full matchbook), with heads of different color for each team member. 20 toothpicks can be used, one set dipped in ink or dye.
3 sheets of paper, each with one of the game matrices duplicated on it. The edges of the matrix squares should be slightly longer (about 1/4 in) than 1 match (1 1/4 in) or 1 toothpick.

To play, matches are placed, one at a time, by each player in turn on the lines of the matrices (including the frame lines), always on an empty line segment. The only way to block an advance is to place a match on a segment that the opponent plans to use. Completed paths from one side to the other need not be straight, but must not be interrupted.

PART A

The algorithm for the first player (Red) to win, with a matrix of 4 squares, is indicated in the chart.

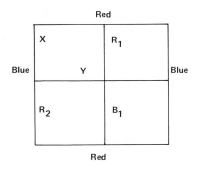

If Blue's second play is X, Red plays Y, and if Blue plays Y, Red plays X. In either case he has a completed path (R_1, Y, R_2 is a continuous path). Red's first match may be on any of the 6 vertical segments, but his second must then be displaced as shown, 1 square to the side and 1 square vertically.

PART B

The algorithm on a 3 × 3 matrix starts on either side of the central square, but further play depends on B's strategy, though in general Red tries to follow the previous algorithm insofar as possible.

PART C

There is no known winning algorithm for a 4 × 4 matrix.

Answers to Questions:

It is clear that adding complexity to a game also adds variations to the possible play. The strategy for a simple game then becomes less and less useful.

Other competitive situations include: checkers, chess, numerous other board games (e.g., Hex, Bridg-it, Twixt).

III. Design of a Remote Electric Heater

This is an open-ended experiment. It gives insight into an actual experimental technique for optimization. Since it is related to both Chapters 2 and 3, it may be done at any convenient time during the class work of these two chapters.

Equipment for Each Lab Team:

Low voltage power supply (10 − 15 volts; Analog Computer supply is satisfactory)

Set of five resistors, 20, 39, 82, 120, 300 ohms, each 1/2 watt

One 82-ohm 5-watt safety resistor

3 short electrical leads, alligator clip at each end

Small block of paraffin

4-in square of asbestos paper (sold for chemistry classes by apparatus supply houses)

Millimeter scale (for Part A)

Watch (or lab wall clock) with second hand (for Part B)

2 sheets of graph paper (4 or 5 squares per inch)

General Lab Supplies:

Extra fuses for power supplies

Extra sets of resistors

Extra leads, or extra flexible wire for leads

Wire clipper, small screwdriver, pliers

Extra paraffin blocks

Extra graph paper

To prepare the paraffin blocks, buy a pound of paraffin (such as Parawax or Household Wax) at a grocery store. It costs about a quarter and comes in four or five flat slabs about 5 × 2 1/2 × 1/2 in. Using a kitchen knife or paring knife, scribe a set of parallel lines across a large face of a slab, about 1/2 in apart. If the knife is placed on these lines one after another, rocked a bit, and tapped on its back with your hand, the strips will (should) split off very neatly and without crumbling. If you wish to have both Part A and Part B done, have the central parts of the long edges used for A, parts near the corners for B (or issue two blocks). There is little advantage in doing both parts, but it may be interesting to assign A to half the class, B to the rest of the class.

If any students are worried about being shocked, reassure them. It is virtually impossible to feel the effect of 15 volts (except by touching both wires to the tongue or to an open wound). Care should be taken, however, not to bring two wires into contact with each other unless the 82-ohm resistor has been connected. The fuse will have to be replaced if anyone is careless.

PART A

Answers to Questions:

*1.(Sample data)

Resistance (ohms)	Notch depth in mm after	
	1 min	2 min
20	1.0	2.0
39	1.5	4.0
82	3.0	5.0
120	2.0	3.0
300	1.0	2.0

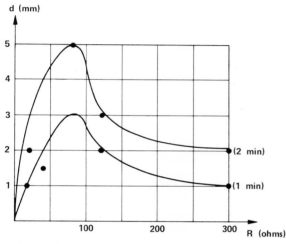

*2.82 ohms

*3.No

Any textbook in high school physics will supply the explanation for most of this. Ohm's Law for a series circuit:

$$(1) \qquad I = \frac{E}{R_1 + R_2}$$

where I = current in amperes, E = potential difference in volts across the circuit, R_1 = cable resistance and R_2 = heater resistance in ohms. It will also explain Joule's Law:

$$(2) \qquad P = I^2 R$$

where P = rate of transformation of electric energy to heat in watts. The matter of optimizing the heater resistor is subtle, and requires calculus for demonstration. It can be made plausible, however, by calculating the heat developed in each of a number of heaters, each in series with the same power cable, and with the same voltage. Equation (1) says that R_2 must be small for maximum current and hence, by Equation (2), maximum heat. But (2) also says that R_2 must be large for maximum heat. A compromise turns out to be best: R_2 should be equal to R_1.

PART B

Answers to Questions:

*4.(Sample data)

Resistance (ohms)	Time (sec)
300	160
120	90
82	60
39	105
20	300

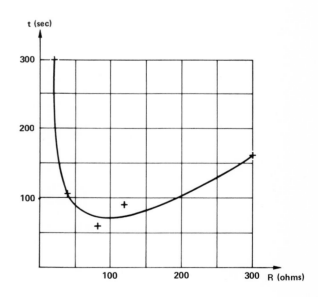

*5.82 ohms

*6.Yes

*7.In Part A the measurement of the notch depth suffers from two uncertainties: the exact edge of the notch, and whether all the melted paraffin was poured out. The chief uncertainty in Part B is in determining the exact instant when the paraffin block has become horizontal, with the resistor just one diameter in. The second method may be more accurate, but neither is highly precise.

E | EVALUATION

The questions in this section are rated according to the chapter objectives and the performance levels stated in the introduction to the teacher's manual. This group of questions is not intended to be all inclusive, but just as a guide to possible questions. Zeros in the chapter objective column indicate no chapter objective for this question.

Chapter Objective	Performance Level	
		Judged to be Relatively Easy:
7	I	1. Given the inequalities $3A + 2B \geq 2$, $A \leq 1$, $B \leq 1$, graph these inequalities on A and B axes, and mark the feasible region (the part of the plane where all three inequalities are satisfied).
5	II	2. Check the best answer:

An old limited-access highway is equipped with two toll booths. In recent years the weekend queues at the toll booths have been intolerably long. The Highway Department's best reaction to the situation would be:

    a) Build some more toll booths and man all of them continuously.

    b) Build some more toll booths and man all of them when traffic is heavy.

    c) Equip one of the existing booths with an exact-change machine.

    d) Report to the Legislature that the highway is outmoded and should be abandoned.

    e) Broaden the highway from two lanes to four each way.

3. Mark *each* of the following statements T, if it is true, or F, if it is false:

Chapter Objective	Performance Level	
4	I	a) It is not proper to apply queueing theory to anything but people.
5	I	b) For maximum profits, a supermarket manager ought to take such action that there would never be check-out queues greater than one.
3	II	c) Queues tend to be longer when service times are random than when they are all equal.
4	II	d) A quick lunch has a counter where people sit at stools. Queueing theory can be applied here even though the customers are side by side.
2	I	e) The statement "after tonight it will be day again" has a probability of 1/2.
2	II	f) When a die is rolled, the probability of a 3 is 1/6. This means that on every sixth roll a 3 comes up.
7	I	g) The sketch shows the graph of $y = x/2 + 3$. The point A is in the feasible area for $y \leq x/2 + 3$. 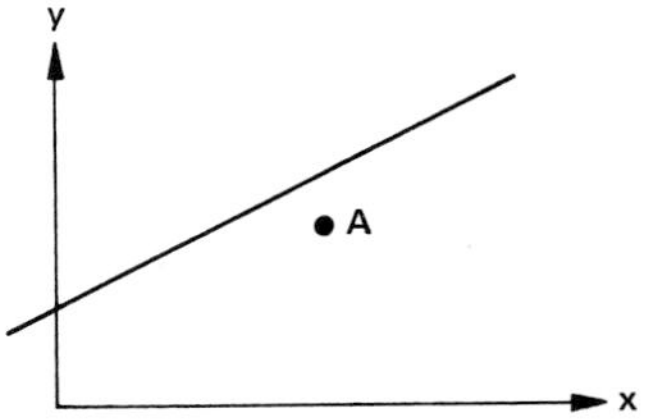
3	II	h) If a service channel is idle part of the time, a queue never forms there.
1	I	i) If a letter is chosen at random from the word "random", the probability that the letter is a vowel is 1/3.
3	I	j) When arrivals at a service counter are random, there cannot be an average interarrival time.
1	I	k) Experience shows that it always rains when the weather report reads "probability of rain 90%."
5	I	l) Experimental studies of queues always agree with the mathematical formulas.
1	I	m) Queueing theory can be successfully applied only to cases where the utilization factor (β) is less than 1.
7	I	n) The symbolic expression $a < x < b$ can be interpreted to mean, in part, that x is larger than b.
7	II	o) The symbolic expression $a < x < b$ implies that b is larger than a.

Chapter Objective	Performance Level	
		Judged to be Relatively Easy:
1 and 7	II	p) The feasible area shown in this graph satisfies the expression $0 \leqslant x \leqslant 4$.
1	I	q) A knowledge of game theory is of little use to players of chess.
3	I	r) If the average interarrival time for a certain service is 5 min, a customer arriving truly at random could not arrive 2 sec after the previous customer.

Judged to be More Difficult:

4. Fill in the blanks with the appropriate fractions:
An integer is chosen at random from the numbers 1 to 20 inclusive.

Chapter Objective	Performance Level	
2	II	a) The probability that the integer is an odd number is _____ .
2	II	b) The probability that the integer is divisible by 5 is _____ .
2	II	c) The probability that the integer is both odd and divisible by 5 is ____ .
2	II	d) The probability that it is not odd and also not divisible by 5 is _____.

5. a) Suppose that when Dick and Joe play the "fingers game" the payoff matrix is as shown. If they play for a long while, each choosing his fingers at random, which will probably be ahead?

		Joe	
		One	Two
Dick	One	10	−10
	Two	0	10

- 5. a) — Chapter Objective 6, Performance Level II
- 5. b) — Chapter Objective 6, Performance Level III

b) What nonrandom strategy would be best for Dick? Show how this was determined.

(Note that the following problem is "different" and hence challenging.)

6. In planning a TV comedy show, the sponsoring advertiser demands at least 3 min of commercials; the network insists that the commercials be limited to 15 min at most. The rest of the half-hour show is occupied by a comedian in either case.

Chapter Objective	Performance Level	
7	II	a) What numerical relationships, equalities or inequalities, are defined by the conditions?
7	I	b) Graph these relationships and indicate the feasible region.
8	I	c) The comedian costs $200 per min and the commercials cost $50 per min. Write the cost equation.
8	II	d) Find the schedule that gives minimum cost. Also, find that cost.

7. For each of the following, mark it T, if it is true, or F, if it is false:

Chapter Objective	Performance Level	
8	I	a) If a cost equation can be written $y = x/2 + C$, and it is desired to have the cost be a minimum, the graph should pass through the lowest possible vertex of the feasible region.
1	II	b) When the average interarrival time at a service facility remains constant, the utilization factor (β) grows smaller when the service time grows smaller.
3	I	c) When service times are random in length, so that some customers are served very quickly, we expect the queue length to be shorter than for constant service times.
6	I	d) A competitor will not always win, even if he knows game theory and follows the best strategy.

68

Chapter Objective	Performance Level

Judged to be More Difficult:

2	I
5	II
7	I
7	II

e) If you reach into a bag full of marbles and draw out a white marble, and then reach in again and draw out a black one, this does not prove that there are equal numbers of the two colors.

f) "Changing the priority system" has the same meaning, in queueing theory, as "increasing the number of service channels."

g) The symbolic expression $a < x < b$ denies that a and b can be equal, under any circumstances

h) If $2 - x \leqslant 0$, it follows that $x \leqslant 2$.

Solutions to Evaluation Questions:

1. (Diagram to the right):

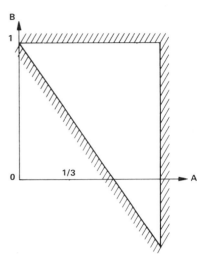

2. b

3.
a) F	g) T	m) T
b) F	h) F	n) F
c) T	i) T	o) T
d) T	j) F	p) T
e) F	k) F	q) T
f) F	l) F	r) F

4. a) 1/2
   b) 1/5
   c) 1/10
   d) 2/5

5. a) Dick

b) Dick should play "One" 1/3 of the time, "Two" 2/3 of the time. The difference of the top row payoffs is 20 (ignoring sign); that of the bottom row is 10. He should play 10 top rows to 20 bottom rows, or 1/3 and 2/3.

6. a) Let x = no. min of commercials.
   Let y = no. min of comedian.
   Also $x + y = 30$.

   Then

   $3 \leqslant x \leqslant 15$

   $15 \leqslant y \leqslant 27$

   b) (Diagram to the right):

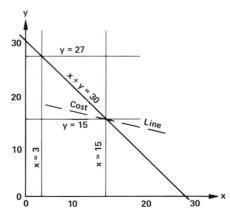

The $x + y = 30$ line is the feasible "area."
Solution: 15 min of each for $3750

Solutions to Evaluation Questions:

c) $C = 50x + 200y$, or $y = -\dfrac{x}{4} + \dfrac{C}{200}$.

d) As indicated on the graph, minimum cost is when $x = 15$, $y = 15$, or Cost = $50 \times 15 + 200 \times 15 = \$3750$.

7. a) T   e) T
   b) T   f) F
   c) F   g) T
   d) T   h) T

F | FILMS

F-0301   OPERATIONS RESEARCH

Recommendation: This film depicts a sample lesson on linear programming. It is useful to teachers who are not very familiar with this optimization technique.

Application: To help in the teaching of inequalities and linear programming.

Length and Type: (Not stated) Color.

Source: Communico, P.O. Box 3000, Fenton, Missouri 63026

F-0302   OPERATIONS RESEARCH TECHNIQUES

Recommendation: Optional film; use only if the teacher feels that additional emphasis on optimization is needed.

Application: Enrichment, during latter part of Chapter 3. Probably, show only first half of film, which is rather heavy.

Length and Type: 30 min (or 15 min at teacher's option), b & w, sound.

Source: Pennsylvania State University, Audio/Visual Service, University Park, Pennsylvania 16802

Summary: Several optimization techniques mentioned in text, but stress is on application to business and industry, not on methods themselves. Also discusses PERT (Program Evaluation and Review Technique).

G | GENERAL

I. Bibliography

C. C. Abt, *Serious Games.* Viking Press, 1970 (B)

> Mostly about games as teaching devices, many of which would require much preparation time. May be a source of inspiration, however.

Association of Teachers of Mathematics, *Some Lessons in Mathematics.* Cambridge University Press, 1964 (B)

> Contains models of lessons in linear programming, binary arithmetic, codes, flow charts, sets, simple logic. Age range of expected pupils is considerable. Even nonmathematicians will gain tremendously from it, and everyone will wish he could teach as well as the simulated instructor.

S. Beer, *Management Science, The Business Use of Operations Research.* Doubleday & Co., 1965 (B)

> Material on queues, models, probability, something on the "philosophy" (to overstate it) of linear programming. Quite interesting, anecdotal, not technical.

D. R. Cox and W. L. Smith, *Queues.* Barnes & Noble, 1961(B)

> Quite short, but has the full apparatus of probability theory. If you don't read mathematics easily, this is not for you; if you do, it may well be just your dish.

A. W. Drake, *Fundamentals of Applied Probability Theory.* McGraw-Hill, 1967 (C)

> Expected background: one year of calculus. The author means it, and the book is mostly unreadable without it.

J. G. Kemeny, J. L. Snell, and G. L. Thompson, *Introduction to Finite Mathematics.* Prentice-Hall, 1957 (C)

> If any book can be called the standard *The Man-Made World* reference book, this is it. Every teacher should own it. Worth every penny. Logic, sets, probability, game theory, and much more.

J. R. Newman, ed., *World of Mathematics*. Simon and Schuster, 1956 (Out of print, but to be found in many libraries)

> This has quite a lot of everything in four volumes. The application here is to game theory.

E. Ruiz-Pala, C. Avida-Beloso, and W. W. Hines, *Waiting-Line Models*. Reinhold, 1967 (C)

> A simple yet complex look at queueing theory.

Scientific American, *Mathematical Thinking in the Behavioral Sciences*. W. H. Freeman, 1968 (B)

> Essays on probability, communication and control, games and decisions, imitation of life (certain aspects of computers), recent computer applications. Many have read most in the magazine; here, all available in one 231-page book.

H. Theil, J. C. G. Boot, and T. Klock, *Operations Research and Quantitative Economics*. McGraw-Hill, 1965 (C)

> Linear programming, optimum and critical path, game theory, queues, etc. Problem suggestions (but not a direct source of problems).

W. Weaver, *Lady Luck, the Science of Probability*. Anchor-Doubleday S-30, 1963 (A)

> Probability and some statistics. As usual with Weaver, delightfully written, full of entertaining and appropriate anecdotes. It is hard to see how a high school student (or a teacher with a knowledge gap) could learn the elements of this very important subject more happily.

J. D. Williams, *The Compleat Strategyst*. McGraw-Hill, 1965 (revised edition) (B)

> An entertaining account, embellished with light-hearted drawings. Because of this technique the book is much longer than some discussions, but many readers will find it so easy to take that they will learn the elements practically as unconsciously as a baby learns to talk.

II. Some Extra Problems

1. A certain part of an oil refinery receives 500 barrels of naphtha a day, which can be refined to produce jet fuel or high-test gasoline. It can produce a maximum of 300 barrels of gasoline per day, or a maximum of 400 barrels of jet fuel per day. Because of the constraints offered by the nature of the plant and the operating costs, these conditions hold:

    a) Amount of jet fuel = 1.5 × amount of naphtha left over.

    b) Amount of jet fuel + 3 × amount of gasoline = 9 × amount of naphtha left over.

The profit per barrel of gasoline or of jet fuel = $1; the profit from sale of unused naphtha = $0.10 per barrel.

How much gas, and how much jet fuel, should be produced per day to obtain maximum profit?

Answer: 250 barrels of gasoline and 150 barrels of jet fuel with 100 barrels of naphtha left over. Profit, $410.

2. Given the conditions of Problem 1, what production runs should be planned, and what is the profit, if the gasoline can be sold at a profit of only $0.50 per barrel, all other conditions holding?

Answer: 300 barrels of jet fuel, no gasoline, 200 barrels of naphtha left over, profit = $320.

3. A cattle farmer wishes to find the cheapest mixture of three available feeds which will contain at least certain specified amounts of several nutrients. The following table lists the specifications (the three feeds are called P, Q and R; the three nutrients X, Y and Z):

Feed	Percent of nutrient in each feed			Cost in cents per bushel
	X	Y	Z	
P	6	2	9	15
Q	3	4	5	12
R	4	1	3	8
Minimum percent required	4	2	7	

What is the cheapest mixture which fulfills the requirements, and what does it cost per bushel?
Answer: 5/8 P, 1/8 Q, 1/4 R; cost: 12 7/8 cents/bushel.

4. Suppose the cost of feed Q in the previous problem were lowered to 10 cents/bushel. What is

now the minimum-cost mixture, and what is the minimum cost?

Answer: 1/2 P, 1/2 Q, none of R, cost 12.5 cents/bushel.

5. In blending a fuel oil, there are three fuels and four ingredients to consider. The table gives the amount of each ingredient (a, b, c, d) in each fuel (P, Q, R), the cost per gallon of each fuel, and the minimum permissible percent of each ingredient in the blended fuel. Find the cheapest permissible blend, and the cost per gallon.

Fuel	Percent of ingredient				Cost in cents per gallon
	a	b	c	d	
P	8	2	13	18	10
Q	3	6	6	24	8
R	5	4	7	21	5.5
Minimum percent required	5	3	8	20	

Answer: 1/6 P, 5/6 R, no Q, 6 1/4 cents/gallon.

III. Another Example of Optimization

In this section, we continue the discussion of optimization by considering an algorithm for an entirely different class of problems. We consider a community which, for all practical purposes, is stretched out along one road. Each building requires a certain number of telephones. Each telephone is connected by a wire to a switching center. When a telephone call is made, the ends of the appropriate wires are connected by switches in the switching center. Where should we construct the switching center in order to minimize the amount of wire? Is there an algorithm for this problem?

This is an idealized situation. The real situation is extremely complicated since we must consider such factors as: price of land, expected growth of the community, cost reduction due to the fact that a cable with n wires does not cost n times as much as a cable with one wire, the fact that in some areas cables can be hung on poles while in others the cable must be buried, etc.

The following drawing shows the simplest possible problem of any interest: namely, 2 buildings, 1 building with 2 telephones (small rectangles) and the other building with 1 telephone. If the switching center (the large circle) is located in the building with 1 telephone, we need 2 wires between buildings. If the switching center is located in the building with 2 telephones, we need only 1 wire between buildings. Obviously the latter location uses less wire.

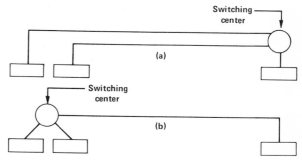

The next drawing shows a slightly more complicated case involving 4 buildings with 3, 1, 3, and 2 telephones, respectively. The 4 possible locations of the switching center are shown. We let the lengths of the segments of wires between buildings be L_1, L_2, and L_3, respectively, as shown in part (a).

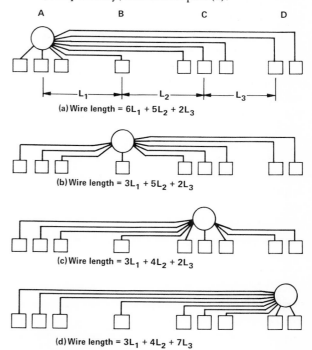

(a) Wire length = $6L_1 + 5L_2 + 2L_3$

(b) Wire length = $3L_1 + 5L_2 + 2L_3$

(c) Wire length = $3L_1 + 4L_2 + 2L_3$

(d) Wire length = $3L_1 + 4L_2 + 7L_3$

In (a), the total length of wire which is required is shown as $6L_1 + 5L_2 + 2L_3$. If we now shift the switching center to building B, as shown in (b), the total length of wire is $3L_1 + 5L_2 + 2L_3$. If we compare this value to the original value above, we note that this new position for the switching center involves less wire: a reduction of $3L_1$ units of length, since the L_2 and L_3 terms are not affected by the change.

If we now shift the switching center to building C, the length of wire required is shown in (c) as $3L_1 + 4L_2 + 2L_3$. This new length is less than that with the switching center at building B by an amount L_2. The L_1 and L_3 terms are not affected by the shift from B to C.

If we now try to shorten the wire length further by placing the switching center at building D, the wire length is found to be greater than the length required from building C by $5L_3$ units, since now the L_1 and L_2 values are not changed. Obviously the location of the switching center which requires the least wire is that at building C. This location is determined without regard to the actual values of L_1, L_2, or L_3 (these lengths can have any nonnegative values).

Can we observe anything about these examples that would help us in more complicated problems with many buildings and many telephones? We see there are three "segments" (intervals) between buildings. We note the following facts.

The discovery that the actual lengths of the distances between buildings is not involved in the placement of the switching center *for minimum wire length* is very interesting. It means that the only factor (which determines the minimum that we seek) must be the number of telephones on either side of the switching center. If we begin our search with the assumption that the switching center is at the building at the extreme left, the first shift of position changes the first length from $6L_1$ to $3L_1$, all other lengths remaining unaffected. In this case, we reduce the telephone-line length.

A shift of the switching center to building C does not affect the length $3L_1$, but requires only 4 lengths of L_2. It is also apparent that the 2 wires ($2L_3$) are not affected. Thus the second shift produces a change only in the second term, which is

equal to the number of phones to the left of C multiplied by L_2. Since the term $4L_2$ replaces the term $5L_2$ of the B location (all other terms remain unaffected), location C is preferable to location B.

How does a shift to D affect the length of line? The $3L_1$ and $4L_2$ terms are not disturbed, but we now have 7 telephones to the left of the switching center, each of which requires an additional length L_3 to reach the center. This replacement of $2L_3$ by a new value $7L_3$ obviously represents an increase in length compared to location C, and this is true, regardless of the actual value of L_1, L_2, or L_3.

This leads to a simple algorithm to find the optimum location of a switching center:

1. In each segment (between buildings), we determine the number of telephones to the left and to the right of the segment, and write these numbers below the segment as (N_L, N_R).

2. We place an arrow below the number pair pointing from the smaller number toward the larger.

3. We find the building where the arrows point to it from both sides; this is the location of the switching center that gives the shortest length of wire.

Let us try the algorithm on the examples of the last two drawings. In the first of the two, there are 2 telephones to the left and 1 to the right of the central segment, so we write (2,1) and put an arrow underneath pointing to the left from the smaller number 1 toward the larger number 2, as shown immediately below. In the "segment" to the left of the central segment there are no telephones to the left and 3 to the right, so we write (0,3) there and put an arrow to the right. Thus the building on the left has arrows pointing at it from both sides and is the best location.

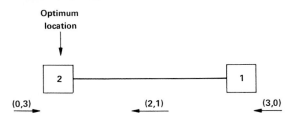

In the 4-building example, next page, arrows from both sides point to the second building from the right as the best location.

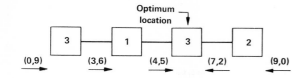

Following, we show an example with more buildings.

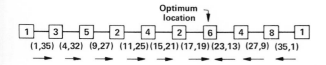

You may ask: *What about a location between buildings?* We can easily show this is not helpful by putting in a "fictitious" building (to house the switching center) with zero telephones in it. Using our algorithm above, we find the same number pair (N_L, N_R) on both sides of this building and hence the arrows point in the same direction on both sides; therefore, this vacant "building" cannot be the optimum location. We conclude that *the best location is always at a building*. Whenever an algorithm has been developed for a type of problem, the computer may be programmed for this algorithm and problems may be solved quickly and accurately.

MODELING

APPROX. TIME: Text: 14 days   Lab: 3 days

A. APPROACH	CLASS PERIODS	B. BLACK & WHITE TRANSPARENCIES	C. CUES (k=key problem) Discussion Questions	Problems Easy	Problems Medium	Problems Hard	D. DEMONSTRATIONS, LABS & PROJECTS	E. EVALUATION	F. FILMS	G. GENERAL
1. The Nature of Models	1	0401	1,4,15				I	1c,e,f 2	0404 0405 0401	
2. The Graph As a Descriptive Model	2	0402a,b	2,3,5,6,7	13k				1a,b,d,j, 5		
3. A Descriptive Model of Traffic Flow	1	0403, 0413	9,10				II			
4. Models for Resource Management	2	0414	11,12				III, IV	1k, 4	0406	
5. A Population Model	2	0404a,b, 0405	13	10k, 12	8			1h,l	0402	
6. Exponential Growth	3	0406a,b,c, 0407, 0408, 0409, 0410, 0411, 0415, 0419		1,4k	11	3,5,6	V	6	0403	
7. An Improved Population Model	1	0412, 0418			7k					
8. Uses of Models	2	0406a,b,c, 0416, 0417, 0420, 0421	8,14		2	9		1g, i, 3		

Modeling
4

A | APPROACH

I. Purpose and Organization of the Chapter

The procedure of rational decision making began with the construction of a model of the system under study. Models serve in more ways than we have suggested, however. A model to aid in focusing the mind is part of nearly all serious thinking, and not only by scientists and engineers. Similes and analogies are models of a kind. For example, in Tennyson's poem on the "flower in a crannied wall" he suggests that the flower is a model of "God and man." In this chapter further benefits furnished by models are indicated, and several new forms of models are examined.

The chapter begins by showing the need for a quantitative model and follows with the presentation of various kinds of models: graphs, equations, simple descriptive models, graphs of exponential growth and their modification into sigmoids. It ends with descriptions of a few of the uses of models.

II. Objectives for Students

By the time a student has completed the activities, discussions, and readings associated with this chapter, he should be able to:

1. Recognize and identify the following terms: *analog computer* including *summing scalor, adder, integrator,* and *coefficient, bar graph, descriptive*

and *functional model, exponential change, extrapolation, interpolation* and *sigmoid growth curve.*

2. Compare a functional model with a descriptive model of the same system, and explain the advantages of each.

3. Discriminate between a correctly made model and one weakened by including irrelevant details.

4. Demonstrate how to test a model by comparing it with the real world.

5. Demonstrate how to construct a graphical model by (a) plotting the results of a number of measurements and (b) drawing a reasonably smooth curve through or near the plotted point.

6. Demonstrate how large masses of data can be modeled by (a) classifying the data somehow (e.g., by year or size range) and (b) drawing a bar graph.

7. Test a table of numerical data (organized by successive equal time intervals) or a corresponding graph, and show that the change indicated is or is not exponential.

8. Construct, from a graphical model which is a straight line, on Cartesian coordinates, a slope-intercept form of equation which is another model representing the same data.

9. Model on an analog computer a linear equation with two or more variables.

10. Prepare a coordinate system with a logarithmic scale on the ordinate (*Y*-axis), and show that exponential change, when plotted on properly chosen coordinates, yields a straight line.

11. Predict, with the aid of a graphical or an algebraic model, results which lie in the future, and explain in what respects such predictions are useful and to what extent they are not reliable.

12. Illustrate the use of a model to aid governmental planning in such areas as transportation, waste collection, construction of housing and schools, and medical services.

13. Justify the use of a single model for two or more systems.

14. Explain what circumstances may cause a single system to require several models.

III. Suggestions for Teaching

Be careful not to let students become so caught up in the details of the anecdotal material that they forget the point each story is designed to bring out.

It would be hard to overemphasize that the most successful model builder is the one who best sees which facts about his subject do or do not bear on the problem before him. He discards the latter and uses only the former.

Section 1. The nature of models. Many teachers have found it a good start for the chapter to read aloud the poem about the blind men and the elephant and after a brief discussion (remarking that even a man with eyes would not know all about the interior of an elephant) go to Lab. I, text page 183.

The elevator supervisor evidently has a complicated queueing problem, and the class should find it both interesting and profitable to use their understanding of queues to organize his operation. Of course, they will have to reach agreement about the model and the criterion to be used; they might investigate more than one, depending on interest and time limitation. This will be useful when the discussion of more than one model for a given problem is discussed in Section 8.

Section 2. The Graph as a Descriptive Model. If possible, get from the athletic or health department figures for your own school with which to make your own graph (the figures will almost certainly be different, and obviously will be very different if you have data about girls). One essential of model building is clearly shown here: instead of height-weight data for everybody, only those numbers which bear on the present problem are used.

An important idea to linger over for a few minutes is the *scatter* of the points (see T-0402a, b). The graph simply gives a rough-and-ready average. This can lead to a discussion of statistics and a sketch of Gauss's famous bell-shaped curve. As you know, there are mathematical ways to get a "best fit" of the curve to the data, but these are not suitable for this course. The amount that a point not on the line is "scattered" can be determined in three ways: go vertically to the line and find the "expected" weight for the given height; go horizontally to the line and find the expected height for the given weight; or drop a perpendicular to the line. The last is wrong, because it changes the measures of both height and weight.

The dangers which lurk in extrapolation, first mentioned here, are commented on again in Section 6. F-0401 is an excellent film on the actual model-development process.

Section 3. A Descriptive Model of Traffic Flow. Bear in mind that most of this text material leads directly to Lab II. Many classes have enjoyed this kind of study very much. But remember that school administrators are too busy trying to find additional classrooms to be apt to cooperate closely in studies of hall traffic.

Section 4. Models for Resource Management. This model may seem like Monday morning quarterback thinking—after all, how many buffalo still roam the plains? But it is an example of numerous studies actually being made today on other kinds of natural resources (cases in point are whales, seals, various kinds of edible fish, and forests). Some of the figures derived are too precise. It would be interesting for someone to work through the model using only two significant figures to see if the final decisions on harvesting were changed appreciably using less precise numbers. This section supplies a good introduction to the study of the human population problem in the next three sections.

Lab IV belongs here but must be preceded by Lab III. The latter is an essential preliminary to the use of the analog computer in a whole series of subsequent lab exercises, and even if you decide to omit IV (which does illustrate use of the analog to solve a linear equation), you cannot get along without III. This is really the best time to perform it.

Section 5. A Population Model. Two of the most important ideas in the course appear here: the population explosion and its possible consequences, and the exponential curve. Point out that exponential decreases are also important (e. g., the decay of radioactivity), and use T-0406a and b. The reduction of unwieldy numerical data to manageable form, first as a bar graph, then as a summarizing curve (which can be expressed as an algebraic equation), is an interesting example of "how to do it." See F-0402 (in light of your locality's customs).

Section 6. Exponential Growth. The characteristic lag between starting a remedy and seeing the effects of the remedy is the most important idea here. This idea becomes quite important if the situation which must be remedied is experiencing exponential growth. Emphasize that exponential growth is very common with living things, such as a colony of bacteria on an agar slant, a seedling plant, or a baby (all shift to a sigmoid pattern after a little). T-0406c is suggestive in connection with sigmoids.

The system of using a logarithmic scale to turn an exponential curve into a straight line is very neat, but might prove troublesome for some of the less mathematically inclined to follow completely. The use of this system of changing a "curve" to a straight line for purposes of extrapolation should be emphasized more than the details of how it is done. See T-0408b, however, to show in more detail the way to interpolate on such a plot. The numbers are appropriate roots of 2 ($2^{1/10}$, $2^{2/10}$, etc.). For example: to find the y - axis value of a point halfway between point a and 2 in Fig. 4-25, look at the scale in T-0408b. The closest approximation to this value using this scale is 1.69. Using the values of Fig. 4-5 we estimate 1.70, which is quite close. As we move up the scale, the error increases. Note that the numerical halfway point between b and 4 in Fig. 4-25 is 3.40 and that in T-0408b it is 3.37.

The solid-waste problem is nearly as important for the United States as the question of starvation is elsewhere. If we analyze the model in Fig. 4-27 (T-0409) and use a logarithmic plot of the data pictured, we can extend the straight line to get an extrapolated prediction of 300 million tons by 1980 (Fig. 4-30). This is much easier to do than to try to extend the curve of Fig. 4-27. F-0403 may be useful here, but it is 68 min long.

Section 7. An Improved Population Model. The decay of an exponential into a sigmoid (T-0412 and T-0406c) is similar to the economists' Law of Diminishing Returns; as production gets nearer to the attainable maximum in a given system, it costs more and more to produce smaller and smaller gains. For such reasons, one investigator has predicted that the population of the world will stabilize at around 10 billion in about a century. This sounds more hopeful than perhaps it is. What will cause the population stabilization if it does occur? Consider such factors as food production, energy production, and disease as you discuss this with your class.

Section 8. Uses of Models. Here we return our attention specifically to the idea of the model itself. "Many models for one system" recalls the blind men and their elephant. In one sense they didn't do badly: to model the animal's trunk it is needless to include data about the tail. On the other hand, once a mathematical model has been developed for one system, a mere change of variables and constants may let it fit another one.

This is a good time to demonstrate exponential change (negative in this case) by keeping track of the temperature of a cup of hot water and graphing temperature against time. This can be accomplished without elaborate equipment. A glass beaker or a coffee cup is excellent. It is interesting to try the same experiment with a styrofoam cup and note the difference in the curves. (Time, the independent variable, should be plotted on the x-axis). The resulting curve will be only approximately exponential. If it were to be truly exponential, the rate of cooling would be proportional to the temperature difference between the water and its surroundings, which implies cooling only by conduction. Radiation and, especially, evaporation steal internal energy from the water.

The refinement of a model may take three forms: (1) the use of more exact statements; (2) the addition of details; (3) the elimination of unessential details. It is worth remarking that trying to take account of every variable at the outset of the modeling process may prove to be too cumbersome; thus the elimination of some details which are in fact essential may enable us to get started. Then when a start has been made, refinement can take place, this time in the second form; but the details are essential ones, not just small improvements.

B | BLACK AND WHITE TRANSPARENCIES

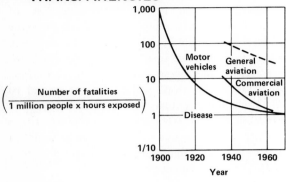

$$\left(\frac{\text{Number of fatalities}}{\text{1 million people x hours exposed}} \right)$$

T-0401 *LEFT*: **RISK OF DEATH CURVES**

T-0402a *BOTTOM, LEFT*: **WEIGHT DATA**

T-0402b *BOTTOM, RIGHT*: **AVERAGE OF HEIGHT-WEIGHT DATA (OVERLAY)**

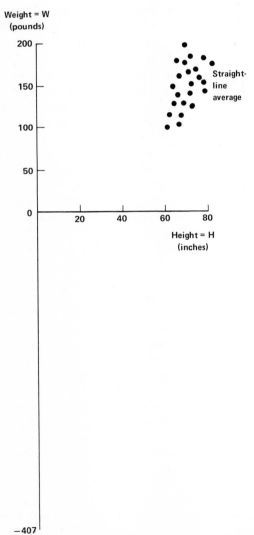

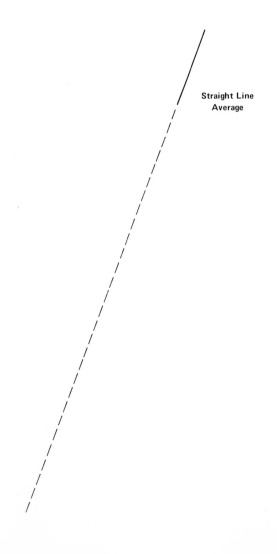

−407

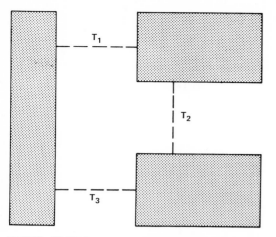

T-0403   WHERE TRAFFIC DENSITY IS MEASURED

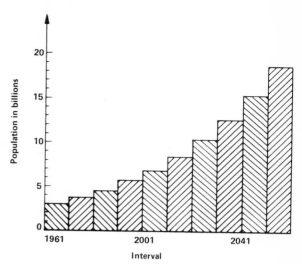

T-0404a   WORLD POPULATION GROWTH

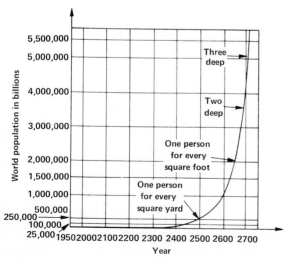

T-0405 MODELING   PREDICTION   OF   WORLD
POPULATION

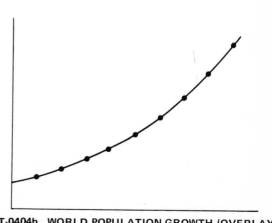

T-0404b   WORLD POPULATION GROWTH (OVERLAY)

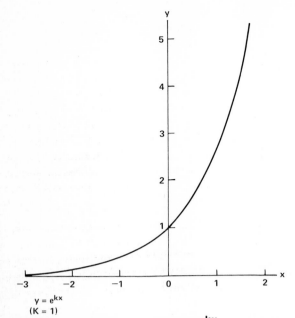

y = e^{kx}
(K = 1)

T-0406a EXPONENTIAL CURVE, $y = e^{kx}$ **(k POSITIVE)**

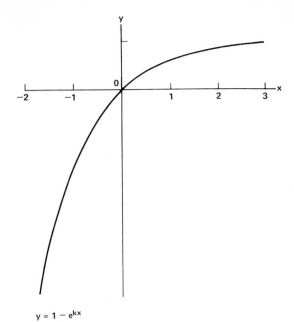

y = 1 − e^{kx}
(K = − 1)

T-0406c EXPONENTIAL CURVE, $y = 1 - e^{kx}$ **(k NEG-ATIVE)**

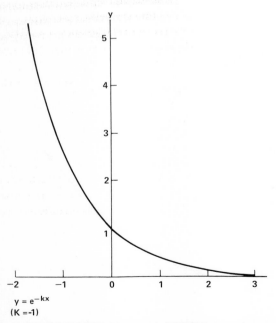

y = e^{−kx}
(K =-1)

T-0406b EXPONENTIAL CURVE, $y = e^{-kx}$ **(k NEGATIVE)**

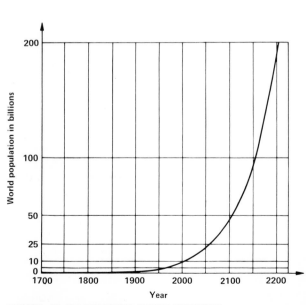

T-0407 PLOT OF POPULATION GROWTH

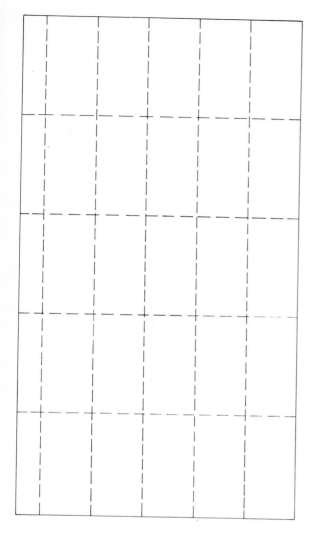

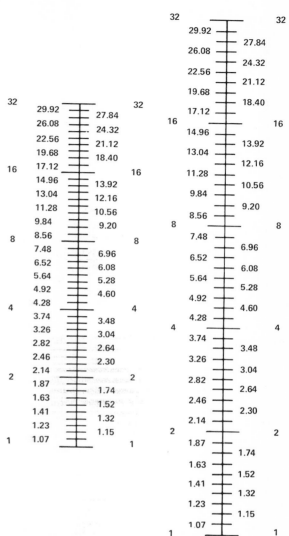

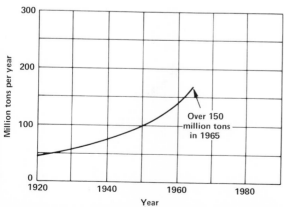

T-0409 UNITED STATES SOLID WASTE PRODUCTION

T-0408a *ABOVE LEFT:* BLANK FORM FOR LOGARITHMIC PLOTS

T-0408b *ABOVE:* INTERPOLATION SCALES FOR LOG GRAPHS

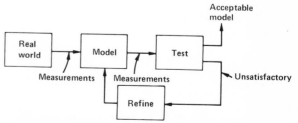

T-0410 BLOCK DIAGRAM OF MODEL-MAKING PROCESS

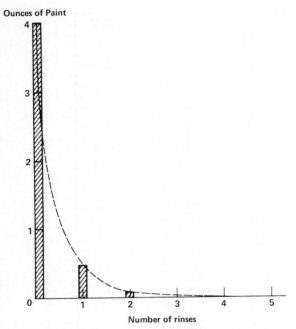

T-0411 PROBLEM 3, CLEANING PAINTBRUSH

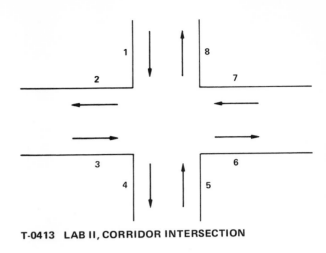

T-0413 LAB II, CORRIDOR INTERSECTION

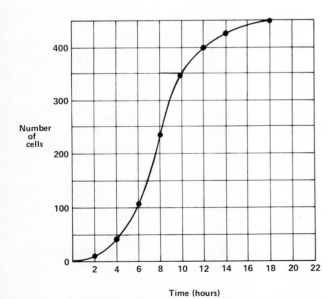

T-0412 PROBLEM 7, SIGMOID CURVE, GROWTH OF YEAST CELLS

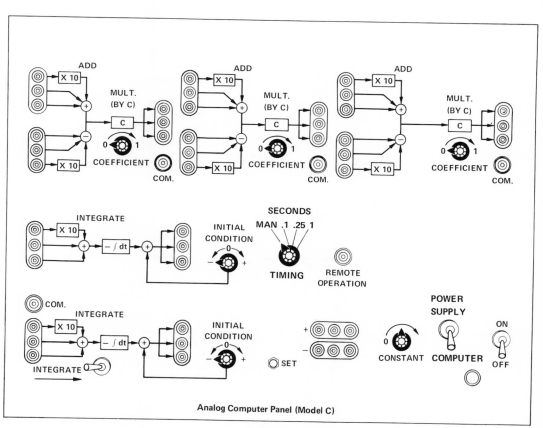

Analog Computer Panel (Model C)

T-0414

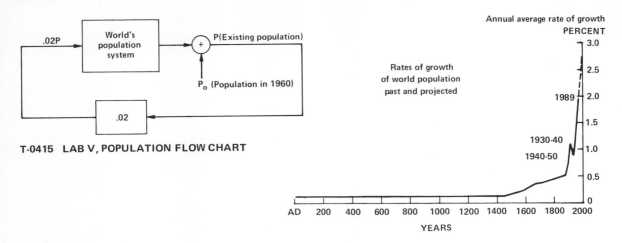

.02P

World's
population
system

P(Existing population)

P_o (Population in 1960)

.02

T-0415   LAB V, POPULATION FLOW CHART

Annual average rate of growth
PERCENT

Rates of growth
of world population
past and projected

1989

1930-40

1940-50

AD   200   400   600   800   1000   1200   1400   1600   1800   2000

YEARS

Beginning with 1920, an average for a ten-year period.
Prior to 1900, crude estimates for fifty-year periods.

T-0416   POPULATION GROWTH RATES

THE POPULATION BOMB
IN THE YEAR 2,000
WHERE THE PEOPLE WILL BE

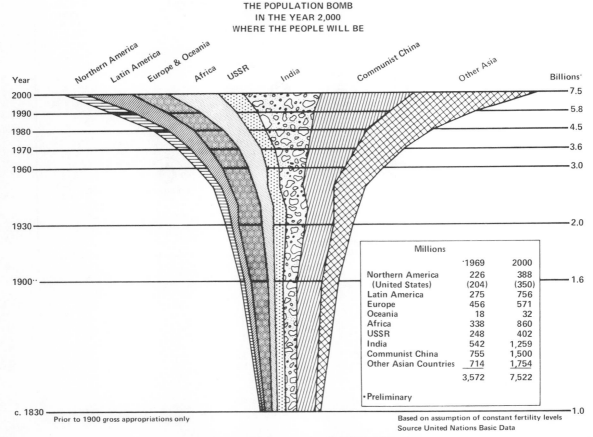

Millions		
	·1969	2000
Northern America	226	388
(United States)	(204)	(350)
Latin America	275	756
Europe	456	571
Oceania	18	32
Africa	338	860
USSR	248	402
India	542	1,259
Communist China	755	1,500
Other Asian Countries	714	1,754
	3,572	7,522

·Preliminary

Prior to 1900 gross appropriations only

Based on assumption of constant fertility levels
Source United Nations Basic Data

T-0417   POPULATION DISTRIBUTION

THE DEMOGRAPHIC TRANSITION

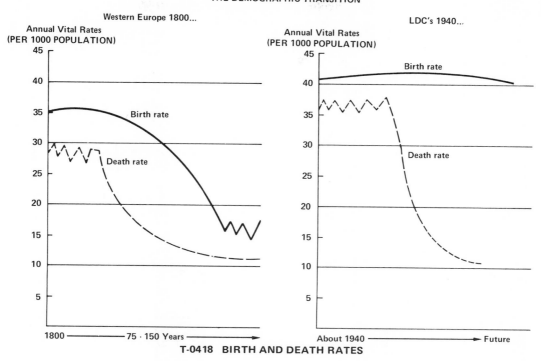

Western Europe 1800...

Annual Vital Rates
(PER 1000 POPULATION)

LDC's 1940...

Annual Vital Rates
(PER 1000 POPULATION)

Birth rate

Death rate

1800 ———— 75 · 150 Years ————→

Birth rate

Death rate

About 1940 ————————→ Future

T-0418 BIRTH AND DEATH RATES

TIME REQUIRED TO DOUBLE A POPULATION

Annual rate of population growth	Number of years to double population
4.0	17.3
3.5	20.1
3.0	23.1
2.5	27.6
2.0	34.6
1.5	46.2
1.0	69.3

Note.   To maintain the same standard of living for its people a country must double its output of goods and services (GNP) in the same time that population doubles.

To improve standards of living it must more than double its GNP in the same time.

T-0419 DOUBLING TIMES

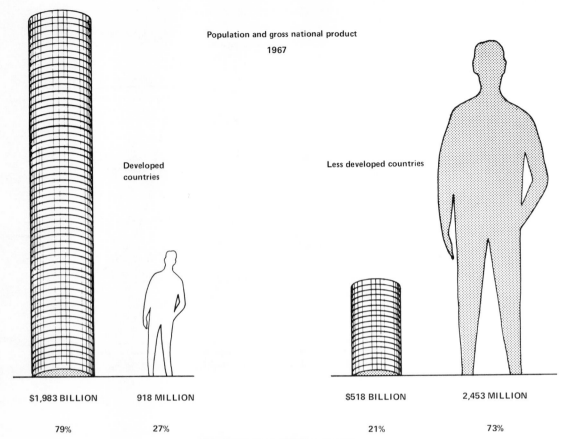

Population and gross national product

1967

Developed
countries

Less developed countries

$1,983 BILLION 918 MILLION $518 BILLION 2,453 MILLION

79% 27% 21% 73%

T-0420 POPULATION VS GNP

Percent of GNP

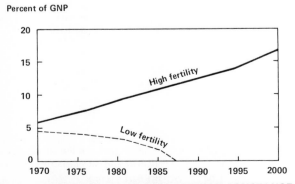

T-0421 NEED FOR UNITED STATES FOREIGN ASSISTANCE

C | CUES TO QUESTIONS AND PROBLEMS

Questions for Study and Discussion

1. A "complete" model would have to be completely equivalent to the entity modeled, and so would lose all the advantages of a model. In essence, the "art of modeling" is the proper balance of completeness and simplicity.

2. a) Functional models are working models of real-world objects. They really work. Descriptive models are descriptions of problematic situations which can be verbal, graphical, or mathematical representations.

   b) Dynamic models represent situations in which events change with time as exemplified by the population model. Static models represent situations in which events do not change with time.

Examples:

Functional model—scaled-down airplane or working replica of nerve cells

Descriptive model—graph of population growth

Dynamic model—graph of speed *vs* time for an accelerating car

Static model—graph of height *vs* weight for 20-year-old men

3. Two desirable qualities of mathematical models:

   a) Mathematical models as *quantitative* descriptions of situations tend to be more objective than other types of models.

   b) Mathematical models are especially useful in situations where prediction is desired ("computerization").

4. After a preliminary model is made, measurements and predictions made with it are compared to the behavior of the real world.

5. One can think of drawing a straight line through the points in Fig. 4-3 as the taking of a "graphical average." The straight-line graph is useful for predicting heights or weights of other 20-year-old men, and is also the source of a mathematical model for the situation.

6. Using Fig. 4-4 to predict the weight of the 6′ 10″ basketball player is valid if no other models are available. Although the data in the model only go up to 6′ 5″, extrapolating for another 5″ does

not seem too unreasonable. Naturally it would be better if our model had been built from data which included 6′ 10″ 20-year-old men.

7. If W = 145 lbs:

$$W = 8H - 407$$

$$H = \frac{W + 407}{8} = \frac{145 + 407}{8}$$

$$H = 69'' = 5' 9''$$

It would be useful to have each student calculate his own expected weight from the equation and suggest (in writing if he would be embarrassed to discuss it in class) the reasons for his weight not fitting into the equation. Reasons may include such considerations as differences in age and bone structure. Girls will usually be taller than calculations indicate, since this equation was determined from data regarding men (who are normally heavier for the same height).

8. Possible "strainers" that a forester might use are: type of tree, age of tree, and type of soil and amount of rainfall in area where the tree is being studied.

9. Engineers take traffic counts by placing sensors along the highway. For example, a cable stretched across a road to an electric counter will count cars that go over it.

10. An incorrect count can occur if two students are walking side by side between the light source and the electric eye. In general, the incorrect count can be minimized in two ways. Students can be prevented from walking side by side (this is not advisable because we are in fact changing the system). Second, more sensors can be placed between the ceiling and the floor, and the degree of accuracy would depend on spacing of the sensors. This question is related to the footnote on page 145 of the text.

11. For example: passenger pigeon, whooping crane, ivory-billed woodpecker, panther, timber wolf, Arabian oryx, Lake Superior lake trout and whitefish, white whale.

12. At appropriate times the satellite sends a signal which triggers a response from the set carried by the elk or other animal, and the response, acting like a kind of reversed radar, triggers the satellite to keep a position record. Some of the information we can gather from this record is: Does the animal have a

fixed range? Does he patrol it regularly? Where does he eat? Where does he sleep? Does he migrate? Is he solitary or gregarious, and always or just sometimes? (The answers to the last question require the monitoring of several animals.)

13. Five other factors which might influence the growth rate of towns are: growth of old industries—increases growth rate because of job opportunity; introduction of new industry—relocation as well as more jobs will tend to increase growth rate; changes in immigration laws such as increase in quotas will tend to increase growth rate in certain towns; improvement of public school system would attract young couples with children which also increases the growth rate (it should be pointed out that taxes would probably go up and encourage the older people in the town to move, but the overall effect would still tend to increase the population); building of better roads and highways would tend to increase the growth rate.

Even though the above factors are all stated in the affirmative, it should be understood that if the reverse of the stated factors occurs the growth will tend to decrease.

14. Three models which could be used to describe a submarine are: model of energy source—for example, a model of an atomic reactor used in atomic submarines; model of air circulation system—description of how the CO_2 of the air and excess water vapor are removed and how the oxygen is replaced; model of torpedo control system—description of aiming and firing mechanism for torpedoes.

15. The only letter which fits the seven descriptions (models) is the letter N.

Problems

1. a) $L/16$

   b) At stop 8: 1/50 sec; at 5.6: 1/100 sec; at 4: 1/200 sec; at 2.8: 1/400 sec

   c) Nonlinear. (Since stop area × time = constant, this curve is a hyperbola.)

2. a) Weight = $(\pi r^2 h)$ (62.4)

Height (ft)	Diameter (ft)	Weight (lb)
2	$\frac{2}{7}$	8
3	$\frac{3}{7}$	27

Height (ft)	Diameter (ft)	Weight (lb)
4	$\frac{4}{7}$	64
5	$\frac{5}{7}$	125
6	$\frac{6}{7}$	216

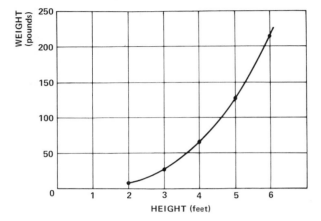

NOTE: It is easily shown that the weight of an object varies as the cube of the scaling factor of its dimensions. In this problem, doubling each dimension results in a multiplication of the weight by 2^3 or 8. Tripling each dimension produces a multiplication of its weight by 3^3 or 27, etc. The analysis is as follows:

$$W = (\pi r^2 h)\,(62.4)$$

Because the diameter is 1/7 of the height, $r = \frac{h}{14}$

$$W = (\pi)\left(\frac{h}{14}\right)^2 (h)\,(62.4)$$

$$= \left(\frac{62.4}{196}\right)(\pi)\,(h^3\,);\text{ but } \left(\frac{62.4}{196}\right)\pi \text{ can be set}$$

equal to k, thus

$$= kh^3$$

b) Since weight is proportional to volume, the curve is cubic. The earlier model (Section 2) was adequate as a linear approximation because only a small part of this curve was represented. The portion from 5 ft to 6 ft is close enough to linear that such a straight-line fit is not too far off. This also illustrates the error pointed out in the text where unwarranted extrapolation led to meaningless results.

3.a)After one rinse the entire uniform solution is composed of 4 oz of paint and 32 oz of solvent. The fraction of paint in the mixture is then:

$$\frac{4}{4 + 32} = \frac{4}{36} = \frac{1}{9}$$

After draining, the brush now contains:

$$(4)\left(\frac{1}{9}\right) = \frac{4}{9} = 0.45 \text{ oz of paint}$$

With the second dilution, the fraction of paint in the new mixture is:

$$\frac{\frac{4}{9}}{4 + 32} = \frac{\frac{4}{9}}{36} = \frac{1}{81} \text{ or } \frac{1}{9^2}$$

and the amount of paint in the brush after draining is:

$$(4)\left(\frac{1}{9^2}\right) = \frac{4}{81} = 0.049 \text{ oz}$$

Continuing this process, it is evident that after the fifth rinse the brush will contain:

$$(4)\left(\frac{1}{9^5}\right) = \frac{4}{59,049} = 6.8 \times 10^{-5} \text{ oz}$$

b)

Rinse number	Paint in brush before rinse (oz)	Fraction of paint in mixture	Paint in brush after rinse (oz)
1	4	$\frac{4}{36}$	$\frac{4}{9} = 0.44$
2	$\frac{4}{9}$	$\frac{\frac{4}{9}}{36}$	$\frac{4}{9^2} = 0.049$
3	$\frac{4}{9^2}$	$\frac{\frac{4}{9^2}}{36}$	$\frac{4}{9^3} = 5.5 \times 10^{-3}$
4	$\frac{4}{9^3}$	$\frac{\frac{4}{9^3}}{36}$	$\frac{4}{9^4} = 6.1 \times 10^{-4}$
5	$\frac{4}{9^4}$	$\frac{\frac{4}{9^4}}{36}$	$\frac{4}{9^5} = 6.8 \times 10^{-5}$

The paintbrush will never get completely clean until just one molecule of paint is left and it happens to remain in the solvent when the brush is removed. So it is with all decaying exponentials which asymptotically approach a limit but theoretically never reach it. Practically, of course, the limit is reached; a paintbrush will get completely clean and coffee will cool to room temperature in a finite time because no process is really continuous. A point is reached where the random variations in the physical system swamp out the residue left in the exponential process.

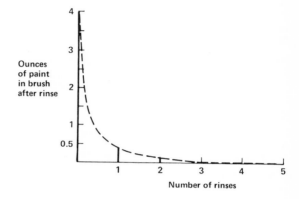

A curve represents a continuous process, and the rinsing is decidedly discontinuous. It can properly be represented only by a bar graph; the ends of the bars terminate on an exponential curve (shown dashed).

4.a)Assuming that his spending starts Saturday, he will have ($150) (1/2) = $75 left on Saturday. On Sunday he will have ($150) (1/2) (1/2) = ($150) $(1/2)^2$ = $37.50. In a similar way, by the following Friday he will have ($150) $(1/2)^7$ = $1.17.

b)

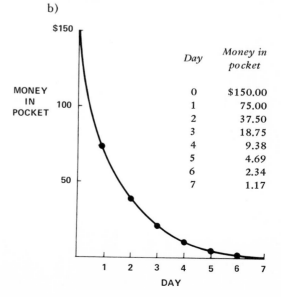

Day	Money in pocket
0	$150.00
1	75.00
2	37.50
3	18.75
4	9.38
5	4.69
6	2.34
7	1.17

90

c)($300) $(1/2)^{14}$ = $0.02. (He would be down to his usual weekly salary after 2 days, with 13 days to go. He would be in pretty bad shape!)

5. STARTING TEMP.

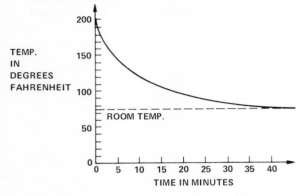

a) From the graph, at $t = 5$ min the temperature is about $155°F$; at $t = 10$ min the temperature is about $125°F$.

b) $T = \dfrac{(40)(1) + (125)(6)}{1 + 6} = \dfrac{790}{7} = 113°F$

c) $T_0 = \dfrac{(40)(1) + (200)(6)}{1 + 6} = \dfrac{1240}{7} = 177°F$

d) $\dfrac{T_0 - 75}{200 - 75} = \dfrac{177 - 75}{200 - 75} = \dfrac{102}{125} = 0.815$

At $t = 10$ min $T = 75 + (0.815)(125-75) = 75 + 41 = 116°F$

e) Since the answer to (d) is greater than the one for (b), it would be better to add the cream first.

6.a) $\dfrac{50,000}{5000} = 10$ half-lives

$\left(\dfrac{1}{2}\right)^{10} = \dfrac{1}{1024}$ of original carbon-14 remaining

b) $\left(\dfrac{1}{2}\right)^{N} = 1.0\% = 0.01$

$2^{-N} = 0.01$

$2^N = \dfrac{1}{0.01} = 10^2$

$N \log 2 = 2$

$N = \dfrac{2}{\log 2} = \dfrac{2}{0.30} = 6.7$ half-lives

(6.7)(5000) = 33,500 yr

c)

No. half-lives	No. years	Fraction of carbon-14 remaining
0	0	1
1	5,000	0.5
2	10,000	0.25
3	15,000	0.13
4	20,000	0.063
5	25,000	0.031

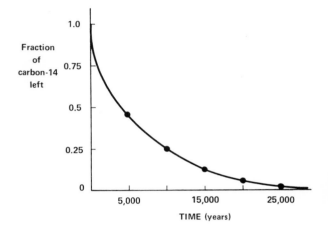

7.a)

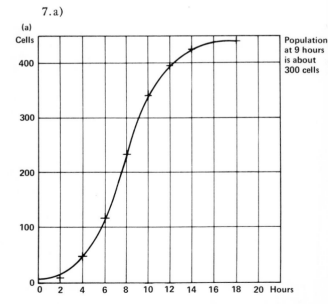

Population at 9 hours is about 300 cells

b) *Apparently* it levels off, so the best guess is about 450 cells. As explained in the problem, however, the population actually begins to drop, reaching a new plateau at about 375 cells. Students have no way of knowing this from given data.

c) Rate of growth is a maximum where slope of curve is the steepest. This is at about 8 hr. From tabulated data, the greatest change is between 6 and 8 hr, 117 cells. Maximum rate of growth is thus 58 cells/hr, or about 1 per minute. The minimum rate of growth is found between 0 and 2 hr, and also between 16 and 18 hr. In each case it is a change of 4 cells, or 2 cells/hr.

8. Remember that a 2% increase means that the population will double in about every 35 yr. This means that in 100 yr the population will be about 8 times (2^3) the original amount. So by 1972, the original population would have doubled 56 times (1972/35 = 56).

Therefore: $P = 4 \times 10^8 (2)^{56}$

$$\log P = \log (4 \times 10^8) + 56 \log 2$$
$$P = 2.8 \times 10^{25} \text{ people.}$$

The exponential equation for population growth is given as follows:

$$P = P_o a^{t/T}$$
$$P = 4 \times 10^8 (2)^{1972/35}$$
$$P = 4 \times 10^8 (2)^{56}$$
$$P = 2.8 \times 10^{25} \text{ people}$$

where:

P_o = original number
a = increase factor
T = time for increase factor
t = total time

If students have not had the benefit of knowing how to handle logarithms, a chart for 20 hundred years can be set up where for each hundred years the previous number is multiplied by 8.

$$P/\text{mile}^2 = \frac{2.8 \times 10^{25} \text{ people}}{5.8 \times 10^4 \text{ mi}^2}$$

$$= 4.8 \times 10^{20} \frac{\text{people}}{\text{mi}^2}$$

Three factors which limit population growth are: amount of food; amount of living space; wars, diseases, and natural disasters.

9. For local elevators (stopping at every floor)— total time/floor = stopping time + running time $t_{total} = 10 + 8 = 18$ sec. For express elevators—

Let N_i = initial floor
N_f = final floor
total time = $3(N_f - N_i - 2)$ +11
      number of floors   time for
      minus first and   starting
      last   and stopping

$$\text{Average time} = \frac{\text{total time}}{N_f - N_i}$$

One further assumption should be: all elevators must start from the first floor. Since as $N_f - N_i$ gets larger, the average time per floor gets smaller, each elevator should have as nearly as possible an express schedule. It should be mentioned that even with express elevators there would still be a waiting period of 10 sec. This, however, does not affect the solution because the more floors between stops ($N_f - N_i$) means less waiting time. For example, in this problem there are 6 elevators in a 20-story building. This means that 1 elevator must have 4 local stops while the other 5 can have only 3 local stops.

10.

Year	Population
1960	3×10^7
1961	3.12×10^7
1962	3.24×10^7
1963	3.37×10^7
1964	3.50×10^7
1965	3.64×10^7
1966	3.79×10^7
1967	3.94×10^7
1968	4.10×10^7
1969	4.26×10^7
1970	4.43×10^7

11. a) $6L^2$
b) $12L^2$
c) $24L^2$
d) Non-linear

12. A loss of 1% per year means 99% remain. Population in 1967 = 9900, in 1968 = .99 × 9900 = 9801.

1969 = 9703	1972 = 9415
1970 = 9606	1973 = 9321
1971 = 9510	1974 = 9228

13. The answer below is one of several possible answers, because there are several ways of "eyeballing" the data.

a)

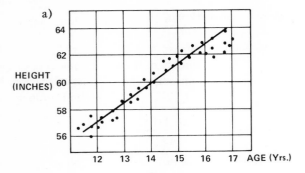

b) 62 1/2 − 59 1/2 = 3/2 in/year.

c) If Sue is an average girl from East High School, then it is reasonable to expect that she will be approximately 64″ tall when she is 17 years old.

D | DEMONSTRATIONS, LABS, AND PROJECTS

I. Is It an Elephant?

Section 1, "The Nature of Models," refers to J. G. Saxe's poem "The Blind Men and the Elephant." This experiment attempts to develop student appreciation for methods and procedures that increase man's understanding of the world in which he lives. Understanding is facilitated by the use of models. In addition to appreciating the value of models, the student will also learn of their limitations.

Two approaches may be used in preparing the container and its contents.

The first is to secure a quantity of cans used in packaging frozen fruit juices. Into each can place such items as: an animal cracker (preferably an elephant), a cube of sugar, a candy life saver, a sour ball, and a marshmallow. The cans, which should all be the same size, may be closed by using a sheet of paper and an elastic band or cellophane tape.

The pupils should have no knowledge of the fact that all the cans have similar contents. After the pupils have answered the suggested questions, the cans may be opened and the contents consumed.

A second approach is to have the pupils prepare the container and contents, then exchange cans at the beginning of the experiment. While this procedure relieves the teacher of the chore of preparing

laboratory material, several extra containers, already filled, should be available in the classroom for use if needed.

Suggestions developed through the use of the discussion questions might be:

*1. Make a model (an outline) of the ideas to be tested. Then prepare sample questions based on this model.

*2. Grades can be predicted with reasonable accuracy if the following items are considered: subject being studied, time spent in studying, the teacher, and relative difficulty of different sections of the course.

These factors are applicable in all subjects.

*3. College Board aptitude tests give a measure of some aspects of a student's potential. They do not measure the numerous other factors that determine success in college work. Some admissions officers use a chart based on pupil performance at the high school level as their model to aid in predicting achievement in college. The form for one such chart is:

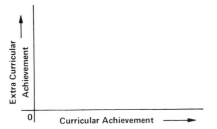

A block diagram of the model-making process may be used in the post-lab discussion. The student should analyze the experiment in relation to the diagram.

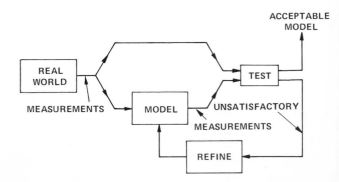

II. Traffic Flow

Section 3 discusses the subject of this experiment. The pupils are asked to obtain data, plot results, and from their graphs make a prediction of traffic conditions at some future time.

In organizing the class for this experiment, be on guard against contributing to congestion by overloading an intersection with observers. Whenever measurements are taken, the presence of the measuring instrument alters the situation. To obtain valid data, the influence of the instrument (in this case, observers) must be kept to a minimum.

Prediction of traffic conditions based on the data obtained will be influenced by the school schedule, the period of the day, and the weather conditions.

As an extension of this activity, the pupils may be asked to study automobile traffic in the general area of the school.

Pupil traffic to and from the school auditorium for school assemblies provides another area where the concepts studied in *The Man-Made World* have an immediate influence on the student.

Pupil investigations into the plans for evacuation of the school building in event of fire or other emergencies have resulted in revision of existing plans.

One ECCP class recommended, after careful study, a change in the traffic pattern for an area of their city. The plan was adopted by the City Council.

Answers to Questions:

*4. It would be possible, but fiendishly laborious, to find the exact destination of every pupil leaving a given room at the end of every period, and the source of everyone who comes to that room. A reasonable approach might be to chart the number of classes in English, History, Science, etc., for each period in the day. Then one could count the *change* in number at each class interval; +3E, for example, would mean that there are to be three more English classes next period than there were last, while OH would mean *no* change in the number of History classes. Next find the net change coefficient: the change in the number of all classes. Do this by adding the change numbers, with due regard to sign. As a rough rule, then, the closer the coefficient at any class change interval is to that at the measured interval, the less change in traffic pattern one expects. It is easy to poke holes in this scheme, and pupils should be encouraged to do so. They should then be encouraged to propose improvements in it. One way to refine the model would be to use the change in number of pupils, not just in number of classes. Thus, instead of +3E one might have +72E. A further refinement might be to find the change in the total numbers of pupils in various closely clustered classrooms. None of these devices, of course, keeps track of the difference between the numbers of pupils who move only a few feet and the numbers who move great distances in the building, which is closer to the heart of the problem.

*5. For every classroom (using the term to include library, cafeteria, gym, etc.) and for every class-change interval, the number of pupils going to, and the number coming from, every other classroom must be counted. From these data the student could predict the expected traffic flow in both directions in every passageway, and the more important 8-way (4 incoming, 4 outgoing) flow where passageways cross.

III. Introduction to the Analog Computer

This experiment is an introduction to the analog computer not only for the student, but also for you if this is your first year in the course, or if you are a bit rusty on the usage of the analog computer. In that case you will be well advised to program some spare time and entertain yourself with the instrument while learning again how to use it. Cassette tapes and a set of diagrams are available for individual use in learning how to use the analog computer. They can be used as supplementary material or in place of a group laboratory.

The following notes are classified in a way that it is hoped will make them easy to consult.

1. *The Meter.* Models C, D, and the demonstration model of the analog voltmeters come with center-reading. If not, a separate meter can be used if it has high impedance. (Many voltmeters found in elementary physics labs have an impedance of 100 ohms per volt or even less. Such a meter is useless in

this application. You need at least 20,000 ohms per volt.) Before the meter is connected, inspect it to be sure it reads 0. If not, look for the adjusting screw (usually just below the point where the needle pivots) and turn it very cautiously with a thin-bladed screwdriver until the needle is where it should be (the correct direction to turn must be found by experiment).

In normal use, start by connecting the commons (COM) of the analog computer and the meter. Then connect the + or − voltage output to the desired scale of the meter.

To protect the meter, always start with a high range setting (15v or even more). Then, if possible, change downward.

2.Setting the Input Signal. Connect the meter as described above. Use a high meter range, turn Constant knob fully counterclockwise and turn instrument On. Slowly adjust the Constant knob until the desired output voltage is recorded. If necessary, change the meter range downward for more accuracy.

The power supply voltage has a nominal value of 15v, but the amplifiers will saturate (no longer give linear response) at about 10 or 12 volts. Always start with an initial input signal low enough to avoid saturation *at any stage* (i.e., after summing and/or integrations).

3. The Summing-Scalors. As far as students are concerned, all the parts of the analog computer should be treated as black boxes. That is, the pupils know that a given input signal produces an output signal that corresponds to the input in a known way. They neither know nor need to know why.

The face of the instrument is marked with lines which show hidden wiring. Thus if a signal is led to the top left-hand-corner jack, it will be multiplied by 10, added to the signals brought to either of the two neighboring jacks, and then carried to the Coefficient black box where it may be scaled up or down by some fraction and then delivered to the three output jacks, which are in parallel (same signal at each). Subtraction is accomplished by the use of the three lower jacks at the left side of the first summing-scalor. Of course the other two summing-scalors are identical with this one. Note that the Coefficient knobs do not have a linear effect: $10°$

of rotation near the start of the possible motion will produce a much smaller change in the output than $10°$ will give near the end of the knob's travel.

Like any electronic device, the analog computer should be allowed to warm up for a few minutes and checked for 0 reading before use. Connect the meter between an output jack of the summer and any Common; turn on power but do not make an input connection; turn C fully clockwise. The meter **should read 0 even on its most sensitive range.** If it **does not, adjust the small screw in the balance control for that stage (see diagram below)** until it does. Check also the other two summers. While these are all balanced at the factory, they may change slightly during shipping or during long periods without use. It is best to let the analog computer "warm up" for 30 min. to an hour prior to use after it has been out of use for any period of time in excess of a month or two.

4.The Integrators. These too may need balancing before use. (a) Turn on the instrument, remove input connections to the stage being tested, turn Integrate switch to Off, connect the voltmeter to the Integrator output and Common. (b) Depress the red Set button and hold it down while adjusting the Initial Condition knob to give 0 on the meter. (c) Release Set Button: the meter should not drift from 0. If it does, adjust the small screw in the integrator balance control on the bottom of the instrument, and repeat the operations from (b).

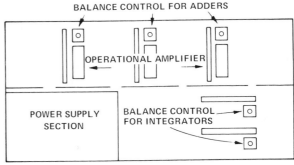

Bottom View of Analog Computer

It is highly recommended that the teacher refer to the AMF trouble-shooting guide when maintenance of the analog computer is necessary.

The output from an integrator can be easily measured with a voltmeter. While charge is accumulating on the integrator's capacitor, the voltmeter needle will be seen to rise at the same rate. In this experiment, then, the water that has flowed into the tank is modeled on the meter by a voltage reading. However, take careful note of the fact that our integrators reverse the sign: a + input has a − output. (This is inherent in the integrator design; the sign could be inverted again to avoid this small inconvenience, but the additional circuitry would not come free.) The voltmeter connection to the output jacks must be properly made with respect to the sign situation.

It would be perfectly possible, evidently, to start with a signal of −10v, cut this to −2v by means of Coefficient C_2, and thus have a positive signal put out by the integrator. But there would be no advantage because, however you do it, you have to measure both positive and negative voltages.

5. *Precautions.* Already mentioned: (a) protect the meter by starting its use at a high range; (b) use a signal small enough to avoid saturation; also (c) never connect a wire (or patch cord) directly from a "hot" terminal in the panel to a Common jack, nor from a + terminal to a − terminal. If this should inadvertently be done, a new 0.2-amp Littelfuse must be installed, at some inconvenience.

In the present experiment, note that we find the initial 10−v output as described under (2); then this signal is led to the first summing-scalor, the meter's positive lead is shifted to the summer's output jack, and the Coefficient knob C_2 is adjusted to get a 2−v signal.

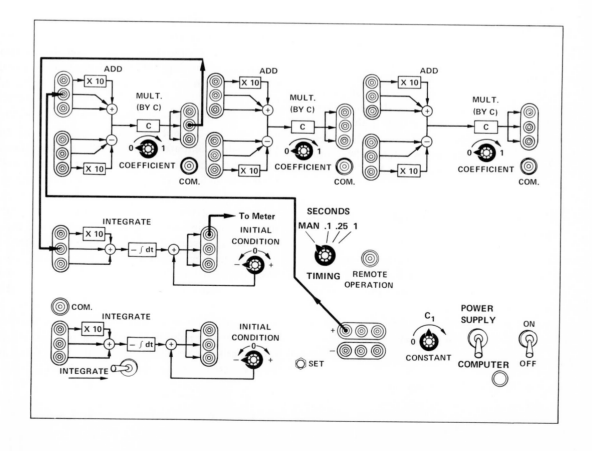

Our expectation is that pupils will very quickly learn to program their analogs for themselves, and no more help should be offered them than is essential. One problem common to teamwork is particularly noticeable here, and you will have to bring to bear all your skill and tact to prevent the best student in the lab team from taking over and running the show for the rest.

Equipment for Each Lab Team (4 students):

> 1 analog computer
> 1 high-impedance voltmeter (if not included with the computer)
> Set of patch cords
> Sheet of graph paper

General Lab Supplies:

> Spare 0.2-amp Littelfuses
> Thin-bladed screwdriver
> T-0413 may be helpful in getting over the start-up problem.

Once the computers have been programmed properly, each student should make a two-column chart, listing in one column the total number of gallons in the tank (2 + what has been added during the simulation); the second lists the corresponding voltage readings. A graph should be drawn, gallons on the *x*-axis (the independent variable in this case), voltages on the *y*-axis. If the integration has been repeated 5 or 6 times, saturation will have begun to set in and will show clearly on the graph.

IV. Analog Computer Model for Buffalo Harvesting

This experiment is important chiefly for two reasons: the first is to demonstrate how to handle a bothersome problem in setting an input signal, as well as how to manage more than one input signal at the same time; the second is to give experience in interpreting an unexpected computer output.

Equipment for Each Lab Team (4 students):

> Same as for Lab. III, omitting graph paper

General Lab Supplies:

> Same as for Lab III

PART A

The basic puzzle in this model is how to represent 15 or 16 million buffalo in terms of volts. The solution is the same as that adopted in scaling the axes of a graph. In this case we are governed by two constraints. First, the scale must be such that the grapher be able to plot the largest measurement on the paper. Second, he must be able to plot fractional values easily. It is easy to estimate halves, quarters, fifths, even tenths of a single graph space, but not (for instance) sevenths. Turning now to the laboratory problem, and remembering to avoid saturation, we see that 17 million buffalo should not be scaled on the voltmeter at 1:1,000,000 or 17 volts; nor is it convenient to use, say, 10v to represent 17 million, nor 4¼ (dividing 17 by 4). Try dividing by 10 million (in other cases one might divide by 5 or 2 times some power of 10). Then 17 million buffalo = 1.7v, and in general the number of animals will always be 10 million times the number of volts.

A voltage of 1.6v can be drawn from the power supply as explained for Lab III. To get the needed 1.5v, use an output jack of an otherwise unused integrator, adjusting the Initial Condition knob while holding down the Set button with the other hand.

The laboratory instructions are quite specific and the class should have little trouble in wiring their analog computers once the above explanations have been understood. However, they may well need help in interpreting the analog model and its results. This is because the instructions will bring them to a negative value of *k* (if all goes well). Let the students find this out for themselves, and then ask them to discuss the significance of a negative *k* value. A leading question, if you have to use it, is: What does k = 0 mean? (Ans.: No harvesting.) Then it follows that a negative value of *k* implies that the buffalo have to be "unharvested" or imported to achieve the desired growth to 17 million. Another question which helps to show if students understand the experiment is: What would be the 1852 value of F_y if k were 0? (Ans.: About 16.4 million.)

Answers to Questions:

> *1. *k* = −0.03 (sample analog value)
> *2. *k* = −0.04

*3. Random variation in individual computers leads one to expect that the final outcome of any two will probably differ somewhat. In this case the answer to Question 1 is so small that it is hard to decide what range of values is "acceptable." You should expect k to lie in the right ballpark: very close to 0, even if it should be slightly positive. Then Question 2 will bring the experimenters to a negative value of k. This all shows that analog computers should not be used when very precise answers are required; nevertheless, they are extremely convenient when we want to discover what mutual interactions in a system, and what sorts of output changes, will be caused by changing one or more of the system variables.

PART B

*1. $k = 0$ means that no buffalo are harvested.
*2. a) $F_{1854} = 18.2$ million (analog value)
   b) $F_{1854} = 18.4$ million (computed value)

V. Models of Exponential Growth

This experiment is designed to illustrate two important concepts of the chapter on modeling. First, students are given a chance to develop a functional model (computer simulation) of systems which exhibit exponential growth. Second, the idea that one model can represent many systems is reinforced by this activity.

Equipment for Each Lab Team (4 students):

Same as for last experiment

General Lab Supplies:

Same as for two previous experiments
1 stopwatch (optional)

As an introduction, go over Fig. 18 (T-0415) in enough detail to recall to the class that the actual size of the increase (or decrease) of a population or any other quantity that is changing exponentially depends on two things: the percent rate of change and also the magnitude itself. With minimal guidance

from Fig. 18 students should by now be able to program the analog computer so that it becomes a model of world population growth. When we use P_0 = 3v (3 billion in 1960) and $C = 0.02$ (2% growth rate) in the simulation, it is very difficult to obtain accurate data from year to year. Therefore, have the students obtain the population after 10 years (at the end of 1969). A sample result for this simulation was 3.6v (3.6 billion) as compared with 3.65 billion in the text.

Answer to Question:

*1. Using a 3% growth rate results in about 4.1 billion people at the end of 1969, while a 1% growth rate yields only about 3.3 billion people.

Another way to use this simulation is to ask students to find how long it takes for the population to double. For example, a 2% growth rate gives a doubling time of about 38 years (the text gives 35 yr). This discrepancy is not unexpected. Without discussing the matter in detail, it may be said here that the integrator is approaching saturation.

There are two ways to use the analog simulation to determine the doubling time. One way is to integrate by 1-sec intervals, counting carefully, until the initial population signal doubles. The other way is to integrate manually and to use a stopwatch to measure the time for the population to double. (When the Timing button of the integrator is set to Manual, the integration process will start as soon as the Integrate switch is pushed and will continue until it is released.) For periods longer than 20 sec the latter method is much simpler. See if your class members notice that the doubling time is independent of the initial population.

Now ask to have the population model modified so that it represents the growth of money in a savings bank. Have the students find the doubling time of a certain amount of money when the interest rate is 5% compounded annually. It turns out to be about 15 years (correctly, 14.2). Compounding the interest quarterly requires the multiplication of 0.05 by 0.25, letting 1 sec of integration represent ¼ year. Theoretically the doubling time should be less (14.0 yr), but the difference is too small for the analog computer to detect it. In this simulation the digital computer would be superior as a modeling

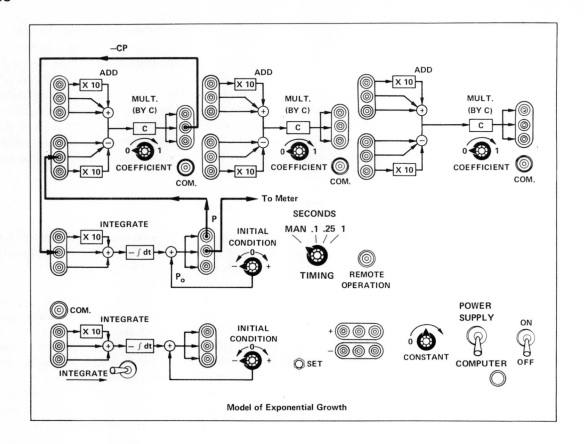

Model of Exponential Growth

device; for one thing, it would not suffer from the saturation inexactness already pointed out.

With many banks offering (or having offered in the recent past) a 6% interest rate for special accounts, you might want to ask the students to use the analog simulation to determine the decrease in doubling time when there is a 1% increase in interest rate. It turns out to be a decrease of about 2 or 3 years (from 15, or 14.2, to 12, or 11.9 yr).

Answer to Question:

*4. To modify the computer simulation so that it represents the growth of solid waste, use Fig. 4-27, which shows that the doubling time is about 20 years. For example, from 1950 to 1970 the amount of solid waste increased from 100 million to 200 million tons per year. This means that the percentage growth per year is nearly 3.5%, which is almost twice the rate of growth of the United States population. All that is required for the analog simulation to represent the growth of solid waste is to set the Constant knob at 0.035 and to let the Initial Condition represent a suitable initial amount of solid waste.

It may be worth remembering that exponential growth can be managed mathematically in several ways, not just those simple cases described in the text. As an example, we can look at bank interest:

$$A = P (1 + r)^t,$$

where A = total amount realized, P = number of dollars at interest, r = interest rate per period (as a decimal), t = total number of interest periods. Thus, to calculate the number of years for any sum to double, at 5% compounded quarterly, we set $A = 2P$, $r = (0.05/4)$, and t = the number of quarters.

$2 = 1.0125^t$. Take the log of each side of the equation:

$$\log 2 = \log (1.0125)^t = t \log 1.0125$$
$$t = \frac{\log 2}{\log 1.0125} = \frac{0.30103}{0.0053950}$$

(With such small numbers, a 5-figure log table helps.) The division is done by logs again and yields $t = 55.901$ quarters, or very nearly 14.0 years.

The growth of solid waste is different in that it grows continuously, not one period after another. Calculation now requires an equation involving e, the natural base of logarithms. The equation is:

$$A = P\,e^{rt}.$$

Using the doubling time of 20 years suggested previously, we have

$2 = e^{20r}$, and taking the (common) log of each side we have

$$\log 2 = 20r \log e = 20r \times 0.43429.$$

This gives $r = 3.47\%$, nearly; or since we recall that the doubling time required an uncomfortable interpolation, we should call it "about 3.5%."

Obviously, this also describes the doubling of a population, but since a census is taken only at intervals, it is reasonable to handle population growth as one does bank interest. In either case, this information is for your use, not to be taught to the class unless they are exceptionally motivated to go deeper into the mathematics of these models.

E | EVALUATION

The questions in this section are rated according to the chapter objectives and the performance levels stated in the introduction to the teacher's manual. This group of questions is not intended to be all inclusive, but just as a guide to possible questions. Zeros in the chapter objective column indicate no chapter objective for this question.

Chapter Objective	Performance Level	*Judged to be Relatively Easy:*
		1. In each of the following cases, mark the statement T if it is true, but mark it F if it is false.
1	I	a) A bar graph is a device used in weather forecasting.
1	I	b) It is always hard to predict the future, but extrapolation is often a help.
4	I	c) After a model is compared with the real world, it can often be improved.
8	I	d) When the equation $y = x - 2$ is plotted on ordinary graph paper, the graph is a straight line sloping downward to the right.
11	I	e) A quantitative model is generally more useful than one without numbers.
1	I	f) A verbal model is often easier to understand than other kinds.
2	I	g) In forecasting the future needs of a city the mayor's Planning Commission use a mathematical formula. Therefore, what they forecast will certainly happen.
7	I	h) If the population of a country is increasing exponentially, it means that the population will double in 35 years.
14	I	i) It is wise to develop several models of a single system (like an air conditioner) so that predictions made by the different models can be checked one against another.
11	I	j) When a model is applied beyond the region that has been measured, the results are always wrong.
0	II	k) If the United States maintained a herd of 40 million buffalo as a source of meat, there wouldn't be a need for all the cattle we now raise.
7	II	l) When a population increases by 2% a year, the gain for any year is always practically the same as that for any other.

Chapter Objective	Performance Level	

Judged to be Relatively Easy:

2. In designing the 747 airliner, plans for the interior were begun during a series of meetings of the designers around a long table. For each of the following, mark the statement *T* if it is true, but mark it *F* if it is false.

2	I
4	I
2	I

    a) The first model of the interior was a verbal model.
    b) It was then necessary to test this verbal model in a wind tunnel.
    c) The only way a functional model of the interior could be made was to build it inside the finished airframe.

2   I

    d) Since the plane was to be so much larger than any existing commercial transport, it was realized that a functional model would not help in the design.

2   I

    e) Photographs for advertising purposes were made of the interior before the plane was released for use. These photographs are a form of model.

4   II

3. The United States government publishes maps (so-called quadrangles) that depict an area about 15 X 20 mi. Gasoline companies furnish motorists with road maps which show a whole state or even several states at once. All of the following statements about these maps are true EXCEPT:

    a) Both kinds of maps are models.
    b) Gasoline company maps would be better models for motorists to use if they showed all the buildings out in the country (as the quadrangles do).
    c) Quadrangles show so small an area that motorists would find them inconvenient.
    d) Gasoline company maps help in planning a trip by trying to show the quality of roads.
    e) All gasoline company maps are not equally reliable for all roads.

Judged to be More Difficult:

4.

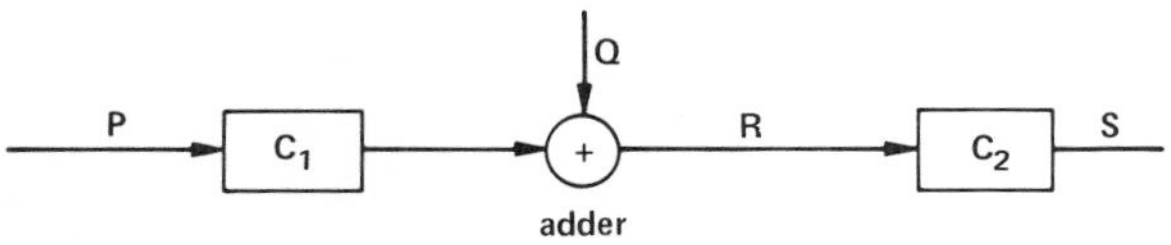

adder

9   II

Use the above diagram of a small analog computer to calculate the signal or coefficient setting marked by a question mark (?) in each of the following four questions. Mark your answers in the column at the right:

	P	Q	R	S	C_1	C_2	*Answers*
a)	2v	?	3v	—	0.7	—	Q = _____ volts
b)	2v	3v		2.2v	0.7	?	C_2 =_____
c)	2v	?		1v	0.7	0.5	Q = _____ volts
d)	?	0.7v		0.7v	0.7	0.5	P = _____ volts

5   II

5. In testing an analog computer, a student used a constant signal of 10.0v as input to a scalor, and measured the output for various settings of the coefficient knob (measured in degrees of rotation).
    a) Graph the following measurements on a chart form:

Knob rotation	Output
40°	0.1 v
90°	0.5
150°	1.0
250°	5.0
300°	10.0

Chapter Objective	Performance Level	Judged to be More Difficult:

b) Estimate the voltage output if the knob were rotated 200°.

c) Estimate the knob setting to produce an output voltage of 7.0 v.

| 10 | II | |

6. The population of Center City (in a certain western state) was 50 in 1900 just after it was founded. It grew rapidly, and the 1960 census counted 400 people in it (both of these numbers are rounded off for convenience).

a) Prepare a suitable exponential graph form and plot these two populations on it.

b) Estimate what the population was in 1920 if the growth was exponential.

c) About when will it become 1000 if the growth rate is maintained?

Solutions to Evaluation Questions:

1. a) F   e) T   i) F
   b) T   f) T   j) F
   c) T   g) F   k) T
   d) F   h) F   l) F

2. a) T   c) F   e) T
   b) F   d) F

3. b

4. a) $Q = 1.6$ v
   b) $C_2 = 0.5$
   c) $Q = 0.6$ v
   d) $P = 1.0$ v

5. a)

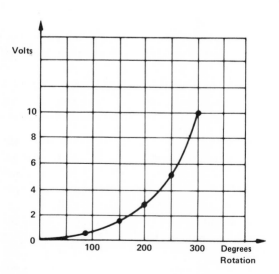

b) 2.5 v

c) 275°

Solutions to Evaluation Questions:

6. a)

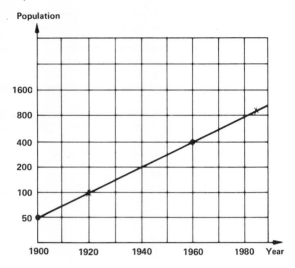

b) 100

c) 1986 (or any year between about 1982 and 1990)

F | FILMS

F-0401   WEATHER BY NUMBERS

Recommendation: Up-to-date illustration of mathematical modeling.

Application: Enrichment. Use it to show how a model is developed and refined.

Length and Type: 30 min, color, sound.

Source: #1 or #5

Summary: Shows the development of a model for weather forecasting, using a digital computer to process the large quantity of data.

F-0402   STANDING ROOM ONLY

Recommendation: Good to stimulate discussion of population explosion.

Application: Enrichment. PREVIEW THIS FILM BEFORE SHOWING IT.

Length and Type: 30 min, color, sound.

Source: #4 (No longer available on free-loan basis from #2.)

Summary: Surveys the population explosion, offering different opinions as to outcome. The emphasis is on birth control as a solution.

F-0403   MULTIPLY AND SUBDUE THE EARTH

Recommendation: Excellent example of how rational planning of land use makes use of ecological models.

Application: To expand text discussion of solid waste in cities to the rest of the country.

Length and Type: 68 min, b & w, sound.

Source: An NET TV film. #5

Summary: Documentary on transformation of natural environment into cluttered wasteland.

F-0404   MANAGERS AND MODELS

Recommendation: Illustrates the use of a digital computer as a modeling tool.

Application: Enrichment after an initial discussion of models.

Length and Type: 30 min, b & w, sound.

Source: One of NET TV series "Computer and the Mind of Man." #8

Summary: Mathematical simulation with a digital computer, in space flight, design of a chemical plant, and management of a sugar refinery.

F-0405   CHANGE OF SCALE

Recommendation: Optional if more emphasis on physical models is needed.

Application: Enrichment, as models are first studied.

Length and Type: 23 min, b & w, sound.

Source: A PSSC film. #7

Summary: Physical effects of change of scale (change of strength-to-weight ratio), and some problems of scale models.

F-0406   THE MATHEMATICIAN AND THE RIVER

Recommendation: Optional—show for additional emphasis.

Application: Enrichment.

Length and Type: 18 min, color, sound.

Source: #11

Summary: Problem of flood control on the Mississippi to show the relationship between the worlds of mathematics ("abstract") and nature ("real").

G | GENERAL

Bibliography

M. B. Hesse, *Models and Analogies in Science.* University of Notre Dame Press, 1966 (B)

> What is an analogy (or model)? When is argument from analogy valid? Mostly philosophy of science, but surprisingly free of the philosopher's technical jargon. Fine bibliography.

H. Leavitt, *Superhighway—Superhoax.* Doubleday, 1970 (B)

> This pulls no punches, and is crammed with useful, astonishing, and depressing facts, figures, and quotations.

D. J. DeS. Price, *Little Science, Big Science.* Columbia University Press, 1963 (A)

> Among many interesting things, study of exponential growth law in scientific journals, scientific and technical manpower, Physical Abstracts, etc.; sigmoids and other functions. Comment on multiple discoverers.

J. Rose, ed., *Technological Injury.* Gordon & Breach, 1969 (C)

> A symposium by 15 British scientists and technologists on pollution of many kinds. They are, of course, as badly off as we, and it is interesting to see their reactions and struggles, which often have a new slant and involve new (to us) data.

K. Sax, *Standing Room Only.* Peter Smith, 1960 (B)

> By an enthusiastic biologist. Packed with facts yet quick reading; from Malthus to the outlook for the future. Probably the best resource if a class takes to the population problem.

Society for Experimental Biology, *Models and Analogs in Biology.* (Symposium #14) Academic Press, 1960 (C)

> Bohr's famous paper on quantum physics and biology. Models in genetics; models of muscle; mechanical models in zoology; physical models in biology; electric analogs in biology; computers and the nervous system; cybernetics; nervous activity. Important and suggestive, even if not immediately applicable to *The Man-Made World.*

G. C. Clough, "Lemmings and Population Problems." *American Scientist,* June, 1965

K. Davis, "Population." *Scientific American,* September, 1963

C. L. Morkert, "Biological Limits on Population Growth." *Yale Scientific Magazine,* November, 1966

A. Rosenblueth and N. Wiener, "Role of Models in Science." *Philosophy of Science,* December, 1945

V. C. Wynne-Edwards, "Self-Regulating Systems in Populations of Animals." *Science,* March 26, 1965

CHECK LIST FOR CHAPTER 5 — SYSTEMS

APPROX. TIME: Text: 12 days   Lab: 5 days

A. APPROACH	CLASS PERIODS	B. BLACK & WHITE TRANSPARENCIES	C. CUES (k=key problem) Discussion Questions	Easy	Medium	Hard	D. DEMONSTRATIONS, LABS & PROJECTS	E. EVALUATION	F. FILMS	G. GENERAL
1. Introduction	} 3		1, 2, 5							
2. Input-Output Ideas		0501, 2, 3, 4 5, 6	3, 4, 6, 7, 9, 10, 11, 12, 13, 14	1, 4	2	3	I, II, III	1, 2, 4a, 5		II
3. Finding the Parts of a System	2	0507, 8, 9, 10 11	8					3, 4b, c, e 6		
4. Rate Inputs	2	0512, 13, 14a, b, 15, 16				5, 6	IV	4d, g, 7, 8		
5. Population Model for a Town	1	0517, 18				7k	V	4h		
6. The Noise-Environment System	2	0519, 20			8			4j	0501	
7. Measuring the System	1									
8. Final Comment	1							4f, i, 9	0502	

Systems
5

A | APPROACH

I. Purpose and Organization of the Chapter

We have by now studied the decision-making process, with extra attention paid to optimization. The first step in decision making was modeling, and this we found has other important uses. Now we expand on a very helpful technique in modeling: the use of a block diagram associated with quantitative information. The topics treated in the previous chapters have been gradually increasing in complexity, and in this one a new plateau is reached with *systems,* where several interacting parts—often more than one cause and as a rule more than one result—are the objects of attention. Modeling a system adequately really demands, as a start, the use of a block diagram. The real goal of the diagram is system analysis, or the "systems approach."

The text immediately introduces several systems, discusses input and output signals, and shows how these are most naturally represented by a block diagram. By means of a thermostat-controlled heating system as a sample, we are shown some of the benefits to be derived from just a good block diagram. The need for quantitative knowledge for a full model is made evident. A population model of a town is chosen as an example of the application of the system idea to a rather straightforward problem

of social importance, and this leads to the examination of the noise-environment system as another, far more intractable problem. The chapter closes with a brief look at the difficult task of making measurements on social systems.

II. Objectives for Students

Upon completion of the activities, discussion, and reading in this chapter students should be able to:

1. Recognize and identify the following terms: *birth rate, block diagram, death rate, decibel, input, output, system, velocity* and *terminal velocity.*

2. Explain the need for quantitative information to convert a block diagram into a usable model.

3. Discriminate between essential and irrelevant inputs in designing block diagrams (for house heating, noise environment, and other systems).

4. Demonstrate the use of the "systems approach" to show how inputs affect outputs, how a system works, and how its operation can be improved, with such systems as thermostatically controlled house heating or laborers working on a job.

5. Explain the integrator as a device for measuring area, and explain why the integral of an acceleration is the velocity and why the integral of the velocity is the displacement.

6. Interpret the effect of noise on a listener in terms of loudness, duration, pitch, and pitch range.

7. Produce examples of the complexity of many social systems.

8. Explain the need for special precautions in making measurements on social systems.

III. Suggestions for Teaching

It will be observed that there is an embarrassment of riches in the laboratory section of this chapter. Many of the exercises may seem similar, but should all be assigned or demonstrated to show the versatility of the computer in simulating a variety of real-world situations. You should plan well in advance whether you are going to assign some and demonstrate others or whether to assign each activity to a different lab team or whether to allow your students to make their own choices.

Section 1. Introduction. Have students write a short statement about the idea of systems.

Section 2. Input-Output Ideas. For strategic reasons, the chapter starts with a number of systems. But tactically it may be better to begin, in the classroom, with the input-output idea (e.g., Questions 11 through 14). When preparing a transparency for T-0504, make enough duplicates for all your students. Use the copies as a basis for discussion. Students should certainly be urged to think up their own examples. The concept is easy, and its relation to the notion of the "black box" should be mentioned. That is, input is cause, output is effect, but in the block diagram no effort is made to work out the details of the linkage inside the "system" block. As a matter of conforming to custom, try to remember that an *input* has an arrowhead on it, an *output* is just a line unless it is also an input to another stage. The black box was first encountered in Chapter 4, Lab III (mentioned in the Teacher's Manual under *Summing-Scalors*). The analog computer itself, when interconnected for a specific end, is an excellent example of a system, in this case employed as a model of some other system. The word "system" was defined as a connection of many different parts which interact; but there is no advantage to be gained by insisting on a census of parts. If you are dealing with an instance with more than one

input or output or working part, it should be regarded as a system. An important distinction, however, is that between block diagram and model. In the model, measured numbers are somehow included, by a graph, a table, or otherwise.

The graph of Fig. 5-6 (T-0505) casts an amusing light on the problem once standard in algebra classes that read something like: "If it takes 5 men 12 days to do a certain piece of work, how long would 24 men take?" For an example close to home, ask whether 6 students could do a lab with the analog computer any faster than 2 could.

Section 3. Finding the Parts of a System. It is possible that there may be objections to Figs. 5-15 to 5-18 on the ground that they are incomplete. The furnace has no fuel to burn, the pump has no electric energy to drive it, etc. If such a complaint arises, grant it and then go to the list of six input signals which control living room, kitchen, and bedroom temperatures (T-0512), and to the comment just below: "There are dozens of different things which affect the inside temperature . . . we have to simplify as much as possible." The omissions mentioned are other details which would be considered at the next level of refinement of the block diagram. This refinement can continue "ad nauseam" down to the grade of oil in the furnace, the cleanliness of the contacts in the thermostat, etc. It is astonishing, and worth emphasis, that so many valuable suggestions for improving the house-heating system can be derived from a careful review of the block diagram alone, without completing the model.

Section 4. Rate Inputs. Prior lab work has made the discussion of operator blocks redundant. But there is one puzzling (though correct) sentence: "The input [of an integrator] is the rate at which the output is changing." This doesn't mean that the output must somehow be plugged into the input. As the examples show, the integrator must be supplied as input with the rate of change, that is, with the increase (or decrease) per unit time, of some measured quantity. Every time the Integrate lever is pushed to the left, a unit of time (1 sec on the model D AMF computer) is supposed to have passed, so the output is a sum: (change during first unit of time + change during second unit of time + . . .). The sum is of course the total change. (Note that the input was, indeed, the rate of change of the output.) The final output is the total change determined just above added to (or subtracted from) the initial condition (it could be 0) that was included. Then if v, velocity, is the input to an integrator, the output is just the net change of position, or the distance covered; and similarly for a, acceleration, and net change of velocity. The mathematical symbol delta, Δ, meaning "change of," may help some students and will no doubt just confuse others. For those who will like it, we can say that $v = \Delta x/\Delta t$. Integrating v means that: $\int v\, \Delta t = \Delta x$ (omitting some boring details about initial and final time and the "constant of integration"). By the same symbolism, $a = \Delta v/\Delta t$, and $\int a\, \Delta t = \Delta v$. This looks like utterly unnecessary complexity. Doesn't $d = rt$? The integrator, and the symbolism, handle cases where the rate which is integrated is changing while the integration goes on. You can't do that with $d = rt$ when r keeps squirming to a new value even as you try to multiply it. This explanation is necessary for a fuller understanding of the process of integration. However, many students might not be ready for such a full explanation at this time. After they have been exposed to some of the laboratory activities in this portion of the course, they may begin to be more interested in this discussion. To insist on their understanding of the concept prior to further work with integration would be contrary to the intended approach of the course.

If you feel that practice on the concept of integration is wise, make duplicator copies of T-0513 for all students. It will be easy to show with the help of the transparency how to use large clusters of squares, grouped into rectangles and "counted" by length times width. From this you can go on to triangles and trapezoids. The idea of cutting down on labor is always appealing, so the class may enjoy the exercise of approximating the area under the curve by one or more rectangles that go outside the curve in some places but compensate by falling short of it in others. If they have first arrived at a fairly close value for the area by the square-counting technique, it will be of some value for them to see

how nearly right they are when they use this "eye-balling" method.

Figure 5-21 will cause some trouble if students did Lab V, Chapter 4. Clearly, this figure has been "simplified" by leaving out the feedback loop (see Chapter 7). Disregarding the sign change introduced by the integrator, that experiment was equivalent to this less-simplified block diagram:

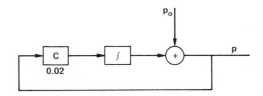

This is not quite the same as the acceleration-to-velocity integration of Fig. 5-30 (T-0515). There, the acceleration is always the same (32 ft/sec every second), provided we don't start the fall far enough out in space for the gravitational attraction to be appreciably less. The velocity grows every second by the same *number* of ft/sec, whereas the population grew every year by the same *fraction* of itself, and therefore by a continually increasing number of people. In practice, as the text implies, this difference in process is entirely swamped out with a falling body because we cannot supply a vacuum for it to fall in, near the earth's surface, more than a very few feet long. In air (unless the body is very heavy and compact, like a bullet or a bomb), it quickly approaches a terminal velocity. For a man falling freely, this is roughly 125 mph, while a parachute will cut the speed to about 25 mph (about 37 ft/sec)—still an uncomfortable landing speed, equivalent to jumping off a wall more than 20 ft high.

Section 5. Population Model for a Town. There is a chance to be confused here by the fact that b is the birth *rate* and bp is the *rate* at which babies are produced, which somehow sounds redundant. The solution is that b is the rate per 1000 people, and bp is the rate in terms of the whole population of the town. But migration, in or out, is treated in terms of actual numbers, not of rates.

Section 6. The Noise-Environment System. In this section the text takes a fairly detailed look at a contemporary urban problem. (Contemporary, but Mayor LaGuardia fought noise in New York in the late 1930's, and authorities in Paris and London took at least some action long ago.) We chose this problem rather than some other, perhaps, because it is rather newly talked about, but almost any urban problem would do to illustrate the points. Looking back at the comment in Chapter 1 on the MHT center, we see the same three difficulties again: that of data pollution interfering with the solution, that of matching any solution to the target public (like many taxi drivers, for instance), and that of avoiding side effects worse than the original trouble.

Much of the factual material here is physics, but it is unlikely that any student who has had a course in that subject will recognize old friends. "Sound" is often played down or skipped nowadays as unimportant even though interesting. Figure 5-41 (T-0520), usually called a Fletcher-Munson curve, has fascinated designers of record players. Occasionally they have fitted a "loudness control," the function of which is to adjust the amplification at various frequencies so that the sound level as heard at all frequencies is about the same number of dB

above the audibility threshold. In other words, even if the *volume* is turned low, the bass and the treble will still be heard.

Section 7. Measuring the System. The possibility that attempts to measure a system will alter the system itself is by no means limited to social systems. For instance, when a voltmeter is connected between two points in a circuit, it draws a little current which may change all the conditions in the circuit. Usually this doesn't matter, but it does matter when high precision is needed. Occasionally a student may have heard about the Heisenberg Uncertainty Principle, which is essentially a restatement of the previous argument but on a submicroscopic level. In general, the act of taking notice of anything modifies the thing by an unknown amount, in an unpredictable direction. A depressing thought, only slightly allayed by all the ingenious techniques described in the text.

Section 8. Final Comment. This is not merely a review section, but mentions several new systems. It would be appropriate to see if members of the class can think of even more.

B | BLACK AND WHITE TRANSPARENCIES

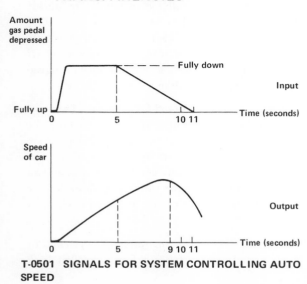

T-0501 SIGNALS FOR SYSTEM CONTROLLING AUTO SPEED

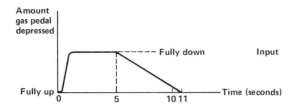

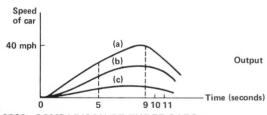

T-0502 COMPARISON OF THREE CARS

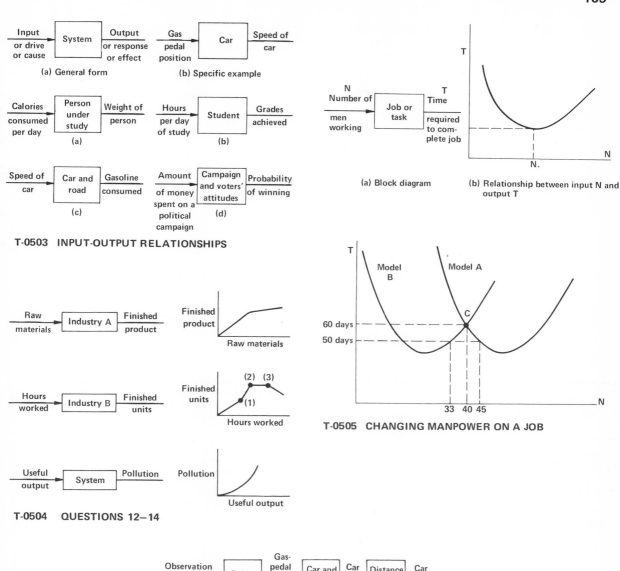

T-0503 INPUT-OUTPUT RELATIONSHIPS

T-0505 CHANGING MANPOWER ON A JOB

T-0504 QUESTIONS 12—14

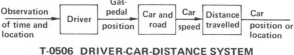

T-0506 DRIVER-CAR-DISTANCE SYSTEM

T-0507 HOME-HEATING SYSTEM

110

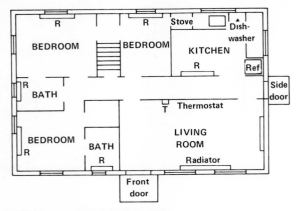

T-0508   HOUSE FLOOR PLAN

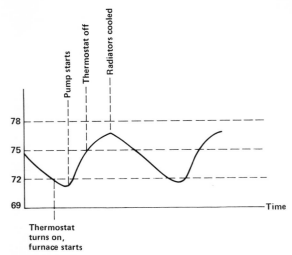

Thermostat
turns on,
furnace starts

T-0509   TEMPERATURE AT THERMOSTAT

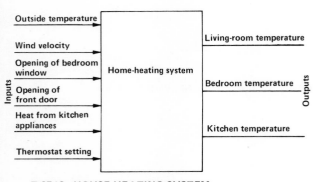

T-0510   HOUSE-HEATING SYSTEM

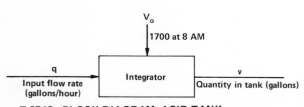

T-0512   BLOCK DIAGRAM, ACID TANK

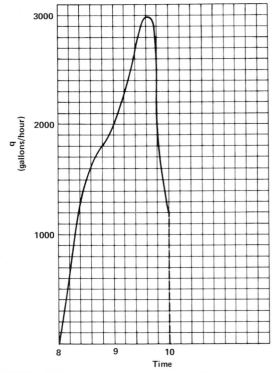

T-0513   RATE OF ACID FLOW 8-10 A.M.

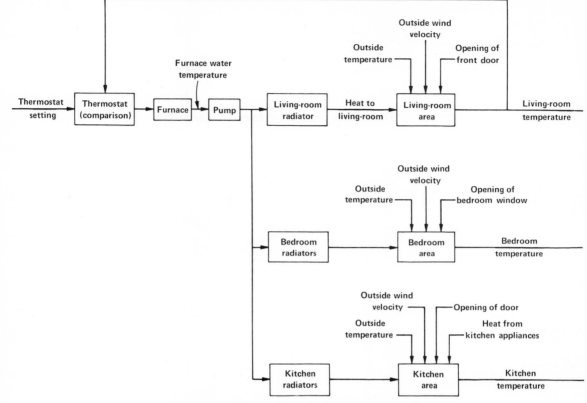

T-0511   HOUSE-HEATING BLOCK DIAGRAM, COMPLETE

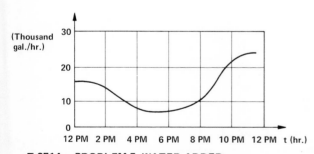

T-0514a   PROBLEM 5, WATER ADDED

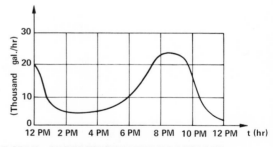

T-0514b   PROBLEM 5, WATER DRAWN OFF

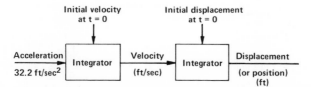

**T-0515   ACCELERATION TO VELOCITY TO DIS-
PLACEMENT INTEGRATORS**

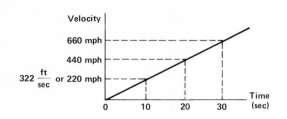

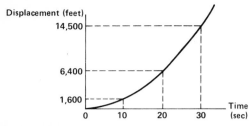

T-0516   FALLING BODY, VELOCITY AND DISPLACEMENT

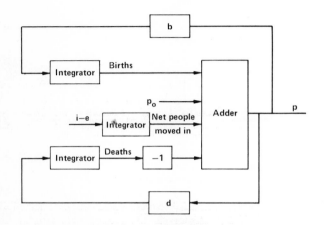

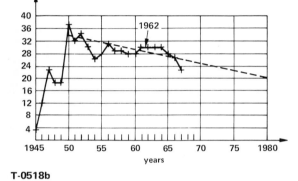

T-0518b

p   population (thousands) at any time
p_o population at start in thousands
i   immigration rate (thousands of people/year moving in)
e   emigration rate (thousands of people/year moving out)
b   births per 1000 population per year
d   deaths per 1000 population per year

T-0517   MODEL FOR TOWN POPULATION

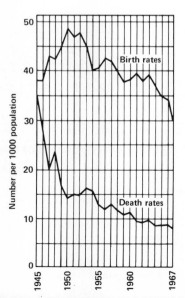

T-0518a   BIRTH AND DEATH RATES, MAURITIUS

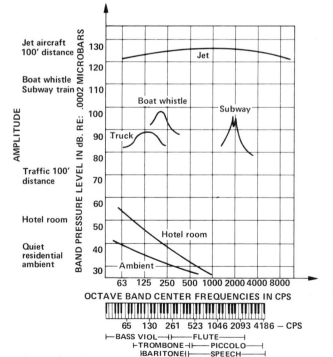

T-0519   NOISE SPECTRA, LEVEL VS FREQUENCY

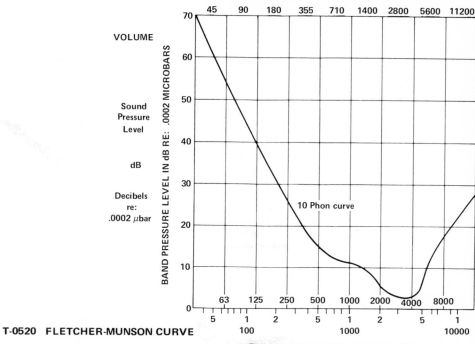

OCTAVE PASS BANDS IN CYCLES PER SECOND

T-0520 FLETCHER-MUNSON CURVE

FREQUENCY IN CYCLES PER SECOND
(FREQUENCY IN Hz (HERTZ OR cps — PITCH)

C | CUES TO QUESTIONS AND PROBLEMS

Questions for Study and Discussion

1. The following definitions of "system" and "dynamic" will be helpful in answering this and the next question.

System: an interconnection of parts or components.

Dynamic: an adjective which emphasizes that the system is described by signals that change with time.

The table which follows is merely suggestive and by no means exhaustive. For example: the reason for referring to SPY in the SKY as a system is also because the satellite is itself only a part of the SYSTEM—the receiving antennae, the data processing machinery, etc., are all part of the spy-in-the-sky system. Similar additional statements can be made about the fish supply system as well.

Example	Why system?	Why dynamic?
Spy in the sky	The various parts of a satellite are interconnected.	The input and output signals of the satellite vary with time.
Fish supply	Fish population made up of fish from different parts of the world.	Fish population changes with time.
1960 Corvair	Car made up of interconnected parts.	Input signal (road) and output signal (ride) vary with time.

2. In trying to decide whether something is a dynamic system, refer to the definitions of "system" and "dynamic" in the answer to Question 1. For example, newspaper accounts of the development of the SST (Supersonic Transport) describe a system (interconnection of components) which is dynamic (signals vary with time) and which can be modeled.

3. Again there are suggested possible answers. Those which your students will provide might well be more appropriate to your situation than these.

Steps against inflation	Segment of population adversely affected
a) Increase income taxes	The middle classes would probably be adversely affected because prices would not come down right away, thereby cutting down the purchasing power of these people. The richer people can go into their savings to maintain purchasing power, while the poor would not be affected much by the tax rise.
b) Raising of interest rates	The small businessman would be hurt most because with his small capital and short-term planning he cannot put off borrowing to a later time.
c) Cut down in government spending	This would hurt educational institutions (with their related projects, e.g., ECCP) as well as other organizations that depend on government support.

4. Starting at the left end of the curve: when there are few workmen (N is small), it takes a long time to finish a task (T is large); as workmen are added (N increases) with automatic machinery to aid them, the time needed rather quickly diminishes (T drops). For any job, there is an optimum number of people and a shortest time (N_0 and T_0). Adding still more workers actually increases the time needed because some machines and their operators have to wait for those earlier in the sequence of manufacturing steps to send along goods for the later steps. Of course, this in turn, since it idles some of the people some of the time, promotes sociability and other ways of wasting time.

5. The dynamic characteristics of the business are:

    a) Growth of population:

        1. How is the population changing in the heart of town?

        2. How will the population of the whole town grow to the point where it will be able to support two supermarkets?

    b) Potential income of the town's people.

    c) Type of people moving into or leaving the town.

    d) Projected profit of supermarket based on current profits and changes in the above variables.

    e) Industrial changes of the town.

All of the dynamic characteristics listed above are important in making a decision. The difference is in the degree of importance. For instance, characteristic (a) is more important than (c).

6.

It would be possible to analyze the "School" block more or less indefinitely, but the question does not ask us to do this.

7.

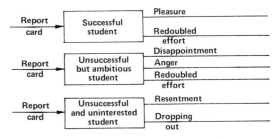

There must be many other ways to discuss this question and should lead to a lively discussion.

8.

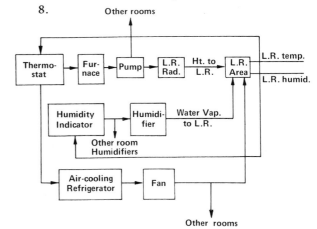

This assumes a not uncommon type of thermostat which does different jobs at different seasons. If the house has a hot-air heating system, the humidifier may moisten the air at the furnace for all rooms.

9. Yes. This system is developed from data concerning past and present population growth. The in-

put signal is a year in the future and the output signal is the population for that year.

10. "The Mississippi River system" is a system made up of tributaries which feed into the main river which has the overall function of transferring water from the head waters (input) to the ocean (output).

11. The students again will have many additional suggestions as to inputs and outputs and block diagrams. It is well to discuss each possibility so that they get the experience in deciding which are useful considerations and which are not. This is also true of the answers to Questions 12 through 14. This is the purpose of the discussion question section of the text. Many teachers have found it useful to have students lead the discussions of these questions while they (the teachers) observe the performance of individuals in this type of activity.

a) 1. Strength of rider
   2. Condition of the road (smoothness or grade)
b) 1. Steep climb
   2. Application of brakes
c) Input—amount of heat applied
   Output—time for water to boil
d)

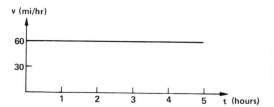

12. At first the input of raw materials and the output of finished product are about equal; but after a time a given input produces a very much smaller output, suggesting that much of the raw material is being spoiled in manufacture. This in turn suggests that the manager, trying to enlarge a profitable operation, took on too many untrained workers and did not have them taught what to do.

13. Between (1) and (2) there was a dramatic rise in output with comparatively little increase in time. This suggests that new machinery was installed at (1). At (2) there was a strike (or a lockout)—no production. After (3) production fell off—the longer

the working time, the fewer units were finished. The end of the strike or lockout at (3) did not occur in a way pleasing to the labor force, and a slowdown began which was joined by more and more workers.

14. As useful output grows, the output of pollution (it could be any kind) grows even faster. The quickest way to cut pollution back is evidently to cut useful output back. This is probably undesirable economically, however, so engineers should be hired to design equipment for intercepting and removing the pollutants (by precipitating particles and chemically neutralizing noxious gases in what goes up the chimney, and chemically neutralizing and filtering effluent water, etc.).

Problems

1. The graph is a horizontal line at 60 mi/hr.

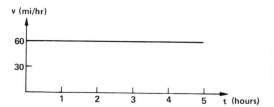

2. a) $v = 0$, because the slope is zero.

b) $v = \dfrac{\Delta x}{\Delta t} = \dfrac{100 - 60}{175 - 137} = \dfrac{40}{38}$

≈ 1 mi/min $= 60$ mi/hr

c) $v = \dfrac{\Delta x}{\Delta t} = \dfrac{60 - 20}{110 - 60} = \dfrac{40 \text{ mi}}{50 \text{ min}}$

$\times 60$ min/hr $= 48$ mi/hr

3. This question is not appropriate in the present context. Your students are familiar with rate-time-distance problems with a fixed rate. Here we have a changing rate (see Section 4), and velocity is no longer rate of change of position. What is it, then? As you recall from your study of physics, the "instantaneous velocity" of a body which is continuously changing speed (a falling body, for instance) can be estimated approximately if we have a graph of displacement against time. Then, if we select the point on the curve which corresponds to the time we are interested in and draw a tangent to the curve

at that point, the slope of the tangent gives the instantaneous velocity. This method has been used in the solution below. It should be pointed out, incidentally, that the tangent at 4 sec is very uncertain because the curve stops at that point, so it is not possible to tell whether the line drawn is indeed a tangent or would intersect the curve if we knew more about it. (Physics teachers will recognize that displacements were calculated from a constant acceleration, $a = 30$ ft/sec^2, and the stated velocities are indeed correct.)

Some students may wish to use the analog computer to check their answers. If this suggestion is made, set the constant at a value which represents a as 30 ft/sec^2 and integrate the signal once to get the velocities at 2 and 4 sec and twice to get the distances.

a)

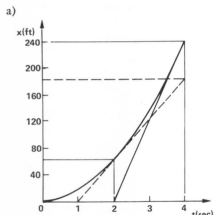

b) $v = \dfrac{\Delta x}{\Delta t} = \dfrac{180 - 0}{4 - 1}$

$= \dfrac{180}{3} = 60 \dfrac{ft}{sec}$

c) $v = \dfrac{240 - 0}{4 - 2}$

$= \dfrac{240}{2} = 120 \dfrac{ft}{sec}$

4. a) Actual velocity = $30 - 10 = 20$ mi/hr.
   b) Actual velocity = $30 + 10 = 40$ mi/hr.

5. Quantity of water stored at 10 P.M. is the area under the q_1, t curve from noon to 10 minus the area under the q_2, t curve from noon to 10 plus 16,000 gallons ($Q = 117,000 - 126,000 + 16,000 = 7000$ gals).

6. Since $V_{max} = 40$ ft/sec

Area of semicircle $= \dfrac{\pi v^2}{2} = \dfrac{\pi (40)^2}{2} = 800\,\pi$

$\therefore \quad 800\,\pi = R\,(80)$

$R = 10\,\pi$ ft/sec (av velocity)

Area of rectangle $= 10\,\pi$ ft/sec (20 sec)
$= 200\,\pi$ ft

7. The graph Fig. 5-39 (T-0518) cannot be read accurately, but we are concerned with trends, not precision. The following values were estimated from the graph, and the differences were taken and plotted below. The dashed line is a trend line.

Year	Birth rate	Death rate	Dif.
45	38	35	3
46	38	26	12
47	43	20	23
48	42	23	19
49	45	16	19
50	50	13	37
51	47	15	32
52	48	14	34
53	46	16	30
54	41	15	26
55	41	13	28
56	43	12	31
57	42	13	29
58	40	11	29
59	38	10	28
60	39	11	28
61	40	10	30
62	39	9	30
63	40	10	30
64	38	8	30
65	36	8	28
66	35	8	27
67	30	7	23

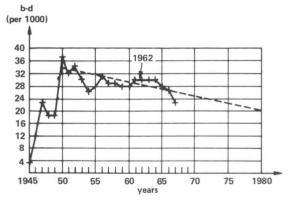

The total estimated gain in population from 1962 to 1980 is 1000 times the integral, the area between those dates under the dashed line, which is a trapezoid. $A = 1/2(28 + 20) \cdot 18 = 432$. Hence the predicted population in 1980 = 700,000 + 430,000 = 1,130,000. Any answer obtained by this method, and without arithmetical error, is acceptable, since the "eye-balled" position of the trend line will vary considerably. (If the trend for the last 4 years shown were projected, there would be a *loss* of population during the last decade.) Therefore only 2 significant digits are retained above.

    8.a) The first sound is at the threshold of audibility. A 2000-cycle sound at the threshold has a volume of 6 dB.

      b) The second sound is audible, the first below the threshold. Therefore the answer is "softer."

D | DEMONSTRATION, LABS, AND PROJECTS

I. Modeling a System on the Analog Computer

III. Modeling Gas Pedal vs Distance

IV. Simulation of a Falling Body

These three exercises are so similar that it is convenient to describe them together. Labs I and III back up Section 2, while IV is described in Section 4. Many teachers have found that it is useful to have one or more of these done as class demonstrations by students. If equipment is available, at least one of these should be done as a smaller group laboratory. If Lab I is done as a demonstration, Lab III should be a small group lab. The chart recorder is particularly useful for this set of labs.

Equipment for Each Lab Team (4 students, ideally):

    1 analog computer
    1 high-impedance voltmeter (if not included with the computer)
    Set of patch cords
    Graph paper (8-12 sheets)

General Lab Supplies:

    Spare 0.2-ampere Littelfuses
    Spare patch cords
    Thin-bladed screwdriver
    Chart recorder (optional)
    Extra graph paper

Lab I, P A R T A

Most students are familiar with the feel of acceleration of a car and they know that it is somehow related to the depressing of the gas pedal. This should help them understand the block diagram. For those who have trouble with the wiring, remind them of Lab III in Chapter 4. The wiring is identical, except for the negative input to the coefficient. Page 121 shows the wiring of the analog computer for this part, where there is no friction. Remember that, since the initial velocity is zero, initial condition of the integrator should be set to this value, with the aid of the meter. You will recall that the sign of the integrator output is the negative of that of the input. This is why the input to C_1 (gas pedal movement) is to the negative side.

Answers to Questions:

    *4. (Sample data)

(1 volt = 20 mph)

Voltage output at constant: 5v

t (sec)	V (volts)	v (mph)
0	0	0
1	0.5	10
2	1.0	20
3	1.5	30
4	2.0	40
5	2.5	50
6	2.9	58
7	3.2	64
8	3.4	68
9	3.5	70
10	3.5	70
11	3.5	70
12	3.5	70
13	3.5	70
14	3.5	70

*5.

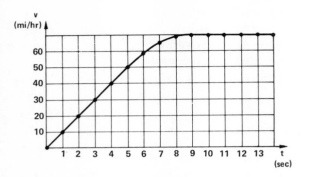

*6. For the first 9 sec, the graphs are quite similar. After the ninth second, the graph in Fig. 5-2 starts to decrease while the experimental graph remains constant.

*7. The difference is caused by the fact that frictional effects were neglected in the experiment. We are modeling an ideal system where there are no energy losses.

Lab I, PART B

The wiring for these appears on page 122. Since the sign of the frictional constant (C_2) has to be opposite to that of the gas pedal coefficient, it is assigned a positive value.

Answers to Questions:

*2. (Sample data)

Frictional coefficient—0.5

t (sec)	V (volts)	v (mph)
0	0	0
1	0.35	7.0
2	0.58	11.6
3	0.73	14.6
4	0.82	16.4
5	0.87	17.4
6	0.85	17.0
7	0.76	15.2
8	0.57	11.4
9	0.40	8.0
10	0.22	4.4
11	0.13	2.6
12	0.07	1.4
13	0.03	0.6
14	0	0.0

*3.

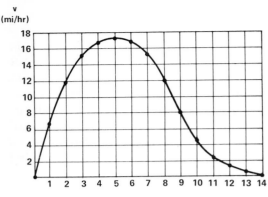

*4. This graph is similar to Fig. 5-2 except that it reaches the maximum velocity earlier than that of Fig. 5-2. This is because the high frictional coefficient diminishes the gain in speed and causes the highest speed to be less and to be reached sooner.

Lab I, PART C

*1. All these graphs would resemble the graph above except for the difference in maximum velocities. They would look very much like those of Fig. 5-3.

Lab III, PART A

When set up as on page 123, the distance will be modeled by a negative voltage. This can be avoided, if desired, by leading the output of integrator 1 to a negative input of summing-scalor 3 (coefficient knob fully clockwise to equal 1), and then returning the signal from here to integrator 2; or by inserting this summing-scalor on the output side of that integrator. It should be observed, however, that the quality of the signal suffers some erosion at every additional stage. A small project for some student would be to compare the magnitudes of a series of output readings, with and without the sign-inverting stage, to see whether there is a perceptible difference.

Answers to Questions:

*1. (Sample data)

$V_{\text{input}} = 0.5\, v$; $C_{\text{friction}} = 0.5$

$v_{\text{initial}} = 0$; $d_{\text{initial}} = 0$

(1 volt = 20 mph)

*2.

t (sec)	Gas pedal depression	Distance traveled (volts)
1	Full	0.22
2	Full	0.77
3	Full	1.5
4	Full	2.3
5	Full	3.3
6	0.8	4.3
7	0.6	5.1
8	0.4	6.0
9	0.2	6.7
10	0	7.1
11	0	7.4
12	0	7.6
13	0	7.7
14	0	7.8
15	0	7.9

*3.

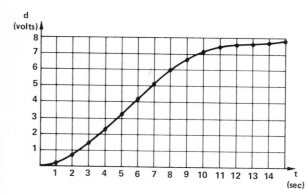

*4. At about the 15-sec mark the v vs t graph (from Lab I) approaches 0 while the d vs t graph approaches a constant value. This is perfectly consistent with the real situation where 0 velocity implies 0 displacement.

Lab III, PART B

*1. The data for different input voltages will be the same as those found in the previous part except for different maximum values.

Lab IV, PART A

The wiring is the same as for Lab I, Part A, except that the summing-scalor stage can be omitted by taking the input voltage for the integrator from the negative side of the constant-controlled supply (see below, however). Question 4 asks to have the simulation run for 30 sec. A real body would reach a speed of 300 m/sec in this time, in the absence of air resistance. To avoid saturation, then, the acceleration signal should be no larger than $1/3v$ (more easily, $0.25v$). If this is hard to achieve accurately, a larger voltage could be taken from the supply and then pared down with the aid of a summing-scalor coefficient. It is evidently futile to try to spot g accurately at 9.8 m/sec^2. Use 10 if necessary.

Answers to Questions:

*1. (Sample data)

Time (sec)	Velocity (m/sec)
1	9.8
2	19.5
3	29.0
4	39.0
5	49.0
6	59.0
7	68.5
8	78.0
9	88.0
10	98.0

*2.

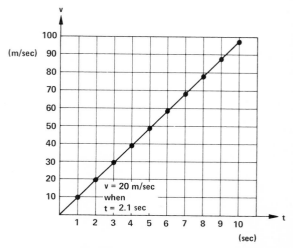

*3. Yes, the velocity increases uniformly throughout the 10 sec.

*4.(Sample data)

Time (sec)	Velocity (m/sec)
5	49
10	98
15	147
20	196
25	246
30	294

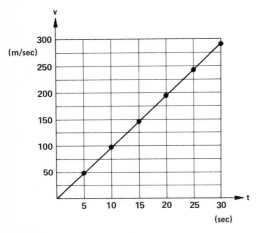

Yes, the velocity increases uniformly throughout the time investigated.

*5.When $t = 30$ sec, $v = 294$ m/sec.

Lab IV, PART B

*1.(Sample data)

Time (sec)	Velocity (m/sec)
5	24
10	33
15	36
20	38
25	39
30	39

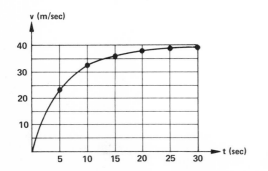

*2.No, it levels off and becomes constant.

*3.The terminal velocity is 39 m/sec.

*4.As the coefficient of air resistance is increased, the graph levels off more quickly and reaches a lower terminal velocity.

Lab IV, PART C

*1.If $a = 9.8$ m/sec^2, $c = 0.1$, $t = 10$ sec, then $d = 55$ m

*2.$v_f = 48$ m/sec

*3.If $a = 9.8$ m/sec^2, $c = 0.4$, and $d = 55$ m, then $t = 35$ sec.

II. Model of the Effect of Manpower on Job Completion Time

This experiment is designed to be used with Section 2. Unless your students need or ask for more experiments with the analog computer, it is best done as a demonstration. The purpose of the experiment is to use a model of the system, manpower-job completion time, to gain insight into the behavior of the system. One arrangement in this experiment might cause confusion; this is the use of each second of integration to represent the addition of one man, and the output of the integrator as a measure of time. It would be well to emphasize this and through reference to the block diagram, show that this is necessary. If this lab is done as a demonstration, it should precede the assignment of the corresponding text pages.

Equipment:

Same as for Lab I (omitting graph paper)

Page 124 shows the wiring for this simulation. Notice that the input to the scalor is at the ×10 hole. This allows us to vary the output of the scalor from 0 to 10; start with a C value of about 0.5, or an output of 5. The time for one man to complete the job (T_0) should be set at about 1 volt. Depending on the type of job, this number can represent 10 hours or 10 days, etc. Make certain that the initial condition of the second integrator (I_2) is set to 0.

When C is varied, a family of curves similar to page 121, bottom, can be obtained. The first curve of the family follows by throwing the Integrate lever N times, taking the meter reading each time. Shut off the power long enough for the integrator capacitors

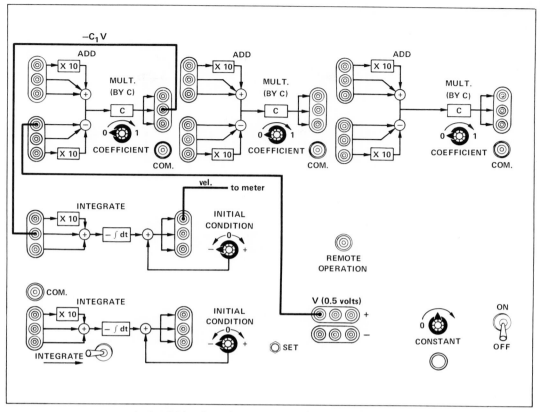

Analog Wiring for Lab I, Part A, and for Lab IV, Part A

to lose their charge, change the setting of C slightly, and produce measurements for a second curve, etc.

What happens is roughly this: the initial reading of the meter is T_0. When one second of integration occurs, the effect of I_1 is to decrease the meter reading to a value T_n (the output sign of I_1 is negative). The scalor output is now CT_n; but I_2 changes the sign of T_n so its output is $-NT_n$ (where $N = 1$ to start, but increases by 1 with each following integration). Hence the input to I_1 for the next second of integration is $T_n(C - N)$. As indicated, $T_n < T_0$, but as one integration follows another, N keeps growing, while C is constant. A time will come when $N > C$, the input to I_1 turns negative, and hence its output becomes positive and begins to raise the meter reading and the curve. Obviously, the number of integrations (or the "number of men added") to produce this result will be greater if C is larger. Basically, C controls the effective use of new men who are added to the job.

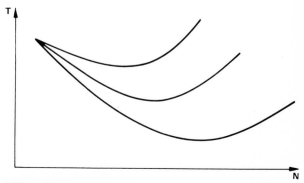

Effect of Varying C

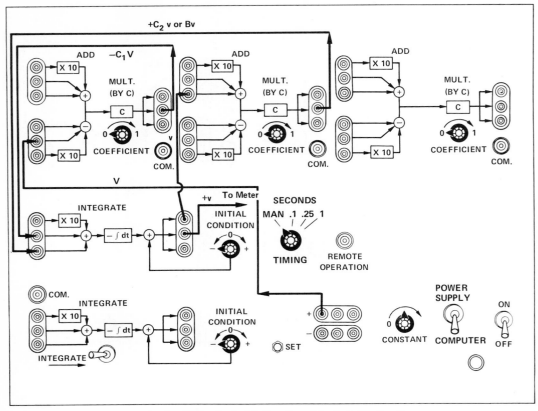

Analog Wiring for Lab I, Part B, and for Lab IV, Part B

Answers to Questions:

*1. The constant C could represent the ability of a foreman to organize his work crew so that new men are used effectively. It could represent the organizational setup of the job itself. If these aspects could be quantified, our simulation could serve as a predictive model.

*2. The summation of T by integrator 2 represents all the negative aspects of adding more men to a job crew. Essentially, it is a summation of the reasons for the increase of job completion time as described in Section 2 of the text.

*3. The factor mentioned above as the summation of T. This can be easily shown by removing the wire from I_2 to I_1 and then running the simulation.

*4. If he has information from previous jobs to help him draw a graph of N vs T, it could be used as a basis for making decisions about adding or removing men to speed up the job completion time. Another possibility is to quantify those aspects of the problem which are related to C, and to determine when the disruptive influences of adding more men become significant. This information together with the analog simulation will make it possible for him to predict the effect of adding more men.

*5. Care should always be taken to find out whether the values used in the model are representative of the real-world system.

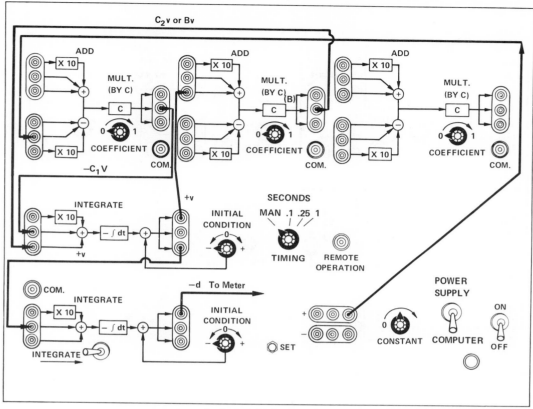

Analog Wiring for Lab III

V. Analog-Computer Simulation of a Dynamic Population Model

The model is probably best used as a demonstration while discussing Section 5, in which it is well described. The output can be taken with a voltmeter, of course, but the small changes (in the hundredths of a volt) are so hard to read, and so misleading when small errors appear (which are in fact probably random fluctuations), that it is far better to use a chart recorder. The general trend is thus made obvious and attention is distracted from the fluctuations. We expect slow growth for the first 4 years, a marked acceleration for the next 10, then a return to the original pattern but at a somewhat greater rate of growth (steeper curve) than before because the town is now larger.

Equipment for Demonstration:

> 1 analog computer
> 1 chart recorder (optional but recommended), or
> 1 high impedance voltmeter (if not included with the computer)
> Set of patch cords
> Spare fuse and patch cords
> Thin-bladed screwdriver

Answer to Question:

*3. If the experiment is used as a demonstration with the chart recorder, only a graph will be obtained, which will resemble the following. If the voltmeter is used, the following are sample data. Included are data for the expected growth of the town without the added industry.

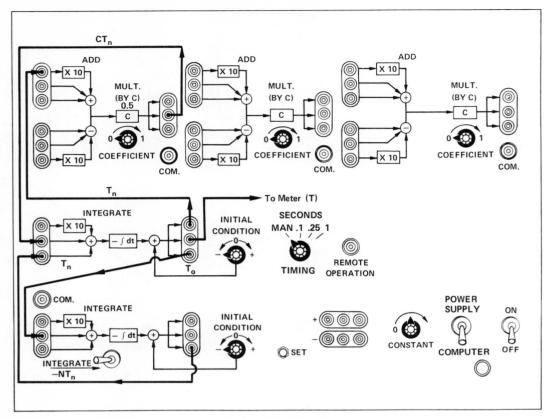

Analog Wiring for Lab II

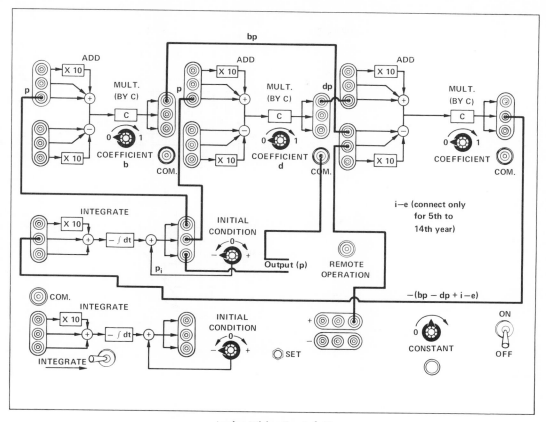

Analog Wiring For Lab V

Year	(With industrial growth) Population (thousands)	(Without extra growth) Population (thousands)
0	100	100
1	103	103
2	106	106
3	109	109
4	112	112
	(New growth rate)	
5	125	115
6	138	119
7	151	123
8	165	127
9	179	131
10	194	135
11	210	139
12	230	144
13	250	149
14	270	154
	(New rate stops)	
15	280	160
16	290	166
17	300	173
18	310	180
19	322	187
20	335	195

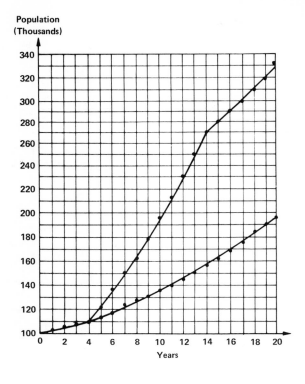

E | EVALUATION

The questions in this section are rated according to the chapter objectives and the performance levels stated in the introduction to the teacher's manual. This group of questions is not intended to be all inclusive, but just as a guide to possible questions. Zeros in the chapter objective column indicate no chapter objective for this question.

Chapter Objective	Performance Level	*Judged to be Relatively Easy:*

In Questions 1 and 2, check the best answer.

Chapter Objective	Performance Level	
3	I	1. → Tax Collector's Office ——— Income for the City

An appropriate input signal for this block diagram would be
  a) the mayor.
  b) the tax rate.
  c) a bill passed by the United States Senate.
  d) the Street Department.
  e) stamps sold at the Post Office.

Chapter Objective	Performance Level	
2	I	2. An engineer wishes to construct a model of a system.

  a) If he can draw a block diagram his task is finished.
  b) The principal reason for wanting a model is to show somebody else what he is thinking about.

Chapter Objective	Performance Level	

Judged to be Relatively Easy:

c) Only a miniature copy of the system is properly called a model.

d) A model must be quantitative to be really useful.

e) Until he has a model he is unable to think about the system.

All of the following statements are true EXCEPT (check the exception):

1	I	3. A system, as the word is used in *The Man-Made World*,

  a) may have only a single input.

  b) may have more than one input.

  c) may have several outputs.

  d) may have several interacting parts.

  e) may have no logical connection between its parts.

Mark each of the following statements *T* if it is true, but mark it *F* if it is false.

4	I	4. a) A block diagram can be drawn only if we know in detail exactly how the input into the system causes the output.
4	I	b) The output of one part of a system may be the input of another part.
4	I	c) In a house-heating system the thermostat is really a device to compare the desired temperature with the actual temperature.
1	I	d) "Terminal velocity" ordinarily means "velocity at the end of the problem."
4	I	e) A thermostat-controlled heating system does not really keep the room temperature exactly unchanging.
4	I	f) In the systems approach we first try to construct a block diagram with easily recognized inputs and outputs.
1	I	g) Velocity is the rate of change of acceleration.
1	II	h) In 1950 the birth rate in Mauritius was 49 and the death rate was 13. (The difference is 36.) Therefore, the gain in population in that year was 36,000.
7	II	i) A really generous welfare system would probably cost less than expected because women could then afford baby-sitters and so would get jobs.
1	I	j) The loudness level of a sound is measured in terms of decibels.

Judged to be More Difficult:

All of the following statements are true EXCEPT (check the exception):

4	I	5. Students of management have shown that,

  a) it really makes no difference how many men are assigned to a job.

  b) for any particular job there is an optimum number of workmen.

  c) adding more workmen to the force sometimes results in finishing the job sooner.

  d) laying off some workmen sometimes results in finishing the job sooner.

  e) subdividing a job into many small tasks may force some workmen to wait for others to do their part.

In the next three questions, check the best answer:

3	II	6. In finding out how a system works,

  a) it is essential not to neglect any possible inputs.

  b) it is necessary to look only for inputs into the first block of the block diagram.

  c) one should ultimately be able to identify just one output.

  d) it is generally important to simplify as much as possible.

  e) nothing can really be understood until the system has been modeled with a computer.

Chapter Objective	Performance Level	

Judged to be More Difficult:

5   I

7. The accompanying graph represents (very much simplified) the motion of a boy on a bicycle.

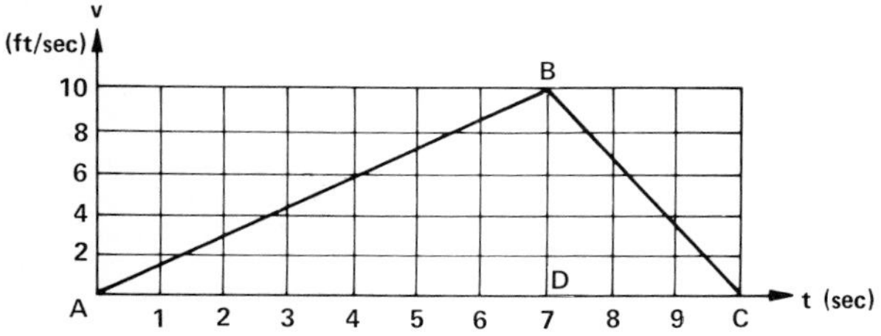

In order to find how far he rode, we could use an integrator, which would actually measure

   a) the slope of AB.

   b) the average slope of AB and BC.

   c) the area of ABD minus the area of DBC.

   d) the area of ABD plus the area of DBC.

   e) the length AB plus the length BC.

5   II

8. An analog computer is connected as shown below, and the Integrate lever is pushed 5 times.

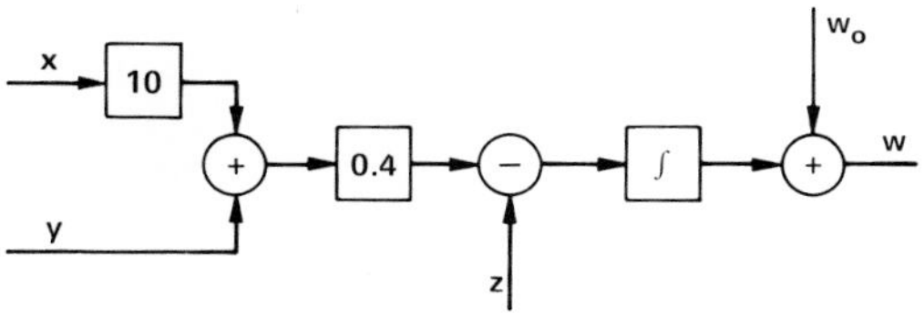

The output w will be the same as would be calculated by the equation

   a) $w = \left[(10x + y - z) \cdot 0.4 \right] \cdot 5 + w_o$

   b) $w = \left[(10x + y) \cdot 0.4 - z \right] \cdot 5 + w_o$

   c) $w = \left[(10x + y) \cdot 0.4 - z + w_o \right] \cdot 5$

   d) $w = \left[(10x + y - z) \cdot 0.4 + w_o \right] \cdot 5$

   e) $w = \left[10 \cdot (x + y) + 0.4 - z \right] \cdot 5 + w_o$

4   II

9. It is possible to consider this course from the system point of view. Let us take the student as one "block" in the system.

Two possible inputs to this block are:

   a)_____ .

   b)_____ .

An output from this block of the system might be

   c)_____ .

A possible quantitative measurement to be used in constructing the complete model of the system is:

   d)_____ .

If the operation of the system proves to be unsatisfactory, two ways to improve the operation could be:

   e)_____ .

   f)_____ .

Solutions to Evaluation Questions:

1. b

2. d

3. e

4. a) F   c) T   e) T   g) F   i) F
   b) T   d) F   f) T   h) F   j) T

5. a

6. d

7. d

8. b

9. It should be apparent that this question has no "right answer." It is hoped that it may stimulate a helpful interchange of views.

 a) and b) Textbook
      Teacher's comments
      Class discussion
      Lab exercises
      Films
      Outside reading, etc.
 c) Increased knowledge
   Activity as a citizen
   Grade in course
 d) Students' IQ's
   Number in class
   Age level and spread
   Average test grade
 e) and f) Try to change inputs:
      Longer class discussion
      More class interaction
      Study text longer
      Perform more labs etc.

      Try to modify some of the system blocks:
      Divide class into 2 sections
      Put upper (or lower) IQ level as admission requirement
      Eliminate sophomores (or some other class) etc.

F | FILMS

F-0501 THE TRAFFIC SNARL

Recommendation: Enrichment, another example of a complex systems problem.

Application: Specific example of a difficult and exasperating social-system problem, familiar enough to everybody.

Length and Type: 60 min, b & w, sound.

Source: #5

Summary: An NET TV film, reporting on some present and future methods of coping with the situation, as tried or projected at half a dozen cities.

F-0502 R. BUCKMINSTER FULLER: PROSPECTS FOR HUMANITY

Recommendation: Enrichment, good for emphasizing "the earth as a spaceship" concept.

Application: To back up the treatment in the text of systems analysis.

Length and Type: 30 min, b & w, sound.

Source: #5

Summary: The highly publicized inventor and engineer speculates about the future, asserting that humanity may yet be unified through the use of the technologies derived from space exploration, computers, and system analysis. Evidently quite talky, but it should be interesting to listen to Fuller talk.

G | GENERAL

I. Bibliography

R. L. Carson, *The Sea Around Us.* Mentor, 1954 (A) (paper)

> A very famous book in its day, and still most applicable in this day of oceanography. But here the point is Chapter 12, on the global thermostat: excellent.

V. C. Hare, Jr., *Systems Analysis: A Diagnostic Approach.* Harcourt, Brace & World, 1967 (C)

> This book is for the teacher, not the pupil. It starts where our text does but goes very much farther. Some topics handled: block diagrams, flow graphs, control systems with feedback at several levels of complication, simulations, system improvements. Numerous problems, some of which might be suggestive of projects. A good text for self-teaching (in the long "vacation").

J. H. Johnson, *Introduction to Electrical Engineering.* International Textbook Company, 1965 (C)

> There is much in this that one will not care to study, but the discussions of operational amplifiers, analog computers, and semiconductors (on a foundation of elementary electricity and a treatment of feedback) are brief, to the point, comprehensible.

J. Singh, *Great Ideas of Operations Research.* Dover, 1968 (B) (soft cover)

> The author, who dates his preface in New Delhi, was a winner of the United Nations' Kalinga Prize for scientific exposition. The small book is a store of information and of examples, many of them with the added interest of referring to Indian experience. The contents include statistics, linear programming, game theory, queueing theory, and the Monte Carlo simulation of problems too difficult for ordinary mathematical theory, among other tasty morsels.

II. Extra Problems

1. An electrical aquarium heater used to provide warm water for tropical fish is an example of thermostatic control. When the switch is on in a certain aquarium, the temperature of the water rises $1°F$ every 10 min, and when the switch is off, the temperature falls at the same rate. (These rates hold only for temperature changes of a few degrees near the desired water temperature.)

a) If the thermostat switch is turned on when the water temperature is $80°F$, what will the temperature be after 30 min?

b) If the thermostat now switches off, what will the temperature be after 20 min?

c) Next, the thermostat is reset to turn the heater on when the temperature (T_L) is $80°F$ or less and to turn it off when the temperature (T_H) is $85°F$ or more. If the temperature is initially $80°F$, the temperature variations can be illustrated.

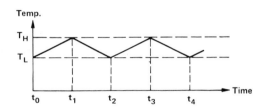

Determine the temperatures T_H and T_L and the times t_1, t_2, and t_3.

d) The thermostat is now readjusted so that the heater is turned on for temperatures at or below $83°F$, and is turned off for temperatures at or above $84°F$. Assuming that the temperature is initially $80°F$, determine the times at the first four subsequent instants when the switch setting changes.

Solutions:

a) $\dfrac{30 \text{ min}}{10 \text{ min}} \times 1° + 80° = 83°F$

b) $83° - \dfrac{20 \text{ min}}{10 \text{ min}} \times 1° = 81°F$

c) $T_H = 85°F$; $T_L = 80°F$; if $t_o = 0$, then

$$\dfrac{t_1 - 0 \text{ min}}{10 \text{ min}} \times 1° = 85° - 80°, \text{ and } t_1$$

$$= 50 \text{ min}$$

Repeating the same process, we find t_2
= 100 min, t_3 = 150 min

d) $\dfrac{t_1 - 0\ \text{min}}{10\ \text{min}} \times 1° = 84° - 80°$; t_1

= 40 min

$\dfrac{t_2 - 40\ \text{min}}{10\ \text{min}} \times 1° = 84° - 83°$; t_2

= 50 min

Similarly, t_3 = 60 min, t_4 = 70 min.

2. The original statement of this problem was in terms of kilowatts of power and joules of energy. In order to avoid the need for lengthy discussion, it is here written in terms of "units" (actually, 1 unit = 1000 joules).

A typical residential furnace is rated at 40 units of energy per second. At the outdoor temperature existing at the time of this problem, the house loses heat energy to the outside at the rate of 15 units of energy per second.

a) For how many minutes in each hour should the furnace run to maintain a constant temperature?

b) The temperature of the interior increases by 1°C when there is a *net* increase of heat energy of 5000 units. How long should the furnace operate on this day to raise the house temperature by 2°C?

c) If the cooling rate is also 5000 units for a 1°C drop in temperature how long would it take the house to cool down 2°C if the furnace was shut?

d) Assume that the interior temperature is 20°C at the time t = 0. Draw a graph of temperature against time if the thermostat maintains the temperature between 20°C and 22°C.

Solutions:

a) It is necessary to make up the energy loss of the house (at the rate of 15 units/sec) by running the furnace (at the rate of 40 units/sec). Therefore the furnace must run 15/40 of the time, or in an hour, 15/40 × 60 min = 45/2 min in each hour.

b) For a temperature rise of 2°C, there must be a net gain of 10,000 units of energy. The net gain of energy is at the rate of 40 − 15 = 25 units per sec. Therefore the time required is

$$\frac{10,000\ \text{units}}{25\ \text{units/sec}} = 400\ \text{sec or } 6\tfrac{2}{3}\ \text{min.}$$

c) The loss rate is 15 units/sec. The time to lose 10,000 units is

$$\frac{10,000\ \text{units}}{15\ \text{units/sec}} = 667\ \text{sec or } 11.1\ \text{min.}$$

d) Combining the results of (a) and (b), we have:

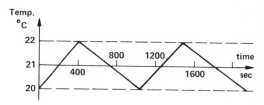

CHECK LIST FOR CHAPTER 6

PATTERNS OF CHANGE

APPROX. TIME: Text: 12 days   Lab: 6 days

A. APPROACH	CLASS PERIODS	B. BLACK & WHITE TRANSPARENCIES	C. CUES (k=key problems) Discussion Questions	Problems Easy	Problems Medium	Problems Hard	D. DEMONSTRATIONS, LABS & PROJECTS	E. EVALUATION	F. FILMS	G. GENERAL
			Before assigning problems, see note at beginning of Problem 6.							
1. The Importance of Change	1	0614	1,2,4,5				I, VI	1a,b,c		II
2. Communication with Language	2	0601 0602	3			2	V	1d,e,f, 2,5		
3. Speech	3	0603 0604 0605 0606 0607 0608 0613		1k,8k	7k,9 / 10, 13k	6,11*	II,III,IV	1g,h,i,3, 6,7,8	0601	III 7,8 / IV
4. Spectrograms	2	0609 0610	12					4,11		
5. Signals Related to Sinusoids	2	0611 0612	10,11		3	4,5,12		1j,9,10	0602	III 1-6
6. Not All Signals Are Sinusoids	1							1k		
7. Person-to-Person Communication	1							1l		
8. Final Comment			6,7,8,9 unrelated to chapter sections, but good for relevant discussions related to GII section of T.M.							

*Do not assign this problem.

Patterns of Change
6

A | APPROACH

I. Purpose and Organization of the Chapter

Hitherto the text has had a noticeable "story line," in which the study of rational decision making brought up the idea of a model, and this led to the concept of system, as a sort of climax. There are, of course, a multitude of other concepts which are important to engineers as they endeavor to fulfill their hopes and plans; many are not really important to the layman who is trying to cope with the world, but a few are so informative they deserve careful thought. Remaining to be looked at are communication, sinusoidal signals, feedback and amplification, stability and its reverse, and (as we saw in Chapter 1) the matching of technology to the human user. The chief concern in the present chapter is communication, in many aspects. Because communication so often occurs by means of wave motion, this directs us to the study of the sine wave. As it happens, both of these subjects not only are important in their own right, but are a vital part of the information-processing story.

The chapter opens with comment on the importance of change, both for interest and for information, and thus is guided to the large theme of communication. The topics treated are language, speech, sine signals, sound spectra, other sinusoidal signals, then nonsinusoids (we have already studied about noise), and other ways in which people communicate.

II. Objectives for Students

Upon completion of the activities, discussion, and reading in this chapter, students should be able to:

1. Recognize and identify the following terms: *bit, cycle, musical scale, randomness, redundancy,* and *spectrogram.*

2. Illustrate by reference to the English alphabet that information content in a message is inversely related to the probability that a letter will occur.

3. Describe the method of studying the structure of English by use of tables of frequencies (individual letters, digrams, trigrams), together with a table of random numbers.

4. Explain in detail why computer translation of one language into another is unlikely in the near future.

5. Demonstrate the use of microphone and cathode-ray oscilloscope to study the structure of sounds produced by musical instruments or the human voice.

6. Demonstrate a method of constructing graphically a sinusoid, and explain with the use of the graph the meaning of the terms *amplitude, frequency,* and *period.*

7. Illustrate the meanings and numerical relationships of the terms *pitch, octave,* and *harmonic.*

8. Repeat the generalization that any signal (if it has some duration) can be represented by a mathematical expression involving the functions called sines, as explained by Fourier.

9. Illustrate the method of sending many telephone conversations over a single telephone cable.

10. Describe the uses of sound spectrograms for teaching deaf children to speak, and for research in equipment for generating artificial speech.

11. Explain the principle of ranging and direction-finding with radar (and also bat navigation with sonar).

12. Illustrate the Doppler effect as applied to sound and to radar signals.

13. Discriminate between sinusoidal signals and such nonsinusoidal signals as stock market quotations, motion of dummies carried in colliding cars, dynamic reactions of human beings to such tasks as steering.

III. Suggestions for Teaching

This is a very full chapter but closely knit. It is hard to point to portions readily omitted. If time is really pressing, part of Section 2 (on studies of language structure), Section 4 (on spectrograms of speech), and Sections 5 and 7 could be skipped without ruining continuity. Labs I and VI are assigned in the check list to Section 1, to call them to your attention early. Both are projects for individuals or small teams and do not necessarily fit in better at one point than at another. Please notice the essay on developing pollution systems as examples where dynamic systems occur, printed in Section G, Part II.

Section 1. The Importance of Change. That it is needless to recite the whole of a well-known poem suggests the habit some people have of leaving a sentence unfinished once its point is made. The dependence on uncertainty or unpredictability for interest (as well as for information) is, of course, one of the reasons that women are interesting to men. "Age cannot wither her, nor custom stale her

infinite variety," said Enobarbus of Cleopatra, according to Shakespeare. However, the fact that not change only, but the nature of the change, is the primary feature of interest should be emphasized repeatedly throughout the chapter.

A slightly longer description of information theory may be useful. See the J. R. Pierce entry in the Bibliography if you wish to go still further.

Section 2. Communication with Language. All this study of basic linguistics will fascinate many of your students, but probably not all. You will have to decide how deeply to go into it by feeling your way. Lab V may be assigned as a homework project that fits anywhere here. Some of your class may find pleasure in reading Poe's short story "The Gold Bug" in which a cipher was unraveled with the help of a table of letter probabilities. T-0601 and T-0602 can be used if you want to explore randomly generated messages in class. Use the masters to duplicate copies for everyone. The example of probability-generated "prose" may recall the child's game of writing a 1-line statement at one end of a sheet of paper, folding it over, and passing it to the next player for a new (and disconnected) line. Usually a small skeleton form is provided, such as "He said," followed by "She said," and then perhaps "Everybody said." It may be worth a minute of class time to try this instance of something quite similar to the text example. The structure provided can make the game hilarious (not to say embarrassing in certain cases: choose your players with some care, and read the result back to the class yourself!).

A puzzling point near the end of the section is this: if information is maximized when the content of the message is least expected, how is it that in all these samples the information transmitted is actually nil? The answer seems to be that the transmission of information demands a context, agreed upon in advance by both sender and recipient. The context is a message form in which every letter has a known probability. In other words, it must be known that there really is a message. If a letter turns up at the expected rate it is more or less redundant. "Information" arises when a letter turns up oftener (or less often) than expected; this in turn means that one must be dealing with a *long* message or sequence of messages, not with a few dozen random letters which are not selected with the idea of giving any other information than the fact that they give none.

Section 3. Speech. It is noticeable that although this long section starts with a consideration of speech, it is necessary to include a certain amount of physics in order to manage the important sine signals. The physics is cut pretty thin, however, and should not be too difficult. Some additional numerical information is added below for reference in case it should be needed; it ought to be avoided if possible, however. It is quite important to perform Lab II (at least as a demonstration) early in this section. Lab III, also, has much inherent interest and is worth using as a demonstration if you feel you cannot spare the extra time to use it as a class exercise.

It is startling to find how small a change in pressure corresponds with a sound. According to Resnick and Halliday, for the threshold of perception by normal young adults, at a frequency of 1000 cycles/sec (not quite the pitch of maximum sensitivity) the pressure change during the passage of the wave train is about 2 tenths of a billionth (2 $\times 10^{-10}$) atmosphere, corresponding to a change in the average position of a molecule in the air of much less than its own radius. At the threshold of pain the difference between maximum and minimum pressure as the wave passes is around 1,500,000 times as much, but the amplitude of change in the average molecular position is still extremely small: of the order of 0.01 mm (about 0.004 in). The intensity of a sound is found to be proportional to the square of the amplitude of the pressure change. It is hardly surprising that in the experiment of Lab II (or Fig. 6–6) it is necessary to use the oscilloscope amplifier at a fairly high level.

Lab IV, again as a demonstration, will pay real dividends during this part of the work; and note the sine-wave transparencies, T-0603, 4, and 5.

It is sometimes convenient to refer to the wave length of a sinusoid. It is related to the frequency by the equation ($\lambda = c/f$,) where λ = wavelength and c = velocity of the wave (see Lab III). It is

important for you to bear in mind that sound waves in air are pressure waves, and the sinusoids of the text represent the pressure variations. The actual motion of the air molecules, however, is "longitudinal"; i.e., back and forth in the direction in which the sound is traveling.

When you come to deal with octaves, you can review the exponential equation of Chapter 4. One may say that $f = f_0 \times 2^n$, where f = frequency of a note n octaves higher than f_0, the initial note. (The exponent t/T becomes n/1.) For the piano scale, for instance, use T-0607. A_4 is the note at the left end of the piano keyboard; the top note is C^{iv} (4186 cycles/sec), 7 octaves and a (musical) third from the start. It must be remembered, in using this transparency, that a musical scale is properly represented by a series of points corresponding to the individual notes, not by a continuous line. When you draw the exponential graph you are not drawing a graph of the scale. Your line connects all the points which lie on any (equally tempered) diatonic scale, starting at *any* frequency whatever. The frequencies of any pair of points that are similarly situated with respect to 2 neighboring vertical lines of the graph chart will be an octave apart. The diatonic major-scale pattern is made up of 5 whole intervals (frequency ratio $2^{1/6}$:1) and 2 half intervals ($2^{1/12}$:1) in an octave: 1, 1, 1/2, 1, 1, 1, 1/2. On the piano keyboard each whole interval is made of 2 halves, the black keys serving to play the intermediate half-interval notes. The scale of C major (T-0608) is the scale obtained by starting at middle C and playing the white keys in order; where the half-intervals occur in the scale pattern, 2 white keys lie side by side with no black one between. This is another way to explain the anomaly of 13 keys in an 8-key octave of 7 intervals. (Contrary to appearances, musicians can count.)

Section 4. Spectrograms. The curious ribbed appearance of Fig. 6-23 is a consequence of the recording method. A sampling of the frequencies in the speech sound is made, the output apparatus is automatically adjusted, one vertical line or set of line segments is printed, and the process is then repeated, about one hundred times a second.

The process of multiplexing a telephone cable to provide many speech channels (T-0610) can be applied in the same way for microwave transmission from one hilltop tower to the next. At each is a radio mirror to reflect the received signal down to an antenna, a receiver, an amplifier, and a retransmitter; the retransmitter also has an antenna and mirror.

In the mention of radio broadcasting (and in the microwave transmission above) there is a sidestepping of one question: What medium carries these waves? Water waves are obvious; speech waves are in the air, and in a telephone there are wires. One thing we may say readily, radio is not carried by the air. Then it gets tough. A radio "wave" is a self-sustaining, self-propagating disturbance in the electromagnetic field which is formed by the radio wave itself. Somewhat like lifting oneself by one's bootstraps. If the question arises, you should sidestep too. Just say this isn't a physics course. There are appropriate references for interested students in the Bibliography of this chapter.

Section 5. Signals Related to Sinusoids. The Doppler effect can be observed by standing beside a road and noticing the change in pitch of the sound of passing trucks. Important: this is not a change in *loudness*. As a truck passes, there is an abrupt drop in the pitch of the sound—especially marked if the driver is blowing a horn. Working out the algebra in detail would gain us little (although it is not difficult); but it is easy to see that if the sound is traveling 1100 ft/sec and the receiving ear is moving at 20 ft/sec to meet it, the *relative* speed of the sound with respect to the ear is 1120 ft/sec (or 1080, if the motion is the other way). Therefore, the number of waves per second received by the ear is greater (or less) in the same proportion than if one were standing still. The result can be written:

$$\frac{\text{change in pitch}}{\text{original pitch}} = \frac{\text{relative speed of source \& receiver}}{\text{speed of sound}}$$

With the numbers just quoted this would mean that the pitch change is (20/1100 x 100) or nearly 2% of the original pitch. If the source of the sound moves, the same equation holds although the explanation differs slightly (the wave *length,* not the wave *frequency,* changes). With radar we use the same equation, except that the speed of radio signals replaces that of sound, and for "there and back" the Doppler effect occurs twice, once for each way; therefore the total pitch change is double that calculated here, or the right-hand fraction must be multiplied by 2.

Section 6. Not All Signals Are Sinusoids. Figure 6-34 is unintelligible without some explanation. The positive direction is to the right. Therefore an acceleration to the left is negative; but a negative *ac*celeration can be (and here is) called a positive *de*celeration. These accelerations must be measured with respect to something, a "frame of reference" (not an actual structure of rods and struts, but probably a graph chart overlaid on the set of photographs, with the origin always at a definite point on the chassis of the Nash). Then when the Nash chassis leaps forward upon being struck by the Hudson, the door post, the head support, and the dummies' heads are more or less left behind. Seen through the graph grid they appear to accelerate to the left; thus we have the "positive deceleration," rather than negative acceleration, of these objects. When the head support (a somewhat flexible structure) starts to rebound *forward*, this is regarded as negative deceleration (positive acceleration to the right), so the dotted curve crosses the abscissa at about 156 ms and stays below it until the support has caught up with the chassis. Some of the variations in the graph are of course caused by the lack of precision of the measuring devices. (Again, it is not the change only, but the nature of the change, that counts: positive or negative, large or small.)

Section 7. Person-to Person Communication and *Section 8. Final Comment.* No comment on these seems necessary.

B | BLACK AND WHITE
TRANSPARENCIES

```
87 35  67 44  51 49  18 98  97 84  75 22  53 29  10 52  26 87  54 92
25 52  29 67  35 99  48 88  40 68  63 68  82 39  38 47  91 39  11 00
87 17  83 31  25 59  87 48  25 80  24 08  81 45  21 32  90 08  44 31
05 04  40 35  72 95  48 56  77 57  63 19  80 16  48 52  06 47  64 98
81 16  09 24  91 71  29 76  54 01  53 47  30 67  62 95  56 58  10 91

54 85  79 88  57 91  11 69  10 22  71 87  24 92  52 64  42 82  78 95
44 78  19 18  35 40  27 66  89 72  21 17  71 69  95 17  97 17  62 60
97 20  98 97  37 33  93 75  18 88  35 85  46 05  07 20  08 17  66 24
98 77  57 51  40 41  76 24  18 54  60 61  79 13  94 57  50 73  89 68
78 12  77 30  83 30  59 28  73 33  47 07  60 07  45 38  82 10  73 19

41 19  70 62  43 46  06 13  22 38  31 18  64 60  07 14  49 16  28 16
70 64  30 55  67 46  95 79  63 66  82 56  67 10  76 77  03 22  42 18
06 56  09 89  68 87  79 19  35 94  66 18  17 94  72 81  72 77  92 39
29 46  18 28  08 88  48 56  49 44  67 82  72 67  28 83  10 26  58 13
42 14  55 51  72 95  29 25  15 18  25 68  48 92  87 16  78 43  17 47

33 75  87 15  15 23  13 79  62 73  76 69  09 77  82 65  72 47  59 56
09 80  99 61  98 08  34 11  88 79  08 32  46 78  33 58  44 16  12 23
98 31  57 50  85 80  53 39  05 92  54 42  29 01  35 23  09 84  96 64
51 70  52 55  83 12  95 02  79 11  49 79  87 95  98 48  88 68  64 77
27 83  61 07  49 05  46 20  35 78  31 34  42 50  68 11  42 14  29 77

78 84  69 15  64 42  92 39  36 08  56 39  35 02  92 78  46 63  82 98
22 12  89 66  49 09  99 10  62 53  19 31  81 83  50 43  37 42  10 00
69 41  59 54  82 72  44 66  64 03  76 59  12 12  41 56  34 90  26 06
54 99  46 54  51 38  59 07  64 21  81 17  88 47  23 05  63 43  08 67
99 91  82 79  92 62  44 24  01 34  45 16  33 56  17 78  42 86  70 94
```

T-0601 TABLE OF RANDOM NUMBERS

Number	Letter
000–186 inclusive	Space
187–293	E
294–378	T
379–444	A
445–509	O
510–567	N
568–622	R
623–673	I
674–723	S
724–766	H
767–797	D
798–824	L
825–848	F
849–870	C
871–890	M
891–910	U
911–926	G
927–942	Y
943–958	P
959–974	W
975–985	B
986–992	V
993–995	K
996	X
997	J
998	Q
999	Z

Notice that more than $\frac{1}{2}$ of the letters will be in this group of 5:

More than $\frac{3}{4}$ of the letters are in this group of 10.

More than 90% are in this group of 16.

T-0602 LETTERS NUMBERED BY FREQUENCY

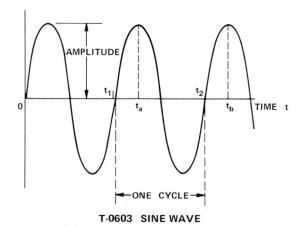

T-0603 SINE WAVE

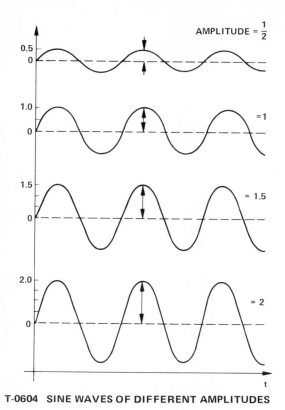

T-0604   SINE WAVES OF DIFFERENT AMPLITUDES

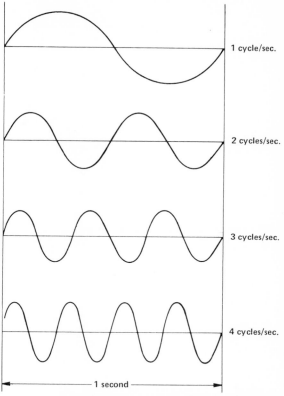

T-0605   SINE WAVES OF DIFFERENT FREQUENCIES

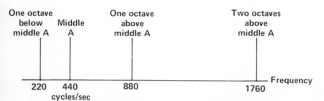

T-0606   FREQUENCIES OF OCTAVES

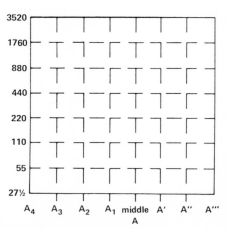

T-0607   EXPONENTIAL OCTAVES

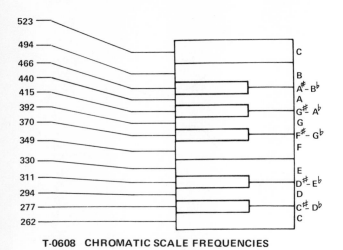

T-0608 CHROMATIC SCALE FREQUENCIES

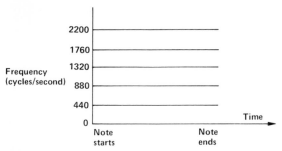

T-0609 SOUND SPECTROGRAM OF FLUTE (MIDDLE A)

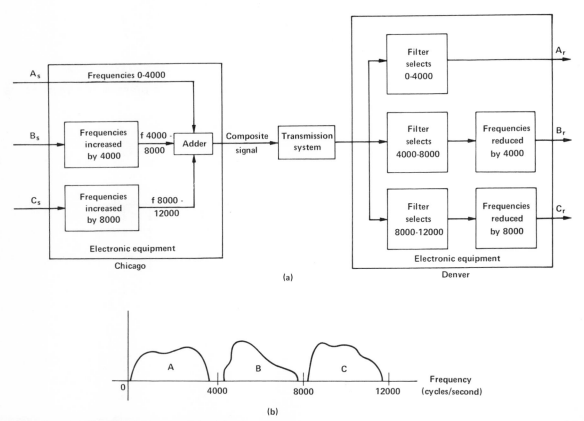

(a)

(b)

T-0610 SHARED COMMUNICATION SYSTEM

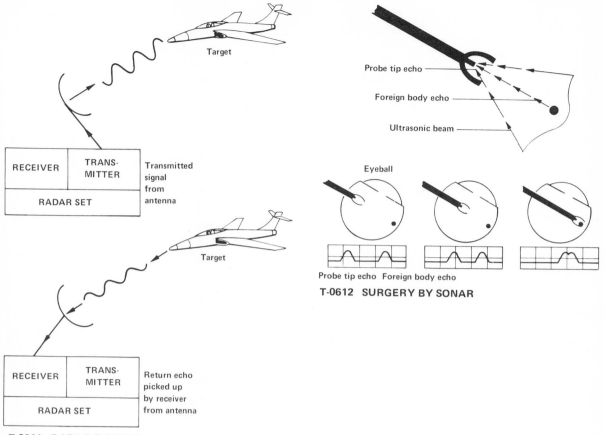

Target

RECEIVER | TRANS-MITTER

RADAR SET

Transmitted signal from antenna

Target

RECEIVER | TRANS-MITTER

RADAR SET

Return echo picked up by receiver from antenna

T-0611   RADAR SIGNALS

Probe tip echo

Foreign body echo

Ultrasonic beam

Eyeball

Probe tip echo Foreign body echo

T-0612   SURGERY BY SONAR

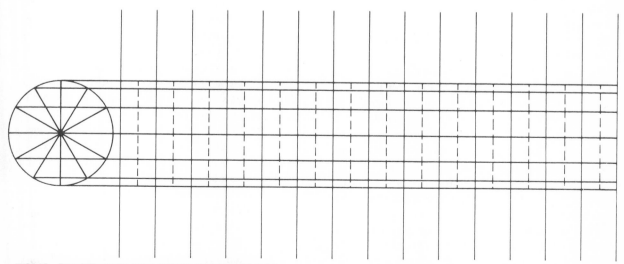

T-0613   FRAMEWORK FOR PROBLEMS 6-7 TO 6-11

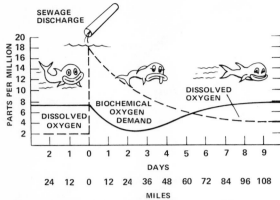

T-0614 THE POLLUTED STREAM ENVIRONMENT

C | CUES TO QUESTIONS AND PROBLEMS

Questions for Study and Discussion

1. Sitting in a waiting room; school every day (maybe?)
A sudden dogfight; a yelling child

2. As worded, this means changes in your life within perhaps 5 years. Not easy! Color TV? Travel by "air bus"? Eutrophication of Lake Erie? Condemnation of a beach because of pollution? Frozen pizzas?

3. Act well.
Good till the last drop.
Turn in here.
We hunted for a yellow-bellied flycatcher. (N.B.: "hunted for" may mean "sought" or "looked for food"; a "yellow-bellied flycatcher" is a kind of bird and also a cowardly left fielder. It may also be a catcher of yellow-bellied flies. Five meanings!)

4. Crowds leave a game that is apparently won several minutes before it ends (in order to get out faster). Children speculate about possible gifts before the birthday party or Christmas day.

5. Notice that this calls for dropping 3 letters out of 4, on the average. Some interesting class discussions may come from this. For instance, can all the students reconstruct the assigned paragraph with about the same number of eliminations, or is there a wide distribution in the maximum number of eliminations before the paragraph becomes unrecoverable?

Questions 6-9 relate to the exponential growth of solid waste (a disturbing pattern of change) discussed on text pages 163-67, Chapter 4.

6. New no-deposit bottles and aluminum cans for soda and beer.
Styrofoam for packaging fragile objects.
The increased use of disposable plastic containers for food.

7. The answer to this question depends on the city or town under discussion. Usually the industry or industries near one's home would be a large source of solid waste. Another would be service facilities such as supermarkets and restaurants.

8. Long-range (5 to 10 years) predictions of such things as production of solid waste and air pollution are necessary because the facilities needed to deal with these problems require 5 to 10 years to design and build. Valuable time is also lost in obtaining the necessary funds from city, state, or Federal governments for the needed facilities.

9. No, not with any degree of precision. These items are technical details which are of great importance to the public servants whose duty it is to plan the disposal methods. Naturally, the informed citizen does need to know, very roughly, about the proportions of various substances, so that he will not back incinerators that handle nothing but old tires, for example.

10. Bat navigation and removal of foreign objects from the eye both make use of the sonar principle. This is an example of how scientific knowledge about the behavior of sound waves and its use by bats leads the way to a technique which helps man, namely, surgery by sonar (see text page 274). This type of interaction between scientific knowledge about animals and technology has been given the name "bionics" (see F-0101, Chapter 1).

11. Radio and television broadcasting: the electromagnetic carrier waves are basically sinusoids.
Phonograph: sound waves can be pictured (on the CRO) as sinusoids.
Radar: uses electromagnetic waves.
Sonar: uses sound waves.
Transmission of electrical energy: the voltage and current in power cables are (ideally) sinusoids.

12. Students should be sent to the public library to look in *Reader's Guide to Periodical Literature*. The most likely heading seems to be "Voiceprints."

Other likely ones are "Sound," "Spectrogram," "Audio spectrogram." The *Scientific American* is always a source to be approached hopefully.

Problems

1. a) period = 1/(frequency); the amplitude is independent of both period and frequency.

   b) Changing the amplitude of a wave does not change the frequency; therefore f = 500 cps.

2. This is probably best done as a class exercise, using T-0601 and T-0602 (they might be duplicated and distributed to the class if you prefer). What is the definition of "most like" in this case? How many 2- or 3-letter English words can you find embedded in your gibberish? There are 6 (including 4-letter "wise") in the first 50 letters of the first sequence, 16 (including 4-letter "rest" and "hind") in the first 50 letters of the second, plus 4 duplicates.

3. A radar signal takes 10.75 μs to travel 1 mi. To travel 200 mi (out and back) it requires 200 mi x 10.75 μs/mi = 0.00215 s, the minimum allowable spacing between successive pulses. At 1 rev/7200 pulses and 1 pulse/0.00215 s there are 1 rev/15.5 sec = 0.065 rev/sec (or 15.5 sec/rev).

4. As stated, this problem has no unique answer, because the distance from the earth to the moon varies from about 221,000 to 253,000 mi, and that to Venus is tremendously variable, depending upon the positions in their orbits of the 2 planets. The mean distance to the moon is about 239,000 mi; the

least distance to Venus is about 25,700,000 mi. We use these distances

$$t_{moon} = 2.39 \times 10^5 \text{ mi} \times 10.75 \times 10^{-6} \frac{\sec}{\text{mi}}$$
$$= 2.57 \text{ sec}$$

$$t_{Venus} = 2.57 \times 10^7 \text{ mi} \times 10.75 \times 10^{-6} \frac{\sec}{\text{mi}}$$
$$= 276 \text{ sec}$$

5. $\Delta f = 2f\frac{v}{c} = 2 \times 3 \times 10^9 \frac{\text{cycles}}{\sec}$

$$\times \frac{80 \frac{\text{mi}}{\text{hr}} \times \frac{1 \text{ hr}}{3600 \text{ sec}}}{1.86 \times 10^5 \frac{\text{mi}}{\sec}}$$

$$= 717 \frac{\text{cycles}}{\sec}$$

If the accuracy required is ±2%, Δf may vary by 717 x 0.02 = ±14 cycles/sec.

If the frequency of the radar is multiplied by 10, so is the permissible variation of Δf: ± 140 cycles/sec. If the frequency is divided by 10, so is the allowed variation: ±1.4 cycles/sec.

6. Problem 6 should not be assigned unless you have preceded it with Problems 7 and 9, text page 283, as well as Problem 7 in Section G, Part III, of the Teacher's Manual. Plot and add two sine waves of the same amplitude which have frequencies of 15 cps and 30 cps.

   a) The 30-cycle wave is shown solid. The 15-cycle wave is shown dashed. The sum-wave is beaded at the measured sum-points.

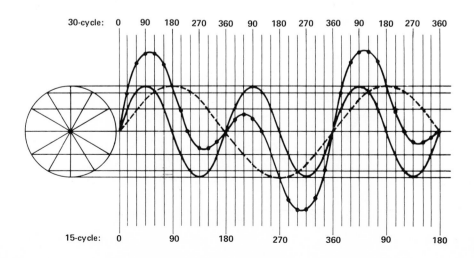

b)Exactly within the space of one 15-cycle wave and two 30-cycle waves the sum-wave shows, in order, a high crest, a shallow trough, a low crest, a deep trough. This pattern would be repeated 15 times in the course of 1 sec.

7. Note: If you assign this problem and Problem 9, you will make everything much easier if you give each student several duplicated copies of T-0613.

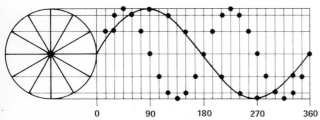

The unconnected dots are the solution to Problem 9.

8. The wave length would have been the same, but the amplitude only 2/3 as much.

9. The new wave has half the length (or double the frequency) of the first, but the same amplitude.

10. At every point, the 2 waves have amplitudes equal in magnitude but opposite in sign (except where both are 0); therefore, their sum is everywhere 0.

11. As with Problem 6, the trick is to draw only a small fraction of what happens in 1 sec, and then extrapolate. Let us try 0.1 sec. This turns out to be extremely awkward: 3 of the 30-cycle waves equal 3 1/2 of the 35-cycle, or 1 of the latter equals 6/7 of one of the former. In a reasonable space, however, it is hard to imagine a better plan. We use 3.5 and 3.0 mm as the basic spacings for the two waves, and draw the perpendiculars for the 30-cycle above the

axis, for the 35-cycle below it, and insert the dots as best we can.

Due to the small scale, it is impracticable to show the sum-dots. Careful inspection will reveal that the sum-wave starts with approximately double the amplitude of the original waves and shrinks to almost nothing. During the next 0.1 sec we expect this pattern to be reversed, the sum-wave swelling out to double amplitude again. Evidently, this will occur during each 0.2 sec: there will be alternate swelling out and dying away of the sound 5 times per sec. The throbbing sound heard by the ear is a phenomenon called "beats."

12. a) One box in the CRO pattern = $1/5 \times 10^{-5}$ sec = 2×10^{-6} sec. In the first picture the distance between "blip" peaks is about 2 1/2 boxes or 5×10^{-6} sec. Hence $d = rt = 5 \times 10^3$ ft/sec $\times 5 \times 10^{-6}/2$ sec (the echo sound must cross the eyeball twice) = 1.25×10^{-2} ft or 0.15 in.

b) In the third picture the blips are about 1/2 box or 1×10^{-6} sec apart, equivalent to 5000 ft/sec $\times 5 \times 10^{-5}$ sec = 2.5×10^{-3} ft = 0.03 in.

c) Ten seconds elapsed from the first to the third picture. The distance moved = $0.15 - 0.03 = 0.12$ in. The speed of movement is 0.12 in/10 sec or 1.2×10^{-2} in/sec.

13. Harmonics have frequencies which are integral multiples of the fundamental frequency. Thus,

$$f_{h2} = 128 \times 2 = 256 \text{ cps}$$
$$f_{h3} = 128 \times 3 = 384 \text{ cps}$$
$$f_{h4} = 128 \times 4 = 512 \text{ cps}$$

Octave frequencies double each time. Thus,

$$f_{octave\ 1} = 128 \times 2 = 256 \text{ cps}$$
$$f_{octave\ 2} = 128 \times 2 \times 2 = 512 \text{ cps}$$

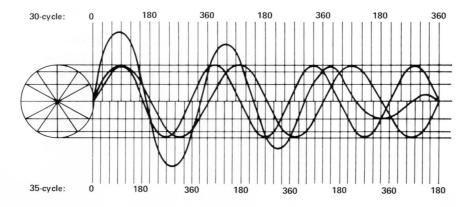

(Note that the last, second-octave, frequency is the same as the last, fourth-harmonic, frequency.)

D | DEMONSTRATIONS, LABS, AND PROJECTS

I. Plotting Tidal Data

Two things are immediately evident: this can be done only if your school is within easy reach of a seacoast; and it is a project, not a class exercise. It is a team project, so that the necessary visits to the tide gauge can be arranged to suit individual convenience. Finally, it will be quite burdensome and should be undertaken only by interested students. They will learn much more, and much more enjoyably, if they do some library research after the experimental part is finished.

In the United States, high tides are likely to range as high as 20 ft above mean low water (Eastport, Maine), approaching 12 ft (Boston), not over 2.5 ft (Key West); on the West Coast they will mostly be not over 7 or 8 ft (except in Anchorage, where a bore causes the spring tide to be as high as 29 ft, which is still far behind the Bay of Fundy). In the Gulf of Mexico the tidal range is small and usually there is only one high tide a day. These figures are given to acquaint you with one serious problem which those who try this project must meet: the length of the tide gauge scale may have to be very considerable, and it probably has to be made for the purpose. You can't just take along a yardstick. The scale will have to be firmly fastened to some support, preferably so placed as not to attract the attention of vandals, and it had best be in a cove or inlet where the waves are unlikely to be very large. Even so, the observer will have to estimate the water height as an average between wave crest and wave trough. It is not impossible that some experimenters will be exasperated enough by this difficulty to want to construct a modified gauge: e.g., a float with enough inertia so that it is little affected by small waves, perhaps guided by a stretched vertical wire (or two), perhaps itself operating an indicator on the end of a line running over a pulley at the top of the gauge support. Inventiveness has unlimited possibilities, and certainly should win high praise even if the result doesn't work very well.

Equipment for Project Team:

Tide gauge long enough to measure the expected maximum range at the station chosen
Watches (synchronized) for all members

PART A

Answers to Questions:

*1. The curve should look like a portion of a sine wave, with one crest and one trough visible (one of these might be divided between the two ends of the curve).

*2. Amplitude means displacement above or below the mean level. It is half the total vertical difference between the level of high tide and the level of low tide. It is half the tidal range on the day in question.

*3. Frequency means number per unit time, most easily found on this short run by finding the number of hours (to nearest quarter) between high tide and low, doubling to get the period of one tide wave, and then taking the reciprocal of the result (thus giving tides per hour). Multiply by 24 hr/day to get tides/day (somewhere around 1.9 if luck is with the experimenter).

PART B

Answers to Questions:

*1. The shape of the curve should still be a portion of a sinusoid, though not the same size (amplitude).

*2. Yes, the positions of crest and trough would be farther to the right (on the average, each high tide is 12 hr 25 min after the previous one, or 50 min later by the clock, one day after the previous measurement; but the actual interval varies throughout the year).

*3. This prediction will be 7 x (time interval between successive crests): roughly 7 x 50 min or nearly 6 hr later by the clock (note that there are two high tides a day, but this investigation always misses one of them). It is also true that generalizations about the tides are likely to be wildly wrong when applied to a particular place.

*4. It is not clear whether the question means "How do you account for being so close?" or "How do you account for being so far wrong?'' In either case, see comment on the previous question.

*5. This question can best be answered by referring students to U.S. Coast & Geodetic Survey (one letter from each class is sufficient).

II. Using the CRO to Analyze Sound Patterns

We preface the discussion of the experiment with remarks about the cathode-ray oscilloscope (CRO). If you are unfamiliar with this fascinating instrument, you should plan some time to find out how it reacts to its controls. There is really only one way to damage the instrument (short of dropping it), and that is to allow a bright spot to remain more than a few seconds in one place on the tube face. This will destroy (''burn'') the fluorescent coating on the inside of the tube face where the spot was. Therefore:

Keep the spot as dim as you can make it and still see it comfortably, unless it is kept in motion. Darkening the room, or shading the tube face with a roll of dark paper and some Scotch tape, or both, may be desirable.

If you can find the manufacturer's instruction book, read it. If not, the following may help.

First plug in the power cord. The controls normally found on a CRO, and their uses, are these:

1. On-off switch: this may be a separate switch, but more often is built into the beam-brightness control. In this case, turn it clockwise, wait a little for warmup, then (if you see no spot) turn it farther in the same direction.

2. Focus: used to vary the size of the spot. A spot which is a little out of focus is a protection for the tube face. Beam and focus controls often interact: get one set, change the other, and the first one is out of whack. You soon get used to managing this.

3. Position controls (often labeled *V Pos* and *H Pos*, for Vertical and Horizontal Position): if the spot is not at the center of the screen (or if for some reason you want it elsewhere), adjust these. It is easy to "lose" the spot if you are heavy-handed. See item 5 below if you do.

4. Sweep or sweep frequency: controls the frequency at which the spot crosses the tube face. Most scopes have a coarse adjustment (0 for a sta-

tionary spot, then perhaps half a dozen ranges) and a fine adjustment (known as the sweep vernier) which varies the actual frequency within the range. Here is the essential adjustment in this experiment.

5. H gain: controls an amplifier which determines the width of the sweep, from none at all (a stationary spot, even if the sweep frequency is not set at 0) to all across the tube face in the x direction, disappearing at each side. Mostly we want to see both ends of the sweep. Nearly always there is some means of introducing an external signal: a jack or binding posts. You may find HAC or HDC labels. The former is used when the signal is a wave, the latter when it is just a voltage which may vary during the experiment, even in the form of a low-frequency wave. If you "lose" the spot, set the H gain to maximum, H Pos to its midpoint, and then adjust V Pos until you find the trace. Then start to cut H gain, adjusting H Pos if necessary, until your spot is centered.

6. V gain is just like H gain except that is has to do with motion of the spot in the y direction. The V inputs are those most often used.

7. Sync, short for synchronizer. If you cannot get a pattern to stand still, a touch here will usually take care of the situation.

Further discussion of the CRO, especially the Sync control, is printed in Section G, Part IV.

Since oscilloscopes, even "cheap" ones, are fairly expensive, many schools will have only one and must perform this experiment as a demonstration. In any case this may be a good idea because several teams producing sounds at once can interfere with each other. It is highly desirable, however, that the experiment be used in one way or another, if only for its inherent interest. A minor clarification: a "transducer" is the general name for a device that translates signals which use one form of energy for their propagation to signals which use some other form. Therefore, the CRO is also a transducer (electrical to light energy). A record player contains two: the pickup which changes mechanical energy signals to electrical and the speaker which changes electrical to sound (another form of mechanical, incidentally), and so forth. A record-player amplifier, then, is not a transducer, because both input and output signals are electrical.

The most important bit of technique for this demonstration is to use a note that lasts as long as possible so you have time to adjust the sweep controls and to touch up the sync. The advantage of photography of the CRO trace is very plain. If you have a photographic enthusiast in the class, tell him that only the extremely high speed black-and-white Polaroid film is usable in the hands of an amateur. In Step 3, remember that in this country we tend to turn vowels into diphthongs (or worse complications: thus "we" may turn out to be "ooeeeuh"). Sounds like the *a* in "father," the *i* in "machine," the *o* in "over," are fairly easy to keep simple and lengthy.

Equipment for Each Lab Team (or Demonstration):

1 oscilloscope
1 signal generator (if available)
1 high-impedance microphone (even a telephone microphone, which is low impedance, can be used with a battery and an audio transformer, if you know how)
1 tuning fork (a second, about an octave different in pitch, will help if available)
Tape player and tapes (or record player and records) of individual instruments and groups
Whatever band and orchestral instruments are available (with players)
Even a whistle (especially if you can find the kind with a slider to vary the pitch)

PART A

Answers to Questions:

*5. The differences observable are in the wavelengths, the amplitude, and the form of the waves, corresponding to the pitch, the loudness, and the "tone quality" or "tone color" or "timbre" of the sound. You will probably have to point these out to the class since they are not trained observers.

*6. The tuning fork, if you had one.

*7. A matter of opinion; a likely choice is an oboe or a clarinet, if used.

PART B

Answers to Questions:

*1. The signal generator and the tuning fork are probably indistinguishable.

*2. Irregular changes in amplitude with the "lively" speech are likely to be the most noticeable difference here. Speech signals are too brief to make it possible to have more than an unreliable impression of possible changes in wave form, and there is no chance to adjust either sweep or sync.

*3. Change in frequency (wave length change is what is actually observed) to match the audible pitch changes is very easy to see.

III. Sonic Displacement Meter

The sonic displacement meter is closely related in its behavior to the radar system for measuring rate of change of range. However, there is no Doppler effect complication, since we are using our primitive sonar device to measure only the difference between two ranges (i.e., the difference between two separations of the microphones), not the time it takes for the moving microphone to change position by the measured amount. Students are likely to be fascinated by the unexpected sensitivity of the experiment. They should have studied Section 5 of the chapter first, not because that section contains much that is essential for their understanding, but because it will add a great deal to their appreciation of the exercise.

The following discussion explains the "displacement meter."

Because the sweep of the CRO is obtained from the Signal Generator, the sinusoidal signal and the sweep signal are synchronized, as shown in drawings (a) and (b). The audio signal from the "sending microphone" is also synchronized to the Signal Generator output even though there may be a pause shift (as shown in (c)) between the output sound wave and the input electrical signal.

The sound waves received by the receiving microphone (d) are of course shifted in time with respect to the outgoing sound wave because of the time it takes the sound wave to travel the distance between the two transducers.

The electrical output (which is the CRO input), (e), may again be different in phase than the incoming sound signal but the two are always synchronized. When one displaces a certain amount the other does too.

As the microphones are moved closer together, the emitted sound is received earlier than before,

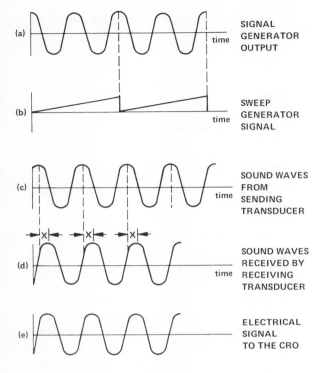

(a) SIGNAL GENERATOR OUTPUT — time

(b) SWEEP GENERATOR SIGNAL — time

(c) SOUND WAVES FROM SENDING TRANSDUCER — time

(d) SOUND WAVES RECEIVED BY RECEIVING TRANSDUCER — time

(e) ELECTRICAL SIGNAL TO THE CRO

which means a smaller phase shift. I.e., the distance x decreases, thereby making the picture on the CRO (e) appear to shift to the left. The sweep signal therefore acts as the reference.

The above explanation can be presented to the students by neglecting the phase shift in the microphone. Then (a), (b), and (d) can be used alone; (a) represents both the signal generator output and the sound wave from the sending transducer and (d) represents both the incoming sound signal and the CRO input signal. The distance x is then measured between the peak of (a) and the peak of (d).

Equipment for Each Lab Team (or for Class Demonstration):

    1 signal generator
    1 CRO
    2 high-impedance microphones, each with its wires connected to a plug fitting the jacks on the generator and CRO
    1 extra wire with plug on one end to fit Sync jack of CRO, and other end to be attached to the output jack of the generator
    1 foot rule or yardstick (or meter stick with inch scale)

PART A

The quarter-inch squares on the CRO screen are made of dots, 5 on each side. Therefore the dots form a convenient scale, spaced at 0.05 in, for measuring the distance through which the wave crest (or trough) shifts as one microphone is moved.

Point out to the students that their plot of 2 measured points plus the origin, for Question 10, defines a straight line only as an act of faith, and if time permitted should be supported by measurements made at many other frequencies. A parabola would do quite as well for the points shown here. But the computation called for in Question 11 is still valid, because a curved line or a straight one would be so close together near the origin.

The sample data which follow were obtained for a particular setting of the H Gain of the CRO. In this experiment it is advisable to use as much horizontal gain as possible because the phase shift will be easier to see. Evidently, measurements made on one instrument by one experimenter will in general differ from those made elsewhere: do not be alarmed if student values of phase shift differ from the sample data.

Answers to Questions:

*2. $f_0 \approx$ 3000 cps. The amplitude is highest at about this frequency.

*7. (Sample data)

Δx (in)	Δy (in)	total y (in)
1	.30	.30
2	.25	.55
3	.35	.90
4	.30	1.20

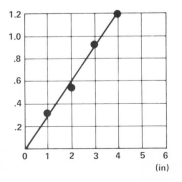

*8.

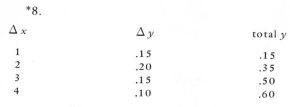

Δ x	Δ y	total y
1	.15	.15
2	.20	.35
3	.15	.50
4	.10	.60

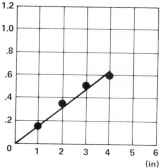

*9. At 4000 cps: .3 in/in
    2500 cps: .15 in/in
For high sensitivity, high frequency is needed.

*10.

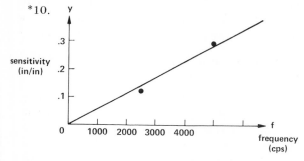

*11. $y = mx + b$. But $b = 0$ and $x = f$. Therefore we may say

$$f = \frac{y}{m} = \frac{\dfrac{1\ \text{in}}{360\ \text{in}}}{\dfrac{.3\ \text{in/in}}{4000\ \text{cps}}} = 37\ \text{cps}$$

*12. About .4 in/in at 6000 cps because we are limited by the decrease in amplitude as we go away from frequency 0.

*13. The resonant frequency (about 3000 cps) might be best, because our system is quite sensitive.

*14. Yes, the signal would have shifted so much that it would be back to its original position.

PART B

At first glance it might seem that Part B has been provided only because the equipment is al-

ready set up. This would miss the point, which really is that the CRO can be used as a clock. The time interval is measured by a phase shift.

Answers to Questions:

*4. 9/10 in
*5. 2/10 in

The derivation of the formula is as follows: when the microphones are brought 1 in closer together, the wave crest shifts a distance Δx. Then

$$\frac{\text{time for sound to travel 1 in}}{\text{time to travel 1 wave length}} = \frac{\Delta x}{\text{wave length}}$$

Hence the numerator (t) equals

$$\frac{\Delta x}{\text{wave length}} \times \frac{1}{3000}.$$

*6. 1/13,500 sec for 1 in.
*7. .0254 m/1/13,500 sec = 343 m/sec.

IV. Periodic Signals on the Analog Computer

What you might expect is found in this experiment to be true. As done previously, this may best be a class demonstration unless you have been flooded with the equipment necessary for a number of small groups. Another approach is to have small groups work on the one or two sets of equipment available while the other students are working on experiment V, "Estimating Your Writing Vocabulary," and then switching assignments at the appropriate time.

Have the class reason out in advance what they expect, and record the consensus on the chalkboard for later reference. Use a sinusoid of about 300 cps. If you have an electronic switch you could show the trace of the original signal and the modified one at the same time. If you do not, be sure (in cases 2 and 3) to connect the output lead from the generator to the scope, note the heights of the wave crests, then shift the lead to the appropriate summing-scalor input and compare with the previous situation. In every case, connect the signal generator output to the sync input, as in the last experiment. In case 2 you would find no effect if you used the VAC input: be sure you use VDC. An easy trick: connect the generator output to one integrator *output* jack, join a second output jack of the same integrator to the CRO, and use the initial condition control to give your constant signal. For case 3, both waves are initially the same, from the generator output. One of them feeds the first summing-scalor, the other the second, and the outputs are then added by use of the third. Thus the two outputs can be separately altered in amplitude before the addition. Another easy trick: plug the generator output into one integrator output jack, and use the other two jacks on the same bar as signal sources for the two summing-scalors. Case 4 is especially instructive, if you have access to two signal generators. Try setting one at 300 cps and the other at 305 cps and demonstrate beats, using a sweep frequency as slow as you can get. If you can connect a small speaker to the adder output this will make the demonstration at least twice as good.

Equipment for Class Demonstration:

> 1 signal generator (better, 2)
> 1 CRO
> 1 analog computer
> 1 small PM speaker, if possible (PM = Permanent Magnet, the only kind currently on sale)
> Suitable connecting wires, terminating in plugs

Answers to Questions:

*1. Starting with C set at 1, the amplitude of the signal is progressively diminished as C grows smaller. One can produce the opposite by starting with C = 0 and plugging the signal into the x 10 input.

*2. A constant signal applied to the VDC input will result in a horizontal line above or below the midline, depending on the sign of the constant. When the sinusoid is added, this line becomes the position of the axis of the sinusoid (but of course no longer visible).

*3. The method suggested results in two signals which are always in phase. In this case, the sum is a wave of larger amplitude (the sum of the original amplitudes) but of the same wave length.

*4. The variety of obtainable patterns is limitless; in general, the high frequency puts "wiggles" on the low-frequency wave.

V. Estimating Your Writing Vocabulary

This individual project for home or library research is completely explained in the directions except for two or three points. (1) Dictionaries seldom or never tell how many words are in their vocabularies. Fortunately, the public library probably has a copy of: Walsh, *Home Reference Books in Print*; R. R. Bowker Co., 1969. This has a complete listing. (2) It is important that the definitions of the words be hidden (so far as possible) from the student while he is trying to decide whether he would ever use the word. Remembering that whole sentences can be reconstructed if half or more of the letters are obliterated, we see that this presents a formidable problem. A partial solution is to take a 3 x 5 index card and clip a rectangular step about 1/2 x 1/8 in at the upper left-hand corner. Then the card can be moved down the page, exposing one word at a time above the "tread" of the step but pretty well hiding the definition. (3) Most dictionary words bring a train of derived words after them which presumably form part of the vocabulary of anyone who knows the primary word. As an arbitrary decision, this "Supreme Court" judgment reads that derived words shall not be counted in either Class A or Class B because to do so consumes a lot of time without making a significant change in the B:A ratio.

VI. Simulation of a Water-Pollution Model

This experiment looks long and complicated, mostly because of the necessary explanation of what is about to go on. It is, however, a very important experiment in that it is unstructured and involves a relevant problem in which most high school students are interested. If you have demonstration equipment only, it is important that a group of students do the demonstration or that individuals in the class devise the simulation as you go along rather than have it presented as a demonstration of something which you have already worked out.

The student by now presumably finds the analog computer fairly easy to use. Now he gets a chance to design a bit of research on his own. The questions should be treated as leads or suggestions rather than as demands for answers (suggested answers are given later), and the young investigator is actually being invited to find out as much as he can, with this model, about the oxygen-sewage-water system (T-0614). Note, however, that the model describes only rather dilute mixtures of sewage and water (about five thousandths of 1% or less). It cannot handle disasters: cases in which the water body is overwhelmed by massive influxes of filth. It would be proper to require a short written report, with graphs drawn either by the student or by the chart recorder. Two additional, though incidental, virtues of this experiment are that this is the first time that exponential decay, rather than growth, has been modeled on the analog computer (compare Fig. 4-35a and T-0406b), and also the first time that the curve shown in Fig. 4-35c and T-0406c has been referred to as an exponential; something very like it was met, however, in Chapter 5, Lab IV. If you do not choose to treat the experiment as a research project, notice that Parts A and B are separate exercises, either of which can be done without the other. Part C is simply a matter of combining A and B.

Equipment for Each Lab Team:

    1 analog computer with meter
    Set of patch cords
    (Optional) chart recorder
    Plenty of graph paper.

PART A

The negative sign in the initial equation is because the rate of change of waste is, in fact, negative. If we plot W against time we have a curve like this:

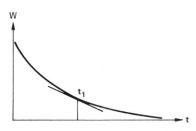

If a tangent to the curve is drawn at t_1 (any selected time), it slopes downward to the right. This slope measures the rate of change of W, or R_w in the notation adopted here *(dw/dt* in calculus terms). Notice that the output of the integrator, in the first portion of the exercise, is positive if it has a negative input; but the latter demands that the signal fed back to the integrator input must go to the subtractor side of the summing-scalor. In the second part of the same exercise the situation is reversed: $R_D - C_w W$ is always positive because $R_D > C_w W$; therefore the integrator signal is negative, so is

$C_w W$, and the patch cord from the integrator must be moved to the + input of C_w.

Answers to Questions:

*1. Increasing the magnitude of C_w increases the rate of decomposition, R_w, and vice versa.

*2. It takes about 14 days (14 sec on the analog computer) to reduce the output signal below the level at which it can be measured. This is exponential decay and can be modeled if you wish by the algebraic equation of Chapter 4:

$$y = Ar^{t/T}$$

In this case $A = 50$, $r = C_w = 0.5$, $T = 1$. If $t = 14$, we find that $y = 0.003$ v (too small to measure). Working the other way to find what value of t would make $y = 0.01$ v, we write:

$$0.01 = 50 (0.5)^{t/1}$$

Take the log of each side and solve for t:

$$t = \frac{\log 0.01 - \log 50}{\log 0.5} = 12 \text{ days}$$

This gives considerable confidence in the behavior of the computer.

*3. Increasing C_w means that R_w increases, as before, but less rapidly. It also means that W, the amount of unchanged waste present, diminishes somewhat as time passes. This new equation translates into a differential equation which is too difficult to be worth discussing here. Intuitively, we would expect the curve to resemble that sketched previously for the value of W vs t in the simple case, but to lie everywhere higher above the abscissa, and this is what is found if we take a series of values and prepare a graph, or use a chart recorder.

*4. The higher R_D becomes, the slower and the less completely the waste is decomposed. In other words R_D and C_w are found to have opposite effects on both R_w and W.

*5. As in the case of simple exponential decay, W may in time grow too small to measure, but it cannot reach 0 (no comment to students is likely to be appropriate about what happens when W is so small that the continuous curve no longer is a proper model).

*6. Both R_D and C_w, as well as W_o, control the amount of waste remaining in the water at any time.

152

PART B

If Part A has been performed, its wiring can be left in place and a new simulation prepared using the second integrator and the third (unused) summing-scalor.

Answers to Questions:

*1. Since turbulence of the water promotes absorption of oxygen, increasing C_A, which measures turbulence, increases the rate of replacement of oxygen.

*2. If A_{max} is increased (by colder weather), R_A will also increase because if the water can dissolve more oxygen, the rate of absorption will increase. Since the oxygen is not being removed in this simulation, A will approach A_{max} and in time will effectively equal it (i.e., the difference between them cannot be detected by our measuring devices).

PART C

Answers to Questions:

*1. Evidently, if the oxygen level may never fall below 5 mg/li, W_o cannot be as large as specified; moreover, R_D must be 0. On the other hand, if we are looking for a final oxygen level of 5 mg/li but are willing to let it go below that magnitude (for about 12 days in this case), then R_D can range up to 0.5 mg/li/day. By now, however, the fish are dead. The data given in the problem are incompatible with the aim of keeping them alive (see T-0614).

*2. It is necessary that $W_o \geqslant 18$ mg/li.

*3. Inspection of the equation makes it plain that if C_w is increased, R_A must decrease, and vice versa; if R_A decreases, then A will have to diminish. Testing the situation with the computer verifies these predictions.

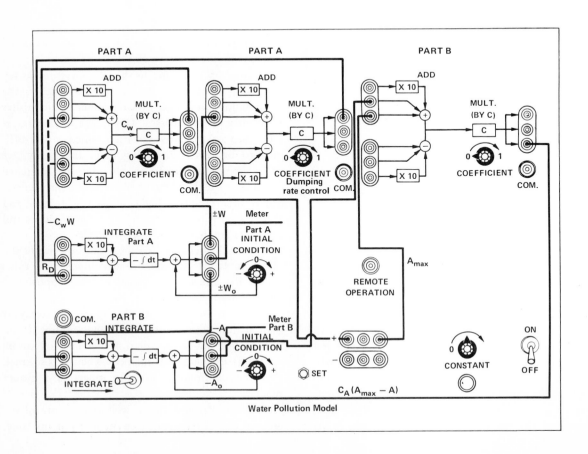

Water Pollution Model

E | EVALUATION

The questions in this section are rated according to the chapter objectives and the performance levels stated in the introduction to the teacher's manual. This group of questions is not intended to be all inclusive, but just as a guide to possible questions. Zeros in the chapter objective column indicate no chapter objective for this question.

Chapter Objective	Performance Level	
		Judged to be Relatively Easy:

In each of the following cases, mark the statement *T* if it is true, but mark it *F* if it is false.

Chapter Objective	Performance Level	
0	I	1. a) Scientists usually find it most rewarding to study stable, unchanging situations.
1	I	b) A *bit* is the name given to the information supplied when there was a decision between two equally probable alternatives.
2	I	c) It is likely to be unwise to try to maximize the information content of written English.
4	I	d) Computers are now being programmed to translate nearly all important languages into English.
4	I	e) The word *fish* may mean either one fish or more than one fish.
1	I	f) A *random* happening means one that can be exactly predicted by using probability.
6	I	g) The frequency of a sinusoid is the number of complete cycles per unit time.
7	I	h) If the pitch of a sound is raised 3 octaves, its frequency is multiplied by 6.
7	I	i) Any note played on a musical instrument may be expected to be a mixture of several harmonics.
11	I	j) Sonar is much like radar except that it uses sound signals instead of radio.
13	II	k) All new business ventures always lose money at the start.
0	I	l) Eyes and ears are not equally sensitive in all respects.

In the next three questions, check the best answer.

Chapter Objective	Performance Level	
2	I	2. A professional student of information theory would assert that in an English message a) the letter *E* carries much information because it is so common. b) the letter *E* carries only a little more information than the letter *Q*. c) the letter *Q* carries only a little more information than the letter *E*. d) all the letters carry equal amounts of information. e) the letter *E* carries less information than any other.
7	I	3. The musical note called middle A and the number 440 are associated because a) the note middle A has a harmonic of 440 cycles/sec. b) the note now called middle A was formerly called 440. c) the octave of middle A has a pitch of 440 cycles/sec. d) the frequency of middle A is an integral multiple of 440. e) a signal of 440 cycles/sec is the note middle A.
9	I	4. To send many telephone conversations at the same time between two cities a) uses a frequency of 4000 cycles/sec. b) means that a frequency 75 cycles/sec must be changed to a frequency 3500 cycles/sec. c) usually requires that each conversation be transmitted by a different route.

Chapter Objective	Performance Level	

Judged to be Relatively Easy:

d) is accomplished by shifting each conversation to a different range of frequencies.

e) requires 2 separate wires for every conversation.

Judged to be More Difficult:

All of the following statements are true EXCEPT (check the exception):

4   II

5. I was hunting for a yellow-bellied fly catcher. This sentence
   a) illustrates a difficulty with computer translation because it has several meanings.
   b) has no intelligible meaning whatever.
   c) may mean that I was searching for a cowardly outfielder.
   d) may mean that I wanted to find a particular kind of bird.
   e) may mean that I was looking for game to give to a catcher of yellow-bellied flies.

In the next five questions, check the best answer.

5   I

6. For the study of the nature of sound, the most convenient and reasonably simple equipment is
   a) a microphone and a digital computer.
   b) a Fourier series and a spectrogram.
   c) a musical scale and some harmonics.
   d) a microphone and a cathode-ray oscilloscope.
   e) a cathode-ray oscilloscope and a digital computer.

8   I

7. The Fourier theorem states that
   a) desert heat is healthy.
   b) sine signals are also called sinusoids.
   c) any signal can be reduced to the sum of several sines.
   d) the frequency of a sine wave is equal to its amplitude.
   e) a sine signal has many periods.

6   II

8.

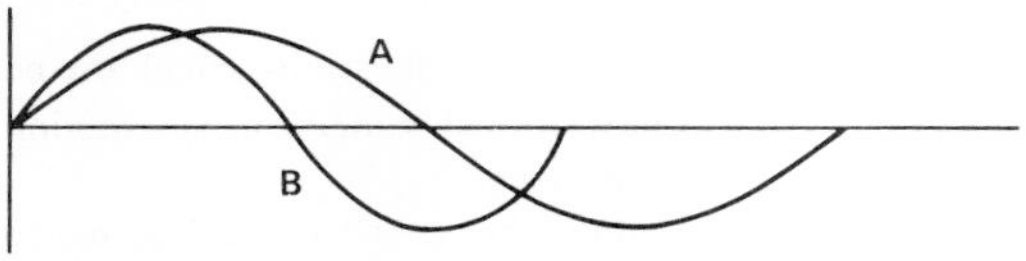

The 2 signals, A and B, in this diagram
   a) differ in both frequency and amplitude.
   b) represent 2 sounds differing by an octave.
   c) have equal periods.
   d) differ in amplitude but not in frequency.
   e) differ in frequency but not in amplitude.

11   I

9. When an airplane approaches an airport it is detected by a radar signal. Because the airplane is approaching,
   a) the duration of the echo is longer than if it were flying away.
   b) the duration of the echo is shorter than if it were flying away.
   c) the frequency of the echo is higher than if it were flying away.
   d) the frequency of the echo is lower than if it were flying away.
   e) the reception time of the echo is later than if it were flying away.

12   I

10. The previous question is concerned with an example of
   a) the Doppler effect.
   b) the Fourier effect.

Chapter Objective	Performance Level	
		Judged to be More Difficult:

    c) the azimuth of the signal.
    d) the sonar effect.
    e) the amplification of the signal.

| 10 | II | 11. The attempt to build a machine that can "speak" understandably is helped by the study of sound spectrograms. Check each statement below that describes an aspect of spectrograms that you believe to be important for this purpose. |

    a) The random quality of the syllable being studied.
    b) The fundamental pitch of the syllable.
    c) The harmonics present when the syllable is pronounced.
    d) The harmonics absent when the syllable is pronounced.
    e) The information content of the syllable.
    f) The redundancy of the syllable.
    g) The attack: the way the syllable starts.
    h) The release: the way the syllable ends.

Answers to Evaluation Questions:

1. a) F   e) T   i) T
    b) T   f) F   j) T
    c) T   g) T   k) F
    d) F   h) F   l) T

2. e

3. e

4. d

5. b

6. d

7. c

8. e

9. c

10. a

11. b, c, d, g, h

F | FILMS

F-0601 SUPERPOSITION OF WAVES
Recommendation: Highly recommended to illustrate the addition of sine waves.
Application: Concept development. Use during study of Section 3.
Length and Type: 4 min, color, silent, 8-mm cartridge film loop.
Source: #13
Summary: The amplitudes and wave lengths of 2 waves are varied and their sum is shown, all 3 simultaneously on a cathode-ray tube.

F-0602 "THE COMMUNICATIONS EXPLOSION"
Recommendation: Enrichment.
Application: Use either with Section 5 or Section 8 (as a kind of review).
Length and Type: 30 min, color, sound.
Source: A 21st Century film. #2
Summary: The next century's worldwide network of communication circuits, using satellites, microminiaturization, and lasers, to provide information, education, and entertainment.

G | GENERAL

I. Bibliography

B. Commoner, *Science and Survival.* Compass-Viking Press, 1966 (A) (paper)

An interesting complement to the HEW paper in Section GII following. His thesis is that all human life is endangered, and that the secrecy restrictions enforced (often for no evident reason) by the government have prevented scientific and technological experts from having the foresight needed to take proper steps to prevent the harmful effects of so many aspects of technology.

R. B. Fuller, *Operating Manual for Spaceship Earth.* Simon and Schuster, 1969 (A) (paper)

The author will be more easily recognized if his "first" name is spelled out: Buckminster. This is a short, nontechnical, very readable account of the author's guess about the next 50 years. But he points out that predictions are self-defeating because of the synergistic effect. By this he means that one event reacts on others in entirely unexpected ways.

R. L. Gregory, *Eye and Brain.* McGraw-Hill, 1966 (B) (paper)

A perfectly fascinating little book, very comprehensive but not repellently so, on the history, physics, physiology, and psychology of vision and theories of vision (one part of communication theory). It may be hard to find in libraries, being steadily circulated (in my experience).

D. R. Griffin, *Echoes of Bats and Men.* Anchor-Doubleday S-4, 1959 (A) (paper)

Sound and sound waves, sonar and radar, and not only bats but also other animals that seem to use wave sensors.

J. R. Pierce, *Waves and Messages.* Anchor-Doubleday S-51, 1967 (revision of part of *Electrons, Waves and Messages*) (A) (paper)

Communication and communication theory, channels and their capacity. As usual with Pierce's writing, he makes the complicated clear and the difficult almost easy.

J. R. Pierce, *Electrons and Waves.* Anchor-Doubleday S-38, 1964 (A) (paper)

Amazingly comprehensive small book. It begins with notes on the scope of science and technology, goes on to provide much essential background, such as Newton's Laws, Law of Conservation of Energy, electric and magnetic fields, and waves. All this is easy to read and appropriate for the high school student as well as for the interested adult who is not especially strong in physical science.

W. A. van Bergeijk, J. R. Pierce, and E. E. David, Jr., *Waves and the Ear.* Anchor-Doubleday S-9, 1960 (2nd edition without Pierce and David) (A) (paper)

These last two authors need no introduction to *The Man-Made World* teachers, being among the originators of the course and David being the author of part of the present edition. The book discusses sound and sound waves as any good large physics text does, but goes on to consider the ear and hearing, speech and speaking, nerves and their action, and quality and fidelity of sound reproduction.

N. Wiener, *The Human Use of Human Beings.* (Houghton Mifflin, 1950). Anchor-Doubleday A-34, 1967 (A) (paper)

Wiener's writing is always stimulating, but should in general be scheduled for times when the pressure of daily commitments is relaxed, if such times can ever be found. This book, mostly about communication (singular, not plural), and always with a strong philosophical approach, is hard reading. The difficulty lies partly in its originality, but also in the author's flattering habit of writing as though his readers had all his background and ability. Some of the topics: feedback and the comparison between automatic machinery and the nervous system; the question whether progress is really possible, considered in the light of the continual increase in entropy and of the exhaustion of the earth's resources.

II. A Discussion of the Problem of Environmental Pollution

The human race is now in peril so grave that most sober warnings by well-informed people sound hysterical and are discounted heavily by the man in the street, and by the Congressman in Washington. This may in fact be our most serious danger, because the time available for effective action is short, and rapidly growing shorter, the lag between planning a reform and benefiting by it is long, and very few of our fellow creatures are willing to give up present benefits for other benefits far in the future which are perhaps fewer and certainly costlier than what we now have. It is literally true that the hope and future of mankind lie in the hands of *The Man-Made World* students and others like them who know the facts and are willing to act on them.

It is necessary to remark that decision making in this case, as in nearly all others, demands compromises. For example, either we stop building power plants (and rapidly lower our standard of living, since the population explosion is bound to continue for at least a generation), or we provide for the power demanded, or at least a part of it. Power plants, whether fossil fueled or nuclear fueled, will cause thermal pollution. The latter type, however, does leave the air clean so the excess heat can be lost by radiation to space. Power plants will also cause air pollution. Which is worse, the mixture of noxious gases emitted by furnaces which burn gas, oil, or coal, or the slight radioactivity produced by nuclear furnaces? Will some of the latter perhaps blow up? Almost no unsensational study of this topic has been reported in the popular press. So what to do? Balance the evidence and compromise, as always. Recommended: "Nuclear Energy: Benefits Versus Risks" by W. H. Jordan in *Physics Today* for May, 1970.

There follows an abridgment of Chapter 1 of *A Strategy for a Livable Environment,* the report by the Task Force on Environmental Health and Related Problems to the Secretary of Health, Education, and Welfare, June, 1967. These pages emphasize the importance of *change* and the problems that are generated by change. The report is not an essential part of the course. It is not necessary background for any of the ideas in subsequent chapters,

but it is an excellent description of the dynamics of technology as they influence the lives of all citizens.

THE ENVIRONMENT

At the two-thirds point of the twentieth century, man has discovered that he cannot act toward his surroundings with the abandon of a caveman. For generations we assumed that Nature had the ability to absorb an increasing number and variety of environmental insults. And for a while it did. Now Nature has rebelled, and we must mend our ways.

We cannot keep adding more wastes in the air.

We cannot turn more rivers and streams into open sewers, and lakes into cesspools.

We cannot befoul the land with the discards of abundance.

In short, we cannot engage in biological and chemical warfare against ourselves. Our health and well-being, and those of future generations, are at stake.

The public will have to understand the limitations of Nature. Understanding begins if we think of the Earth as somewhat like a submarine or a space capsule. Air and water supplies are limited. All of us must understand what is required to live in the finite capsule of air, water, and land that is our environment.

The Task Force has examined the history of environmental health problems and has scanned the broadest possible variety of these hazards to Americans. One paramount conclusion resulted from the many lines of inquiry which the Task Force pursued: An effectively coordinated environmental health protection system is mandatory, one based on the premise that the environment affects man's mental as well as his physical health and welfare. An approach toward environmental health protection which is limited to concern for less than the total range of hazards that do or may exist in man's environment must be viewed by the Department as inadequate.

Many cities have reached or are approaching a crisis in air pollution. It might seem at first that there is enough air to absorb whatever insults man might hurl at it. Under normal conditions the atmosphere does have a large capacity to cleanse itself. Nuclear testing has given us knowledge of the global transport of air masses. Radioactivity from atomic bomb tests in China can be detected in the United States because the air mass circulates around the planet in a matter of weeks. But when the winds stop blowing, the pollutants concentrate in the lowest levels of air and then trouble begins. This is most common during the fall and winter when there is less sunlight. Then the ceiling tends to dip closer to the ground so that under conditions of a temperature inversion the mixing air is confined to a layer approximately 2500 to 1500 feet above city streets and factories.

This year, the 90 million motor vehicles in use will burn an estimated 60 billion gallons of gasoline, or about 700 gallons for the typical automobile. This means that each automobile in the country will discharge in a single year over 1600 pounds of carbon monoxide, 230 pounds of hydrocarbons, and 77 pounds of oxides of nitrogen.

It is difficult to predict future levels of sulfurous air pollution from the burning of fossil fuels, because such a prediction depends on assumptions about trends in fuel use and advances in pollution-control technology. Authorities agree that premium fossil fuels will be in short supply in the near future. According to one estimate, continuation of present control practices would see a 100% rise in sulfur levels by 1980, from a present level of 24 million tons to 48 million tons per year, as a result of increased consumption of sulfur-bearing coal and oil. If even the most rigorous control technology were developed and applied, sulfur emissions by 1980 would reach an estimated 32 million tons per year. Electric power plants, which account for about half of the sulfur discharged to the air as a result of fuel burning, will continue to be a major source of sulfurous pollution long after nuclear energy becomes a mainstay of electric power, simply because so many coal- and oil-burning power plants will be built in the next 25 years to supply rising demands for electricity. Without nuclear power and without controls, by the year 2000 Americans would have to restrict their use of electricity or pay much more for the kilowatt-hour because of the scarcity of cheap low-sulfur coal and oil.

Some 50,000 people die each year from traffic accidents. However, the driver or the pedestrian has some control over his safety. But many environmental hazards are more subtle and are beyond an individual's perception and control. For example, the development of efficient braking systems for motor vehicles has led to increased exposure of the public to asbestos particles produced by the wearing of brake linings. There is scientific basis for concern that these particles may promote lung cancer over long periods of time. Similarly, the change from hard to soft detergents, a move aimed at reducing a serious water pollution problem, led to the introduction into the environment of a new compound which is believed to be killing large numbers of fish by attacking their eggs. By allowing tiny amounts of pesticides to enter our waters, we have set in motion processes that can lead to the destruction of birds that feed on fish that feed on plants that draw the pesticide from the water. Though the bad effects of radiation have been known for several decades, many uranium miners in the United States are today being exposed to excessive amounts of radioactive gases. Such exposure has produced a marked increase in the incidence of lung cancer among them. Infectious hepatitis appears to be directly related to contaminated drinking water, but very little is known about how the disease-causing agent gets in the water or how it can be taken out.

The Food and Drug Administration has estimated that the American people are being exposed to some 500,000 different substances, many of them over very long periods of time. Yet fewer than 10% of these substances have been catalogued in a manner that might provide the basis for determining their effects on man and his environment. Health experts have repeatedly pointed out that delayed damage to health can result from repeated exposure to concentrations of pollutants so small that they do not make one ill enough to send him to the doctor. Environmental pollutants can have cumulative effects. These effects can take delayed forms such as cancers, emphysema, and reduced life span, and they can even extend to following generations. In other words, the most serious effects of pollution may be those we do not fully appreciate or take steps to prevent. Our ignorance of potential hazards is perilously great.

This is a time when our capacity to enhance or degrade the environment is literally beyond reckoning, but we do not now fully understand how to use this capacity for the benefit, rather than the harm, of mankind. The effects of environmental change are not manifested solely in threats to man's physical well-being. The pressures of our industrial culture must certainly produce threats to social and psychological welfare. These psychosocial effects of environmental hazards are cause for concern in a nation where mental and social ills are recognized as major problems. Certainly they are to a significant degree major environmental problems.

Man's affluence has its source in the extraction and exploitation of natural resources. But the use of these resources has resulted in an environment abused. Strip mining has left ulcers on the land. Our forests have been emptied of their timber. Dust storms of the thirties recall the price of land neglect. Chemical agriculture has laid down a barrage of deadly insecticides, fungicides, and herbicides to kill off plant pests and diseases: but the residues infiltrate the food chain. Banks of rivers are littered with the accumulated debris of fish kills due to these water-borne residues.

In a recent report dealing with the increasing pollution of the air, water, and land, the National Academy of Sciences National Research Council stated:

Pollution increases not only because as people multiply, the space available to each person becomes smaller, but also because the demands per person are continually increasing, so that each throws away more year by year. As the earth becomes more crowded, there is no longer an "away." One person's trash basket is another person's living space.

Americans make more things than other people, and they make far more than half of the world's trash. This year's rubbish would fill 36 lines of boxcars stretching from coast to coast.

In 1900 the population of the United States was 76 million, and urbanization was still a trend of the future. Our population today approaches 200 million and may reach 235 million by 1980. Already, nearly three-quarters of this nation's inhabitants are densely packed into 200 urban centers. Demographers estimate that before the next turn of the century, "super-cities" will stretch from Boston to Washington, Buffalo to Milwaukee, San Francisco to San Diego. The problems of these huge urbanized land masses will be vastly greater than those of the present cities. The impact of population growth, technology, and urbanization on man's environment is accelerating. There is no sign of any stability in man's collision with his environment. As people crowd more densely together, the environment changes with increasing effect, often unpredictably, and what is most serious of all, possibly irreversibly.

The United States needs to take stock of its environmental condition and to recognize the urgency of the situation. Since the environment and man's relationship to it are so complex, no simple solution or simple approach can be sketched out which will allow the Federal government to correct centuries of abuse overnight. The tools available to the nation to do the job are insufficient. Jurisdictional disagreements among those responsible for environmental protection create problems and too often inaction. Nowhere is there the capability of making enlightened assessments of policy affecting the economy. Yet one is no less important than the other. A weak economy means human distress. A diseased environment also means human distress.

Even the abbreviated effort which the Task Force has made to examine the nature and extent of the nation's environmental problem leaves no doubt that there must be a radical increase in the national commitment to protection of man's health and welfare from threats, present and future, in the world about him.

III. Some Extra Problems

1. A radar system emits pulses of 2 microseconds duration at a rate of 500 pulses per second. What is the maximum range from which a pulse can return before the next one leaves?
10^6 $\mu s/s /(500$ pulses/s$) = 2 \times 10^3$ μs between the start of one pulse and the start of the next.
$2000 - 2 = 1998$ μs of silence between pulses.
Each pulse can travel out for half this time, 999 μs
$d = rt = 3 \times 10^5$ km/sec $\times 999 \times 10^{-6}$ sec $= 299.7$ km.

2. a) What is the length in meters of a 0.001-sec burst from a sonar transmitter in air? (c = 350 m/sec)

b) In water? (c = 1440 m/sec)

c) How long would it take the sound pulse caused by an earthquake in Japan to reach California through the ocean, a trip of 9600 km?

The length is the distance which the leading edge of the sonar burst travels during the burst.

a) $\ell_a = 350 \dfrac{m}{sec} \times 10^{-3}$ sec $= 0.35$ m

b) $\ell_w = 1440 \dfrac{m}{sec} \times 10^{-3}$ sec $= 1.44$ m

c) $t = \dfrac{d}{r} = \dfrac{9600 \text{ km}}{1.44 \text{ km/sec}} = 6670$ sec

3.a) If an insect is 18 ft from a bat, what is the time delay between transmitted and echo pulses? (c = 1100 ft/sec)

b) What is the maximum range of the bat's cruising sonar system if an echo must be received before the next pulse is transmitted? (Assume pulses are emitted every 0.1 sec.)

c) If the bat approaches the insect at the relative speed of 10 ft/sec and the transmitted frequency is 30,000 cps, what is the received frequency?

a) $t = \dfrac{d}{r} = \dfrac{2 \times 18 \text{ ft}}{1100 \text{ ft/sec}} = 0.0327$ sec

b) $d = rt = 1100 \dfrac{ft}{sec} \times \dfrac{1}{20}$ sec $= 55$ ft

c) Notice first that the Doppler effect is applied twice here: the pitch as heard by the victim is raised, and this raised pitch is then echoed and elevated again upon reception.

$$\dfrac{\Delta f}{f} = \dfrac{2v_{rel}}{c} \quad ; \quad \dfrac{\Delta f}{3 \times 10^4 \text{ cps}} = \dfrac{20 \text{ ft/sec}}{1.1 \times 10^3 \text{ ft/sec}}$$

$\Delta f = 546$ ft/sec. Since the motion is an approach, the pitch is raised. $f_{final} = 30,546$ cps.

4. Standing on a platform when a train with its whistle blowing goes past, you observe a frequency of 550 cps when the train is approaching, and 450 cps when it is receding. What is the speed of the train? (c = 1100 ft/sec)

$f + \Delta f = 550$ cps; $f - \Delta f = 450$ cps; $2f = 1000$, $f = 500$ cps, $\Delta f = 50$ cps

$$\dfrac{50 \text{ cps}}{500 \text{ cps}} = \dfrac{v_{rel}}{1100 \text{ ft/sec}} ; v_{rel} = 110 \text{ ft/sec}$$

(It should be pointed out that the formula used is approximate and gives a good result only when the relative speed is much smaller than the speed of the wave. A more accurate solution gives v = 100 ft/sec.)

5. A musician with a perfect sense of pitch hears an approaching train whistle which seems to produce a frequency of 1500 cps. The pitch of the whistle drops to a frequency of 1300 cps after the train has passed him.

a) How fast was the train moving, if c = 1150 ft/sec?

b) What advantage can be gained with the use of higher frequency for the transmitter of a Doppler unit?

Answer to Question 5:

a) As shown in the previous problem, we can readily find that the whistle frequency = 1400 cps. Then,

$$\dfrac{100 \text{ cps}}{1400 \text{ cps}} = \dfrac{v}{1150 \text{ ft/sec}} ; v = 82 \text{ ft/sec.}$$

b) For a given ratio of relative speed to velocity of the wave (radio, for Doppler speed checking), the change in frequency is a constant fraction of the original frequency. Therefore, if the original frequency is raised, the magnitude of the change in frequency will be raised in the same ratio. If the sensitivity of the detecting circuit does not change, a smaller Doppler shift can be measured and therefore a smaller relative speed can be detected.

6. A sound wave having a frequency of 12 kilocycles/sec is used with a sonar unit to measure the speed of a moving vehicle. If the smallest frequency change that can be detected is 50 cps, what is the speed which the moving vehicle must have to reach this limiting value on the instrument? (c = 1150 ft/sec)

As in Problem 3c, the Doppler shift is involved twice.

$$\dfrac{50 \text{ cps}}{12,000 \text{ cps}} = \dfrac{2v}{1150 \text{ ft/sec}} ; v = 2.4 \text{ ft/sec}$$

7. To add two sine waves, use the following graphical method. Draw both waves on the same basic framework. Every one of the lines perpendicular to *AB* crosses both curves. Measure the distances of each of these 2 crossing points from *AB*, add

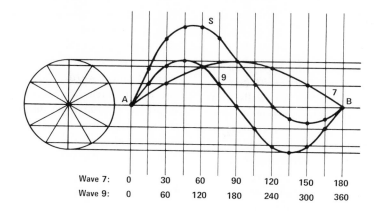

Wave 7:	0	30	60	90	120	150	180
Wave 9:	0	60	120	180	240	300	360

them, and mark a new point on the perpendicular at the sum of the distances from AB. This is done most easily by setting a compass to one distance, and using it to add this distance to the other. Pay attention to sign: all the crossing distances which are below AB count as negative.

Add the wave of Problem 9 in the textbook to the first half of the wave in Problem 7.

A useful additional question: If the graph were extended to bring in the whole of Wave 7 and two cycles of Wave 9, how would Wave S look?

Answer:

An inverted mirror image; or rotate the whole figure

$180°$ around an axis set perpendicular to the plane of the paper at point B.

8. On a fresh framework, again draw the wave of Problem 9 from the textbook. On the same framework, draw an identical wave $60°$ earlier in phase; i.e., when Wave 9 is at the point determined by the $60°$ radius of the guide circle, this new wave will be at $60° - 60° = 0°$. Add the two waves by the graphical method, having carried the graph of the second wave to $360°$ by its phasing (or $420°$ for Wave 9). (Students may be surprised to find that the Sum wave has exactly the same wave length as the component waves, although its amplitude has been changed.)

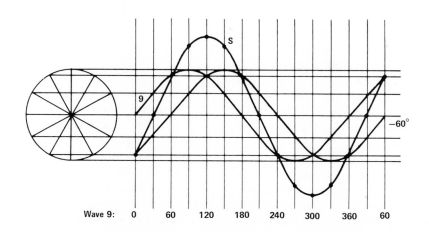

Wave 9:	0	60	120	180	240	300	360	60

IV. More on the CRO

THE CRO SWEEP

The CRO "gun" is a source of a slim beam of (negative) electrons. These pass between a pair of metal plates arranged on edge, like two walls with the beam between. At a certain instant one of these plates (on your left, as you face the screen) is electrically positive and the other is negative, which deflects the beam toward the left, and the fluorescent spot on the tube face is also at the left. These charges are gradually reversed, causing the beam and its spot to move toward the right, until suddenly the charge is restored to the original condition and the beam flies back (called appropriately enough, flyback). This description corresponds to what is called a sawtooth voltage wave, produced by electronic gear within the oscilloscope.

The flyback occurs at the (almost) perpendicular portions of the wave. Often a "blanking" circuit is incorporated, to suppress the beam (and hence the spot) during flyback. The frequency of the sawtooth wave depends on the setting of the sweep-frequency control.

CRO SYNCHRONIZATION

To obtain a stationary picture of a periodic wave form on the CRO screen, the frequency of the horizontal sweep must be equal to the frequency of the vertical movement or to that frequency divided by a whole number. Or stating it another way, the frequency of the wave form being viewed must be some whole multiple of the horizontal sweep frequency. When this situation exists, the sweep signal and the waveform are said to be in *synchronization*.

When the CRO sweep is not adjusted properly, the picture moves across the screen. The same thing happens in the TV set; when it is not properly adjusted, the picture appears to "roll." The rolling of the TV picture can be stopped by adjusting a knob on the set, and the movement of the CRO picture is stopped in the same way.

The movement which occurs when the wave form being viewed is not in synchronization with the sweep frequency is due to the fact that the signal wave form is different during each successive sweep of the electron beam spot across the screen.

The CRO then presents a rapid sequence of different pictures. This situation is illustrated below. The wave form of the signal x is shown in this figure and successive sweep intervals of duration T are marked on the graph. The signal wave form is different during each of these sweeps, and the picture displayed by the CRO during successive sweeps is shown below the wave form. Under this operating condition the wave form seen on the CRO seems to move across the screen from right to left.

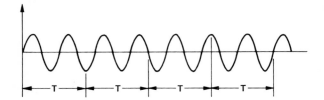

A little thought shows that if the sweep duration T, above, is made exactly equal to one period of the wave form being viewed, then the wave form is exactly the same during each sweep. With this adjustment the picture on the CRO remains stationary, and the picture on the TV screen does not roll.

At high frequencies, when the phosphor persistence is several times longer than the period of the sweep signal, a lack of synchronization will produce traces on the CRO similar to that shown below.

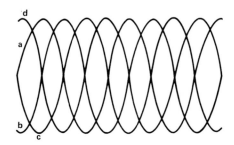

This trace can be explained by studying the next diagram, where the sweep time, T, is made equal to 7/4 of the sinusoidal signal period. The trace for 4 successive sweeps across the CRO screen is shown in (a), (b), (c), and (d). Because of the high sweep frequency, several traces persist on the CRO screen. Thus we see the traces in (a), (b), (c), and (d) *simultaneously* on the screen. The result is the one shown above.

(a)   (b)   (c)   (d)

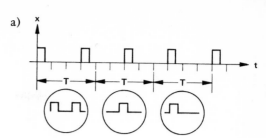

a)

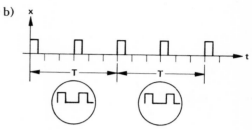

b)

A stationary picture is obtained on the CRO when the sweep duration is made equal to 2 periods of the wave form being viewed, or 3 periods, or any whole number of periods. In (a), opposite, none of these conditions exist, but (b) illustrates the situation when the sweep duration is exactly 2 periods of the wave form (some of the right-hand horizontal line is lost during flyback).

FEEDBACK

APPROX. TIME: Text: 10 days   Lab: 7 days

A. APPROACH	CLASS PERIODS	B. BLACK & WHITE TRANSPARENCIES	C. CUES (k = key problem) Discussion Questions	Problems Easy	Problems Medium	Problems Hard	D. DEMONSTRATIONS, LABS & PROJECTS	E. EVALUATION	F. FILMS	G. GENERAL
1. A Feedback System	1	0701a-f	12				I,VA	1a,b,c,e 4	0701	II
2. Goal-Seeking	1	0702a,b	1,2,9					2,3		
3. Feedback as Self-Regulation	1	0703	3,4,5,6, 15,16							
4. Feedback for Disturbance Control	2	0704a,b,c 0705a,b 0706 0707	10	2k	1,3k,4	5,8	II,III	1d,f,6		
5. Automatic Compensation	1	0708 0709 0710 0711	13		6		IV,VI,VII	1k,7	0702	
6. A Human Feedback System	1	0712	14		7			1l,5		
7. Instability in Feedback Systems	2	0713 0714	7,8,11				V	1g,h,i,j 8		
8. Final Comment	1		17							

Feedback 7

A | APPROACH

I. Purpose and Organization of the Chapter

If any single concept of today's technology is more widely used than any other, it is feedback. The chapter might plausibly have closed the course or it might have opened the book, except that the subject is easier to appreciate if the student knows something of technology first. Its placement in the middle of the course, therefore, meets both criteria. The students have run into feedback situations prior to this chapter. Those situations will now be clearer to them. Feedback considerations later in the text will require less explanation. All of the following topics, and others too, could have been developed from the point of view of feedback: the yellow light problem; modeling; optimization; linear programming; population studies; the home heating system; pollution in various aspects. That is, in each case we can find a goal and an actual output; we can determine the error signal; we can describe means of diminishing the error. To a degree, all this is what we have been working toward. This is the culmination of our technological study of *The Man-Made World*. The next chapter could have preceded this one without confusion, although the feedback concept is employed in it. Chapter 9 culminates the study in another and more important way, because human

beings are more directly involved, and in Chapters 10 through 15 we have an exciting example, on a large scale and in some depth, of the technological enterprise.

The chapter opens with a qualitative account of an easily comprehended feedback situation; later it shows how feedback is used to make systems self-regulating and also to control the effect of disturbances. Easy examples of quantitative applications follow, and the lessons are driven home by a biological example, the intricate ways in which the internal (core) temperature in a healthy person is kept constant. Finally we learn how feedback may lead to instability, either wanted or undesired.

II. Objectives for Students

Upon completion of the activities, discussion, and reading in this chapter, students should be able to:

1. Recognize and identify the following terms: *ataxia, comparator, endocrine gland, error signal, goal seeking, hormone,* and *vasomotor control.*

2. Explain the functions of the various parts of a simple feedback system: input and output, comparator, and feedback loop.

3. Demonstrate how an error signal can be used to initiate and control corrective action.

4. Compare the goal-seeking aspect of feedback with its use for self-regulation.

5. Outline how feedback from the environment

may result in adaptation of the organism in organic evolution.

6. Compare the process of counterbalancing an undesired disturbance (noise) with that of counterbalancing changes within a system itself.

7. Show why an intermittently operating feedback loop is inferior to one with continuous operation.

8. Calculate the amplification factor of a given amplifier with a feedback scalor of a given size.

9. Explain how a suitable feedback loop may diminish the effect on system output of an undesired disturbance, and calculate in specified numerical cases what improvement will be produced.

10. Explain how automatic decision making is made possible by the use of feedback in such cases as the control of a machine tool or the banking of an air-cushion (Hovercraft) train.

11. Identify the advantages of feedback as gained at the price of more complicated apparatus and of instability.

12. Recognize cases of instability (both oscillatory and runaway), and predict when instability is likely to occur.

13. Show how a delay in a feedback loop may cause instability, particularly oscillation.

14. Illustrate how oscillation may be put to use.

15. Describe as a group of feedback processes, the physiological system for the control of the core temperature of the human body.

16. Reformulate other kinds of homeostasis as possible effects of feedback loops.

III. Suggestions for Teaching

Feedback, in the technical sense, requires a comparison between a desired state or goal and an actual state or goal; it also requires corrective action, controlled by the result of the comparison. Not all alleged examples of feedback are that. Many are just reactions. Dog bites man on ankle, man kicks dog. Not controlled feedback. Child is naughty, parent metes out punishment. Yes, this *is* feedback. The error is the difference between an "ideal" child and the actual child; the punishment (unless dictated solely by temper) is intended to change the child

toward the ideal. Some other examples: Automatic Frequency Control in a radio receiver; a man balancing his checkbook (if there is an error, he takes steps to correct his record—or the bank's); a spring-mass system (see Section G, Part III, in Teacher's Manual for Chapter 8); osmosis (when the concentration or mass per unit volume of water within a cell is less than that without, osmosis occurs. The "goal" is equal concentrations; there is a comparison—a thermodynamic difference—followed by a shift of the system toward equal concentrations). The hormone vasopressin, secreted by the pituitary gland at the base of the brain in an amount controlled by the water concentration of the blood—the comparison mechanism—stimulates the kidneys to restore the normal water concentration (the regulator mechanism controlled by the feedback; it is an osmotic process). One of the very early applications was to steam-driven steering gear on a ship. When the steersman put the wheel over, the steam engine started to move the rudder; the difference between the steersman's signal and the rudder position signal was used to control the amount of steam admitted to the cylinder of the engine. (Sometimes it was unstable: the rudder went too far each way alternately and "hunted" for its proper place.) See Wiener item in the Bibliography. Wiener named his book *Cybernetics* from a Greek word for "steersman."

Notice that in technological application, the error signal (which is normally very small) controls an amplifier (for definition, refer to Chapter 1, Lab II, Part B).

If your class members are having trouble with algebra, you may omit the three boxed developments (Box 7-1, 7-2, and 7-3) without serious loss.

Section 1. A Feedback System. One of the best ways to start the chapter is to describe the rolling-pencil example of this section with the help of T-0701a–f (a series of overlays). Then do Lab I, and perhaps show F-0701. If all goes well, the section need be assigned only for review.

Section 2. Goal-Seeking. Students who have studied biology should be able to produce numerous examples of feedback in living beings. The action of hormones (like that of vasopressin, mentioned earlier) is generally a feedback process.

Section 3. Feedback as Self-Regulation. The fact that the input to the feedback block diagram is sometimes called the "goal" is a source of confusion to beginners. Naturally enough, they read from start to finish and expect the finish to be the goal. What they are missing is that the block diagram does not portray a manufacturing process; its input is not a supply of raw materials, nor is its output the finished product. The block diagram is a way of describing a series of cause-and-effect relationships. The following modified structure of the block diagram of T-0702a may make it easier to grasp what is going on.

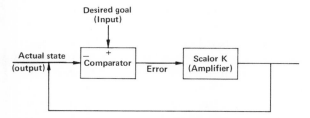

The trouble with this way of drawing the diagram evidently is that the output is quite certainly at the wrong place, but this may be useful in explaining why the diagram is drawn as it usually is.

The shoe-factory example ought to strike your class as oversimplified. Of course it is. Just as in the case of the house-heating system of Chapter 5, we omit the extraneous details like the influence of fashion, of advertising, of charming salespeople, etc. The whole story is much more complicated than they guess and probably not fully understood even by professional economists. The function of the example is to illustrate not the laws of economics, but the self-regulating effect of feedback and the fact that it doesn't always work that way. Lab V, Part A, is helpful in demonstrating both kinds of instability: oscillation is likely in Step 1, and an output growing indefinitely in Step 2.

Section 4. Feedback for Disturbance Control. Lab II illustrates the navigation problem so beautifully that you may gain both understanding and time if

you assign it to start with, and then tie up the loose ends by describing the text discussion yourself, using T-0704a–c and T-0705a and b. Don't fail to emphasize the main point, that feedback may help to control the effect of disturbances.

Answers to Feedback Questions in Text: (Note: Skip Q3 if you are omitting the algebraic development in the boxes.)

1. To diminish the effect of a disturbance signal.
2. The output signal must be measured and compared with the desired goal (input), in order to find the magnitude and sign of the necessary correction.
3. In the simple system, $y = 5x + u$. In the feedback system, $y = (x - y/6) K + u$, whence $y + Ky/6 = Kx + u$. Then $y = [Kx/(1 + [K/6])] + [u/(1 + [K/6])]$ Now if the part of the output due to x is the same in the two systems, $K/[1+(K/6)] = 5$, or $6K/(6+K) = 5$, and $K = 30$. In the first system, the output contains u; in the second, it contains $u/[1+(K/6)] = 6u/(6 +K) = 6u/36 = u/6$. Therefore u has less influence in the second system, by a factor of 6.

Section 5. Automatic Compensation. Nearly all this material keys directly to the Chapter 5 discussion of a house-heating system, and therefore students should be advised beforehand to review the appropriate pages. Lab. VII is one way to manage this review. Lab IV, Part A, is closely related to the original analog lab exercise, Chapter 4, Lab III. Part B will require some close reasoning. This is a better automatic control than that shown in Chapter 5, Section GIII. Demonstration (lab) VI is interesting, unexpected, not easy to understand, but an excellent example of feedback for automatic compensation.

Answers to Feedback Questions in Text (Q2 and Q3 require the use of algebra):

1. To diminish the unwanted effects of disturbance signals, and to eliminate variations caused by amplifier changes.
2. At first, $y = 100(x - y)$, or $y = 100x/101 = 0.990x$. When amplifier gain falls to 80, $y' = 80(x - y')$, or $y' = 80x/81 = 0.988x$. The change in $y = 0.002x$, and the percent change = 0.002/0.990 x

100 = 0.202%. (It is a bit startling to work this out with common fractions, when the percent change = $(8100 - 8080)/81 \times 100 = 0.247\%$. The reason is that in the first case the presumably proper amount of rounding off has resulted in a quite unexpectedly large percentage change in $y - y'$, but this does not happen when we keep all the digits as in the second method.)

3. The expected way to attack this is to follow the algebra in the text. Then $y = 1000 (x - y/10 + z)$. But then we attempt to find z; we go to the middle amplifier, the output of which is $10(x - y/10 + z)$, and this times $1/10 = z$. The outcome is that z drops out! x is now found to equal $y/10$; therefore the signal from the comparator is 0, and everything has collapsed. One may attack the problem by the following abnormal method. Leave out the letter z, insert v and w as shown, and call the gain of the large amplifier G. Then if we work backwards, $y = Gw$, but $w = 10v$, so $y = 10Gv$. However,

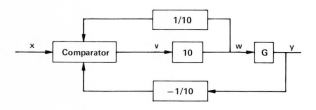

at the comparator we see that $v = x + w/10 - y/10$. Now substituting $10v$ for w and $10Gv$ for y we get $v = x + v - Gv$ or $x = Gv$. If $y = 10Gv$, $y = 10x$ and the gain of the main amplifier has no effect on y. The system is equivalent to a single amplifier of gain 10, and is therefore as good as (and only as good as) the first, gain 10, amplifier.

Section 6. A Human Feedback System. This should interest students who have studied biology, because it is probably a more complete statement than they have seen. Many of the details are still under investigation, so it is unsafe to make categorical statements. One interesting set of questions concerns the ways in which the brain exercises control. Sometimes it is by electrical (nerve-carried) signals; in other cases the message is transferred by a hormone secreted by a gland which also presumably receives an electrical command.

An Answer to Final Feedback Question (Text page 318):

The input temperature is lowered, so sweating would be inhibited and shivering would occur at a much lower temperature (assuming that woodchucks do sweat and shiver). Blood flow to the skin would be diminished by the vasomotor constriction. The skin sensors would be less sensitive or would be adjusted to respond to a lower temperature. The core sensor would be similarly readjusted. Metabolism would be slowed. The lower temperature is desirable because there will be less heat loss through the skin to be made up by metabolism, and the chemical reactions of metabolism will slow down at the lower temperature. Therefore the woodchuck's supply of fat (his fuel) can last all winter.

Section 7. Instability in Feedback Systems. A familiar example of instability induced by feedback is the squeal or roar heard with a public address system when a loudspeaker is behind the microphone, so that sounds emitted by the loudspeaker are picked up by the microphone. This is much like a reaction system (see Manual page 166), rather than a feedback system. There is no clearly evident comparator, no error signal, no machinery for reducing the error. However, if the feedback were delayed enough to put the output signal out of phase with the input we would find no buildup to a roar and the system would behave more as in conventional feedback, so perhaps it is hair-splitting to speak of reaction. There can be no question that it is instability.

An easily demonstrated example of real feedback instability, similar to that by which a pendulum can be made to swing with constant amplitude, is an ordinary electric bell or buzzer. If you show one to your class you can use a simplified diagram similar to this:

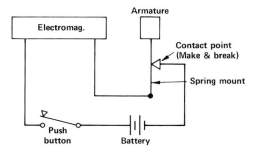

When the button is pushed, the electromagnet is energized, attracts the armature, and by pulling it over breaks the circuit at the tip of the contact point. The spring mount then restores the armature to its first position, and the cycle repeats indefinitely. A block diagram is difficult. What is the goal? The choice is really arbitrary, but since the immediate result of pushing the button is to establish a current, we choose this. Then the output is the actual condition: current or no current. The make-and-break mechanism may be considered the comparator; the magnet's condition depends on it and the armature position in turn depends on the fact that the energized magnet exerts more force than the spring can.

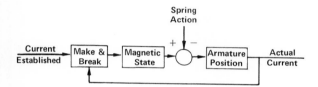

Your class may be curious about the clock mechanism that keeps a pendulum swinging. The balance wheel of a watch is kept vibrating in a similar way. Notice, by the way, that the envelopes of the damped oscillation curve of Fig. 7-33 are exponentials if each oscillation is diminished from the previous one by a constant fraction. Both clock and watch are really amplifiers (and so was the buzzer), self-controlled (like the oscillator in a radio transmitter or in most receivers). The energy source is a spring, or in a pendulum clock, a weight on the end of a wire; as the weight very slowly descends it rotates a drum and this in turn, through gears, turns the toothed wheel in the diagram. But the wheel can only turn intermittently. Most of the time it is prevented from turning by the escapement, which catches and holds a tooth on the wheel. This form of the mechanism is known as the anchor escape-

ment. When the pendulum swings back from the end of its arc it rocks the escapement and when it reaches a certain position the wheel is released. During the release the wheel tooth gives a nudge to the escapement tooth, and thus to the pendulum, because of the shapes of the two teeth. From the point of view of the wheel's teeth, one side of each escapement tooth is an inclined plane or wedge. Thus, as the escapement tooth is pulled aside, the gear tooth that is being released gives it a push, as just described (the energy coming from the weight), much as a tiddlywinks player projects his chip, which has a wedge-shaped edge.

Section 8. A Final Comment. The historical part of this review is perhaps more interesting than the description of the automated railway freight yard. The latter may appeal more to students who live in cities near freight yards than those who do not, but it is such an elegant description of automation on a large scale that it was included for study by all.

B | BLACK AND WHITE TRANSPARENCIES

Input
Pencil
Position →

Output
Hand
Position

T-0701a FEEDBACK: INPUT AND OUTPUT

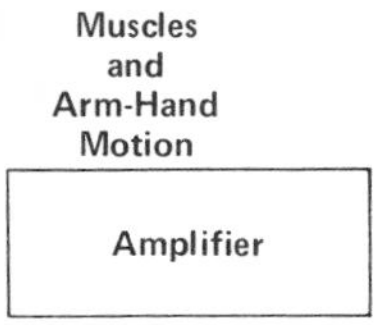

Muscles
and
Arm-Hand
Motion

Amplifier

T-0701d FEEDBACK: MAN-PENCIL SYSTEM
MODELED

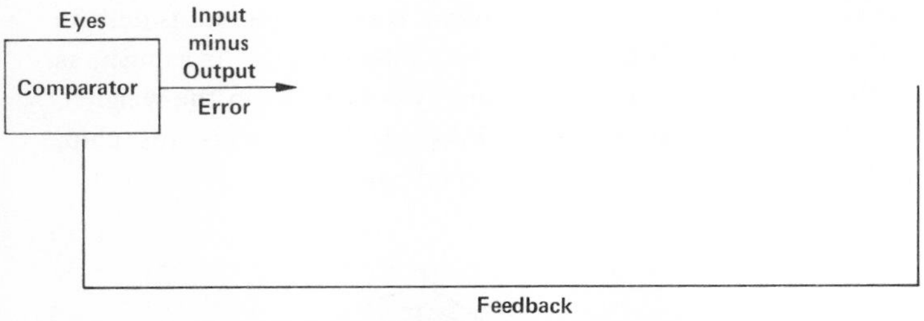

Eyes

Comparator

Input
minus
Output

Error →

Feedback

T-0701b FEEDBACK: SYSTEM MEASURES ERROR

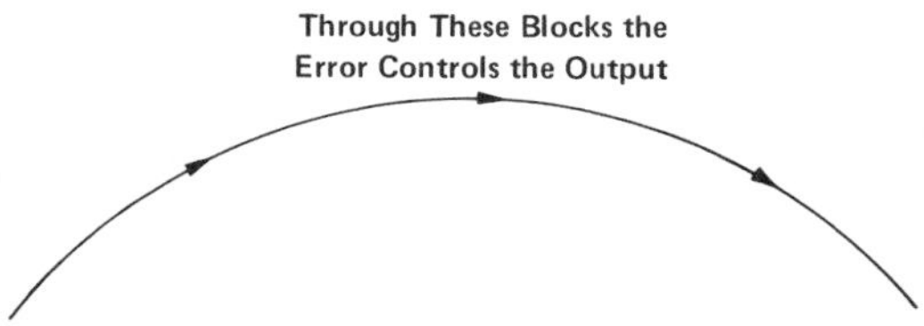

Through These Blocks the
Error Controls the Output

T-0701e   FEEDBACK: AN ERROR CHANGES OUTPUT

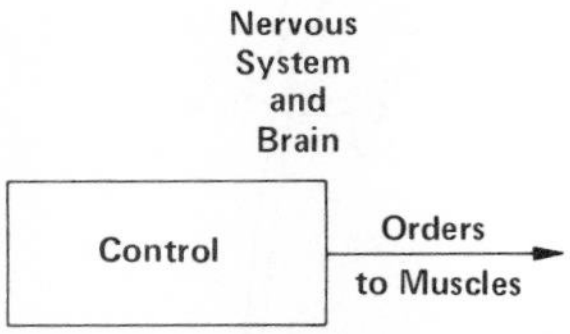

Nervous
System
and
Brain

Control

Orders
to Muscles →

T-0701c FEEDBACK: DECISION-MAKING

A Loop to Travel Around in Cause-Effect Relations

T-0701f FEEDBACK: A FEEDBACK LOOP

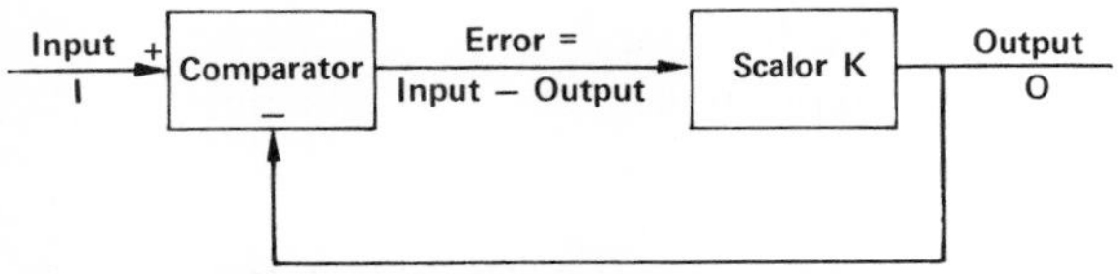

Input
I

+ | Comparator | −

Error =
Input − Output

| Scalor K |

Output
O

T-0702a   A SIMPLE FEEDBACK SYSTEM

Loop

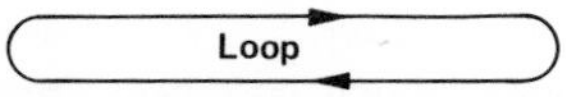

T-0702b LOOP IN SIMPLE FEEDBACK SYSTEM

Input
normal price
of shoes
$12

− | Comparator | +

Error
Difference in
price from
normal
$2

| Number of
manufacturers |

Quantity
manufactured

| Marketplace
(supply and
demand) |

Output
Price of shoes
$14

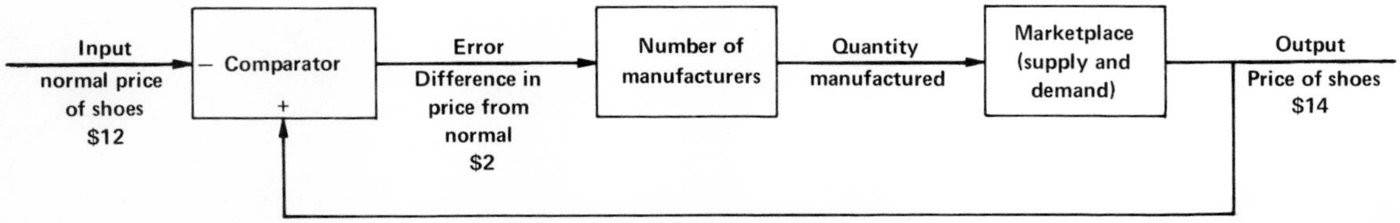

T-0703 SYSTEM REGULATING PRICE OF SHOES

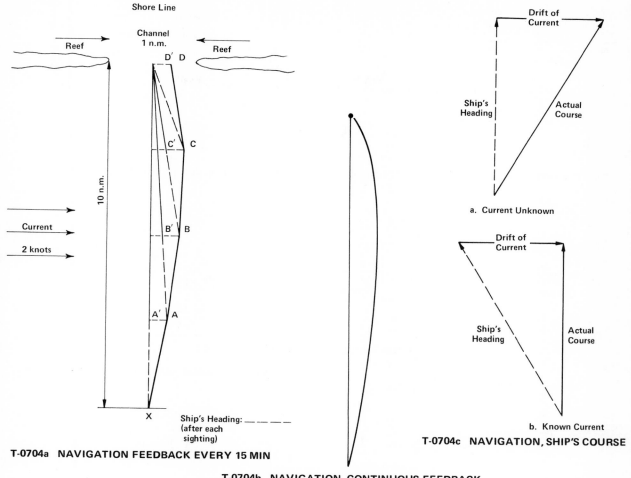

Shore Line

Channel
1 n.m.

Reef

Reef

D' D

10 n.m.

C' C

Current

B' B

2 knots

A' A

X

Ship's Heading: _ _ _ _ _
(after each
sighting)

T-0704a NAVIGATION FEEDBACK EVERY 15 MIN

Drift of
Current

Ship's
Heading

Actual
Course

a. Current Unknown

Drift of
Current

Ship's
Heading

Actual
Course

b. Known Current

T-0704c NAVIGATION, SHIP'S COURSE

T-0704b NAVIGATION, CONTINUOUS FEEDBACK

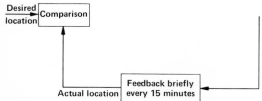

Current

Heading
offered → Adder → Actual
heading
of ship → Ship's
character-
istics → Location of
ship (relative
to channel
center)

T-0705a BLOCK DIAGRAM, NAVIGATION PROBLEM

Desired
location → Comparison

Actual location → Feedback briefly
every 15 minutes

**T-0705b NAVIGATION SYSTEM, INTERMEDIATE
FEEDBACK**

Disturbance
u

x
Main input → 2 → Adder → 10 → y
Output

y = 20x + 10u

(a) Original system with no feedback

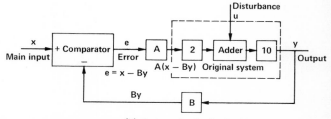

Disturbance
u

x
Main input → + Comparator
− → e
Error → A → 2 → Adder → 10 → y
Output

A(x − By)   Original system

e = x − By

By

B

(b) System after feedback added

T-0706 SYSTEMS FOR BOX 2 PROBLEM

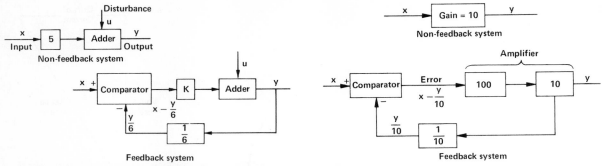

T-0707 SYSTEMS FOR QUESTION 3, SECTION 4

T-0709 SYSTEMS FOR PROBLEM OF BOX 3

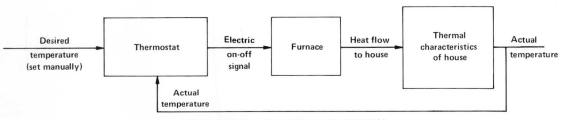

T-0708 HOUSEHOLD-HEATING SYSTEM

T-0710 SYSTEM FOR QUESTION 2, SECTION 5

T-0711 SYSTEM FOR QUESTION 3, SECTION 5

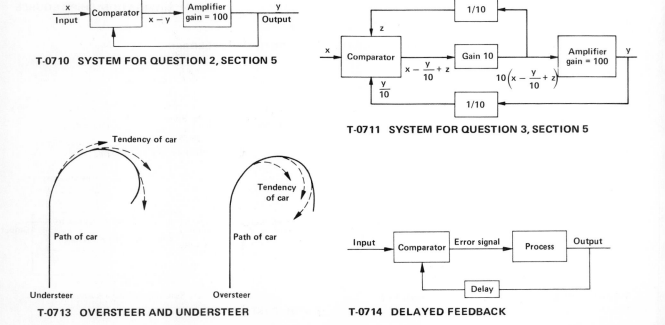

T-0713 OVERSTEER AND UNDERSTEER

T-0714 DELAYED FEEDBACK

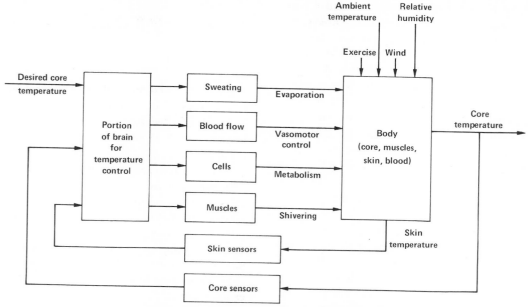

T-0712   SYSTEM FOR BODY CORE TEMPERATURE

C | CUES TO QUESTIONS AND PROBLEMS

Questions for Study and Discussion

1. Either yes or no. Yes, because presumably he wants to keep your favor. This implies, of course, that he possesses at least some reasoning power. Or no, because presumably his training has been so good that the sound of the whistle produces a "conditioned reflex" of returning to his master. This implies no reasoning power on his part, but does imply a feedback mechanism in his brain.

2. A root hair which extends into dry soil either withers or at least grows only very slowly, but those which reach moist soil containing plant foods will grow longer and faster than the rest. The result is that the whole root structure develops better on this side. Feedback is involved because the growth of root hairs is enhanced by the presence of moisture and fertilizers, while lack of these results in slow growth or none at all. The moisture is literally fed back into the root.

3. a) An error signal, which is obtained by comparing the actual to the desired speed, controls the power fed to the motor which runs the escalator.

b) The input is the desired speed; the output is the actual speed.

c)

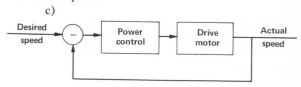

4. a) Input is desired frequency; output is the frequency at which the tuning circuit of the radio is set.

b) Input is the direction to which the steering wheel is set (or its angular position); output is the direction in which the wheels actually point.

c) Input is a weight of 2 lb; output is the weight of sugar which has been added to the box up to this point.

d) Input is a position of the pickup head closer to the center of the record than the inner edge of the grooves; output is the actual position of the pickup head on the record.

e) Input is desired temperature inside the refrigerator (setting on temperature dial); output is the actual temperature inside the refrigerator.

(Note: this is unrealistic, because the control is actually arranged to allow a certain lag—the pump goes on when the box is warmer than some selected level, and goes off after it drops below that level. Moreover, the control is usually actuated by gas pressure in the freezing coils, not by temperature at all. When the pressure rises too high, the pump is started to *reduce* this pressure, thus accelerating the rate of evaporation of the liquefied gas which, in evaporating, absorbs heat from the box. In the process, the gas which has been pumped off is liquefied and passed on to the cooling coils. An advantage of this method is that the pump doesn't start every time the refrigerator door is opened.)

5. The feedback mechanisms of examples (a), (b), and (c) are probably not familiar to most of the students. Therefore, it is suggested that if there are students who have experience in these feedback mechanisms, they should be asked to make a report to the class. A description of the feedback mechanisms of examples (d) and (e) is within the experience of most students and they can be assigned as homework questions. For example, most students have record players and can see that when the pickup arm nears the center of the record, a switch is operated mechanically (tripping action) and the pickup arm returns to the starting point. As for the refrigerator, see answer to Question 4 (e).

6. The sliding collar is connected to the steam inlet valve in such a way as to close it slightly if the sliding collar rises, and open it slightly if the collar falls.

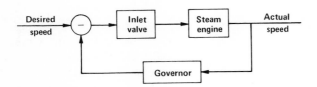

7. The cause is evidently feedback in the wrong phase ("positive feedback"). Aside from the electrician's usual effort to eliminate the cause by improved placement or "dress" of the wiring or even redesign of the circuit, it is possible to add a loop to provide enough negative feedback to balance out the positive feedback.

8. a)

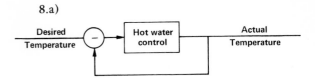

b) This is rather similar to the navigation problem shown in Fig. 7-18. Here the intermittent character of the feedback is equivalent to delay, as though it took 15 min for course correction to become effective.

In the shower case, let us assume that the water is initially too cold. The man in the shower wishes to avoid being scalded and so sets the valve for a temperature lower than the desired one. If, on the other hand, the water is already too hot, he will do the same thing in order to protect himself. Most people, of course, would step out of the spray and then make the adjustment with a correction factor *greater* than 1.

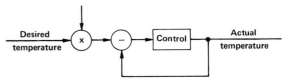

c) Because he underestimates the time delay, he will make a second warming adjustment after he supposes his first valve setting has produced its effect. This will result in the water presently getting too hot. Similarly, two cooling adjustments will make it too cold. And so on.

d) This is equivalent to a time delay. The first adjustment has no effect. Because of impatience, the second adjustment is probably overdone. Thereafter the situation continues to resemble that of (c).

9. a) There is no feedback. There is no comparison device to balance the actual backspin with what is needed.

b) There is feedback. The spring and gravity together always apply a force to the weight tending to return it to the rest position. Moreover, this force is always proportional to the distance between the instantaneous position of the weight and its rest position—but this fact is probably known only to physics students.

c) Except that the elastic rail exerts a restoring force proportional to the distance it has been distorted by the ball (much as in the previous case), there is no feedback, no goal seeking.

d)There is no feedback. The coin's weight actuates a mechanism which unlocks the door: straight cause and effect (unless there is a device to reject slugs, which does use feedback).

10.

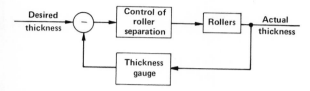

11.He might (for example) reach first for the hay, then decide that he was really too thirsty to eat, and swing his head toward the bucket; but then, before drinking, his hunger might get the upper hand and swing his head back. And so on.

12.

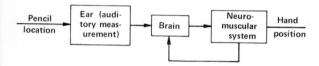

Since the only knowledge of the pencil's position comes from hearing it put down, this auditory clue must be compared in the brain with the neuro-muscular sensations which tell where the hand is. That is, the brain, not eyes or ears, is the comparator. The input and output are the same as in the ordinary case.

13.References for this question: *The Human Use of Human Beings,* by N. Wiener (Houghton Mifflin, 1950) has a good discussion with photographs in Chapter XI. In *Scientific American,* May, 1950, is "An Imitation of Life," by W. G. Walter, who has written also "A Machine that Learns" in the August, 1951, issue. Both of these include photographs and also a print of the electronic circuit he used.

These machines depend, evidently, on feedback loops. A bumper bar in front actuates a sequence of operations: stop, reverse, turn the guide wheels slightly to one side, go ahead again. Lowered battery voltage may permit a relay to open which throws one or more phototubes into operation, which, in turn, through a feedback circuit, aims the device toward a bright light. When the voltage has risen enough, a reversing switch causes the machine to back out of its kennel. A spring-loaded feeler sliding over the floor out in front could actuate the avoidance operation at a precipice.

14.a)The BMR is a measure of the rate at which a man is converting fat to energy internally. Temperature control is achieved by control of the metabolic rate through an endocrine gland which receives electrical signals from the brain, and so dictates an increased or decreased metabolism.

b)The muscles also provide a source of heat. If the skin detects a sharp drop in outside temperature, electrical signals are transmitted from the brain to the muscles to order shivering. Here adjacent muscles (the same ones normally used for motion or useful work) operate in an uncoordinated fashion, with the result that there is very little useful work and most of the energy is converted to heat. (Metabolism in the muscles also results in heat generation.)

c)The skin is used to effect changes in internal temperature in two ways. First, the blood flow to the surface of the skin can be controlled (this is called the vasomotor effect). When heat flow out of the body is to be decreased, less of the warm blood goes to the skin (e.g., during a cold shower). Second, sweating permits the loss of heat by evaporation, and is particularly important when the temperature of the surroundings is higher than the body temperature. (Dogs have very few sweat glands; they pant to increase evaporation from the tongue and the mouth.)

15.

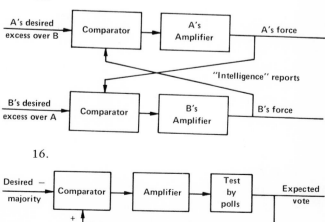

16.

The amplifier represents all such redoubled efforts as TV and radio spots, stump speaking, newspaper publicity, and handshaking. Notice the reversal of the usual signs in the comparator: if the expected vote minus the desired vote is negative, all this extra work must be done.

17. It is important for the students to remember that the input is the goal, not the actual situation. The goal may vary, from the most general (well-educated graduates) to fairly specific (graduates able to vote, read, and think intelligently) to highly specific (graduates able to program a computer, keep double-entry books, make a professional athletic team). The difficulty comes in actually describing the amplifier or correction system. More or better tests? More A/V aids? More interviews with the teacher? (Or maybe less of something?) The point is to get your young people thinking *constructively* about some facet of the educational system.

Problems

1.

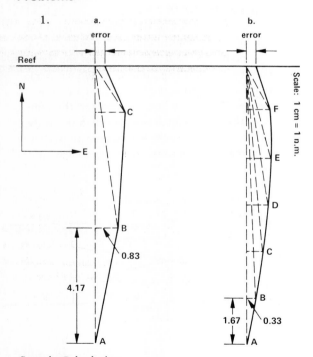

Sample Calculation:

a) For each 25-min interval
$\Delta d_{north} = (5/12)(10) = 4.17$ n.m.
$\Delta d_{east} = (5/12)(2) = 0.83$ n.m.

b) For each 10-min interval
$\Delta d_{north} = (1/6)(10) = 1.67$ n.m.
$\Delta d_{east} = (1/6)(2) = 0.33$ n.m.

2. $y = [20 (E_i - .009y) + E_n] \ 50$

$20 = [20 (E_i - .009(20)) + 2] \ 50$

$2 = [20E_i - 3.6 + 2] \ 5$

$2 = 100E_i - 8$

$E_i = 0.1$ volt

If there were no noise ($E_n = 0$)

$y = [20(E_i - .009y) + E_n] \ 50$

$y = [20(.1 - .009y) + 0] \ 50$

$y = [2 - .18y) \ 50 = 100 - 9y$

$y = 10$ volts

3. $y = (x + 0.05y) G$

$y = \dfrac{G}{1 - 0.05G} (x)$

a) If $G = 5$, $y = 6.7 (x)$
b) If $G = 10$, $y = 20 (x)$
c) If $G = 20$, $y = \infty (x)$

Not recommended.

4. $v = x - 0.03 \ y$

$w = v - 0.01y = x - 0.04y$

$y = 400w = 400x - 16y$

$17 y = 400 x; \quad y = \dfrac{400}{17} x. \quad \text{Gain} = \dfrac{400}{17} = 23.5$

5.

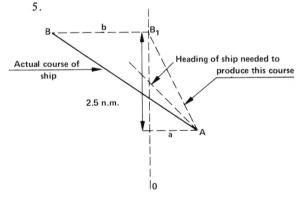

In 1/4 hr the ship drifts $P/4$ n.m. eastward; therefore $a = P/4$.

The course is then set for B_1 assuming that the current is $+P$. Actually the current is $-P$, so that instead of B_1 being $P/4$ to the east of the point for which the ship is headed, it is (or rather B is), $P/4$ to the west of that point, or 2P/4 to the west of the point marked B_1 on the diagram. Hence, $b = -P/2$.

On the next leg, the actual current is $+2P$ more than the expected $-P$. Hence, $c = +P/2$. The ship then continues indefinitely to oscillate back and forth between $+P/2$ and $-P/2$.

6. a) $y = 100x = \dfrac{1000}{1 + 1000B} x$

$B = 0.009$

b) $y = 10x = \dfrac{1000}{1 + 1000B'} x$

$B' = 0.099$

7. If the ambient temperature rises, the skin sensors detect this fact and feed it back to the brain. The latter orders sweating, but because of the raised relative humidity there is little evaporative cooling, and the core temperature will start to rise. The core sensors feed this in turn back to the brain, which issues signals to counteract the effect: blood flow to the skin for radiative cooling, and diminished metabolic rate.

8. $x = 20w = 2v$

$y = (2 - 0.2y)\, 400$

$\quad = 800 - 80y;\ 81y = 800$

$y = 9.88v$

$z = (9.88 - 0.4z)\, 100$

$\quad = 988 - 40z;\ 41z = 988$

$z = 24.1v$

D | DEMONSTRATIONS, LABS, AND PROJECTS

I. The Tantalizer

Equipment for Each Lab Team:

1 Tantalizer

1 sheet of paper with the rectangular design (about 2 × 3 in) duplicated on it

Several sheets of tracing paper, onion skin, or manifold paper

Plain white paper for block diagrams

PART A

Students are likely to find it easier to trace the pattern provided than to explain what is happening. A proper explanation is quite subtle.

PART B

Answers to Questions:

*1. The pencil and its image travel in the same direction, either to right or left (parallel to the abscissa of coordinate axes).

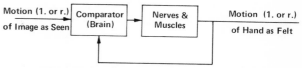

*2. Pencil and image both approach or withdraw from *the mirror* at the same time, hence on opposite sides and in opposite directions (parallel to y and $-y$, the ordinate of coordinate axes).

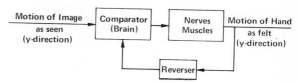

Hitherto, block diagrams have always involved magnitudes, and the function of the feedback process has been to reduce the difference to 0. Here the magnitudes (speeds) are always equal but the y-direction motions are 180° apart; that is, if one goes in the $+y$ direction, the other goes in the $-y$ direction. These can only be compared by (mentally) reversing one of them. Otherwise the error signal will always be 180°.

*3. When the pencil image is seen to move from 1 toward 3 on the diagram (left to right, and away from the mirror, hence away from the experimenter), the pencil itself should also move left to right and also away from the mirror, but therefore toward the experimenter. The brain has to manage to handle simultaneously a hand motion which matches that of the image and another motion of the hand which is opposite to that of the image, and similarly for motion from 4 to 2.

The confused feedback messages and the inability of the coordination system to handle the confusion often results in the situation of being unable to move the pencil at all, or of moving it at right angles to the desired direction, causing unwanted oscillations.

With practice and perseverance this can be overcome. This device is used to work with people who have left-right or up-down confusion in reading. Such people cannot readily distinguish between *b* and *d* or *p* and *q*. The forced concentration which this exercise provides is one system for helping to overcome this confusion.

II. A Triangulation Problem

In preparation for this exercise you will need to mark a line on the classroom floor which is as accurately parallel to one wall of the room as possible. To locate the line, locate its ends first, equally distant from the selected wall. Have a student hold one end of the tape measure, and both of you can agree when it is perpendicular to the wall (or use a carpenter's square). To mark the line is less easy. Chalk won't "take" on many floorings, and will scuff off in any case. Paint may not be welcomed by the authorities. If you can, insert a thumbtack at each end point, then you can stretch a length of white string just before the line is needed, and replace it if necessary.

To shorten the time needed for the exercise, you could measure the room yourself, make a scaled map, and distribute duplicated copies. This removes an interesting construction problem, which some will look upon as busywork, but it makes one source of error less important. If students do the work, they should collaborate on the measurements. Each group's results may be copied on the board, and the averages used in preparing the maps.

Here is the first laboratory exercise in which error of measurement seems to be important. Those of you who have a strong physics background may be tempted to discuss percentage errors in detail, but please resist the temptation. It is interesting to see *why* results are imperfect, but it is of no value in this course to worry about *how* imperfect they are.

Equipment for Each Lab Team (2 or more persons):

1 theodolite
1 protractor (the theodolite base can be used, but inconveniently)
Straightedge or foot rule
Drawing compass

It may cause less confusion in the room if only one set of equipment is available and is used by each lab team in turn. In this event a lab team may consist of 4 or 5 students, each bearing taken by a different student, so each has an opportunity to manage the instrument.

General Lab Supplies:

50-ft (or longer) tapeline
Carpenter's square (optional)
Spare thumbtacks
White string

PART A

Answers to Questions:

*3. If the 4 lines on the map intersect at one point, it is almost certain that results have been fudged. Failure in concurrence is caused by several errors: the theodolite's 0-180° line may not be accurately parallel to the reference line (check by actual measurement of distances from the ends of the instrument line to the reference line, first extending the former if possible); the sighting bar may have play at the axle (make numerous check measurements, each after resetting the bar); front and rear sights may not both have been properly focused by the eye (stand farther back); the theodolite scale may be badly divided (make 4 measurements each time, rotating the base 90° before each extra sighting, and average); the theodolite may have been unsteadily held (place it on a table); the protractor may have been carelessly set before drawing the lines on the map (use great care, and recheck the placement of the center point and of the scale angle each time before drawing the line); the pencil lines may be thick (sharpen the pencil).

*4. (Sample data)

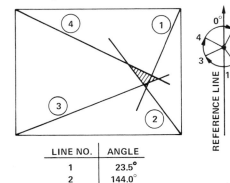

LINE NO.	ANGLE
1	23.5°
2	144.0°
3	248.0°
4	296.5°

The "error polygon" is shaded. One way to estimate actual location is to take the midpoint of the longer diagonal. It may be remarked that each of the lines drawn is actually uncertain in direction. This uncertainty is less uncertain if the landmark observed is near than if it is far (the diamond formed by the uncertainty lines from C and D is smaller than the one formed by lines from A and B):

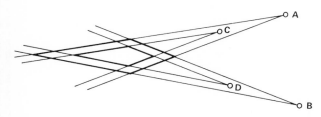

It is less important when two observations are nearly at right angles than otherwise (lines 1 and 4, or 2 and 3, on the sample map, or as shown here):

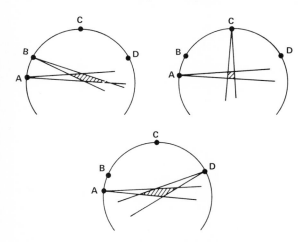

*5. The position may be marked on the map by setting the drawing compass to the (scaled) distance from one corner and swinging an arc. Repeat for one other corner. The intersection of the arcs marks the position. Using more than 2 corners will simply multiply confusions. You should accept any result which is not so grossly erroneous as to show failure to understand the process.

PART B

It may simplify the process if the "ship" can carry a small table or short stepladder to support the theodolite. The "navigators" need a foot rule and protractor as well as the scaled map. The chief problem in this part is to keep the theodolite's axis parallel to the reference line. This may be extended, if necessary, as far as the "reef" or a wall of the room.

Answer to Question:

*1. In Fig. 7-17 the starting point of the ship is directly "south" of the opening of the reef. Point *A* is indicated well to one side (a good place for it). In comparing the chart with the figure, this cause for the difference should of course be kept in mind.

III. Feedback for Disturbance Control

This experiment reinforces the algebra explained in Boxes 7-2 and 7-3, and will not be helpful if they have been omitted. It will be very useful, however, if any of your class have studied the boxes and are still confused. You may wish to use it as a demonstration for review.

Notice that in the first simulation the input to the summing-scalor which represents *B* should be to the x 10 jack; otherwise the amplifier will merely diminish. Having set the coefficient knob to a known value (say 0.5), then y should be $10 (0.5)x$. Now when u is added (and it can be either + or −), y is changed, as shown, to $10(0.5) (x \pm u)$.

The answer to the question that follows the addition of the noise signal—Why two amplifiers?—may be too brief for some of your class. The reason is that the feedback signal Cy diminishes x; amplifier A is inserted to counterbalance this effect. This should become clear to your students during the exercise.

Equipment for Each Lab Team:

> Analog computer
> High-impedance VM (if not included with the computer)
> Set of patch cords

If the experiment is done as a demonstration, a chart recorder is good, but it is not recommended for individual lab work.

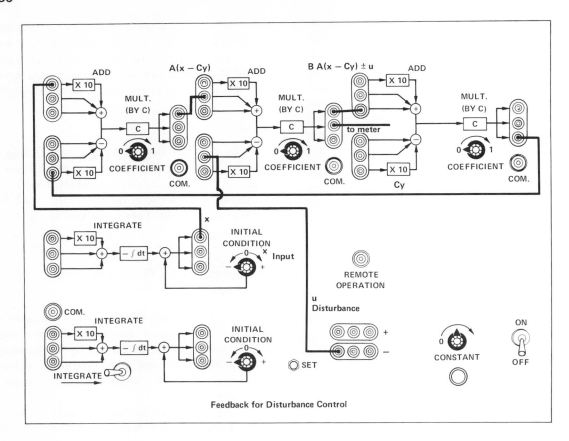

Feedback for Disturbance Control

Answers to Questions:

*1. $C = 1.4$ (approximately)

*2. $y = 0.45$ (a change of 0.05 volts)

*3. To retain y at 0.5 v, C would have to be lowered and A raised.

*4. (Do not let x be larger than 1.0 v, to avoid saturation.) With this equipment, we are likely to find that particular values of A and C work best for specific values of x and u; however, it remains true that feedback somewhat lessens the effect of disturbances (u) regardless of amplification factors.

IV. Feedback Control Systems

There are moments when this may seem to be a course in plumbing. In Chapter 4, Lab III, a simulation was shown of a tank-filling system with a hand-controlled valve, and Part A of the present exercise is identical, except that now the connection to the integrator should be made to insert a negative signal, so the tank will fill from the bottom up and not (apparently) from the top down. In Chapter 5, Section G, Part III of the Manual we presented a tank-filling simulation which had an automatic shut-off feature but showed no way to sense the liquid level in the tank; there was merely a predetermined maximum depth d. This was all right on the computer, but would work in reality only if some means were available to measure the error signal $d - h$. Part B of this exercise simulates the shutoff of an ordinary water closet controlled by a float, the needed sensor. Auto mechanics in the class will recognize this as the float mechanism in the carburetor.

In text Fig. 8, when the float goes up a certain distance, the valve will close. But how high is the "certain distance"? In general, this is determined by experiment. When he installs a water closet, the plumber will often bend the rod carrying the float until operation is satisfactory. The apparatus shown in Fig. 8 has a more elegant method: the adjustment of the screw that carries the pivot. Working out the details of the process in algebraic form is much too difficult for most students. This part of the exercise should be reserved as a project for a good student.

In the diagram below, we start with the control pivot at P_1 and the filler pipe shut off (float at F_1, valve at V_1). Now, in order to fill the tank further, the adjusting screw is backed off to raise the pivot to P_2, a distance p. The valve opens and water can flow in without any check until the float rises to F_2, a distance f, while the valve rises a distance v to V_2. (Further water flow will ultimately raise the

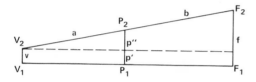

float enough to close the valve.) In what follows, we ignore the fact that the float really follows an arc, which introduces no serious error. The dashed line is parallel to the base line. It therefore cuts off a portion of p, labeled p', which is equal to v. The rest of p (p'') can be found as follows (a line parallel to one side of a triangle divides the other two sides proportionally):

$$\frac{p''}{f - p'} = \frac{a}{a + b}$$

$$p'' = \frac{a}{a + b}(f - p') = \frac{a}{a + b}(f - v)$$

But $\quad p = p' + p'' = v + p''$,

or $\quad v = p - p''$

$$= p - \frac{a}{a + b}(f - v)$$

$$= p - \frac{a}{a + b} f + \frac{a}{a + b} v$$

Then $v(1 - \frac{a}{a + b}) = p - \frac{a}{a + b} f.$

The left side reduces to $v \dfrac{a + b - a}{a + b} = v \dfrac{b}{a + b}$.

Measurement of an actual structure will show that a is only a small fraction of $a + b$ (perhaps 3/8 in vs 1 ft or about 3%). The error is therefore negligible and the algebra easier if we make the following approximations:

$$\frac{b}{a + b} \approx 1$$

$$\frac{a}{a + b} \approx \frac{a}{b}$$

Hence it is nearly true that

$$v = p - \frac{a}{b} f$$

$$= p - \frac{a}{b} b \qquad (1)$$

since f, the height the float is raised $= b$, is the depth of water added to the tank.

The volume of liquid already in the tank is $b_0 A$, where b_0 is the original depth and A is the area of the bottom. The volume added, Q, is therefore $Q = bA$; (the total volume is, of course, $(b + b_0)A$, or $b + b_0 = V/A$). Q is evidently the integral of the volume added per unit time, and this is proportional to the amount of valve that is lifted, which may be called Cv, C being the constant of proportionality.

$$Q = \int CV, \text{ or }$$

$$b = \frac{Q}{A} = \int \frac{C}{A} v \qquad (2)$$

Now substituting equation (1) into (2) we find that

$$b = \int \frac{C}{A}(p - \frac{ab}{b})$$

This is shown wired up in the diagram on page 182.

PART A

Answers to Questions:

*1.

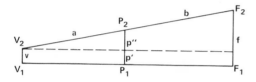

*2. See Chapter 4, Lab III. It is needless to wire this up again, and the wires need not be left since the new simulation is quite different.

*3. No. There is nothing to simulate the float-operated valve.

PART B

Answers to Questions:

*1.

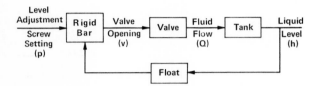

*2. See diagram below, wiring diagram at end.
*3. See labels on diagram below.
*4. The level screw adjustment, *p*, is the original control.
*5. The integrator controls the elapsed time.

V. Feedback and Instability

The reason for this experiment is plain, the instructions are clear, the game is fun. The only equipment needed is chalk and a blindfold. Remember that many people can see, even if blindfolded, by squinting down alongside the nose. This will be of no consequence here if the subject of the demonstration is required to keep his head inclined slightly forward so that he cannot see the board even if he knows the trick.

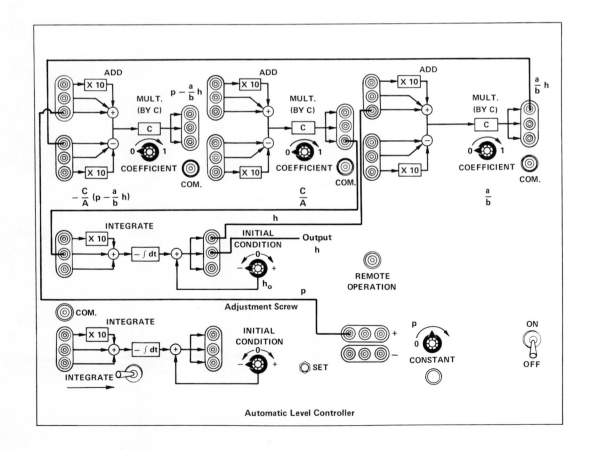

Block diagrams as required in Step 5, Part B:

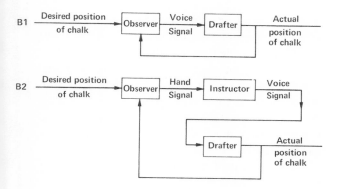

A2 Same but without input or feedback

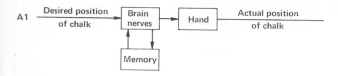

PART B

Answer to Questions:

*3.In Step 1 there is some feedback from storage in the memory to the part of the brain which issues orders to the arm-hand-finger system. There is none in Step 2 (except possibly the same brain-to-brain process, which offers no help in this case.

*4.Although we recognize feedback every time, it is by a path of increasing length and inaccuracy, with consequent delays; these are expected to cause instability.

VI. Unique Spring Scale (Classroom Demonstration)

This curious device is in a sense an application of the mechanical amplifier. An amplifier, however, puts out more work (force times distance) than its controller puts in. For simplicity, we used a static demonstration in Chapter 1, Lab II, Part B; no work was done, but forces were compared, and the machine became, technically, a transformer or coupler. Here we again have a coupler, not unlike a lever in its principle, in which the "effort" exerts a force, that of the spring, f, which is matched by the agency of the machine to another force. Since the

pulley divides the weight between the two strands of cord, this force is half the load, or $F/2$.

It will be recalled from the earlier experiment that the force exerted by a stretched spring is proportional to the amount it has been stretched. If we call the increase in length x, then

$$f = -kx$$

We can neglect the minus sign because we can handle directions differently. The matching process was accomplished by the mechanical amplifier, and we calculated the amplification factor, which was

$$A = \frac{\text{force exerted by amplifier}}{\text{force exerted by experimenter}}$$

If we examine the accompanying diagram, below, of the machine as used in the first part of the demonstration, we see that the load F is initially supported equally by 2 strands of cord; i.e., the weight F causes a tension $F/2$ in the cord, or the cord pulls down on the point P in the diagram with a force $F/2$. This force does not change when the amplifier motor starts, but friction between the drum and the cord causes a drag F_f clockwise which moves the point P up until $F_f = kx$. But $F_f = A\,F/2$, so

$$A\,\frac{F}{2} = kx + \frac{F}{2}$$

Hence $\dfrac{x}{F} = \dfrac{A-1}{2k}$, and the block diagram is

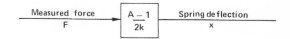

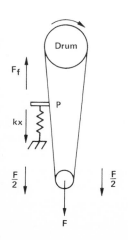

In the feedback case, we have acting on the pulley a downward force F, an upward force kx, and two upward forces each of which is the tension T in the cord.

$$2T + kx = F, \text{ or}$$

$$T = \frac{F - kx}{2}$$

Then, by the same argument as before, $F_f = kx + \frac{F - kx}{2}$, and

$$F_f = A \, \frac{F - kx}{2}$$

So $\quad \frac{F - kx}{2} + kx = A \, \frac{F - kx}{2}$

$$\frac{kx}{2}(A + 1) = \frac{F}{2}(A - 1)$$

$$\frac{x}{F} = \frac{A - 1}{k(A + 1)}$$

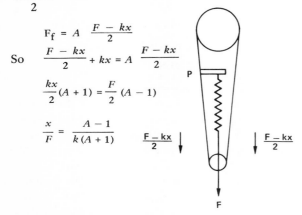

The block diagram now becomes:

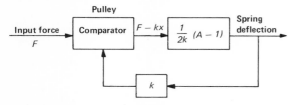

Equipment for Demonstration:

"Unique" spring scale
0.05-kg mass
Centimeter scale (preferably) or foot rule

Answers to Questions:

*3. With a simple spring balance, the addition of more force causes the suspension hook (at the bottom) to be pulled down by an amount proportional to the force. Here the addition of weight causes the hook at the top of the spring to rise. It might be rather useful to have this type of spring scale at a weighing station for trucks, so that the platform supporting the truck would not sink below the road level.

*7. Sample curve:

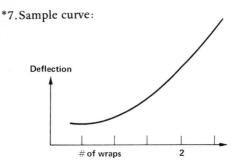

*8. By extrapolation, the result reached is about 6 or 7 times the deflection with 1/2 wrap.

*9. Without feedback, $x = AF/2k$; with feedback, $x = AF'/k \, (A + 2)$. If x is the same in each case, $AF/2k = AF'/k \, (A + 2)$, or $F' = (A + 2)F2$. Hence the force being measured on the scale with feedback is much larger (about $A/2$ times, very roughly) than the force on the scale without feedback.

*12. Movement of the spring can only be detected by close examination. To measure small weights, a very weak spring (with small k) should be used.

*17. Sample curve:

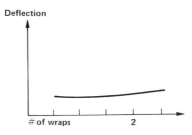

*18. This curve is much flatter. Increasing the amplification factor of the windlass causes almost no change in the reading of the balance. In fact, if $A \gg 1$, the scale with feedback is almost independent of the amplification, it is nearly true that $x/F = 1/k$ (or $F = kx$), which is the equation describing the behavior of an ordinary spring scale.

VII. Model of a Home-Heating System

This experiment gives students practice in using the analog computer to simulate the performance of systems. It also serves as a review of the heating system of Chapter 5, and a preview of the reappearance of that system in Section 5.

Before starting to model the system, the student should be given some new items of information. The teacher will decide which of the following are suitable for his particular class. The output of the comparator is evidently a temperature difference, whose magnitude and sign determine the action of the furnace. But the output of the furnace is *heat*. In a thermal system, temperature difference determines heat flow. Heat flows from the hot radiators to the cool rooms. The temperature of the air in the rooms depends on the amount of heat flow but also on the "thermal characteristics" of the air and of the rooms. In a physics course one would write $\Delta Q = mc\ \Delta t$, and thus $\Delta t = (1/mc)\ \Delta Q$. Here ΔQ stands for the thermal energy absorbed or the heat which flowed into the room: $1/mc$ is a factor depending on the "thermal characteristics." In the computer simulation, the error signal $T_d - T_a$ is

connected to the x 10 input to the integrator, as a means of indicating that the furnace is actually an amplifier (an outside source of energy controlled by a much smaller input). The factor 10 can be assumed to include also something like mc, and thus to lead to a rate of gaining heat (Btu/sec, for example). Then the integration gives the actual amount of heat supplied. Next the integrator part of the furnace is connected to a scalor, $1/k$ (which stands for 1/mc), and then a term is added to stand for the initial temperature.

Equipment for Each Lab Team:

> Analog computer
> High-impedance VM (unless supplied with computer), or Chart recorder (preferable)
> Patch cords

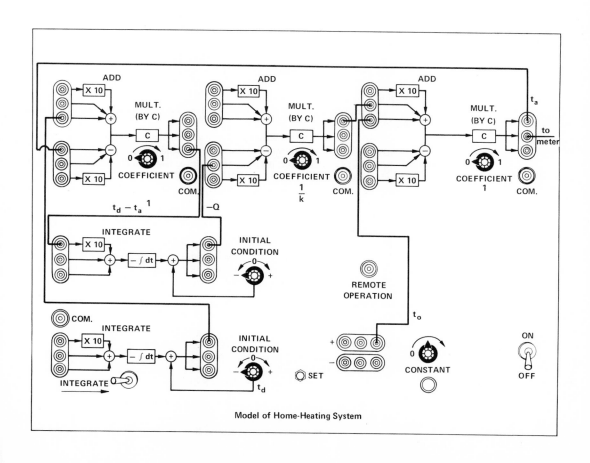

Model of Home-Heating System

Answers to Questions:

PART A

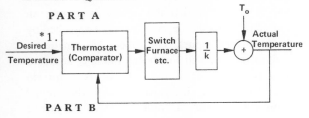

*1. Desired Temperature → Thermostat (Comparator) → Switch Furnace etc. → $\frac{1}{k}$ → + (T_o) → Actual Temperature

PART B

*1. The only important changes to be tried out are changes in the thermostat setting and in the ini-

tial temperature (it might be set low, comparable to a cold house in the morning). It will take a long time for T_a to equal T_d on the analog because the heat added per unit time grows less and less.

*2. No. A real furnace continues to run full blast until the thermostat turns it off. As implied in the answer to Q1, our model peters out, so to speak, along an exponential curve as in Fig. 4-35c.

E | EVALUATION

The questions in this section are rated according to the chapter objectives and the performance levels stated in the introduction to the teacher's manual. This group of questions is not intended to be all inclusive, but just as a guide to possible questions. Zeros in the chapter objective column indicate no chapter objective for this question.

Chapter Objective	Performance Level	*Judged to be Relatively Easy:*
		In each of the following cases, mark the statement T if it is true, but mark it F if it is false.
2	I	1. a) The input into a feedback system is the desired goal.
1-3	I	b) The error signal is what is obtained when output is subtracted from input.
3	II	c) The error signal changes the input.
7	I	d) When feedback is interrupted at intervals, the desired output is not always attained.
2	II	e) Feedback systems would be much better if a way could be found to eliminate the loop.
1	I	f) An unwanted disturbance signal is often called an error signal.
13	I	g) The only kind of instability that is really troublesome is oscillation.
6	I	h) If a car understeers it means that the driver has to pull harder on the wheel than he expects.
5	I	i) The evolution of plants and animals, as described by Charles Darwin, shows little or no evidence of the effect of feedback.
13	I	j) When a feedback signal is delayed in reaching the comparator, the system often becomes unstable.
6	II	k) Even a well-designed feedback system is helpless if the gain of the main amplifier drops below 50% of its original value.
15	II	l) The chief reason for making a model of the body's system for controlling the temperature of the core is to make the system easier to teach.
		In the remaining questions, check the best answer.
4	II	2. One way in which living things differ from nonliving is:
		a) Living things are controlled only by earlier events.
		b) Living things seek goals which are useful to them.
		c) Living things never change their goals.
		d) Living things expect to find their feedback comparators to show zero error.
		e) Living things make use of feedback only occasionally.
2	II	3. A pitcher throws the baseball and the batter makes a two-base hit.
		a) In this case the feedback has introduced an unwanted disturbance.
		b) The hit occurred because the pitcher failed to regulate the feedback to his delivery.

Chapter Objective	Performance Level	

Judged to be Relatively Easy:

c) This is not a good example of a feedback situation.

d) Here we have a case where the feedback sent the system out of control.

e) The batter has hoped for a hit, so this was a case of feedback for goal seeking.

2   **II**

4. When he makes a study of the pollution of the water in a river, an engineer may be taken as an example of a feedback system.

a) If he tells the newspapers that the phosphate content is 10 times what is normal for a river, his mind is the comparator in the system.

b) If he tells the newspapers that the phosphate content is 10 times normal, this is the output of the system.

c) The feedback loop in the system is the return of water to the headwaters by evaporation, condensation, and rainfall.

d) The amplifier of the system is the widely read newspaper account.

e) The phosphate content is a disturbing signal, the effect of which is diminished by feedback.

Judged to be More Difficult:

16   **II**

5. If a man becomes too cold, he often starts to shiver. The shivering may be considered to be the result of feedback which

a) produces a self-regulating system.

b) causes a disturbance (noise) signal.

c) results in goal seeking.

d) tends to cause automatic compensation.

e) has put the system out of control.

12   **II**

6. In this simple feedback system, if the input x and the signal y/K which is fed back were added in the comparator, the output y would be expected to

a) increase without limit.

b) oscillate.

c) shortly become 0.

d) quickly approach the input x.

e) become smaller than desired.

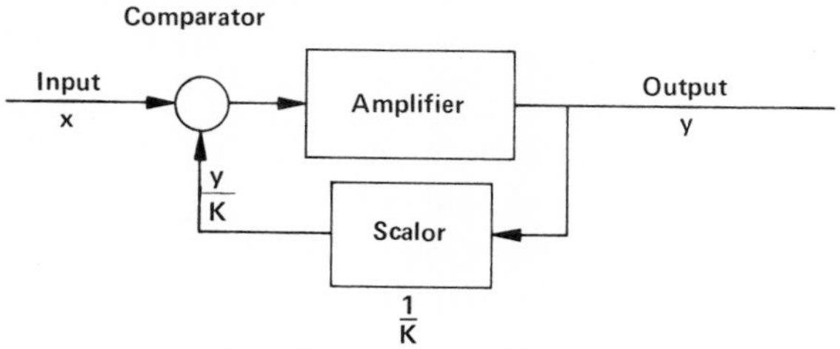

8   **II**

7. In this system, the known values are as shown. In order to find the magnitude of y, one should solve the equation

a) $y = 1 - \dfrac{1}{25} y$

b) $y = (1 - \dfrac{y}{25}) \, 100$

c) $y - \dfrac{100 \, y}{25} = 1$

d) $1001 - \dfrac{y}{25} = y$

e) $(1 - \dfrac{1}{25}) \, 100 = y$

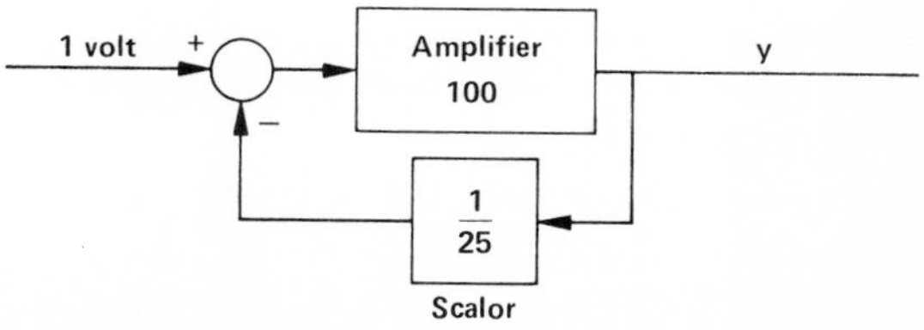

Chapter Objective	Performance Level	Judged to be More Difficult:
11	II	8. One way to diminish the likelihood of instability in a system is to cut down the amount of feedback. An undesirable result of this measure might be that

        a) the magnitude of the output signal would diminish.
        b) the input signal would grow smaller.
        c) a new goal for the system would have to be set.
        d) the feedback has now become a disturbance signal.
        e) the output signal would become more variable.

Answers to Evaluation Questions:

1. a) T   e) F   i) F
   b) T   f) F   j) T
   c) F   g) F   k) F
   d) T   h) T   l) F

2. b

3. c

4. a

5. d

6. a

7. b

8. e

F | FILMS

F-0701 INTRODUCTION TO FEEDBACK

Recommendation: Highly recommended for development of this concept.

Application: Concept development. Use early in the chapter.

Length and Type: 10 min, color, sound.

Source: #2 (Ask for free IBM films.)

Summary: This film does not go into technical detail, but shows the wide application of feedback in many fields. The cycle of measuring, evaluating, and correcting is illustrated, and the consequences of overcorrecting are pointed out.

F-0702 THE CONTROL REVOLUTION

Recommendation: Good film for illustration of closed-loop control systems.

Application: Enrichment. Best used after some discussion of feedback.

Length and Type: 30 min, b & w, sound.

Source: #8

Summary: Starts with animated pictures of a modern control system, using the thermostat as a simple example. Most of the pictures have to do with control systems built around digital computers, and the point is repeatedly made that release of management from routine decision-making frees it to consider the really hard problems.

G | GENERAL

I. Bibliography

N. Wiener, *Cybernetics.* M.I.T. Press, 1961 (2nd edition) (B) (paper)

> Chapters 2 and 3 are largely unreadable except to genuine mathematicians. The introduction (much interesting history) and Chapter 1 are fine. Chapter 4 requires the reader to broadjump across notational booby traps. All the rest is comprehensible (with brief exceptions) and well worth the trouble. Wiener was not only the inventor of the word in the title, but also was at least even with von Neumann, if not ahead of him, in foreseeing the future of the stored-program computer.

W. A. Lynch and J. G. Truxal, "Control-System Engineering." *International Science and Technology,* March, 1966

> In particular, the impossible problem of maneuvering a VTOL aircraft without the aid of computer control aided by feedback.

R. Bellman, "Control Theory." *Scientific American,* September, 1964

> Particularly on the use of mathematics and control with the aid of computers. Reflective and somewhat philosophical.

O. Mayr, "The Origins of Feedback Control." *Scientific American,* October, 1970.

> Surprising results of historical studies, which trace the subject much farther back than ordinarily expected. A water-clock flow-regulator in Greece, third century B.C. A wine dispenser by Hero of Alexandria (the early steam turbine man), first century A.D. Then the Arabs, the Dutch, the British, etc., etc.

"Automatic Control." *Scientific American,* September, 1952, entire issue.

> A. Tustin, "Feedback," including much on oscillations, rabbit-lynx population, nervous system, economics. G. S. Brown and D. P. Campbell, "Control Systems," rolling steel, locking radar to target, ruling engine for diffraction gratings. Other articles on automatic petroleum refinery, control of machine tools, the role of the computer (just at the start of the transistor revolution), information processing, effect of all this on people.

II. Demonstrating Feedback

The match game of Chapter 2, Lab III, illustrates a kind of feedback, since as the game progresses each player reacts (with increasing tension) to the other's play. An alternative and rather simpler game of the same kind is Nim. Here one sets out any number of matches (except a number which can be written as $6n + 1$), and each player, picking up from 1 to 5 in turn, tries to force the other to take the last match. The winning algorithm (if you play first): mentally divide the number of matches by 6. For your first play, take one less than the remainder. Thereafter, at each play pick up 6 minus what the other player just took. Thus your next-to-last play leaves 7 on the board and you can win whatever he does. This is evidently pure feedback: comparison of an output signal and a desired-result signal to generate an error signal, which determines your play.

CHECK LIST FOR CHAPTER 8

STABILITY

APPROX. TIME: Text: 10 days Lab.: 2 days

A. APPROACH	CLASS PERIODS	B. BLACK & WHITE TRANSPARENCIES	C. CUES (k=key problem) Discussion Questions	Problems Easy	Problems Medium	Problems Hard	D. DEMONSTRATIONS, LABS & PROJECTS	E. EVALUATION	F. FILMS	G. GENERAL
1. Introduction	1		1,2,3,16		4k,5k		I	5		
2. Skyscrapers Beget Skyscrapers								1a	0801	
3. Stability in Traffic Flow	1	0801 0802	4,5					1b, 2		
4. The Black Death	3	0803a-c 0804 0805a, b						1c		
5. Epidemic Model			6,7,9,10, 11, 12		1k, 2			1d,3,6		II
6. An Improved Epidemic Model	1-2	0806a-d 0807a, b	8,13,14 15		6	3				
7. Law of Supply and Demand	2	0808 0809 0810 0811 0812a,b 0813a,b 0814a,b		7,8k	9			1e,4,7		
8. Instability in Physical Systems	1/2	0815 0816 0817 0818	18				II, III	1f, 1g	0802	III, IV, V
9. Uses of Instability	1		17					1h		
10. Final Comment										

Stability

8

A | APPROACH

I. Purpose and Organization of the Chapter

> The best laid schemes O'mice and men
>   Gang aft a-gley.

These famous lines from Burns have become a cliché, but generally we go no farther. We don't ask, Why do they? This chapter gives a glimpse of the kind of reasoning which enables a systems analyst to predict that one structure (organization, plan, set of events) will prove to be unstable and another stable, and contains hints of his ways of turning the first into the second. The topic is enormously important, especially in its political, economic, and social applications. It is unfortunate that too little attention has been given to rules or algorithms for these non-physical aspects of our world.

In this chapter we develop the concepts of stability and instability by contrasting business-district buildings before and after the invention of the skyscraper. Then we go on to study traffic patterns, epidemics (introduced by the history of the Black Death), the Law of Supply and Demand, and one or two physical systems, always contrasting the conditions of stability and instability. As a final twist, we learn that even instability has its uses.

II. Objectives for Students

Upon completion of the activities, discussion, and reading in this chapter, students should be able to:

1. Recognize and identify the following terms: *Black Death, bubonic plague, center of gravity, instability, operating point, stability,* and *torque.*

2. Explain what the term *equilibrium* means, in the case of particular systems.

3. Describe the effect of a disturbance on a system in (a) stable equilibrium; (b) unstable equilibrium.

4. Distinguish between stable and unstable equilibrium in such systems as (a) a real-estate market, with reference to a change of building styles; (b) a stream of traffic.

5. Explain how public understanding of the technologies used is necessary for successful application of systems to control economic or social instabilities.

6. Calculate in detail, from information about rate of infection, the expected course of an epidemic (using a simple model that does not include recovery rate).

7. Translate into ordinary speech the details of a block diagram of an epidemic ("Improved Model").

8. Predict by calculating the critical number of

susceptibles, whether or not the onset of a disease in a population will lead to an epidemic.

9. Justify the employment of immunization or of quarantine in controlling an epidemic.

10. Prepare and interpret graphs which represent various business strategies, of both buyer and seller.

11. Infer from general principles whether a particular combination of such strategies leads to stability, instability, or a "neutral" cyclic state.

12. Identify the parts played by gravitational force and other forces in producing stability or instability in simple physical systems (pendulum, levers, and the like).

13. Cite examples of useful instabilities.

14. Interpret such statements as: "Stability is undesirable in the economic status of the world's population."

III. Suggestions for Teaching

The basic idea of stability is familiar; that of an unstable equilibrium perhaps is not. Instability has a bad name which is not always deserved. Remember the punch line on the first page of Chapter 6: *"Change* is essential in an interesting, exciting, and challenging life." Consider, for instance, the familiar pattern of planetary winds. The stable trade wind belt can be rather boring. The fun and thrills come in the stormy westerlies, where the weather patterns are typically unstable; even the instability is unstable, and sometimes we have a week at a time without variation.

Stability demonstrations can be found in most science departments, especially physics, physical science, or elementary science. One of the best examples, for our purpose, is the Tower of Pisa, which is stable without its top story but not in equilibrium at all when the top story is added. This suggests an interesting project. Let a student drill an axial hole part way into a wooden cylinder, cut off the ends of the cylinder along two parallel planes at an angle of 70° or so with the axis. Put some lead shot into the hole and then plug it with a dowel. If the depth of the hole and the weight of the shot are right (plenty of room for experiment here), the cylinder is stable when set on one end but will tip over when set on the other. Analysis shows that the center of

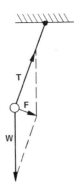

gravity of the weighted cylinder should be less than 1.5 diameters (nearly) from the lower base, measured along the axis, if the bases are at 70° with the axis. The simple pendulum is a good example of stable equilibrium, because the weight of the bob and the tension of the supporting wire always combine to exert a restoring force when the bob is displaced in any direction. One of the best demonstrations of unstable equilibrium is the familiar supersaturated solution of photographer's hypo (hydrated sodium thiosulfate, $Na_2S_2O_3 5H_2O$). To prepare this, put a couple of hundred grams or so of the compound into a 250-ml Erlenmeyer flask and cover its mouth with a bit of aluminum foil. Warm the flask in a bath of boiling water until the contents are *completely* liquid, pour into at least 3 or 4 test tubes (because 1 or more are likely to crystallize on cooling), and then set them aside until they have reached room temperature. The test tubes should also be covered with foil to keep out dust. It is a good idea to insert thermometers through the foil because the evolution of heat when the liquid freezes is quite noticeable. If you have difficulty preparing the supersaturated liquid, a *small* amount of water (10 or 20 ml) may be added before melting the hypo. Each of the tubes is seeded in front of the class with a tiny crystal of hypo and the liquid hypo will promptly solidify. The test tubes can be inverted to prove it.

The exponential growth of population studied in Chapter 4 is another example of instability, where the "small disturbance" was a birth rate greater than the death rate. Some other examples of instability: the stressed rocks on either side of a fault just before the slip that causes an earthquake; a nuclear chain reaction; plants and animals in ecological equilibrium which is upset by introducing a foreign population (e.g., Australia when rabbits were imported; Jamaica, to which the mongoose was imported in an initially successful effort to eliminate rats, after which the Indian animal became a worse pest); the start, and then the end, of the Pleistocene ice age; panics on the stock market; the rise to the best-seller lists of occasional books unnoticed, or panned, by critics.

Two of the three demonstrations and labs (like many of the suggestions just given) are classified to go with Section 8 on the check list. However, since only Lab II depends upon specific remarks in the text, the other may easily be inserted at whatever moment is convenient.

Section 1. Introduction. Call attention to the term *operating state*, which occurs repeatedly in the chapter. It is a term hard to define concisely, but its usage will make its meaning clear to the forewarned reader.

Section 2. Skyscrapers Beget Skyscrapers. In the real-estate business of city business districts before the turn of the century, there was a stable operating state. The shift from this to instability with the invention of the skyscraper is quite important as an illustration of the basic phenomenon. It is hardly important at all for its own sake today, but call attention to the fact that stability was achieved again, once a new operating state was achieved. This operating state describes the situation when all structures, practically speaking, within a certain area had become skyscrapers. This way of building was no longer a threat nor bitterly resented; it had become normal and was expected. A drawback to the skyscraper subculture, not mentioned in the text, is the increasing difficulty of getting its occupants there in the morning, and home at night. The city transportation system goes into an unstable state, motor traffic becomes impossible, even sidewalks are clogged. Some architects and some of the corporations which build skyscrapers are conscious of this problem, but it is rare indeed to find more than token efforts to solve it. It is even doubtful whether it can be solved at a price the taxpayers are willing

to pay. The essential lesson to be drawn from the section is the contrast between the effect of a disturbance on a stable system and on an unstable system. This is the best place to demonstrate the two conditions with a pendulum and with a solution of hypo. In addition there are a great many examples of instability in economic life. Consider the effect of the automobile on the horse-and-buggy era in transportation, on the petroleum industry, on the organization of labor, on the railroads. Here as in many other cases the complications and ramifications are nearly impossible to keep track of. Again, petroleum largely replaced coal as a raw material for synthetic dyes, after which chemists went on to pharmaceuticals, plastics, fertilizers; botanists at the same time were developing improved varieties of food plants; fertilizers plus better seeds plus tractors from the automobile industry meant fewer farmers were needed to raise more crops, and the United States population shifted from being chiefly rural to being chiefly urban. And so on and on.

Section 3. Stability in Traffic Flow. All of this descriptive matter must be familiar to everybody who rides in a car or watches television. The term *stability* in this context had better be defined. It means that people can drive ahead at a fixed speed without needing to use the brakes. It is evident that a flow of traffic which is stable at 40 mph might not be at 60 mph, and vice versa, which is the reason for setting minimum speed limits as well as maximum speed limits on many expressways. The little story of the transition to stability as the author drives home each evening may be taken to exemplify another lesson, repeatedly met in this course: the frequent unexpectedness of the results of a small change. Such shifts from instability to stability are less often noticed, however, than the more dramatic shifts in the opposite direction.

Section 4. The Black Death. These pages are intended to show why a study of epidemics may be far more important than one might suppose from everyday experience in school. There is little reason to spend much time on them in class (note T-0801 and 0802). Students with an interest in looking more deeply into the history of the situation will probably enjoy reading the P. Ziegler and W. L. Langer items listed in the Bibliography of this chapter.

Section 5. Epidemic Model. Even though this model is admitted (in Section 6) to be unrealistic, it is worth spending enough time and care to be sure that everybody is clear about the way it is developed, if only to be certain that the class will understand the improved model. But work it all out as a team operation, teacher and class together, before assigning any text. The chances are that even the nonmathematical will readily buy the idea that R_i is not proportional to the sum of s and i, but to their product (though clearly N *equals* their sum). There is no need to insist on the use of 0.01 as a proportionality factor, but it is plausible, easy to use, and makes it possible to leave out a k. There are many facets of this infectious factor; among them are: crowding of population, air quality, climate, and virulence of infection. As a matter of fact, the prediction of when the infection will reach maximum is affected by many seemingly unrelated factors. For example, the 1968 flu epidemic in New York City reached its peak earlier than predicted from the model because the oil truck drivers went on strike in early December and many people were in crowded apartments with reduced heating during an unusual cold snap. From here on use the set of overlays T-0803a, b, and c. To make the algebra less confusing, the definitions of the variables are listed as they appear. Then work out the calculation of Table 8-1. T-0804 provides the table headings for projection on the board, where the numbers can be written in (or on the transparency itself if preferred, or you can duplicate this master and distribute it to the class for use in making copies of the table). T-0805a is a graph form on which to plot the results, and T-0805b is an overlay to make it into Fig. 8-7, but with s plotted too. Notice its resemblance to the sigmoid of Fig. 4-33 (or T-0412).

Section 6. An Improved Epidemic Model. In this section we look at the epidemic from a much more realistic position, using the rate of recovery of those infected. Again, the factor of recovery (0.1 in the example) depends on many things, amount of medical aid available, strength of medicines, general level of health of the population, and possible isolation of infected people from the susceptible group. The set of overlays T-0806a-d can be used as you did T-0803a-c, and T-0807a and b are comparable to T-0805a and b. However, working out Table 8-2 in detail is likely to prove much more of a chore than is needed. It is worth noticing that although this model is a feedback chart, there is a change in terminology: N, called the input, is hardly the desired state or goal. But what is the goal? If you are involved with a time-sharing computer system which uses BASIC Language, it would be quite useful to have a student program it to simulate this epidemic model. Now it becomes possible to alter such parameters as original population, infectious factor, and recovery factor to find out their possible effects on the stability or instability of the epidemic system. This is much more satisfactory than having the students do the mathematics by hand. The computer study will be helped if you have examined Box 8-2; this is well worth pursuing with your class if they are at ease with symbols, computer connection or none; or it can be assigned to some of your better students in order to give them a new insight into the reasons for immunization or quarantine.

Section 7. Law of Supply and Demand. This is a complicated and puzzling story (to be omitted if necessary, but it might be offered to your class as a challenge). Notice, to begin with, the reasons assigned for studying the example (in the "Final Comment" part of this section), particularly that it is a new illustration of stability and instability, and an example of what can be learned by "relatively simple" analysis. The classroom approach should certainly depend heavily on the use of the overhead projector. Transparencies T-0808 − T-0814 duplicate most of the diagrams in the book; but Fig. 8-12 (T-0810) is offered with no labels. It can be used in advance to develop the ideas of stability or instability of business strategies, or alternatively afterward as review and on-the-spot testing. A suggested value of A_1 is provided (but not placed as in Figs. 8-13 and 8-14). T-0812 − T-0814 appear without "spider webs," which are provided as overlays. It would be less complex, perhaps, to use only 5 unlabeled curves to be overlaid in pairs; but it was felt that you would find yourself pulling out the wrong sheet if you had to divide your attention between your class and a series of unlabeled (or only partially labeled) transparencies. Incidentally, the 3 combinations mentioned but not illustrated can be shown by using T-0811 — T-0813 and temporarily reversing the labels for Crafty and Discount.

A helpful tip: Discount always starts; he orders. The price, however, is always set by Crafty to fit this order, and the price governs Discount's next order. In other words, the first line is drawn from A_1 vertically *to the Crafty curve.* The second line runs horizontally to the Discount curve, and so on. At first glance, the initial step appears artificial and inexact. Who puts an order in before he knows the price? But each illustration must start somewhere, and after the first action-reaction pair, every order is made with knowledge of the existing price, and every price is set with reference to the current market. But rules like this probably should not be shared with the class; their task is not to learn to draw spider webs but to understand whether the system is stable, neutral, or unstable, and why, in terms of the mutual influence of Crafty's prices and Discount's purchase orders.

Section 8. Instability in Physical Systems. The aerodynamic instability described here is also of-fered as a laboratory demonstration, which should probably be shown in advance of any discussion. There is a fairly detailed treatment in Section G, Part IV ("Stability, Instability, and Oscillators"). F-0802 is a dramatic and most useful aid in this part of the work, showing an actual case of destructive aerodynamic instability: the wreck of the Tacoma Narrows Bridge. Before showing the film loop, tell the class to look for the 8-ft-high girders that made up the sides of the bridge span. Since the roadway was 2800 ft long and only 2 lanes wide, the narrow steel ribbon had what engineers call a span-to-depth ratio of 350:1. The ratio was double the span-to-depth ratio of any bridge in existence at that time or since the collapse. The Golden Gate Bridge had a span-to-depth ratio of about 175:1, and it has been stiffened since November, 1940, the date of the now famous collapse.

Section 9. Uses of Instability. Refer to the Teacher's Manual for Section 7 of Chapter 7. The electric buzzer exemplifies useful instability, and so does the ticking pendulum. The ticking pendulum would evidently be stable, and seeking its equilibrium position, if it were not for the repeated application of force from the drive weight.

Section 10. Final Comment. No comment is needed here.

B | BLACK AND WHITE TRANSPARENCIES

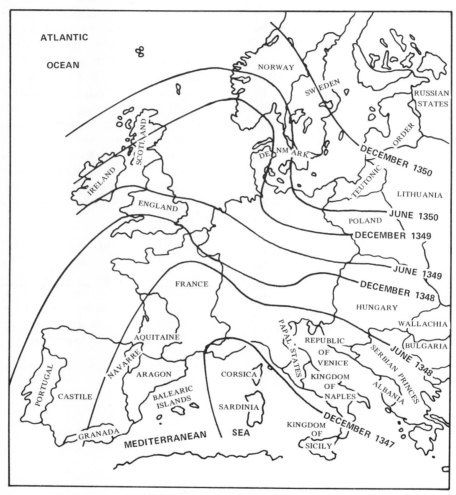

T-0801   SPREAD OF THE BLACK DEATH

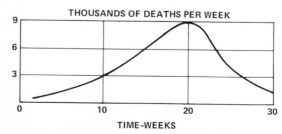

T-0802   BLACK DEATH: LONDON DEATH RATE

N = Number in population
i = Total number infected
s = Total number susceptible

T-0803a BLOCK DIAGRAM, SIMPLE EPIDEMIC MODEL

T-0803b BLOCK DIAGRAM, SIMPLE EPIDEMIC MODEL

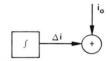

T-0803c BLOCK DIAGRAM, SIMPLE EPIDEMIC MODEL

Day Number	i at start of day	s = 100 − i	si	$R_i = 0.01si$	$\triangle i = R_i \times 1$	i at end of day
1						
2						
3						
4						
5						
6						
7						
8						
9						
10						

T-0804 HEADINGS FOR TABLE 1

198

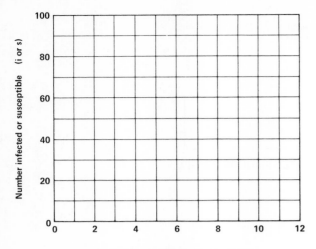

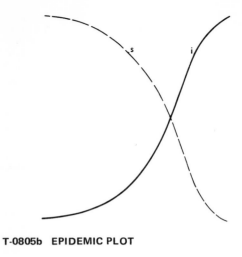

T-0805b   EPIDEMIC PLOT

T-0805a   GRAPH FORM FOR EPIDEMIC PLOT

T-0806a   IMPROVED EPIDEMIC MODEL

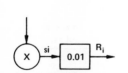

T-0806b   IMPROVED EPIDEMIC MODEL

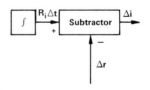

T-0806c   IMPROVED EPIDEMIC MODEL

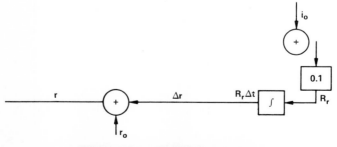

T-0806d   IMPROVED EPIDEMIC MODEL

199

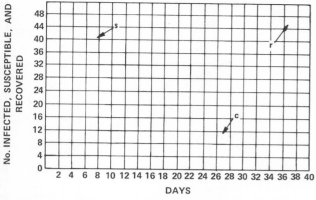

T-0807a GRAPH FORM, IMPROVED EPIDEMIC PLOT

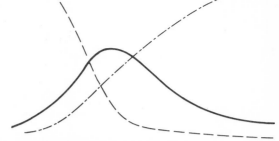

T-0807b ADVANCED EPIDEMIC PLOT

Discount's Probable Buying Strategy

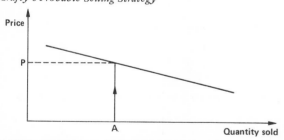

Crafty's Probable Selling Strategy

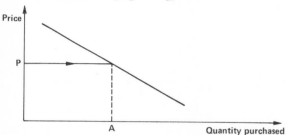

T-0808 PROBABLE STRATEGIES FOR CRAFTY AND DISCOUNT

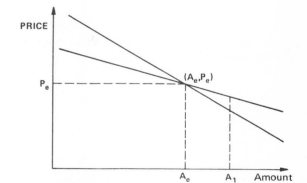

T-0810 TWO STRATEGIES

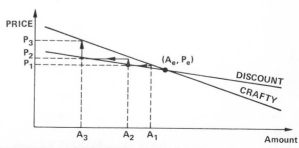

T-0809 STABLE AND UNSTABLE EQUILIBRIUM FOR CRAFTY AND DISCOUNT

Discount's Improbable Buying Strategy

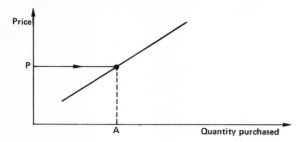

Crafty's Improbable Selling Strategy

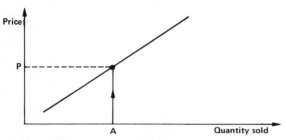

T-0811 IMPROBABLE STRATEGIES FOR CRAFTY AND DISCOUNT

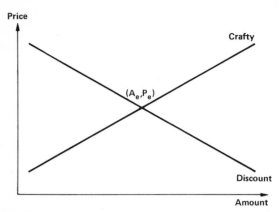

T-0812a CRAFTY'S UNLIKELY STRATEGY WITH DISCOUNT'S LIKELY STRATEGY (SLOPES HAVE EQUAL MAGNITUDE)

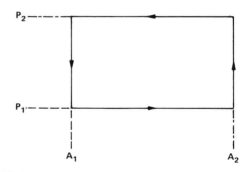

T-0812b CRAFTY AND DISCOUNT, EQUAL SLOPES

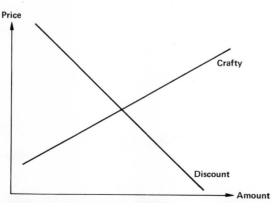

T-0813a CRAFTY'S UNLIKELY STRATEGY WITH DISCOUNT'S UNLIKELY STRATEGY (DISCOUNT'S SLOPE HAS GREATER MAGNITUDE)

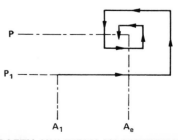

T-0813b CRAFTY, UNLIKELY, VS STEEPER DISCOUNT

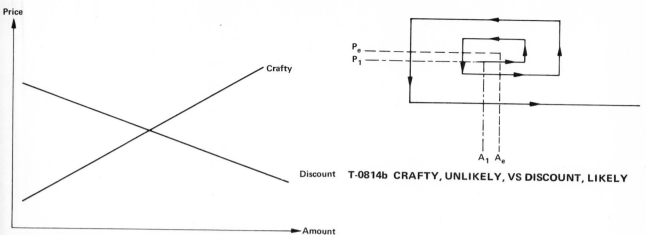

T-0814a CRAFTY'S UNLIKELY STRATEGY WITH DISCOUNT'S LIKELY STRATEGY (DISCOUNT'S SLOPE HAS LESSER MAGNITUDE)

T-0814b CRAFTY, UNLIKELY, VS DISCOUNT, LIKELY

| | Going Down | | | | Going Up | |
a	v	x	Positions	x	v	a
Maximum −	Instantaneous 0	Maximum +	Top	Maximum +	Instantaneous 0	Maximum −
Shrinking −	Growing −	Shrinking +	Half Way	Growing +	Shrinking +	Growing −
Instantaneous 0	Maximum −	0	Middle	0	Maximum +	Instantaneous 0
Growing +	Shrinking −	Growing −	Half Way	Shrinking −	Growing +	Shrinking +
Maximum +	Instantaneous 0	Maximum −	Bottom	Maximum −	Instantaneous 0	Maximum +

T-0815 CHART OF SPRING-MASS ACTION

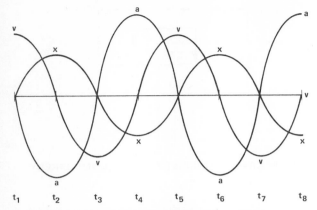

T-0816   GRAPHS FOR SPRING-MASS ACTION

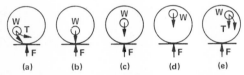

T-0817   BALANCED AND UNBALANCED WHEELS

T-0818   BRIDGE ROCKER FOR EXPANSION JOINTS

C | CUES TO QUESTIONS AND PROBLEMS

Questions for Study and Discussion

1. The principal idea is that motorists flock to a new road because of its speed, lack of red lights, comfort, and safety. When they are forced to leave at either end, they must follow already-existing highways which are inadequate for the greatly increased traffic, become choked, and as a result a public outcry arises for improvement. Each added segment of superhighway-type exit road simply transfers to its remote end the same old conditions. A similar situation exists in the case of the entrance roads, of course, because they are the same roads as those used for exit. It is worth noticing that a highway built with 2 traffic lanes each way may foster so much use that it has to be widened to 3, then to 4 lanes, etc. A second point is that people making long trips tend to use superhighways and resent it when they must use older roads between superhighway segments; this promotes the integration of interconnecting superhighway networks.

2. Assuming that the stable situation for a particular highway is cars traveling at 50 mph, we can then consider the slowing down of traffic as instability. If the original disturbance, the entrance of cars onto the highway, does not reduce the speed of the cars, then the system is stable. However, if the entrance of cars reduces the speed of the cars already there, then the system is unstable. Some forces (factors) which tend to drive the system toward or away from stability are traffic density, road conditions, weather, and accidents.

3. An obvious example of an unstable system which is not discussed in the text is an uncontrolled nuclear reaction (e.g., an atom bomb). When the fission material (fuel) is above the critical mass, a neutron (disturbance) can set off a chain reaction (unstable system). The forces (inputs) which drive the system away from stability are extra neutrons resulting from the splitting of nuclei. These neutrons are able to split other nuclei and cause a chain reaction if the amount of fissionable material is above the critical mass.

4. Information on the number of cars on a controlled stretch of highway is communicated to a computer in which are stored the model (maximum number of cars for the system to remain stable) and current data on weather, time of day, and location of accidents or stalled cars. The computer then analyzes the information and transmits appropriate control signals to the traffic lights at each entrance of the highway.

5. One fundamental limitation of a traffic-control system is derived from the necessity for achieving public acceptance. If motorists are expected to wait at a traffic light at an entrance to a superhighway, they would like to understand the reason behind the wait. Another major limitation is the interaction of the controlled system with other parts of the total automobile transportation system.

6. The forces (factors) which tend to drive an epidemic toward instability are:
   a) Number of susceptible persons
   b) Number of infected persons
   c) Degree of contact of infected persons with susceptible persons
   d) Long contagious period
   e) Bad hygienic conditions in the region.

7. The forces (factors) which tend to drive an epidemic toward stability are:
   a) Number of immune persons
   b) Quarantine of infected persons
   c) Short contagious period
   d) Good hygienic conditions.

9. The number (0.01) in ($R_i = 0.01si$) can be determined from data of previous epidemics of a particular disease. The constant could be computed if R_i, i, and s from a previous epidemic were known. The use of the computer can provide a more reliable constant in two ways:
   a) Trying out different constants to see which results in data which fit the real epidemic.
   b) If data from previous epidemics are incomplete or inaccurate, a computer simulation using data concerning factors which affect epidemics could be programmed. Data from this type of simulation could then be used to compute the constant which relates R_i, i, and s.

10. For the first 3 days, the graph in Fig. 8-7 does not show that an epidemic is imminent. The main reason is that the slope of the curve is very gradual. After 5 days an epidemic appears imminent because the graph shows that the rate of growth of the number of people infected has increased appreciably.

11. Since Fig. 8-7 is a graph for the simplified epidemic model, the flattening out is caused by the whole population having become infected. The same question asked about Fig. 8-9 would have a different answer. That curve reaches a maximum and then decreases. This occurs when $\Delta i = 0$ because the epidemic model has been improved to include the recovery rate. The comparison of Fig. 8-7 and 8-9 might be a good quiz question for this section of Chapter 8.

8.

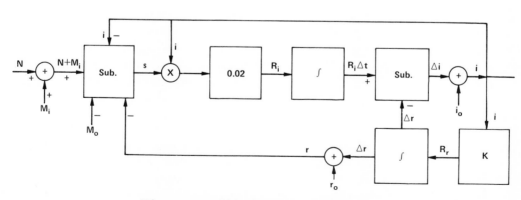

K is a constant which relates R_r (recovery rate) to i.
In other words, $R_r = Ki$.

12. Since Fig. 8-7 plots i vs t for only 10 days and all the people are infected after 10 days, the fact that people recover and become immune 10 days after the infection would not affect Fig. 8-7 at all. However, if the time base were extended to 20 days, then the number infected would decrease after 10 days and become 0 at the end of 20 days.

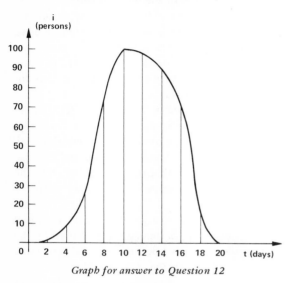

Graph for answer to Question 12

13. After 1 year the population (N_1) will be N_0 plus the increase for that year (Δn):

The problem requires us to compute Δn. We know the change in population per annum per 100 (R_i); it is $P_i + R_b - P_o - R_d$, which we can symbolize with a summer:

But to turn this into rate of increase per annum of the whole population (R_n) we must multiply by 1% of the population for the year in question (N_t):

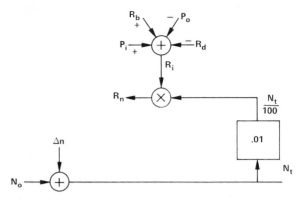

Now to find the actual increase for each year in succession (Δn) we must integrate R_n to give $R_n \Delta t = \Delta n$, which we have already used to get N_t:

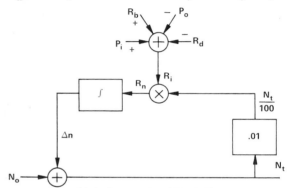

This is the completed block diagram

14. No. In New York many (if not most) people have been vaccinated; therefore f_i will be lower there than in Asia. In New York skilled medical and hospital care are more readily available than in almost any part of mainland Asia; therefore f_r will be greater there than in Asia.

15. If f_r is increased by 50%, then $s_{cr} = 3f_r/2f_i$ compared to its original value; but if f_i is decreased by 50%, then $s_{cr} = 2f_r/f_i$ which is larger than the other fraction. Hence, to decrease f_i by 50% is more effective.

16. This is, of course, a very complex question, only a few phases of which are here touched upon. Ford expected (correctly) that he would force wages up in many other industries as well as his own and that a wide market for his cars would thus develop. He also expected (correctly) that he would

make a large overall profit from large sales, even though the profit per car was much smaller than the industry standard. He probably did not foresee how unstable the labor market would become (e.g., the new CIO industry unions upsetting the dominance of the old AFL craft unions). Some results: many other companies brought out low-priced cars in order to compete (the Model T was extremely reliable, but neither comfortable nor good-looking, and these last points offered ways to compete successfully); wages were raised elsewhere, but only grudgingly, so unions grew and forced wage rates even higher; presently car prices were raised again in order to maintain a profit margin. The *price* instability turned out to be self-limiting, but the *wage* instability was not. (The effect on the steel industry might be examined, with the interaction between cheaper large-volume operation and the limit imposed by total plant capacity.)

17. They "break" the dam in a controlled way by opening a gate at the top of a pipe through the dam and use the water to run a turbine at the pipe's lower end, or just let it spread through a water-supply system.

18.

Situation	Desired State	Disturbance	Forces which tend to return system to desired state
Smallpox epidemic	No Disease	An infected person	Quarantine, Vaccination
Gasoline price war	Stable price	A gasoline station lowering its prices	Profit motive, actual cost of gasoline to dealer.
Bridge rocker support	Stable position	Weight of bridge and vehicles	Force of gravity (mg)
Urban riot	No riot	Arrest by police, gang fights, etc.	Riot-control police, local leaders
College student strike	No strike	Grievance of students ignored by administration	Good communication between student leaders and administration
Soil erosion	Soil maintenance	Rain and wind	Contour plowing, or planting of trees
International boundary "situation"	No boundaries disputes	Accidental injury to boundary guards	Communication between governments, machinery for "airing" problems
Sudden banking of planes	Stable flight	Gust of air	Reaction of pilot
Depletion of minerals in soil	Maintenance of materials	Plants: e.g., corn removes nitrogen from soil	Replace minerals by fertilizer or leguminous plants

Problems

1.

Day	i at start of day	$s = 1000 - i$	si	$R_i = .01\,si$	$\Delta i = R_i\,\Delta t$	i at end of the day
1	1	999	999	9.99	10	11
2	11	989	10,879	108.79	109	120
3	120	880	105,600	1,056.00	880	1,000

From the data on the preceding page we can see that the total population (1000) became infected between the second and third days. These results suggest that different epidemic models are needed for different sizes of population.

2.

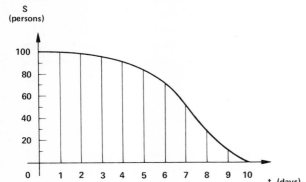

S (persons)

3. From the block diagram (see answer to Question 13) for this population situation, the following mathematical model can be obtained:

$$N_t = N_{t-1} + (P_i + R_b - P_o - R_d) \times \frac{N_{t-1}}{100}$$

$$= N_{t-1}\left(1 + \frac{P_i + R_b - P_o - R_d}{100}\right)$$

With the given rates of change,

$$N_t = N_{t-1}\left(1 + \frac{0.6 + 1.7 - 0.4 - 0.9}{100}\right)$$

$$= N_{t-1}\left(1 + \frac{1}{100}\right)$$

$$= N_{t-1}(1.01)$$

Years	N_{t-1}	N_t
1	40,000	40,000 + 400 = 40,400
2	40,400	40,400 + 404 = 40,804
3	40,804	40,804 + 408 = 41,212
4	41,212	41,212 + 412 = 41,624

This is an exponential equation of the form $P = A(\alpha)^{t/T}$, where $T = 4$ yr, $t = 10$ yr, $\alpha = 1.0406$, $A = 40,000$. Then $P = 40,000 (1.0406)^{10/4} = 40,000 \times 1.1046 = 44,184$. Since the graph is practically linear at first, the mathematical model may take the form $y = mx + b$ where $y = N_t$, $x = t$, $m = 406$, and $b = 40,000$.

$N_t = 406t + 40,000$

For example if $t = 10$ yr

$N_t = 406 (10) + 40,000$

$N_t = 4060 + 40,000$

$N_t = 44,060$, an error of about 0.3%, much less than the uncertainties of the data.

4. $\Delta N_A = 0.10 N_B \qquad N_A = N_{A-1} + \Delta N_A$

$\Delta N_B = 0.10 N_A \qquad N_B = N_{B-1} + \Delta N_B$

The situation is an unstable system where the rate of growth increases and never stops.

5. 2357 each. By simple arithmetic:

End of week no.	Men in force
1	1000
2	1000 + 100 = 1100
3	1100 + 110 = 1210
	etc.

Note that each new levy comes the week *after* the corresponding intelligence report, so that only 9 troop additions have been made in 10 weeks.

An extension to this question is to have the students solve the problem via a mathematical model. The variables can be expressed algebraically. Let N = original force, R = weekly rate of increase, S_t = force after t weeks.

End of week no.	Men in force
1	$S_1 = N$
2	$S_2 = N + RN = N (1 + R)$
3	$S_3 = N(1 + R) + RN(1 + R)$ $= N(1 + R)(1 + R) = N(1 + R)^2$
4	$S_4 = N(1 + R)^2 + RN (1 + R)^2$ $= N(1 + R)^3$

We now notice that the expression for day No. 1 can be written as $N(1 + R)^0$, so the general expression must be $S_t = N (1 + R)^{t-1}$, and $S_{10} = 1000 (1.1)^9 = 2358$, using 4-digit logarithms.

6.

$$s_{cr} = \frac{f_r}{f_i} = \frac{0.6}{0.001} = 600$$

7. Evidently, Crafty's price equals the number of toys bought the previous week, and the situation is unstable; i.e., Crafty's price curve is steeper than Discount's buying curve. To produce stability, Discount's curve must be made steeper than Crafty's;

i.e., the instruction should be to buy *less* than previously when prices are low, *more* than previously when prices are high. Or you might put in the same order every week.

8. In discussing the stability of a simple supply-and-demand curve one merely has to apply the simple rule: the equilibrium point is stable if the magnitude of the slope of Discount's buying strategy exceeds that of Crafty's selling strategy.

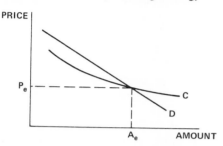

The above curve shows one equilibrium point A_e, P_e, and since the magnitude of the slope of D is always larger than the slope of C the system is stable.

9.

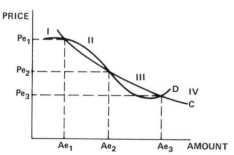

Since there are three equilibrium points and the slope of curve D is constantly changing, the simple rule used in Question 8 must be used with caution for this more complex situation. In order to simplify the discussion of the stability of this system we will discuss the behavior of the system in terms of regions I, II, III, and IV and their relationship to the three equilibrium points. In region I and the left portion of region II, D's curve is less steep than C's and Pe_1, Ae_1 marks an unstable equilibrium point. But if the instability leads to an order to the right of the amount where the curves have the same slope, the situation will shift to a stable equilibrium at

Pe_2, Ae_2. Similarly, Pe_3, Ae_3 is an unstable equilibrium point, but it is likely that the increasing oscillations will again lead over the border of equal slopes and stability will be reached at Pe_2, Ae_2. (Note that the regional division would have been more convenient if only 3 regions had been marked, separated at the 2 places where the curves have equal slopes.)

D | DEMONSTRATIONS, LABS, AND PROJECTS

I. Dynamic Stability Demonstration

The essential purpose of this demonstration is to illustrate the idea that a system under certain circumstances will be stable while under other circumstances it will be unstable. The demonstration can be used as an introduction to this chapter. The idea that unstable and stable systems differ in behavior if a disturbance is applied to them can be developed in conjunction with this demonstration. Basically, a stable system when disturbed will return to the equilibrium point while an unstable system will not.

Equipment for Each Lab Team:

    Stability demonstrator (3-wheeled cart)
    Length of fishline or other strong string
      (2-3 ft)
    Thumbtack or piece of masking tape

General Lab Supplies:

    Extra fishline
    Extra thumbtacks or masking tape

Answers to Questions:

*2. The optimum location of the point of attachment is directly over the swivel wheel. Any other point of attachment will result in different degrees of instability.

*3. Some other systems that can be modeled by means of the 3-wheeled cart are:

    a) Tripod for television cameras
    b) 3-wheeled cars (at one time quite popular in England) and motorcycles, or delivery tricycles

II. Analog Simulation of Aerodynamic Stability (Classroom Demonstration)

PART A. DEMONSTRATION OF THE SPRING-MASS SYSTEM

This demonstration is necessary to show the meaning of certain terms to be used in Part B (Manual page 211) on Aerodynamic Stability, and its simulation on the analog computer. It also serves as a review of part of the discussion of sinusoidal signals, in Chapter 6.

Equipment for Demonstration:

Spring-mass system
Meter stick
Spring balance
Equal-arm balance and set of weights
Stopwatch

The spring-mass system, which many schools possess, has been specially prepared for the demonstration. It consists of a cylindrical mass, weighing about half a pound. The mass is suspended by a spring. The mass looks like a piston inside a glass cylinder. The cylinder guides the motion of the mass. The upper end of the spring is attached to a disc which is rotated by a motor drive with speed control. It is best to use the innermost of the 3 screw holes to attach the spring. Thus a sinusoidal signal, of variable frequency, is imparted to the spring and transferred to the mass. Damping holes which can be covered in whole or in part allow more or less air to be pushed through and help to control the motion.

Here it is necessary to state without proof an equation. The proof can, however, be found in most elementary physics books. The equation is:

$$f_o = \frac{1}{2\pi} \sqrt{\frac{k}{m}}$$

It refers to the behavior of the mass when suspended freely from the spring and set into up-and-down motion. The term f_o is the natural frequency (in cycles per second, from the top of the motion back to the top for example). The mass of the piston is m, and k is the spring constant. (If necessary, refer to Chapter 1, Lab II, Part B, or Chapter 7, Lab VI.) The equation is intuitively reasonable: if the spring is strong and stiff, then k is large and any motion of the mass will be quickly stopped and reversed, making f_o large; if the mass is large it will respond sluggishly to the spring, making f_o small.

A troublesome difficulty with the equation is the need to use comparable units. If the mass is determined in kilograms on an equal-arm balance, then k must be measured in newtons per meter. In Chapter 1 we found k in grams-weight per meter, using a spring balance to measure the force applied to the spring in order to stretch it, and taking the scale reading of the spring balance without modification. To change grams-weight to newtons, divide by 1000 (thus changing to kilograms-weight) and multiply the result by 9.8 (newtons per kilogram-weight). This is equivalent to dividing grams-weight by 102, or nearly enough by 100. Thus in that Chapter 1 experiment the sample data gave $k = 2500$ gm-wt/m, which is 25 N/m within 2% (actually, about 24.5). Using newtons per meter and kilograms in the equation stated, f_o comes out in cycles per second. The English system of units is just as puzzling (pounds-force and slugs-mass, the latter being the weight in pounds divided by 32). 9.8 and 32 are (to 2 digits) the acceleration due to gravity in the International (or metric) and English (or British engineering) systems respectively.

Sample data:

$m = 0.24$ kg, $k = 42.3$ N/m,

$$f_o = \frac{1}{2\pi} \sqrt{\frac{k}{m}} = \frac{1}{6.28} \sqrt{\frac{42.3}{0.24}} = 2.1 \text{ cps (theoretical)}$$
$$f_o = 1.9 \text{ cps (experimental)}$$

Demonstrate the general operation of the system. Show how the maximum piston displacement or output amplitude changes as the frequency is increased from its minimum value through the resonant frequency. The piston and the motor drive are in resonance when the drive frequency is the same as f_o, the natural frequency of the spring-mass system. It will be best to cover about half the area of the damping holes. This will permit the transients in the vibration to settle out quickly at each frequency. Always let the vibration reach a steady motion before taking any readings or making any observations. Be careful when the system is operated near the resonant frequency. If the damping is set very low the piston may jump out of the cylinder. At very high frequencies you can set the spring itself into a resonant vibration. The numbers on the dial next to the motor are not calibrated. They should be used only as a rough indicator. To measure f_0, time a convenient number of vibrations, say 10, with the stopwatch.

Effect of Frequency on Amplitude (sample data with partial damping, about half the area of damping holes covered):

f (cps)	y (mm)
1.3	5
1.7	20
1.8	38
1.9	50
2.1	37
2.3	8

Next, it is necessary to make a study of the damping process. With the motor turned off, displace the piston downward about 2 in inside the cylinder (you can do this by pulling down on the spring). Release the piston and count the number of oscillations it takes for the piston to come to rest. Observe how the number of oscillations changes at different settings of the lower collar (fraction of damping holes covered). Try to find the setting at which the piston just returns to its neutral position without overshooting it.

Sample data:

Amount of covered area of damping holes	Number of oscillations before stopping
None	8
1/4	7
1/2	5
3/4	4
All	0

Then determine what effect changes in damping have on the output amplitude at resonance.

Sample data:

Fraction of damping-hole area covered	Output amplitude (y) for resonance
None	70 mm
1/4	65
1/2	50
3/4	8
All	2

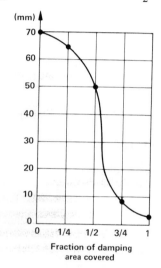

More exact experiments show that the damping is always caused by a force F_d opposing the motion of the piston, and proportional to the piston's speed,

$$F_d = -bv$$

where b is the "damping coefficient." The negative sign is used because the force acts in opposition to the motion. The spring also exerts a force F_s on the piston proportional to its extension, as we have seen:

$$F_s = -kx$$

We now include the negative sign, previously rejected as unnecessary, because when the spring is stretched one way the force acts the other way. This is only a partial derivation; when the piston is above its "neutral" point the spring is not pushing down on it, but the pull of gravity is always there and is in effect diminished by the spring's action. Detailed analysis shows that the net force (gravity and spring) acting on the piston is always $-kx$, where we now measure x from the neutral point. The total force acting on the piston is therefore:

$$F_t = F_s + F_d = -kx - bv$$

One of Sir Isaac Newton's great contributions to physics and engineering is the equation:

$$F = ma$$

Here F is the *net* force acting on a mass m; by "net" is understood that force which causes the mass to acquire an acceleration a. Hence $a = F/m$, or in the present case, where we have called the net force F_t,

$$a = \frac{F_t}{m} = -\frac{kx}{m} - \frac{bv}{m}$$

This equation is necessary if you wish to model the spring-mass system on the analog computer; the model is especially revealing if you have a chart recorder. The motion is found to be sinusoidal. The equation is also required for the aerodynamic simulation in Lab II, Part B.

Just about here the student is likely to be sure he is in trouble. If a is always negative, how can the motion be sinusoidal? (Let us discuss the undamped case for simplicity.) If $a = -kx/m$, then a is $-$ when x is $+$, but a becomes $+$ when x is $-$. (Similarly, the bv term changes sign according to the direction of v.) When $x = 0$ (the piston at its midpoint), a must also be 0, and when x is at maximum (the endpoints) so is a, though with the opposite sign. Again the student balks, because he sees the piston come to rest, instantaneously, at the endpoints. How can there be an acceleration when there is no velocity? Straightening this out is a real challenge to the teacher's skill. The velocity *was* +, is *about to become* − (or vice versa), and is therefore indeed *changing*, so there *is* an acceleration.

To help the discussion we offer a tabulation (T-0815) and a set of graphs (T-0816). The former should self-explanatory except for the arrows, added to emphasize the directions of v and a, not the directions of change (up is +, down is −). In the

graphs the ordinate scales are different for the 3 curves to make it easier to keep them separate. They should be different anyway, since each quantity is measured in different units. It will be recalled from Chapter 5, Section 4, or Lab III or Lab IV, that if an acceleration is integrated we obtain the velocity change produced by the acceleration, and if we integrate the velocity we obtain the change of displacement caused by the velocity. (Conversely, notice on T-0816 that the magnitude of v varies with the slope of the x curve, that of a with the slope of the v curve. The slope of a curve like these is always 0 when it crests or bottoms, always maximum (+ if upward to the right, − if downward to the right) as it crosses the axis. The slopes show the derivatives or rates of change; the derivative of $x = v$, the derivative of $v = a$, just the converse of the integration results.)

See Part B for the wiring of the analog to simulate the spring-mass system. If the second summing-scalor is omitted, the simulation is of the undamped system. For the damped system, connect the output of the upper integrator to input jack S (Stable) of the second summing-scalor, and also to the lower integrator as shown in the diagram.

For the undamped case, set the first coefficient at 1 (so $k/m = 10$), initial displacement at +1 volt, initial velocity to 0, and integrate continuously if you have either a chart recorder or a voltmeter with center 0. This shows the analog of the piston's motion beginning at the top of its upward journey. Then set initial displacement to 0, initial velocity to −2 volts (2 ft/sec downward), which means that the simulated motion starts in the middle of the down journey, at maximum speed. When the damped case is studied, use the same initial conditions as before, and set b/m to 1 at first, then to other values.

If you select any particular values of k/m and x_0, the maximum velocity (at x_0) will be found to be about $\sqrt{k/m}$ times the maximum displacement (that when $v = 0$).

To vary the constant knobs, be sure to stop integrating and reset the initial conditions.

To carry the study of this system further, see Section G, Part III ("Simple Harmonic Motion and the Mass-Spring System").

PART B. Analog Simulation

The demonstration is an excellent illustration of the difference between stability and instability in physical systems. It should be performed while studying Section 8 of this chapter. The apparatus is depicted in Fig. 8-21.

For Simulation:

>   Aerodynamic stability demonstrator, including fan
>   Analog computer with high-impedance VM, or Chart recorder
>   Set of patch cords

Set up the apparatus with the round side of the cylinder turned toward the fan, but leave the power off while determining the relationship between the amplitude of an initial displacement and the number of cycles that occur until rest results. Remember that a cycle is a complete to-and-fro excursion (which simplifies the counting problem). As we saw in Part A (Manual page 208), a count of the frequency enables us to calculate k/m, needed for the computer simulation. Repeat with the fan turned on. Here we increase the damping effect by raising the velocity of the air relative to the vane. This velocity has 2 components as seen by the vane: a small one parallel but opposite to its motion, and a much larger and more important one perpendicular to its motion. Reverse the half cylinder, turn on the fan, and observe that a small initial displacement results in vibrations of increasing amplitude (perhaps until the cylinder strikes the supporting frame). Physics teachers will be able to relate this to the curving of a baseball, but the full explanation is complicated and probably not very well understood. See Section G, Part IV ("Stability, Instability, and Oscillators") for a partial discussion. It is probably adequate to refer, as the textbook does, to the shedding of eddies, alternately from the 2 edges; then it may be plausible to postulate that eddy-shedding occurs at the leading edge when the result is to damp the motion, at the trailing edge when instability follows, and also that this difference is related to the surface presented to the airstream from the fan.

If the demonstrator is not available, refer the students to Fig. 8-21 and explain that this experiment involves the simulation of the pictured system. The analog simulation can be set up by using the wiring diagram, shown on next page, with minor adjustments to be mentioned later.

Answers to Questions:

*1. The springs in this case tend to cause sinusoidal oscillation, just as the mounting spring and gravity do together. The effect of the air is somewhat different, however. For one orientation of the half cylinder it acts purely to damp the motion, though in 2 ways, as previously indicated; for the other orientation it acts as a "positive damping" to build up the oscillations. The first case is stable, the second unstable.

*2. We assume now that the force exerted by the airstream on the half-round bar is, as before, proportional to its speed, whichever kind of effect it has:

$$F_d = \pm bv$$

The negative sign goes with ordinary damping, the positive with what we referred to as "positive damping." In this case, if $F_d > F_s$ the spring force will be overpowered and instability follows.

When using the analog simulation, change the value of b/m until the output of the analog matches the output of the physical system. The easiest way is to plot the number of cycles that result from a given displacement against the magnitude of the displacement, for the physical system. Then plot on the same axes values obtained from the simulation, until a match is obtained. To save time in class, this had better be tried out in advance, so that the coefficient knob can be (by a lucky chance!) set right at the first trial.

Sample values:

Displacement amplitude (in)	Number of complete cycles to rest
0.25	10
0.50	20
1.0	30
2.0	40
3.5	50

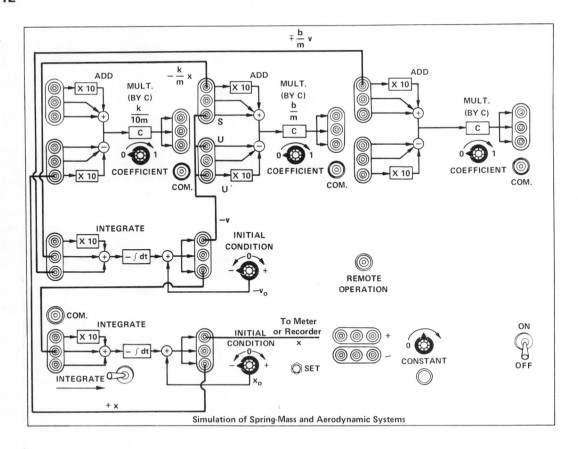

Simulation of Spring-Mass and Aerodynamic Systems

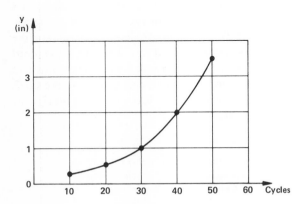

The simulation is a valid model of any type of periodic motion with a restoring force and a damping (or alternatively, driving) force which is proportional to the speed, such as a pendulum swinging in a resisting medium like water; here gravity and the supporting wire collaborate to act as the springs do. It may also be adjusted to simulate a wide variety of unstable situations where the force which causes the instability increases with the velocity of the system. As already suggested, the curving baseball is one; another is the sailing ships once tried out which used huge vertical rotating cylinders (employing the Magnus effect); another is the skidding of an automobile on a curve. The friction between the tires and the pavement is fairly constant at different speeds, but the "centrifugal force" is greater at higher speeds, though the actual physics of the case is too subtle to go into in this course.

*3. This question is evidently worded backward. To change the stable system to instability, we must change b/m from $-$ to $+$; that is, the $-v$ signal must now go to the $-$ input to the b/m summing-scalor, and possibly to the × 10 terminal (from S to U or U' on the figure).

*4. The first scalor simulates the action of the springs, the second that of the airstream.

III. Demonstration of Static Stability

Your students may have noticed while riding in a car that the roadway of most bridges seems to be cut completely across at least once. If they stopped and looked at the underside of the bridge they would find that this is true. At least one end of the bridge deck rests on rollers or is pinned to a rocker. Often both ends are mounted in this way. A long bridge is thus broken into a number of segments. The reason for such construction is to allow for expansion or contraction of the bridge deck with changes of temperature (below).

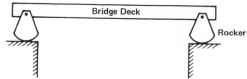

Bridge deck on rockers to allow for thermal expansion

The purpose of this demonstration is to find out whether the design of the rockers makes any difference to the stability of the bridge. Of course it does, and it is remarkable that this apparently trivial demonstration recalls an accident that really happened: the collapse of a bridge while under construction. The designer had failed to take account of an elementary principle of physics, the "lever law." (See "Torques and the Unstable Bridge," Part V in Section G).

Equipment for Demonstration:

2 pairs of bridge-support rockers, stable and unstable

Plank for bridge deck, grooved (see end of discussion)

Ring stand and ring or burette clamp

Strong string

To perform the demonstration, hang one end of your bridge deck by a piece of string from the ring stand, if convenient, so you can concentrate on the rocker end, but be sure to place the ring stand in a stable position, with its base extending under the supporting clamp that holds the string. To make things simpler, our bridge will not be pinned to the rockers. Instead, 2 rocker patterns are supplied. One is shorter than the other and its top corresponds to pin joint 3 in T-0818, while the other, taller one corresponds to pin joint 1. Evidently, if the bridge is supported at 3, the situation is like that shown in (b), T-0817, whereas supporting it at 1 produces an unstable situation like (d) in the same transparency. If a rocker were supplied with its top at the center of the circular arc, it would be like case (c); this is the so-called critical condition which separates stability from instability. In each case the rockers alone are stable because their centers of gravity are low, as T-0818 shows. Notice that with care the bridge can be balanced even on the unstable rockers: this is unstable equilibrium, as a small push on the bridge will demonstrate. Experience suggests grooving the underside of the bridge deck and putting the rockers in the grooves to keep them from slipping.

E | EVALUATION

The questions in this section are rated according to the chapter objectives and the performance levels stated in the introduction to the teacher's manual. This group of questions is not intended to be all inclusive, but just as a guide to possible questions. Zeros in the chapter objective column indicate no chapter objective for this question.

Chapter Objective	Performance Level	
		Judged to be Relatively Easy:
		In each of the following cases, mark the statement *T* if it is true, but mark it *F* if it is false.
4	I	1. a) The invention of the elevator was the only thing needed, at the turn of the century, to make skyscrapers possible.

Chapter Objective	Performance Level	

Chapter Objective	Performance Level
4	I
1	I
9	I
10	II

b) Traffic on an expressway is likely to become unstable when the traffic density (number of cars passing a given point per minute) falls too low.

c) The most important agent in spreading bubonic plague is believed to be fleas.

d) Epidemics are always best treated by quarantining all those who become infected.

e) This diagram represents unusual strategies by both the seller, C (Crafty) and the buyer, D (Discount). Since graph line C is steeper than line D, this represents an unstable system.

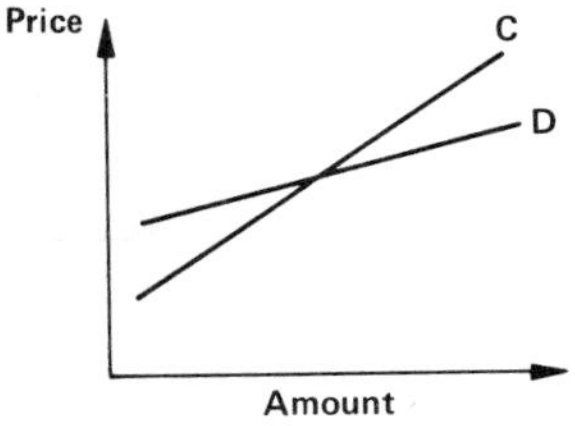

Chapter Objective	Performance Level
12	I
12	I

f) A pendulum is in equilibrium even when it is swinging, because all the forces acting on it are balanced.

g) This diagram represents a rocker to allow for the expansion of a bridge. The structure will be stable if the bridge is pinned to the rocker at a point below C, the center of the circle.

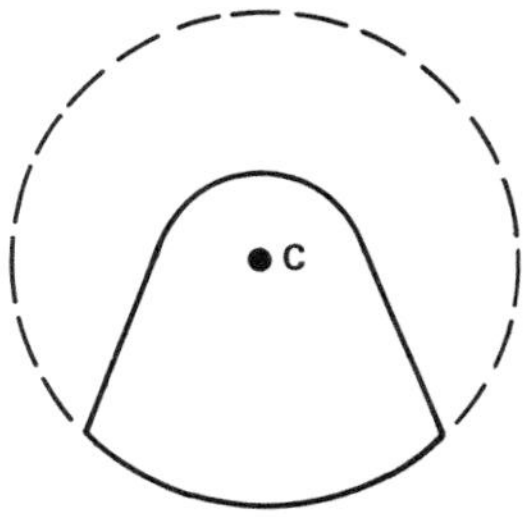

Chapter Objective	Performance Level
13	I
4	II

h) Unstable systems are always undesirable.

In the next two questions, check the best answer.

2. Traffic on a certain highway is moving steadily, at 5 o'clock, at a speed of 20 mph. It is correct to say that the traffic pattern

a) is unstable because the speed limit is 45 mph.

b) is unstable because there are no traffic lights.

c) is unstable because traffic as slow as 20 mph is always considered to be unstable.

d) is stable because the movement is steady.

e) would become stable if the speed were checked by radar.

Chapter Objective	Performance Level
7	II

3.

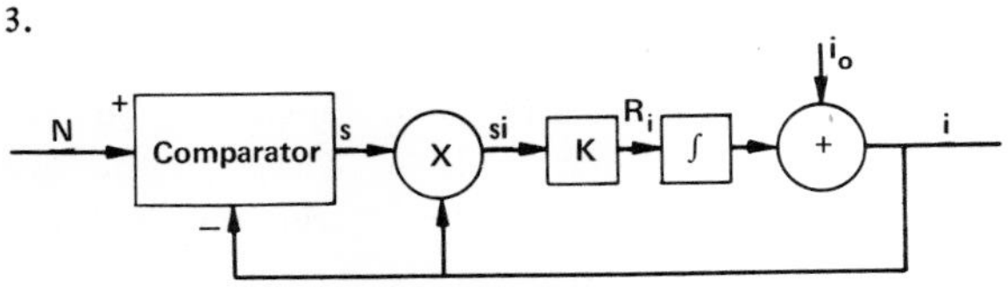

The above diagram represents a simple model of an epidemic system.

a) If i increases by 1, s must increase by 1.

b) If i increases by 1 and s decreases by 1, si must remain unchanged.

c) If i increases by 1, s must decrease by 1.

d) The output of the scalor, K, is the integral of the system output.

e) The output of the multiplier, X, is the rate of increase in the number of infected cases.

Chapter Objective	Performance Level	

Judged to be Relatively Easy:

10   II

4. Show, by drawing lines on this graph, whether an order by D of an amount of goods A_1 leads to stable equilibrium or to unstable.

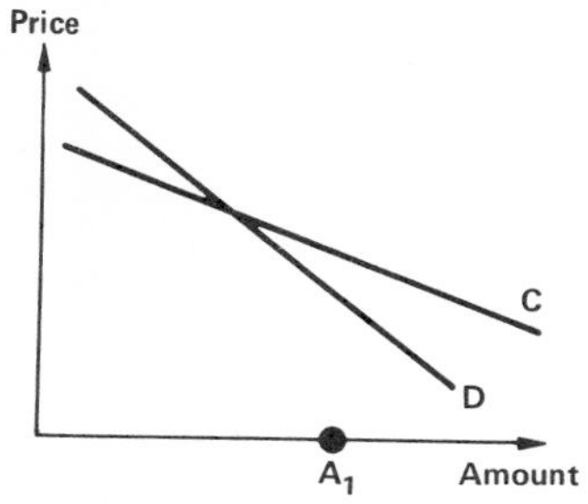

[Graph: Price vs Amount, with curves labeled C and D, point A_1 marked on Amount axis]

Judged to be More Difficult:

In each of the following questions, check the best answer.

2   II

5. Which of the following systems are apparently in a state of stable equilibrium at their present operating points?
   1) The railroads
   2) The petroleum industry (wells, refineries, sales outlets)
   3) Network television
   4) The women's clothing industry
   5) The planetary system
   6) The motel (or motor hotel) industry
      a) All 6   d) 2, 3, 4
      b) 2, 3, 5, 6   e) 1, 4, 6
      c) 1, 3, 4, 6

6   II

6. When a graph is drawn to show the course of an epidemic (plotting i, the number infected, against the number of days since the epidemic began), the curve bends over into a sigmoid at the top. This is mostly because
   a) as time goes on, there are fewer and fewer people left to infect.
   b) the factor of proportionality (which was 0.01) was incorrectly chosen.
   c) i was shown being fed back partly to one point, partly to another in the block diagram. Thus i became too small.
   d) the calculated figures were spoiled by the process of rounding off decimals.
   e) The graph ought to show f_i, the fraction of si infected each day, plotted against the number of days.

10   II

7. The diagram represents a manufacturer's selling strategy (labeled S) and a customer's buying strategy (labeled B). Initially an order is placed for the quantity A.

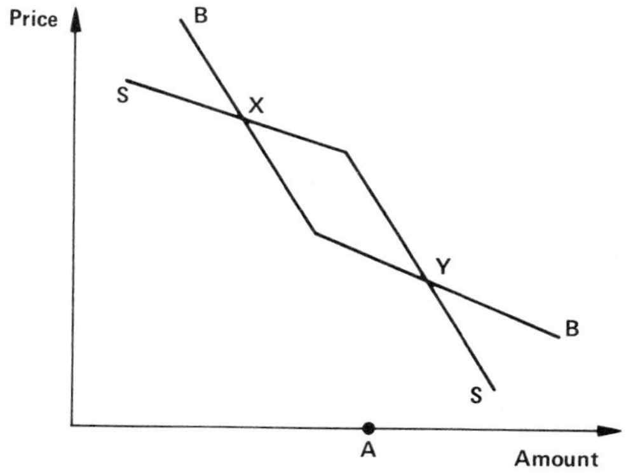

[Graph: Price vs Amount, with curves labeled B and S intersecting at points X and Y, point A marked on Amount axis]

Judged to be More Difficult:

a) The situation is unstable and analysis shows the adjustment process moving off the diagram to the right.

b) The situation is unstable and analysis shows the adjustment process moving off the diagram to the left.

c) Y represents a point of stable equilibrium to which the adjustment process tends.

d) X represents a point of stable equilibrium to which the adjustment process tends.

e) There would be a cyclic pattern developed somewhere in the part of the diagram between X and Y.

Answers to Evaluation Questions:

1. a) F   e) T
   b) F   f) T
   c) T   g) T
   d) F   h) F

2. d

3. c

4.
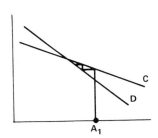

5. b

6. a

7. d

F | FILMS

F-0801 PANDORA'S EASY-OPEN POP-TOP BOX

Recommendation: Not yet previewed.

Application: This film, and similar ones, can be used to show how unstable situations can come about if proper planning is not used, when trying to solve environmental problems.

Length and Type: 15 min, color, sound.

Source: #20 (No charge)

Summary: Dramatic presentation of effects of uncontrolled urbanization. Emphasizes the need for proper planning and foresight to minimize the creation of urban sprawls.

F-0802 TACOMA NARROWS BRIDGE COLLAPSE

Recommendation: Highly recommended as a dramatic example of an unstable system.

Application: Use to illustrate aerodynamic instability.

Length and Type: 4 min 40 sec, color, silent, 8-mm cartridge film loop (also available in 16-mm form for purchase from Macalaster Scientific Corp).

Source: #19 (Purchase only)

Summary: Shows the oscillation and ultimate collapse of the bridge.

G | GENERAL

I. Bibliography

L. J. Batten, *The Nature of Violent Storms.* Anchor-Doubleday S-19, 1961 (A) (paper)

Thermal instability (convection) in fronts, thunderstorms, tornadoes and waterspouts, hurricanes. An admirable source of examples which have been made familiar either by experience or by reading the papers.

H. Brown, *The Challenge of Man's Future.* Viking, 1968 (A) (paper)

This skillful writer and noted geochemist gives a marvelous capsule history of the rise of civilization from the first hunting cultures to the contemporary age, in the form of the story of an imaginary tribe. He goes on to a pretty hair-raising account of the past, present, and future prospects of world populations and of sources of energy, food, and materials. Almost all has a direct bearing on *The Man-Made World.*

R. L. Carson, *Silent Spring.* Houghton Mifflin, 1962; also Fawcett-World, 1964 (A) (paper)

A celebrated, extremely influential description of instabilities forced upon a previously stable ecology by the side effects of insufficiently tested insecticides. Horrifying, and every person who cares for our race and its future must read it.

E. J. Kormondy, *Concepts of Ecology.* Prentice-Hall, 1969 (B) (soft cover)

The unifying theme of this book is the structure and function of ecosystems, with reference to energy flow, nutrient cycling, population growth and regulation, and community organization and dynamics. It contains many examples of how the ecosystem can be maintained.

L. J. and M. Milne, *The Balance of Nature.* Knopf, 1960 (B)

Ecological stability and instability. There is much matter here that can be usefully introduced to the classroom. It is served up in a manner that is extremely easy to take: it reads like a book of anecdotes, but is concerned with documented facts; it is full of surprises, and brings up to date such old stories as the mongooses introduced into the West Indies to eliminate rats (in the long run they didn't and have become an almost equally vexatious pest).

J. H. Storer, *Man in the Web of Life.* Signet Books (New American Library) 1968 (A) (paper)

An excellent treatment of how man upsets the stability of natural ecosystems. It does not stop with the disruptive influence of man but contends that with proper planning and application of science and technology the stabilization of the human environment is possible.

P. Ziegler, *The Black Death.* John Day, 1969 (B)

The bubonic plague of the fourteenth century is described in detail. The book is a natural extension of the text's discussion of epidemic models in Sections 4 through 6.

W. L. Langer, "The Black Death." *Scientific American*, February, 1964

The article mentioned in Section 4 of the text; it can be used by teachers who wish to elaborate on the study of the bubonic plague of the fourteenth century.

A partial list of publications useful in providing background for discussion of the ecological and environmental crises:

Newsweek, January 26, 1970 (entire issue)
Scientific American, September, 1970 (entire issue)
Time, February 2, 1970 (entire issue)

Scientists' Institute for Public Information (SIPI): a series of eight workbooks ($5 each) obtainable from SIPI Headquarters, 30 East 68 St., New York, N. Y. 10021:

1. Air Pollution
2. Environmental Cost of Electric Power
3. Environmental Education, 1970
4. Environmental Effects of Weapons Technology
5. Hunger
6. Nuclear Explosives in Peace Time
7. Pesticides
8. Water Pollution

II. An Extra Problem

Calculate the course of an epidemic for the simple model that does not include the effect of recovery. Assume $N = 151$, $i = 1$, and $f_i = 0.02$ (i.e., $R_i = 0.02$ si).

Day	i at start of day	$s = N - i$	si	$R_i = 0.02$ si	$i = R_i t$	i at end of day
1	1	150	150	3	3	4
2	4	147	588	12	12	16
3	16	135	2160	43	43	59
4	59	92	5428	109	109	all

III. Simple Harmonic Motion and the Mass-Spring System

1) MOTION OF A MASS SUSPENDED FROM A SPRING

Suppose we have a coil-spring ℓ units long, represented in diagram by a slender rectangle (a). If a mass m is hung from the end of the spring, as in (b),

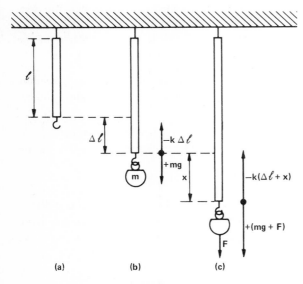

(a)   (b)   (c)

Mass-spring-force relationships

the spring will be stretched by an amount $\Delta\ell$. By Hooke's Law (Chapter 1, Lab II, Part B), once equilibrium has been reached and the mass hangs quietly (provided that the elastic limit of the spring is not exceeded), the forces acting on the mass are those shown in the sketch: an upward force $-k\,\Delta\ell$ and a downward force mg, such that $mg - k\,\Delta\ell = 0$. As shown in the discussion of Lab II, Chapter 8, mass in kg × acceleration due to gravity = force in newtons.

Now let us apply a further downward force F (c), for instance by pulling the mass by hand. Then of course the spring stretches a further amount (here called x), such that $F - kx = 0$. If we now let go, this upward force is no longer balanced, so there is a net force acting on the mass, which accelerates upward. But not with uniform acceleration. At every instant, as the extra length shortens, the extra upward force diminishes at the same rate. When the total length of the spring has been reduced to $\ell + \Delta\ell$ again, the *net* upward force on the mass is 0 and momentarily it has no acceleration, though it has acquired a velocity upward. This causes the follow-

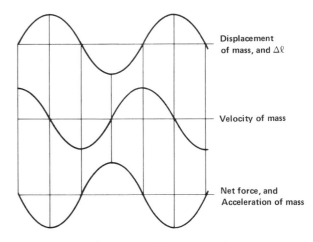

Graphs of force and motion, mass-spring system

ing sequence: (1) the mass overshoots; (2) the spring is now elongated less than $\Delta\ell$; (3) therefore $|mg| \triangleright |k\,\Delta\ell|$, so there is a net downward force on the mass; (4) hence there is a negative acceleration; (5) the net downward force and so the acceleration increase, both reaching a maximum at the instant when the mass stops rising; (6) the whole process repeats in the opposite direction, and the mass continues to bob up and down until frictional forces in the spring and the air bring it to rest (compare diagram above with T-0816).

2) SIMPLE HARMONIC MOTION

The preceding is a wordy description of simple harmonic motion (SHM). The essential feature is a net force acting toward the equilibrium position, proportional to the displacement of the mass, when the system is disturbed.

The motion just described can be mimicked very easily. All that is needed is a wheel supported by an axle, a lump of putty on its rim, a strong light shining edgewise on the wheel (the sun is perfect), and a screen for the shadow (below). If the wheel rotates at a uniform speed, the shadow of the putty performs motion like SHM. It is easy to see that when the putty is at the spot shown, the speed of the shadow is maximum, and identical to that of the putty. When the putty reaches position 2, the shadow is at the end of its trace and its speed is, at that instant, 0. Available films usually show by such mechanical means that SHM can be modeled by means of a sine curve, or that when displacement from rest is plotted against time, a sine (or cosine) curve results. For our present needs it is enough to point out that the time for one rotation of the putty lump, whose speed is v, is the circumference of the wheel divided by v. This time is known as the period (P or T):

$$T = \frac{2\pi x}{v}$$

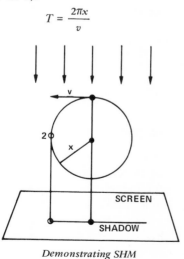

Demonstrating SHM

The number of rotations per second, or the number of complete sine waves plotted per second, or the frequency, is the reciprocal of the above: $f = 1/T$ (in cycles per second, or Hertz: Hz), so

$$f = \frac{v}{2\pi x} \text{ and } v = 2\pi f x$$

These relationships are also true of the mass vibrating on a spring. In this case, v = the instantaneous speed of the mass as it passes through the equilibrium position (which equals the derivative of the sine curve representation of displacement plotted against time at its intersection with the axis). The last formula will be important in the subsequent development.

3) CONSERVATION OF ENERGY IN THE MASS-SPRING SYSTEM

We now proceed to derive the expression for the frequency of a mass-spring system from the Law of Conservation of Energy (L.C.E.).

We have to distinguish and examine three kinds of energy in this case. The first of these is gravitational potential energy, which represents the work a body could do if it fell from an elevated position. Clearly the word "elevated" is relative. If we raise a body which weighs 10 n from a classroom floor to a table 1 m high we have done 10 joules (j) of work and have given the body 10 j of potential energy (E_p). But if the classroom is on the second floor and we use a windowsill instead of a table, the body would have much more than 10 j of E_p with reference to the ground level outside. Of course work

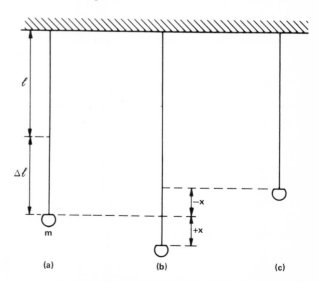

Mass-spring system in motion

was done when the body was carried upstairs, but so long as we stay in the classroom we are justified in ignoring this source of E_p. In a somewhat similar way, it is convenient and entirely proper to assume that the E_p of gravitation in the equilibrium position (a) is 0. In (b), then, it is negative, in (c) positive. The second form of energy to consider is the potential or elastic energy stored in the spring when it is stretched. This is the work done in stretching the spring. But the force exerted increases linearly from 0 to kx, and therefore has an average value $\bar{F} = 1/2$ kx (below). The work done, then, is W = 1/2 kx·x = 1/2 kx^2, and this is the basic expression for E_p of elastic energy. The third form of energy is the kinetic energy (E_k) of the mass when it is in motion. It is proved in textbooks of physics that $E_k = 1/2 \ m \ v^2$.

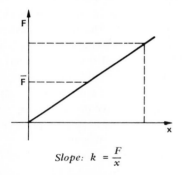

Slope: $k = \dfrac{F}{x}$

Each of the three forms of energy is continually changing during the SHM of the mass; but the L.C.E. insists that the total energy of the system remains constant (if we ignore the very slow bleeding off of energy in the form of thermal energy in the air and in the spring).

Let us calculate the amount of energy in each of the three forms in (a) of the "Mass-spring system in motion" diagram. We have already specified that E_p (grav.) = 0, shown that E_p (elastic) = 1/2 k $(\Delta\ell)^2$, and remarked that $E_k = 1/2 \ mv^2$. The total energy E = 1/2 k $(\Delta\ell)^2$ + 1/2 mv^2. In (b) the mass has been lowered a distance x; therefore, E_p (grav.) = − mgx. E_p (elastic) = 1/2 k $(\Delta\ell + x)^2$ E_k = 0, because the mass is at the bottom of its path and momentarily at rest. The total energy

$$E = \frac{1}{2} \ k \ (\Delta\ell + x)^2 - mgh$$

$$= \frac{1}{2} \ k \ (\Delta\ell)^2 + k \ \Delta\ell \cdot x + \frac{1}{2} \ k \ x^2 - mgh$$

However, we already know that mg = k $\Delta\ell$, so k $\Delta\ell x$ − mgh = 0. Thus

$$E = \frac{1}{2} \ k \ [\ (\ \Delta\ell)^2 + x^2]$$

In (c), E_p (grav.) = + mgh; E_p (elastic) = 1/2 k $(\Delta\ell - x)^2$ = 1/2 k $(\Delta\ell)^2 - k \cdot \Delta\ell x$ + 1/2 kx^2. E_k = 0 again, so

$$E = \frac{1}{2} \ k \ (\Delta\ell)^2 - k \ \Delta\ell x + \frac{1}{2} \ kx^2 + mgh,$$

which reduces to the same value as in (b):

$$E = \frac{1}{2} \ k \ [(\Delta\ell)^2 + x^2]$$

Thus the total energy in (a) must be the same as that in either (b) or (c):

$$\frac{1}{2} \ k \ (\Delta\ell)^2 + \frac{1}{2} \ mv^2 = \frac{1}{2} k \ (\Delta\ell)^2 + \frac{1}{2} \ kx^2$$

$$mv^2 = kx^2$$

$$v^2 = x^2 \ \frac{k}{m}$$

$$v = x \sqrt{\frac{k}{m}}$$

We have already shown that for SHM v = 2πfx. So

$$2\pi f = \sqrt{\frac{k}{m}}, \text{ or}$$

$$f = \frac{1}{2\pi} \sqrt{\frac{k}{m}} \cdot \text{ Q.E.D.}$$

IV. Stability, Instability, and Oscillators

We know that physical systems obey the law of conservation of energy. According to this law, if a physical system becomes unstable and goes into some violent, uncontrollable motion, it must somewhere get the energy to execute that motion. Indeed, as we shall see, a reservoir of available energy is a requirement if instability is to occur. However, in other than simple static systems without friction, the role of energy in stability can be quite subtle and unanticipated. An example which is of great engineering importance is instability of structures induced by aerodynamic forces. Engineers have become conscious of this sort of instability only recently as the result of applying well-studied principles to the structural design of bridges and airplanes.

AERODYNAMICALLY INDUCED INSTABILITY

A simple illustration of it is the fan and the spring-supported half-round section of Lab II in this chapter. When the fan is aimed at the flat side of the section, the latter will begin to oscillate with ever-increasing amplitude until it bangs against the frame or until the springs give way.

This phenomenon can be explained as follows. Imagine that we fix the section, say in a wind tunnel, and measure the vertical force F as we vary the angle A of the wind direction:

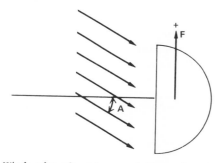

Wind and resultant force on half-round section

If we take F as positive when it is upward and A as positive when it is clockwise, the curve of F vs A will look something like the diagram below. That is, for a *downward* directed wind-stream, as shown in the first diagram, the vertical component of the force will be *upward*. Obviously, there is also a component directed horizontally to the right, but we are not interested in it in this experiment.

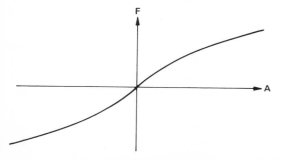

Force vs angle, flat side to wind

The aerodynamic phenomena involved are very complicated, and the reasons for an *upward* vertical component of force for a *downward* vertical component of velocity are not well understood. An explanation that seems plausible is this. *Streamlines* are the trajectories along which particles of a fluid move. P (below) is an example of such a particle. In the flow around the half-round section, the streamlines must look something like those shown below, which recall the streamlines in the airflow past an airplane wing. The streamlines over the upper part of the section are very sharply curved. To make the air follow such a course the forces in the airstream must act downward on the particles near the top of the section. This means that the pressure at the

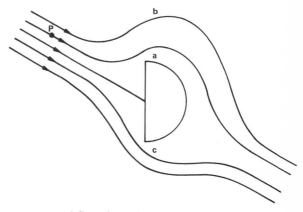

Airflow about the half-round section

point b is higher than that at a. But the pressure at b is the atmospheric pressure. Therefore there must be a partial vacuum at a, and by similar reasoning at c. However, the pressure at a must be even lower than that at c, because the streamlines curve more abruptly at the top. Moreover, these pressures act not only on the air but also on the parts of the half-round section in contact with the air. Hence the net vertical force on the section is upward.

This plausibility argument asks us to assume that the streamlines are arranged like those shown above, and further, that this is the pattern when the half-round section is moving. It is in fact difficult to check these hypotheses experimentally.

This situation is not uncommon in engineering. Very often the physicist has not sufficiently unlocked the secrets of nature to provide the engineer with all the basic theory he needs, or at other times the theory is so complex as to be of no use. In such cases, gross experiments such as those summarized by the second diagram on page 221 are done. Although such experiments lump together detailed phenomena the physicist would like to separate and study individually, they enable the engineer to make progress. Such is the case in the present example.

Let us therefore proceed under the assumption that the curve of the second diagram is correct. We consider a horizontal airstream of velocity V_{air}, as occurs when we turn on the fan, and a moving rather than fixed section. Say the section is moving upward with a velocity V_{sect} (below). Then to an observer moving with the section, the airstream

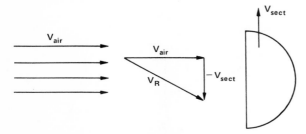

Velocity diagram for an upward-moving section

appears to have two perpendicular components, V_{air} and V_{sect} (the latter directed downward, naturally), and he sees a resultant airstream, V_R, which is pointing downward. When we compare this situation with that in the first diagram on page 221 we see that when the section is going *upward* the force F is also *upward*! The force thus tends to push the section in the direction in which it is already going. Since the force F is in the direction of the motion, it continually does work on the airfoil, or, if you prefer, on the springs which support it. Energy is constantly being taken out of the airstream and put *into* the section. The result is an ever-increasing buildup of oscillations.

It is interesting that when the fan is aimed at the round side of the section, the buildup does not occur. Instead of as in the second diagram, we get a plot like that in the next diagram. The force now always opposes the motion; it acts like a damping force, and any oscillation quickly damps out. Here, the airstream continually draws energy *out* of the section.

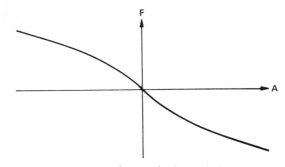

Force vs angle, round side to wind

As we have indicated, it is hard to predict from aerodynamic theory whether a cross-section will be stable or unstable. Usually, extensive wind-tunnel testing must be done to determine this for a given design. The diagrams below show some unstable cross-sections and some stable ones.

We have noted that the presence of a reservoir of energy is a requirement for a system to be unstable. On the other hand, just because there is a

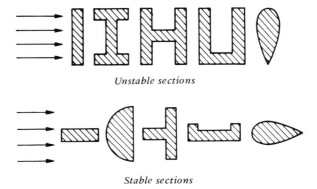

Unstable sections

Stable sections

supply of energy available it does not follow that a system will be unstable. In the case of the half-round section, the airstream provided a reservoir of energy for both stable and unstable sections, but the flow of energy was oppositely directed in the two cases. Likewise, the 3-wheeled cart has a reservoir of kinetic energy when it is moving along the desired straight-line path. Again energy will flow either from or into the reservoir depending on whether the cart's orientation is stable or unstable. Generally speaking, analyses of the type indicated above are required to determine stability or instability in any given case.

OSCILLATORS

The unstable cross-section we have been considering is set into uncontrolled oscillation. It is possible to use instability in a more subtle way to produce controlled oscillation. Oscillators like this are of tremendous importance to technology. In order for Station WNBC to transmit a signal at 660 kc/s, it must have a means of generating 660 kc/s. Radar signals must be of high frequency to get good discrimination; again an accurate high-frequency source is required. A single telephone cable can carry thousands of telephone calls, each call being carried at a different frequency; accurate frequency sources are required to keep the calls from getting mixed up. Examples of the use of oscillators abound in our modern, electronic society.

The device we seek is one which will oscillate at precisely a desired frequency. In addition, the device must produce enough energy for our needs at the desired frequency. How do we reach these goals?

The need for a precise frequency immediately calls to mind the use of the natural frequency of a vibrating system. But a vibrating system without an external energy source always has friction or damping present that eventually causes the system to come to rest. It is, in fact, an energy extractor rather than an energy source.

In order to get a finite amplitude and energy, we could think of driving the system at resonance and applying suitable damping. But that would require a frequency-controlled excitation—the very thing we are looking for. We might think next of coupling a source of energy with a naturally vibrating system. We have in fact already met an example of an oscillator of just this sort in our model of aerodynamically induced instability. By taking energy out of the airstream, the half-moon section oscillated at ever-greater amplitude until it started slapping against the frame or the spring failed. If we measure the frequency of the oscillation just before the final collapse, we find that it is very nearly the natural frequency of the mass-spring system. Also, we notice that the oscillation is of sizable amplitude: it has enough energy to use.

How does the behavior as an oscillator come about? Let us look at this system again, this time including damping. Below, we have written the force

from the airstream as $f(v)$ and have assumed it to be in the direction of motion of the mass m. For a given velocity of the airstream we can easily obtain $f(v)$ from the curve of F vs A (page 221, bottom left). To do this we note that a given A corresponds to a certain velocity of V_{sect}, the vertical velocity of the section (page 222, column 1). From this figure we see that V_{sect} is related to A by the formula $V_{sect} = V_{air} \tan A$.

Having the force F for a certain A we therefore have it for a certain V_{sect}, and hence we can make a plot of F vs V_{sect}. For simplicity, we replace V_{sect} by the symbol v, and to bring out the fact that F varies with v, we rename it $f(v)$ as above. The curve of $f(v)$ vs v then looks something like that shown in the diagram at the bottom of the page.

Mass-spring model of oscillation of the half-round section

If we look at the diagram above we can see that three forces are acting on the mass m: an upward (therefore negative as we have selected directions

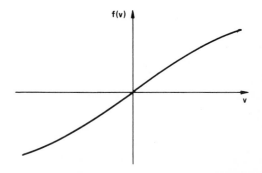

Aerodynamic force vs vertical velocity for the half-round section

here) force $-kx$ exerted by the spring (Hooke's Law) where k is the spring constant and x the displacement from the rest position caused by gravity; an upward damping force $-Bv$, where B is the damping coefficient; and of course $f(v)$. The total force, then, is $-kx -Bv + f(v)$, and by Newton's Law

$$-kx \; - \; Bv \; + \; F(v) \; = \; ma$$

If we apply energy considerations we see that we can ignore the force $-kx$, since it is concerned only with transformations from potential to kinetic energy and back, with neither gains nor losses (see Manual page 219 of this chapter). However, the damping force is always applied in a direction opposite to the motion and hence represents a loss of energy by the system, whereas the airstream force represents a gain of energy. If on the previous diagram we plot $f(v)$ and Bv we get a graph like that shown below. For a given v the net force $f(v) - Bv$ will be the vertical distance between the curves (shaded area). Where the shaded area is positive, the net force will be in the direction of the velocity and energy will be extracted from the airstream by the system. Where the shaded area is negative, the net force will be opposed to the velocity and energy will be lost by the system.

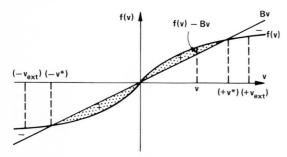

Net effect, aerodynamic and damping force, for the half-section

What do we expect to happen finally? By conservation of energy, we know that when the system reaches a final or steady oscillatory motion, energy cannot be extracted or lost, overall, in each cycle. For then the system's amplitude would either grow or decay each cycle, which would contradict the observed steady state. Likewise, the system cannot

operate at one of the velocities $(+v^*)$ or $(-v^*)$ where the curves cross, for then the mass would be going in one direction indefinitely (except for the effect of the force $-kx$). Clearly, what must happen is that the system oscillates between two extreme velocities $(+v_{ext})$ and $(-v_{ext})$ in such a way that the net energy gained or lost in a cycle is zero (essentially like the simple mass-spring system). If we add some other "load" which consumes energy from the airstream, the system will settle down to a steady state at some other, smaller amplitude.

Thus we have seen that by capitalizing on an instability we can get a system which takes a steady, nonoscillatory energy source and produces an oscillatory motion of a closely controllable frequency. This mechanical system is, of course, not suitable for producing high-frequency oscillations in a radar set. But it is a model or analog of the electrical oscillators one might in fact find in a radar set.

V. Torques and the Unstable Bridge

Everyone is familiar with the principle of the lever, which enables two unequal forces to be in balance if they are also at unequal distances from the fulcrum or pivot: the product of one force multiplied by its distance (measured at right angles to the line which shows the direction of action of the force), called its moment or torque, must be equal to the torque of the other force, figured about the same point.

In Demonstration III the lever is not readily apparent, but the torques are easy to figure. T-0817 is a useful introduction. Here we have a wheel with an off-center weight, W, in four positions, as well as a wheel with central weight, (c) in the diagram. In this case, the weight W measures the earth's gravitational attraction. The wheel does not fall under the influence of this force because it elicits an equal, opposite force F to support it. (From Newton's First Law we know that a motionless body, or one moving with constant speed in a straight line, must have no unbalanced force acting on it; hence W, the force of the earth's pull, equals F, the force of the table's push. If the teacher is not a physicist, and he would not be reading this discussion if he were, he must be warned that this is *not* a case of "action and reaction are equal and opposite.") The same argument applies in (b) and (d); the first is in stable equilibrium, the second in unstable. If wheel (b) is turned slightly, as in (a), the forces are still equal, but now a torque has developed about the point of support. F has no "lever arm" and no torque, but W does. Its lever arm is the distance from W to the vertical diameter of the disc, the one which passes through F. This torque tends to rotate the disc counterclockwise; it rolls until it is in position (b),

and after a number of rockings back and forth, settles into this position. This is indeed stable equilibrium, because a disturbance gave rise to "forces" (here, actually, a torque) that restored the original state. In (d), on the other hand, a disturbance results in a state like (e), the torque developed is clockwise, and the disc rolls further from equilibrium; this is the mark of instability. Of course, the disc finally finds itself stable, in position (b). In the words of the text, a new operating point has been reached.

CHECK LIST FOR CHAPTER 9   MACHINES AND SYSTEMS FOR MEN

APPROX. TIME: Text: 7 Days Lab: 2 Days

A. APPROACH	CLASS PERIODS	B. BLACK & WHITE TRANSPARENCIES	C. CUES (k=key problem) Discussion Questions	Easy	Medium	Hard	D. DEMONSTRATIONS, LABS & PROJECTS	E. EVALUATION	F. FILMS	G. GENERAL
1. Introduction			2							
2. Man as a Controller	1	0901 0902 0903 0904 0905	4,9,10				I, II	1a,e,2,3,5		II, III
3. Man in Communication	1	0906a,b 0907a-d 0908	3,5,6,7,8, 13					1b, c, g, 4		
4. Man Limited by Environmental Needs	1							1d		
5. Man and Sensing	1		14					1f, h, i, 6	0901	
6. Prosthetics	1	0909						1j,k,l	0106	
7. Matching Technology to Man	2	0910 0911	1,11,12					1m,n,o 7	0902 0903 0904 0905	
8. Final Comment										

Machines and Systems for Men

9

A | APPROACH

I. Purpose and Organization of the Chapter

Nearly all the emphasis of the book until now has been on how to use the concepts which have been found by engineers and technologists to be so helpful. In this chapter we look at some of the developments which the use of these concepts has helped to bring about and why they were (or were not) worthwhile. We ask the question: What *should* technology do? Implied, of course, is the question: What should technology *not* do? The answer given is that technology should make life pleasanter, fuller, and richer by providing ways to do worthwhile things that man, unaided, cannot do or, for good reasons, does not wish to do.

The discussion concentrates on five areas in which the technologist can help the human being: (1) in controlling devices too intricate, or too quick in action, for him to handle; (2) in communicating important information without error; (3) in working in hostile environments; (4) in sensing signals which he cannot perceive; and (5) in assisting or replacing damaged or useless parts of his body. Finally, the point is made that the technologist can help only where he knows and understands the needs, and further, that efforts to help are futile if faulty design interferes.

II. Objectives for Students

Upon completion of the activities, discussion, and reading in this chapter, students should be able to:

1. Recognize and identify the following terms: *electromagnetic wave, noise (as unwanted signals), prosthetics, robot, sensor, VTOL.*

2. Judge in specific cases whether a man or a technical device would be superior.

3. Illustrate by example the limitations of a human being as a controller of difficult or unstable systems.

4. Predict the impossibility of human control when his innate time delays prevent him from taking proper action.

5. Explain the production of "artificial gravity" by revolution of man-made satellites.

6. Justify the necessity for redundancy in the transmission of information.

7. Discriminate between the "Hamming code" and word-spelling with respect to their relative values as information transmitters.

8. Describe the "cocktail party effect" in listening to messages.

9. Interpret the method of recovery of a desired signal, lost in a noise background, by multiplication of samples of the signal as received.

10. Give illustrations of the bearing of a human being's environment on the effectiveness of his performance of tasks.

11. Contrast the service of a man with that of a mechanical substitute when working in a particular environment.

12. Identify those external signals that can be sensed by a man and those which require instruments.

13. Describe the use of filters with films sensitive to visible light or to infrared radiation to increase the information obtainable by study of the prints.

14. Foresee the need to develop new sensors for the study or control of problems created by the interaction of technology and people.

15. Cite in general terms the structure and action of the human ear and eye.

16. Explain the importance of current research in prosthetic devices, especially the efforts to link the devices directly with the nervous system.

17. Contrast the pattern-recognition ability of man with the corresponding weakness of present technical devices.

18. By the use of specific examples, show how the match between a user and a technological device can be helped or hindered by its design.

19. Distinguish between technology which serves genuine human needs and that which has little value to humanity.

20. Identify side effects of such technological systems as automobiles, power plants, and modern cities, and forecast likely side effects associated with systems not previously studied.

III. Suggestions for Teaching

Notice how this chapter reflects the profound change in contemporary philosophy. At one epoch pride was often expressed in "man's conquest of nature." Now we know that the conquest was a Pyrrhic victory, and we seek merely to "maximize the benefits" of the technical skills which were usually acquired as part of the effort to conquer. We hope that as new skills are gained, they will be genuine assets to humanity.

Section 1. Introduction. A couple of questions may occur to students: (1) Why does racing an automobile motor cool it? When the motor is not moving the car, little fuel is required to race it, so not much extra heat is produced; but the water pump and the fan both go faster too; the results are more coolant through the radiator, and more air past the cooling tubes. (2) Why are "idiot lights" so commonly used, if they are so bad? The real reason is that they are much cheaper than gauges. The rationalization may be that they are easier (for "the idiot") to interpret: red light = stop!

Section 2. Man as a Controller. Figure 6-36 should be reviewed at this time (the human tracking experiment). The experiment in moving the jacket should certainly be done by students, also the variant with the pockets loaded, perhaps with a couple of half-kilogram laboratory weights, or just the normal junk found in the jacket pockets of students. Some will quickly find that a fairly slow motion seems to contradict the text: the jacket just moves without unstable swinging. It doesn't really, however; it just means that the braking motion is so slight as not to be noticeable. Try the inverted pendulum (which everyone has played with) but use a meter stick, not a broom: its period is shorter, its inertia much less, so it is harder to keep it upright very long. This attempt to maintain stability in an inherently unstable system is so fine an example of feedback that students should not be allowed to miss it. Probably nobody will believe the account of the Stanford cart; point out that rod A is longer and slower than B, so there is time for the cart to get B under control first and then go back for A. For any pendulum, whether erect or inverted, $T = 2\pi \sqrt{\ell/g}$, where T = period or time for one back-and-forth swing, ℓ = length from support to "center of percussion," about two-thirds of the way along a uniform stick, and g = acceleration due to gravity. For a discussion of the imitation gravity which can be produced in artificial satellites, and of the VTOL aircraft, see Section G, Part II ("Dynamics for Chapter 9"). Section G, Part III is an extra lab project known as "The Flying Saucer" which is pertinent, and especially interesting because the circuit was first developed by a student in this course. It requires a CRO.

Section 3. Man in Communication. Use the game described at the beginning of this section in class, using only English. Have the message transferred in a whisper or a low voice, and meanwhile play a good loud record or encourage other conversation. The only rule: it is forbidden to repeat the message. If someone is sure he missed it the first time he must pass on *something*, no matter how garbled, just as a telegraph or radio channel does. The Hamming code has nothing to do with radio amateurs: Dr. Hamming works for Bell Labs (use T-0907a–d). In case there is a high level of interest, directions for the use of five Logic Circuit Boards to make an automatic encoder, decoder, and error corrector are given in Part G of the Teacher's Manual for Chapter 13. This device may seem like a lot of work for not much reward, but it *is* a little surprising to be able to create an error by short-circuiting or even breaking a connection and still see the correct message come through; that is, the proper lamps light up. It may be worth reviewing binary numbers briefly (probably already studied in math class), at least enough to remind students that even numbers always must end in 0 and odd numbers in 1. We finally come to the matter of multiplying received signals. The student may not see the point of the statement "if r_1 is positive, r_2 is as likely to be positive as negative." It sounds like weighting the odds, but it is not. Left unsaid: "and if r_1 is negative, r_2 is still as likely to be positive as negative." Therefore there are two positive products: $(+r_1) \times (+r_2)$, $(-r_1) \times (-r_2)$; and two negative ones: $(+r_1) \times (-r_2)$, $(-r_1) \times (+r_2)$.

Section 4. Man Limited by Environmental Needs.

This section contains a useful lesson for students who drive cars. A good driver takes care to accelerate and decelerate slowly for the sake of his passengers' comfort, even if he doesn't mind paying for wasted fuel and tires worn out before their time.

Section 5. Man and Sensing.

Some students will probably know about dog whistles pitched too high for most human ears (we once measured the highest pitch audible to a group of young men and found, to our astonishment, one who could have heard such a whistle). This whole section should serve as a reminder of a fact often repeated: when we want precise knowledge of almost anything, we are generally dependent on instruments for the measurement.

We have met such problems as that of handling traffic where lack of appropriate instrumentation has turned out to be the major part of the problem. In the last part of Section 5 a statement is advanced which may promote some valuable discussion. It is: "10% of the earth's land area is cultivated; an additional 21% can be..." Why, then, is it not? Some of the answers are: large private estates and public parks; land so low in fertility that although it could be cultivated it does not seem worth the trouble; forested regions which would first have to be cleared, and in any case they may be in use for raising trees for lumber; the rapid loss of plant foods in the tropics by leaching, especially in places with excessive rainfall.

Section 6. Prosthetics.

In connection with the search for an artificial heart you may like to use this quotation: "While it may be ridiculous to compare a heart with a washing machine, the reliability problem is emphasized by the relatively few washing machines which operate for 15 years without maintenance or repair." It is probably needless to remind students of the remarkable British hand, Figs. 7-10 and 7-11. The whole section has so much human interest (even though artificial teeth are omitted!) that you may find it difficult to break away and get on with other subjects. However, weighing relative importance is, as usual, an optimization problem that is yours alone.

Section 7. Matching Technology to Man.

The part of this section that really demands careful treatment is the very end: "Controlling Technology's Side Effects." The difficulty of and the need for foreseeing these side effects can hardly be overemphasized. Build more reservoirs to increase our dwindling water supplies—and drown valuable farmland (a British problem)? Dispose of radioactive wastes in deep wells—and set off earthquakes (as near Denver)? Keep down the cost of gasoline by cheaper oil shipment in giant tankers—and cause endless damage to beaches and wildlife when one is wrecked? Improve agricultural practices so we can feed more of the earth's exploding population—and ruin lakes and watercourses by eutrophy fostered by excess fertilizer in runoff water (Lake Erie, for instance)? Any of these will serve to make the point, but class members should be urged to think of their own examples. Some interesting ideas were expressed by A. W. Eipper in *Science* (July 3, 1970): "It is far easier to prevent pollution (or nuclear warfare, or overpopulation) than to correct for it after it has occurred." Last thought: nothing useful was ever accomplished by people sitting on their hands;

things can be put to rights only by active effort on the part of many people. Several good films are suggested that are especially helpful in winding up this part of the course. See Section F, Films.

Section 8. Final Comment. We have none.

B | BLACK AND WHITE TRANSPARENCIES

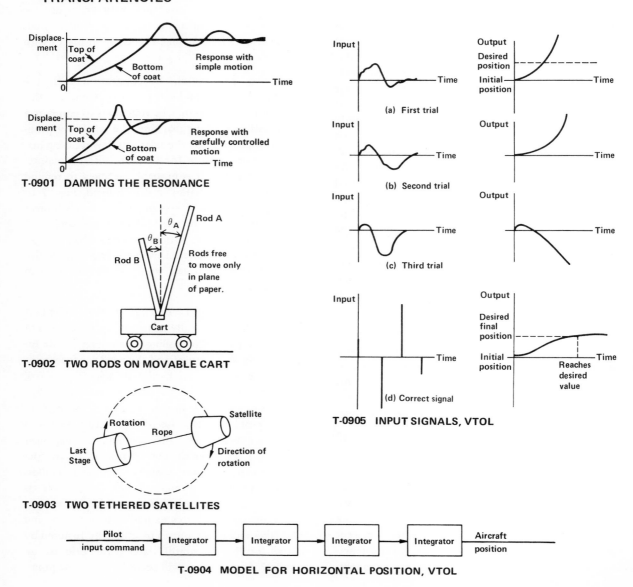

T-0901   DAMPING THE RESONANCE

T-0902   TWO RODS ON MOVABLE CART

T-0903   TWO TETHERED SATELLITES

T-0904   MODEL FOR HORIZONTAL POSITION, VTOL

T-0905   INPUT SIGNALS, VTOL

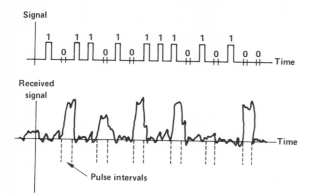

T-0906 TRANSMITTED AND RECEIVED PULSE TRAINS

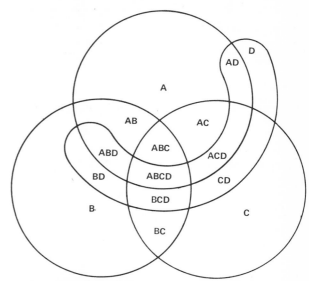

T-0908 FOUR REGIONS OVERLAPPING IN ALL POSSIBLE COMBINATIONS

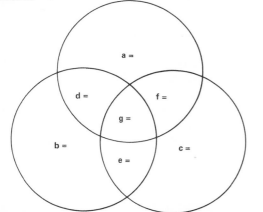

T-0907a OVERLAPPING CIRCLES, HAMMING CODE

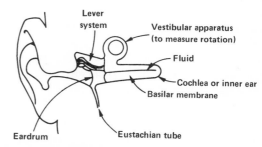

T-0909 DIAGRAM OF AN EAR

T-0907b SIGNAL DIGITS, HAMMING CODE
T-0907c REDUNDANT DIGITS, HAMMING CODE

T-0907d SIGNAL RECEIVED, ERROR IN "e"

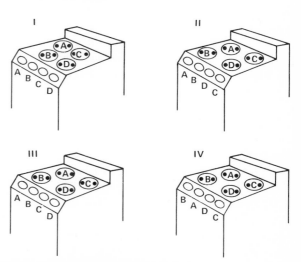

T-0910 MODELS OF FOUR STOVES

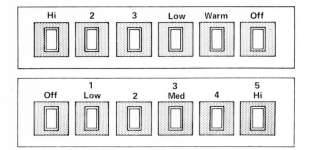

T-0911 PUSHBUTTONS FOR ELECTRIC STOVE

C | CUES TO QUESTIONS

Questions for Study and Discussion

1. Comfort, convenience, safety

a) The shift selector on automatic cars has changed recently from PND21R to PRND21. The reverse (R) position has been moved from the extreme right to between park (P) and neutral (N). There are at least two reasons for the change, convenience and safety. For example, when parking, reverse is almost always used; it is not necessary to go through all gears to get from reverse to park; and there is now no danger that in going from reverse to first the gear will inadvertently be shifted to second, with a resulting fast jerk forward, perhaps into the car in front.

b) Many small appliances have been changed to accommodate the user: Teflon-coated frypans, electric can openers, electric carving knives, toasters, small mixers, blenders, and many others. These products have been introduced for the convenience of the customer. Great attention has been paid to the ease of cleaning, handling, repair, safety, appearance, and ease of storage.

2. a) Ability to go great distances

b) Ability to travel at high speeds

c) Ability to transport large numbers of people

3. a) Ability to understand many languages

b) Ability to adapt to many dialects

c) Ability to read many styles of handwriting

d) Ability to separate message from noise

e) Ability to learn different means of communication

4. a) Ability to make measurements and to take necessary action almost instantaneously

b) Ability to exert a much larger force than a man can

c) Ability to expend a much larger amount of power (force x speed) than a man can

5. Electronic noise from components or external disturbances.

6. Man has the ability even under great noise intensity to select the signal he wants to hear and reject those portions that he doesn't wish to hear. Examples of this are a husband ignoring his wife while he is listening to an exciting part in a ball game, or a student listening to a friend while their teacher is talking in front of the class.

7. When heard during the chaos of combat or other peril, or in the presence of noise, words with similar vowels and syllable structures are likely to be confused. Several such pairs are: *able, baker; dog, yoke; easy, zebra; item, mike; jig, king; peter, zebra.* Moreover, many of these words would be strange to a person whose native language is not English, and therefore would be very easy to miss or confuse.

8. a) To average out the noise and make the primary signal more easily recognized.

b) In determining whether a person is dead or not (for example, before transplanting healthy organs from an accident victim), doctors are becoming more cautious about relying on traditional tests (e.g., hearbeat audible through a stethoscope). "Brain waves" recorded by an electroencephalograph may be more reliable, but it is necessary to make sure that the noise of a received signal is indeed only noise.

9. The purpose is to add an artificial effect of gravity by spinning the 2 tethered satellites. An astronaut in a capsule tends to keep moving in whatever direction he already happens to be moving (by a principle first fully understood by Newton). If the tether forces the capsule to follow a circular path, its floor presses against the astronaut's feet and turns his straightline motion into circular motion, too. The force of the capsule's floor against his feet feels to him exactly the same as the force of the ground against his feet under ordinary conditions on earth. The speed of spin is controlled by reeling in or play-

ing out the rope tethered to the 2 vehicles—the longer the rope, the slower the rate of spinning and the less the artificial gravity effect.

10. We use a bicycle as the example. The rider controls his balance helped by signals from the middle ear. Whether he touches the handlebars or not, the rider senses whether or not he is balanced and his actual position, then feeds this information back through the brain to his muscles so that he leans to the right or left or turns the front wheel just enough to restore his balance or cause the bicycle to turn the desired amount.

11. a) The advantage of an airplane's automatic pilot is that it frees the human pilot from having to concentrate over an extended time period on flying and enables him to save his faculties for the landing details.

b) Radio time signals are a far more accurate means of telling time than the human body's own time-keeping mechanism, which can, nonetheless, be relatively accurate. Have you ever awakened minutes before the alarm sounded?

12. a) Pound for pound, man is still the least expensive device which can reason and thereby control and report on a space flight (of course, assuming no disaster occurs).

b) Man is still required to program, operate, and service computers, although computers are now being designed which "repair" themselves (i.e., switch from a circuit which fails to a standby circuit).

13. It enables messages to be transmitted which are virtually error-free without wasting the time required to repeat everything at full length.

14. Partial lists

No help needed (except in unusual cases):

> Pain
> Flavor, odor
> Assonant pitch (sound)
> Surface texture of fabrics, etc.
> Own posture

Help sometimes needed:

> Color
> Brightness
> Exact pitch

> Very faint sounds
> Very dim shapes
> Intensity (loudness) of sound
> Relative roughness or smoothness
> Degree of acidity, alkalinity, sweetness, saltiness
> Temperature
> Lapse of time
> Very short distances
> Very long distances
> Speed
> Presence of small electric potentials

Many others will need to be judged individually as they are mentioned by students.

D | DEMONSTRATIONS, LABS, AND PROJECTS

I. Man as a Controller

PART A

This exercise is designed to demonstrate the inability of man to control oscillations which are above 1 or 2 hertz (cycles/sec) in frequency. It should be used when Section 2 is being discussed. The demonstration should be set up before class starts.

Equipment for Demonstration:

> 2 analog computers
> Cathode-ray oscilloscope (DC-coupled, with slow sweep)
> Patch cords, connecting wires
> Watch with sweep-second hand (stopwatch, preferably)

The square wave is obtained by preparing an analog oscillator (Manual page 208) and then amplifying its signals, use × 10 inputs, so that they saturate the analog amplifiers. The signal observed is a sine wave with tops and bottoms cut off. The initial condition of the lower integrator should be set to its maximum value. It is advisable to reset the initial condition after each run because a slight imbalance in the amplifiers can change the signal amplitude.

The manual control circuit permits the student to vary the amplitude of the controlled signal between plus and minus one-half the amplitude of the input voltage E. This should be considerably larger than the square wave amplitude so that signal cancellation is possible with only a small motion of the manual control knob.

The CRO display of the signal from analog computer #1 should appear as:

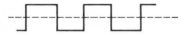

When the signal from the student-controlled analog is combined with the signal from analog computer #1, the composite signal should appear as:

The initial spikes (leading edge of the square wave) will always be present, but as the frequency increases the student will be unable to adjust the composite signal to 0 before the beginning of the next pulse. This, then, will mark the limit of his response time.

Start the square wave frequency at a low value to give the student some experience in manipulating the signal control, and use the slow sweep of the CRO. Start to increase the frequency after the operator learns the technique. Although the oscillations can be timed with a stopwatch much more quickly

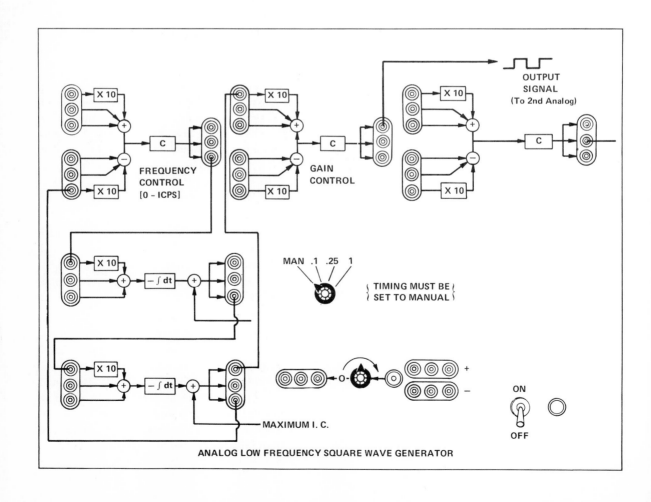

ANALOG LOW FREQUENCY SQUARE WAVE GENERATOR

and accurately than otherwise, use of a simple sweep-second hand is quite successful after a little practice. The reaction time is one-half the inverse of the frequency of the square wave oscillation, if this detail is of interest.

Answers to Questions:

*1. Most people will lose control between 1 and 2 hertz.

*2. People are distinctly variable in their ability to control dynamic signals.

PART B

The boat-docking simulation will probably be looked upon (and properly so) by the students as fun, and it may be classified as a simple optional exercise requiring little or no write-up. As with Part A, the setup should be prepared in advance, either by the teacher or by interested and able students.

Equipment for Demonstration:

    Analog computer
    High-impedance VM, or CRO, or chart recorder
    Patch cords
    Watch (if competition is desired)

Only a smooth performance of the docking maneuver is acceptable. The object is to touch the dock gently, not bump into it or go beyond it (i.e., crash through it). The pilots will probably discover on their own that the manual blade-angle control must be turned cautiously at first until they acquire a feel for the "throttle."

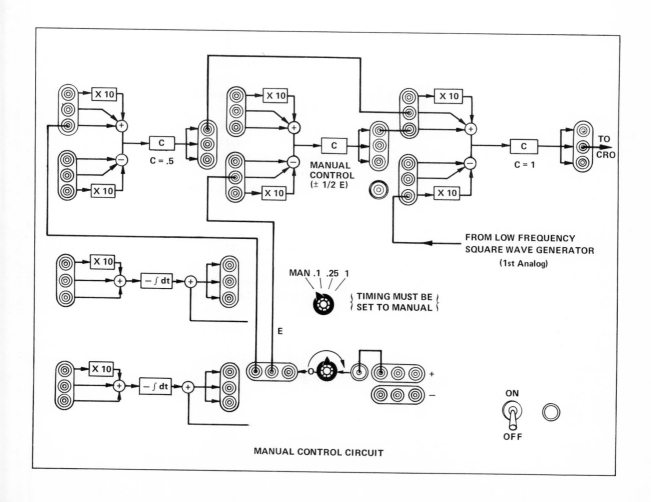

MANUAL CONTROL CIRCUIT

For general entertainment, you may wish to organize a class contest to see who can drive his vessel across the lake without damage to the dock in the shortest time.

Answers to Questions:

*5. Once the boat gets moving, it takes longer for it to slow down when the coefficient of resistance (*B*) is small than when it is large. In the former case it is therefore more difficult to dock the vessel properly. The difficulty is caused partly, in every case, by lack of information about the rate of change of speed. The pilot might be aided in controlling the boat if its velocity were to be monitored on a second meter.

*6. For reasons just given, it is easier to dock the boat with an opposing current, harder to dock it with a favoring current.

In case of questions, it should be added that the resistance offered to motion through a fluid is not correctly described by any simple law. If the speed is so slow that the fluid flow follows streamlines, the resistance does vary nearly as v; when the speed is fast enough for turbulence to occur, the resistance is nearly proportional to v^2, but at still higher speeds this rule fails, too. We may assume that we are dealing only with streamline flow, or realize that at low speeds Bv (with high B) is not far different from Bv^2 (with low B). But in any case it doesn't matter: the point is that there *is* a resistance and that it *does* depend on v. (Moreover, we have no multiplier on our computers, so we couldn't use v^2 if we wanted to.)

II. LEM Landing Simulation

This exercise should convince students that astronauts cannot land a lunar excursion module (LEM) safely unless they are assisted by technological devices. Even though it is difficult to achieve a soft landing at first, most students should be able to do it with a little practice. Monitoring the velocity will improve the student's ability to control the position of the vehicle. In early trials, v_0 should be set at 0.

The sign convention adopted may cause trouble for a time. It may help to draw a large circle

("Moon") on the chalkboard, together with two arrows. One points "up" or away from the Moon and is labeled "$+a$, $+v$, $+S$"; the other points "down" or toward the Moon and carries negative labels.

Just as in docking a boat, a landing that penetrates the surface is frowned upon. A meter reading of a fraction of a volt negative implies that the LEM hit hard. You may want to decide on appropriate criteria in the light of your experience after a few preliminary trials, determining the dividing line between a jolt and a wreck.

PART A

Equipment for Each Lab Team:

Analog computer
Meter, CRO, or chart recorder

Answers to Questions:

*1. Landing technique will definitely improve with practice. In fact, learning curves can actually be obtained: plot number of volts past 0 vs number of trials.

*2. At first it will be more difficult to control the LEM. The operation of the ascent-engine control knob will be different, depending upon whether the initial velocity is toward the moon (negative) or away from the moon (positive).

PART B

When we add another integrator to the system, we are removing the output (displacement) farther from the input (now rate of change of acceleration or "jerk"). The third integrator is procured by connecting 2 analog computers; to do this, join the "remote-operation" jacks on the two instruments by a suitable patch cord. The extra integrator makes it even harder to control the system, which now begins to be rather similar to the VTOL example discussed at the end of Section 2.

Equipment for Demonstration:

Two analog computers
Meter, CRO, or chart recorder

E | EVALUATION

The questions in this section are rated according to the chapter objectives and the performance levels stated in the introduction to the teacher's manual. This group of questions is not intended to be all inclusive, but just as a guide to possible questions. Zeros in the chapter objective column indicate no chapter objective for this question.

Chapter Objective	Performance Level	Judged to be Relatively Easy:
		1. In the following question, mark each statement T if it is true, but mark it F if it is false.
3	I	a) When a man attempts to control a complicated system, he is helped if he uses feedback.
7	I	b) The word-spelling method of eliminating message errors is still used in spite of the invention of the Hamming code.
9	I	c) The most effective way to recover a radar reflection signal that is lost in background noise is to multiply together many samples of the reflection signal, all equally delayed after the transmission.
10	I	d) People often become carsick when their "environment" of acceleration is changed too rapidly and often.
2	I	e) A properly trained man could be used in place of any machine that a man can design.
12	I	f) The only signals a man cannot sense are the electromagnetic ones like radio, radar, and infrared.
7	I	g) When the Hamming code is used to transmit a message, any number of mistakes can be automatically corrected.
12	I	h) Man is supposed to have 5 senses, but we all know that he actually has exactly 6.
13	I	i) Infrared photographs cannot be taken successfully through smoke or haze.
16	I	j) False teeth can properly be considered prosthetic devices.
16	I	k) If sound signals could be converted to electrical signals and correctly inserted into the proper nerve, many people now totally deaf could hear.
17	I	l) The fact that man can be easily fooled by optical illusions shows that he really does not readily recognize patterns.
19	I	m) The proper use and only important purpose of technology is to aid man in his effort to control nature.
18	I	n) Since most people are right-handed, the buttons to control an electric stove should have lowest heat at the right, highest at the left.
20	I	o) Thermal pollution is bad for some kinds of fish.

In the next three questions, check the best answer.

2. Of the following advantages that technology can bring us, the most important is

a) color TV sets that are really portable.
b) the invention of new ways for people to enjoy themselves.

19	II	c) mankind's new ability to set foot on the moon.

d) knowledge of new, more effective insecticides.
e) the control of systems that man, unaided, cannot manage.

3. In the "human tracking experiment" of Chapter 6, man tried to control one spot of light on a screen to make it follow the random motions of a second spot. In such a control problem, a man should expect to be defeated because

a) the control machinery is too complicated for him to master without long study.

Chapter Objective	Performance Level

Judged to be Relatively Easy:

4 — II

   b) the task is so boring that he quickly loses interest.

   c) there is always a time delay between seeing the light spot move and his response.

   d) there is a device inside the mechanism that makes it impossible for anyone to succeed.

   e) his arms are too short to move the control lever properly.

4. Redundancy is a useful way to
   a) control an unstable system.
   b) avoid misunderstandings in conversation.

6 — I

   c) encode a message.
   d) eliminate noise.
   e) match technology to man.

Judged to be More Difficult:

In the three following questions, check the best answer.

5. The attempt to make artificial gravity in satellites by spinning them about each other in pairs

5 — II

   a) will not really work because the artificial gravity is not enough like the real thing.

   b) is an interesting idea but the artificial gravity must always be too weak.

   c) has had to be given up because the satellites tend to break up.

   d) was at first unsuccessful because the system proved to be unstable.

   e) worked beautifully except for minor, unimportant side effects.

6. In the early days of airplanes good pilots claimed that they flew "by the seat of their pants." By this they probably meant that

5 — II

   a) when the airplane, taking a curve, was tilted just right it produced an imitation gravity that made the pilot's chair feel directly under him.

   b) they thought that they had developed a special gravity-sensing ability.

   c) flying had become so natural to them that it was as easy as sitting down.

   d) the unstable aircraft made them slide around in their seats.

   e) they had motors that they thought were powerful enough to make them fly, even if they used their trouser seats for wings.

7.

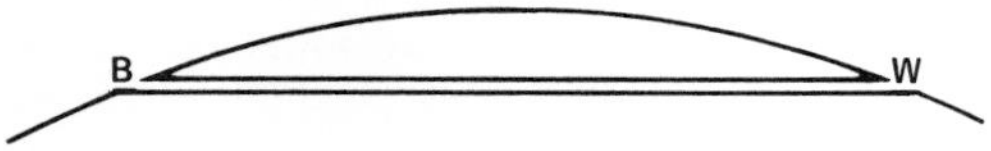

20 — II

A proposal has been made to construct a tunnel from Boston to Washington in a straight line as in the diagram (it would therefore have to lie much farther below the earth's surface in the middle than at the ends); thus trains traveling between the cities would gain speed by coasting "downhill" to the center, and would then slow down on the uphill journey the rest of the way. Hence gravity would supply most of the needed energy. The most appropriate response to this proposal is the following:

   a) What are we waiting for? Let's start digging!

   b) What makes anyone suppose the scheme would work?

   c) What side effects might result?

   d) This is a silly idea because it leaves New York out of the picture.

   e) It would obviously cost too much to be practicable, so it isn't worth thinking about.

Answers to Evaluation Questions:

1. a) T   f) F   k) T
    b) T   g) F   l) F
    c) T   h) F   m) F
    d) T   i) F   n) F
    e) F   j) T   o) T
2. e
3. c
4. b
5. d
6. a
7. c

F | FILMS

F-0901 CONTROLLING THE FUTURE
Recommendation: Useful, if students show an interest in this area of technology.
Application: Should be shown during Section 5 for examples of sensing and control using the currently interesting fluidic devices.
Length and Type: 29 min, b & w, sound.
Source: #5
Summary: NET film showing examples of both bistable and proportional fluidic devices and explaining their action. They are displayed in use to sense malfunctions of a pumping station and to control jet engines, as well as to control the aerodynamic lift of an airfoil.

F-0106 BIOMEDICAL ENGINEERING
For details, see recommendation in Chapter 1. The film is appropriate here also, in Section 6.

F-0902 OF MEN AND MACHINES
Recommendation: Good film to illustrate engineering psychology, an area not well known. Also shows a special case of optimization.
Application: Enrichment, very good illustrations of man-machine relationships.
Length and Type: 30 min, b & w, sound.
Source: #5 or #8
Summary: Shows some of the ways in which man handles and processes information, problems and dynamics of information feedback between men and machines, the human being's behavior in complex man-machine systems, and the way in which all this has led to redesign of equipment to fit human capabilities.

F-0903 ENGINE AT THE DOOR
Recommendation: Good for limited application.
Application: Enrichment. Probably best used near end of Section 7. Considerable conversation; if students react negatively, point out that people are just as important as principles and machinery; probably more so.
Length and Type: 30 min, b & w, sound.
Source: #8
Summary: NET film in which J. P. Eckert, co-inventor of ENIAC, asks if machines will ever run man, and E. Nagel, Columbia professor of philosophy, and C. R. DeCarlo, director of education for IBM, point out that only man has responsibility to use science and technology wisely; science does not dictate uses to which it is put.

F-0904 AMERICA: ON THE EDGE OF ABUNDANCE
Recommendation: Excellent film to start a discussion of the social and economic impact of automation.
Application: Can be used anywhere in course, but best just after discussion of what automation is.
Length and Type: 60 min, b & w, sound.
Source: #5
Summary: Far-reaching economic and social conse-

quences of our automated and computerized society examined by British commentators. What will be the effects on training, leisure, values?

F-0905 CITIES OF THE FUTURE

Recommendation: Good film for illustrating the importance of rational planning.

Application: Evidently belongs at the end of this chapter to bring this work to a conclusion in a somewhat different way.

Length and Type: 30 min, color, sound.

Source: #2 (No charge)

Summary: Study of planning problems which must be solved to prevent the city of the twenty-first century from becoming a disorganized, unimaginative megalopolis. (A 21st Century film)

G | GENERAL

I. Bibliography

W. H. Davenport and D. Rosenthal, *Engineering, Its Role and Function in Human Society.* Department of Engineering, Reports Group, University of California at Los Angeles, 1966.

> An anthology of writings which deal mostly with the human use of engineering. The treatments include sociological, philosophical, economic, and political discussions about the future use and role of science and technology.

R. L. Gregory, *Eye and Brain, the Psychology of Seeing.* McGraw-Hill, 1966 (B) (paper)

> A perfectly fascinating little book, very comprehensive but not repellently so, on the history, physics, physiology, and psychology of vision and theories of vision (therefore part of communication theory). Pattern recognition, optical illusions, and other perception problems.

E. G. Mesthene, *Technological Change.* Mentor, 1970 (A) (paper)

> Is technological change good, evil, or overrated? These common views are shown to be inadequate because change is outstripping traditional categories of thought. The book argues for a response to technology that will make man its master, not its slave. Important background

reading for students if there is to be adequate discussion of the impact of technology on man and society.

E. E. Morison, *Men, Machines, and Modern Times.* M.I.T. Press, 1966 (B)

> A first-rate historian takes a long, thoughtful look at a number of case histories of the man-machine interaction, particularly when it is complicated by man-man interaction. His comments on the nineteenth-century Navy in its reactions to suggested improvements in gunnery practice and in ship design, on steelmasters and financiers trying to make and market steel, and on a range of other subjects, are all delightful, unpressured reading.

R. Theobald, ed., *Dialogue on Technology.* Bobbs-Merrill, 1967 (A) (paper)

> The impact and implications of technology in our society. An important prefatory article describes both the body of knowledge on which experts are mostly in agreement, and a series of disagreements: on facts and their interpretation, trends and *their* interpretation, constraints imposed by the environment, the nature of man, and the nature of a desirable world to live in. Fine background for discussion (which, after all, should be based on facts and not on unsupported opinions).

R. Bellman, "Control Theory." *Scientific American,* September, 1964

W. A. Lynch and J. G. Truxal, "Control-System Engineering." *International Science and Technology,* March, 1966

M. May, "The Road to 1977." *Fortune,* January, 1967

"A Study of Technology Assessment." U.S. Government Printing Office (send to Superintendent of Documents, Washington, D.C. 20402), $1.25

> Study by committees of the National Academy of Engineering indicating that reliable forecasts of potential impact of future technologies are essential to guide decisions.

II. Dynamics for Chapter 9

Section 2 has two particular puzzlers. The puzzler to discuss first is the statement that it takes no less than 4 integrations to get a VTOL aircraft off the ground and moved from here to there. This is because 2 kinds of motion are required, linear and rotational. All the propellor (or jet) does is exert a force. The force is directed in such a way as to cause 2 accelerations: rate of change of linear velocity and rate of change of angular velocity. It is necessary to tilt the aircraft, change its angular posture more or less so that it will not merely mount straight up but will also, later, move to the side. Newton's Second Law may be written, for the first case, $a = (1/m)F$, acceleration is proportional to net force (with the reciprocal of the mass as constant of proportionality). When this acceleration is integrated for a stated time it yields change in velocity, and a second integration (for the same time) gives change in displacement. Another derivation from the Second Law is written $\alpha = (1/I)\tau$. Alpha is angular acceleration, in radians-per-second/second ($360° = 2\pi$ radians), and I is moment of inertia. I depends on the distribution of the mass of the object; a wheel with a light rim and a massive hub is easier to spin than a wheel of the same total mass but with a heavy rim and a light hub. If a rotatable object is considered to be the sum of many small masses, each of magnitude m and each at its own measured distance r from the axis, then $I = \Sigma\, mr^2$, the sum of the mr^2 products for all the tiny individual masses. The magnitude of I for our VTOL aircraft is fixed by its structure, its load, and how the latter is distributed, and need not trouble us further. Lastly, τ is torque, the product of F and its lever arm. Much as before, if α is integrated for a stated time it yields the change in angular speed in radians per second (usually symbolized ω, omega), and a second integration gives change in angular posture, radians from the start (θ, theta). Thus we see the reason for 4 integrations. Of course, the magnitudes of the integrations (the time that each one must last) change with change of loading, wind speed, and direction, and even with temperature, relative humidity, and barometric pressure, which alter the properties of the air.

The other puzzler in Section 2 is that of imitation gravity in a man-made satellite, produced by whirling the satellite and another object, probably a piece of a rocket, about each other. On its face this is not too difficult to manage. The 2 bodies revolve about their common center of gravity. The tether supplies each with a centripetal force which causes the angular accelerations. For each as it whirls in its orbit the motion keeps changing direction, and this rate of change of direction, in radians/sec², is the angular acceleration. Clearly, the men on board the capsule must have angular accelerations identical to that of the capsule; the floor of the latter exerts centripetal force on them. This force is the gravity analog, and in fact is indistinguishable from gravity in its effect on the men.

This is very much like the motion of the earth-moon system. Here gravity supplies the tether, and if one could maintain a position directly "above" the center of gravity of the combination, the center would be seen to move uniformly (to a first approximation; to a second approximation it moves with slowly varying speed in an ellipse, thanks to the sun's attraction; to a third approximation: Oh dear! The other planets cause variable and minute but important changes). The earth's center describes a smallish circle about the common center of gravity (which lies inside the earth, about 1000 mi under the surface), the moon's center a large one (to a first approximation). One can show that the product mvr (the "angular momentum") is the same for each, and unchanging in time. The earth's mass m is much larger than that of the moon, but the moon's distance r from the center of gravity and its speed v in its orbit are much larger than the earth's. Since r varies, so does v.

It is very simple to demonstrate the interdependence of orbital speed and radius. The PSSC course has an experiment on centripetal force which uses simple equipment, but because we are not concerned with the quantitative details we can be even simpler. It is sufficient to tie a small weight to a piece of string and whirl it about your head. A #5 or #6 rubber stopper makes a nice safe weight, 5 or 6 ft of fishline are enough. Hold the free end in one hand, and whirl with the other. Threading the line through a 1-hole stopper provides a convenient grip

242

to avoid wear on the fingers of the whirling hand and to make it easy to pull in or let out line with the control hand.

All this analysis ought to apply to the capsule-rocket combination; since *mvr* is constant for each, if the tether is shortened (both *r*'s made less) the speed in orbit of both objects increases (both *v*'s made larger), and vice versa. The fact that waves were set up in the tether, so the system was unstable, was as unexpected as it was unwelcome. The solution to the difficulty, a constant readjustment of the length of the tether according to computerized instructions, is mentioned in the text.

III. The Flying Saucer

(Originally devised by John McConkey, student at James Caldwell High School, West Caldwell, N. J., 1966–67.)

In Lab I, Part B, we assumed the acceleration of a boat to be a quantity $(a-Bv)$, where a depended on the angle of the propellor blades and B was the coefficient of water resistance, taken to be 0.7. In this simulation of a flying saucer we assume that the part of the acceleration of the saucer caused by a given engine is, as before, $(a - Bv)$, where the magnitude of a depends on the throttle opening for the

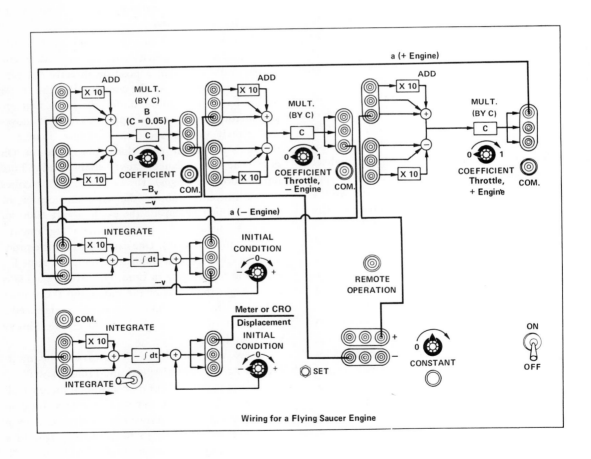

Wiring for a Flying Saucer Engine

engine and *B* is arbitrarily given the value 0.5 (students may find it amusing to vary this and find how *B* affects the ease of "flying" the saucer).

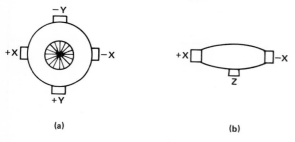

(a)   (b)

Engine placement

The engines are located as shown above, where (a) is a top view and (b) is a side view. To "fly" the machine in the *X* direction (+ or −), wire up an analog computer as shown opposite. Notice that although *B* is to have the value 0.5, the coefficient is set to 0.05 because the output has to be inserted into the ×10 input to the integrator. The thrust of each engine is controlled by the setting of its Coefficient control. The "displacement" wire goes to the HDC input of a CRO. Center the dot on the screen, and defocus slightly to enlarge the saucer image. Set vertical and horizontal controls to the low range. Turn on the − engine all the way, and push the Integrate lever; the image should move to the left. Adjust the horizontal gain until it is at the edge of the screen. Wire a second analog in exactly the same way for the *Y* engines, and lead the displacement connection to the VDC input. Make adjustments similar to the previous ones and you are ready to fly in a horizontal plane.

To add the third dimension, we must include gravity instead of a − engine. Use the Coefficient knob to get −10 volts at the output of the middle summer. This will subtract 10 m/sec^2 (gravitational acceleration, 2% high) from the acceleration supplied by the Z engine (+ only). Otherwise, the third analog computer is set up as at the bottom of page 242.

If 2 oscilloscopes are not available, use a voltmeter as an altimeter and connect it to the Z displacement.

If you wish, you may use 3 oscilloscopes to get 3 views of the saucer. The connections are as follows: for the *x*, *y* plane (below), the displacement leads of X and Y engines are connected as before. For the *y,z* plane, connect a second displacement lead from another outlet of the second integrator of the Y engines to HDC of a second scope, and the Z engine output to its VDC input. Similarly, arrange to show motion in the *x,z* plane by connecting the X engine output to the HDC input of CRO #3, and the Z engine to the VDC input. Flying the machine under these conditions is quite a rigid test of the chauffeur's ability to visualize in three dimensions.

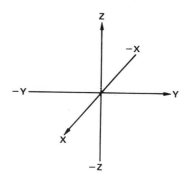

Three-dimensional coordinates

CHECK LIST FOR CHAPTER 10 — THE THINKING MAN'S MACHINE

APPROX. TIME: Text: 9 Days Lab.: 1 Day

A. APPROACH	CLASS PERIODS	B. BLACK & WHITE TRANSPARENCIES	C. CUES (k = Key problems) Discussion Questions	Problems Easy	Problems Medium	Problems Hard	D. DEMONSTRATIONS, LABS & PROJECTS	E. EVALUATION	F. FILMS	G. GENERAL
1. The Key to Man's Survival	1		8					2,6	1001 1002 1003 1004	
2. Man as a Symbol Maker	1							1		II
3. Ciphers and Codes	1		9				III	3		
4. Symbols and Machines	1	1001						4,5	1005	III
5. Digital Computers: What Goes In and What Comes Out	2	1002 1003 1004 1005	1,2,3							
6. Digital Computers: What's Inside?	3	1006 1007a,b 1008 1009 1010 1011a,b,c	5,7,10,11				I, II	7,8,9		
7. Past, Present, & Future of the Computer	1		4,6						1006 1007	

The Thinking Man's Machine
10

A | APPROACH

1. Purpose and Organization of the Chapter

We have now completed the discussion of "engineering concepts," which led us from decision making through modeling to the study of several kinds of systems. The last part of the book explores a most important system, technologically speaking: the digital computer. This is done in considerable depth, much more than there was either time or room, or indeed need, for with the systems investigated up to now. The stages of this study are logical. It leads from the question "What *is* a computer?" through the foundations of computer programming (using only machine language with the briefest glance at a compiler language); it continues to the basic switching circuits found in computers; it ends with the conceptual assembly of a "minimicro" general-purpose computer by combining just the circuits described (or a few other very similar ones).

This first chapter starts by showing that digital computers deal with symbols, explains what symbols are, and then takes a look at a very simple computer program. By means of this approach, the need for input and output devices, for memory, for a processor, and for control are clarified. The chapter closes with a history of computers and a look ahead.

II. Objectives for Students

Upon completion of the reading, discussion, and laboratory in this chapter, the student should be able to:

1. Recognize and identify the following terms: *accumulator, address, binary code, code, computer memory, input* and *output, instruction decoder, instruction register, operation code,* and *program counter.*

2. Describe the importance of the digital computer in the history of the development of the human intellect.

3. Discriminate between "symbols" and "objects."

4. Justify the statement that the digital computer deals with ideas, not only with numbers.

5. Distinguish between tasks which can be performed by a computer and those which cannot (at present) be done and justify the distinctions made.

6. Reproduce the basic operation cycle of a stored program computer and explain the purpose of each step.

7. Describe the functions of the control unit of a digital computer.

8. Compare a flow diagram with a program, explaining the purpose of each.

III. Suggestions for Teaching

It is important not to bog down in this chapter's fascinating details, most of which do not in fact get one ahead very much in the main work. If the class is short of time, Sections 5 and 6 contain the essential material introductory to the later chapters.

Section 1. The Key to Man's Survival. It would be hard to quarrel with this assessment. Students may be interested to know that the manufacture of stone tools (not just of flint) still goes on. The work is done by archeologists in order to find out how primitive man went about it. Mostly, it appears that pieces of bone or horn or even hard wood (believe it or not) were employed as tools to shear flakes off bits of stone and thus shape them into arrow points, axes, or scrapers. The hypothesis that man with his brain saw how to use his hand with its opposable thumb to make and use tools has a counterpart (like the chicken-or-egg-first?) argument. Some people argue that the hand was the first essential, that with it sticks and stones were picked up and used, and the early brain then evolved toward our present organ because those who had better gray matter used their tools better.

Section 2. Man as a Symbol Maker. It is perhaps worth reminding the class that there is no logical necessity that dictates 26 letters in the alphabet. Classical Greek used 24, several different from ours. In classical Latin there was no need for *J, U,* or *W.* Modern Italian does without *J, K, W, X,* and *Y* (except in some foreign words).

The nub of this section is the fact that a symbol means what we choose it to mean, and therefore that communication can only take place between people who have *agreed* on the meanings of their symbols. This is a good place to remind the class of the importance of order and place value in our number system. The symbols 264 and 642 are very different as are 5500 and 5005.

Section 3. Ciphers and Codes. These fascinate young people. Some teachers exploit this fascination by setting the working out of a cryptogram as a class project, suggesting also that students invent and explain their own codes. It seems to be a question of best use of time, and each teacher has to be his own decision maker, given the constraints in his situation. Once more, the essential point, not to be missed, is that a symbol is no more or less than what we decide it should be. Students really enjoy doing Lab III, and it provides a concrete experience for the ideas in this section.

Section 4. Symbols and Machines. It is too soon to spend time on the details of binary arithmetic but not too soon to entice your students to "discover" that if you use n binary digits you can write 2^n different numbers. Work out charts on the chalkboard: with 1 digit you can write 0 or 1 (2 numbers); with 2 digits, 00, 01, 10, 11 (4 numbers). Hence 2^6 yields 64 entries in Table 10-3 (T-1001). At the same time, introduce the system to be used later for writing a chart of all possible numbers having n digits: in the 2^0 column, alternate 0 and 1; in the 2^1 column, alternate two 0's and two 1's; in the 2^2 column, four 0's and four 1's, and so forth. But don't worry about the place value unless it seems appropriate. About now may be the time to point out that one can study computers in two ways: (a) How are they used? (b) How do they work? In this chapter and the next we investigate (a); finally we will get to (b).

Section 5. Digital Computers: What Goes In and What Comes Out. Here we get down to cases. As much practice as necessary should be given to writing flow diagrams, and at this stage the diagrams should be as informal as possible. For example: the flow diagram of the process of making a telephone call when you don't remember the number; of opening a safe with a combination lock (coded ECCP, of course); of starting a car; of ordering a mid-morning snack; of your morning's activities; of calling a girl for a date; of tossing a coin for a decision; or of sharpening a pencil. Be sure all the cases of choice are recognized, and all the loops. The flow diagrams in the text are important only as examples of how a computer follows instructions, and of how looping and decision stages make it needless to write a program in absolutely complete detail.

Section 6. Digital Computers: What's Inside? Several kinds of sensor were discussed in

Chapter 9. The simplest sensor for reading punched cards is like a doorbell, which senses the presence of a caller. Much faster ones exist with a light and photocell, just as in the ECCP card reader.

It is a needless distraction just now to spend classroom time on the Rand table or the light pen, though it is certainly worth pointing out that these optical output attachments are extremely convenient for instant, but temporary, use, while permanent records need a print-out unless the user is prepared to process something like magnetic tape or punched cards or tape. Do move along to the development of Fig. 10-11. T-1007a and b should be quite helpful here. Notice the heavy black borders of the boxes which stand for selector switches, and the fact that Control works by controlling these, not otherwise. The same thing is emphasized in T-1011 and its overlays. Take up the *idea* of memory, stressing the organization with addresses (T-1008) and also the device of stacking core planes (T-1009), but soft-pedal the detailed instructions in Fig. 10-13. "Check bits," mentioned in this part under "Memory," are described in Section G, Part II ("Error Detection and Error Correction").

There is apt to be trouble with the understanding of the Control unit but it will become clear enough as time goes on. The problem no doubt stems from two sources. Partly it is because the student is still vague about what the difference really is between data words and instructions. Data words as such do not usually appear in programs. The English translation of instructions is apt to refer to just "the word": Copy *the word* on the top card into memory cell 18. Add *the word* in cell 27 to the contents of the accumulator. Print out *the word* stored in memory at address 36. However, every one of these instructions has two parts: an "operation," an order to do something, and an address where "the word" is to be stored or from which "the word" is to be obtained.

The second source of trouble is the student's failure to distinguish sharply among 3 computer units with somewhat similar names. These are the instruction decoder, the program counter, and the instruction register. The first job of the instruction decoder (part of Control) is to send the address of the first instruction in the program to the program counter. The counter will be updated step by step as the computing process continues, since subsequent addresses normally follow in order; but a point easily missed is that in case of a loop the counter will be reset, after the looping is finished, to the original count at the start of the loop, by a circuit under control of the decoder and having just this job. The counter *may* also be reset if a decision instruction is met. Again, the decoder is in charge. The decoder's second job is to "look" in the *address* just sent to the program counter, "fetch" from it the whole of the first instruction and send it to the instruction register. (Fetching and sending are accomplished in the minimicro computer we are working toward by throwing switches, or using electromagnets to throw them.) In the instruction register the instruction is stored in 2 parts, an op code and an address. Once the instruction register and program counter have been set, the decoder takes over again, "looks" in the register to find what to do (op code) and where to find the data or put the result (address); and then looks in the now-updated program counter to learn where to find the next instruction for the register.

Fig. 10-18 is copied on T-1011a (with 3 overlays to be used one after another, not together), except that in the text the figure depicts an input instruction (or data word) being stored, while the transparency is arranged to show what happens when the instruction "209" comes up during the execution of a program. At Step 04 of the program (see the program counter on overlay b) the selector switch in Memory (which is a decidedly short one in this case) and the decoder switch in Control connect cell 04 in Memory with the instruction register, thus "fetching" its contents. The instruction in 04 is not physically moved, of course; it is just a matter of arranging things so that the switches in the instruction register are set like those in cell 04. Thus the instruction is *copied*, but the original remains unchanged in the memory cell. It may be needed again later if looping occurs. In overlay c the program counter is updated and nothing else happens. Then in d the address part of the instruction causes the selector switch to be moved to cell 09 in Memory so that the instruction can be executed: the word "XYZ" (it must be a number) stored in cell 09 can be copied (again without being removed from its place in Memory) into the accumulator, which has been connected to it by the action of the instruction decoder, together with the op part of the instruction. We are now ready to go through the cycle again.

The "Fetch, Update, Execute" cycle is absolutely basic, and must be stressed repeatedly. Using CARDIAC for this purpose can be very effective.

All of these details fall into place easily and quickly with the aid of CARDIAC. Give a very simple program such as described in this chapter and Fig. 11-1 of the next (T-1101) to be worked out in class. (Notice that this chapter includes all the work with CARDIAC in the lab. After Part A of Lab I has been done, it would be wise to run through some of the simple programs printed in the Questions and in the Problems, until familiarity has brought ease, and only then go on to Part B.) Lab II can be done when studying Chapter 11.

Section 7. Past, Present, & Future of the Computer. It is interesting that Napier's bones, the device for multiplication mentioned here, were essentially a device designed to crudely mechanize the multiplication process shown in Fig. 1-8. The slide rule, invented about 1630 by Delamain or Oughtred (there was controversy, the latter claiming theft of the idea by the former), was circular at first.

The UNIVAC computer was introduced to a wide public when it was used to forecast over the radio the result of the 1952 Presidential election after only a few key districts had reported. (Eisenhower defeated Stevenson. There was a row later because the announcement of UNIVAC's forecast was made before all polling places had closed, so at least some of the last voters may have thought they were voting without having any effect on the outcome.)

A device to use in this section is to send the class members to the Sunday paper to find how many different kinds of programmer they can find mentioned in the "help wanted" ads.

B | BLACK AND WHITE TRANSPARENCIES

0	000000	↑	100000
1	000001	J	100001
2	000010	K	100010
3	000011	L	100011
4	000100	M	100100
5	000101	N	100101
6	000110	O	100110
7	000111	P	100111
8	001000	Q	101000
9	001001	R	101001
[	001010	-	101010
#	001011	$	101011
@	001100	*	101100
:	001101	)	101101
>	001110	;	101110
?	001111	'	101111
(space)	010000	+	110000
A	010001	/	110001
B	010010	S	110010
C	010011	T	110011
D	010100	U	110100
E	010101	V	110101
F	010110	W	110110
G	010111	X	110111
H	011000	Y	111000
I	011001	Z	111001
&	011010	←	111010
	011011		111011
]	011100	%	111100
(	011101	=	111101
<	011110	"	111110
\	011111	!	111111

T-1001 SIX-BIT CODE FOR ALPHANUMERICS

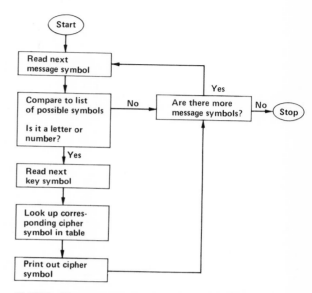

T-1003 FLOW DIAGRAM FOR ENCIPHERING

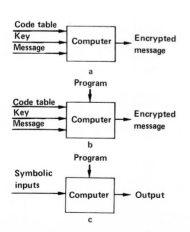

T-1002 BLOCK DIAGRAM OF COMPUTER USES

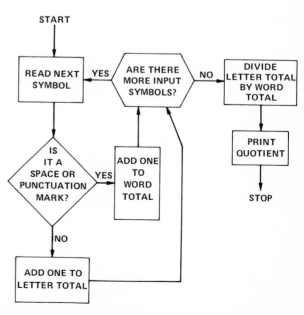

T-1004 FLOW DIAGRAM, PROGRAM FOR AVERAGE WORD LENGTH

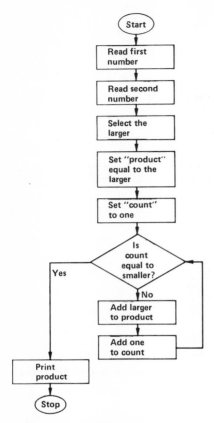

T-1005 THE "IDIOT MULTIPLIER"

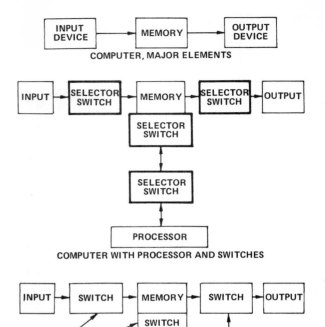

T-1007a COMPUTER BLOCK DIAGRAMS

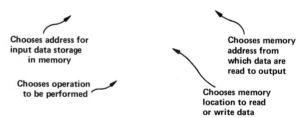

T-1007b SWITCH FUNCTIONS, COMPUTER DIAGRAM

Memory	Access time to any stored bit (seconds)	Typical size		Cost
		Bits	Typed pages	($ per bit)
Transistor (solid state)	50×10^{-9}	128,000	8	1
Typical magnetic cores	$0.5 - 1.0 \times 10^{-6}$	5×10^{6}	250	0.1
Magnetic drums	2×10^{-6} to 30×10^{-3}	130×10^{6}	800	0.01
Magnetic disc	10×10^{-6} to 0.5	10^{9}	5000	0.001
Photographic	0.25 to 10	1000×10^{9}	A library of books	0.00001

T-1006 ACCESS TIME, VARIOUS MEMORIES

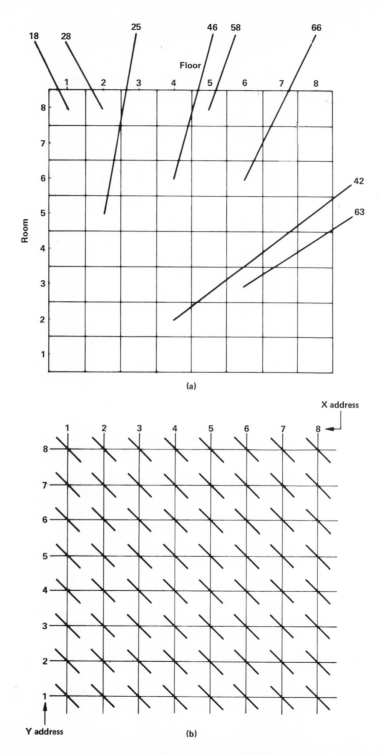

(a)

(b)

T-1008   MEMORY ADDRESS SCHEME

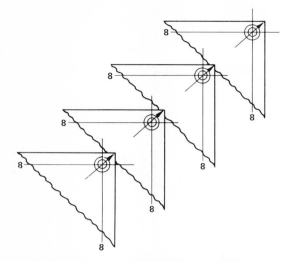

T-1009 FOUR CORE PLANES FOR 4-BIT WORD

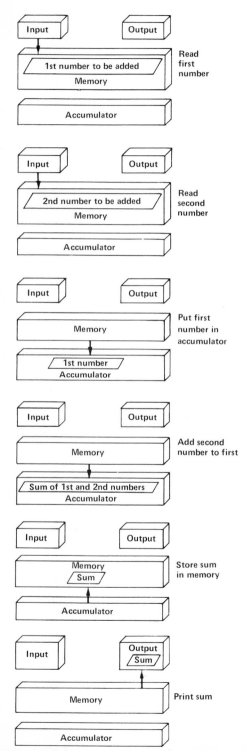

T-1010 BLOCK DIAGRAM

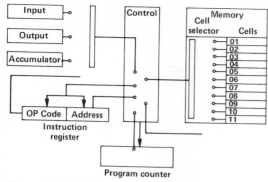

T-1011a THE COMPUTER CYCLE

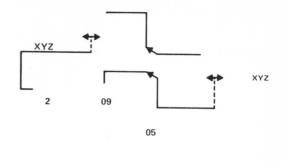

T-1011d INSTRUCTION EXECUTED

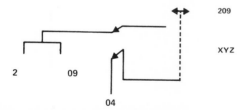

T-1011b FETCHING THE INSTRUCTION

48	0	60
49	0	61
50	0	62
51	1	60
52	2	61
53	6	63
54	1	61
55	2	62
56	6	64
57	5	63
58	5	64
59	9	00
60	-	- -
61	-	- -
62	-	- -
63	-	- -
64	-	- -

1st card:	111
2nd card:	222
3rd card:	444

↓
05

T-1011c PROGRAM COUNTER UPDATED

T-1012 SUPPLEMENTARY PROGRAM FOR PRACTICE

C | CUES TO QUESTIONS AND PROBLEMS

Questions for Study and Discussion

1. Finding Pythagorean triples, airline reservations, bank deposits and withdrawals, automobile assembly, including customized interiors and options. (But, as always, results are no better than the efforts of the key puncher. As the writer was starting to answer this question, the mail came, bringing a canceled check that had missed the bank statement. When he put this check with the others, he found one belonging to someone else.)

2. The first problem here is to decide on the amount of detail expected. In general, the computer would be used for:

> sorting (by Social Security numbers; sorting is not essential because the computer can scan its whole memory quite quickly)
>
> comparison (taxpayer's statements with other information)
>
> arithmetic (to check the return, make corrected computations)
>
> print-outs (return is correct or in error; prepare bill for amount due)

Clearly, there is plenty of employment for key-punch operators, who are needed to enter all the information in memory.

3. In the view of this writer this question (taken literally—in both senses) is better suited for a dissertation at a second-rate university than for *The Man-Made World.* However, there are reasonable shortcuts. It seems like unconstitutional punishment to make any student count *all* the letters on a page. The point of the question can be felt if each boy or girl counts the occurrence of, say, 3 letters. If you have enough students you can thus cover 6 or 9 letters in the chapter. The number of letters on a page can be estimated by counting lines and multiplying by the average number of letters on a few lines (the variation comes mostly from spaces and punctuation). It is necessary to define a "page" as one without illustrations breaking into the text. For part (c) the page size must be specified—2 books of

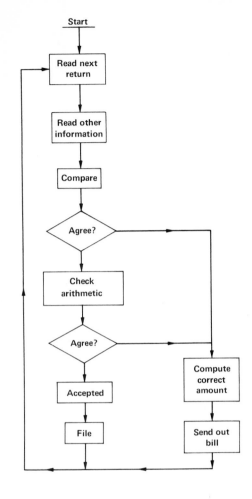

the same size and degree of difficulty as *The Man-Made World.* Compare Section 2, Chapter 6, and Section 3, Chapter 3. In the light of the second reference especially, it is apparent that the proper answer is very large, perhaps even more pages than occur in any one book!

4. a) A lawyer thinks logically just as an engineer does.

b) A biologist models the structure of the living world to help his students learn.

c) Engineering affects our social science (as this book aims to show).

d) We have repeatedly cited aspects of environmental and urban problems, which are going to demand steadily more of the politician's attention.

5. No, but in some cases solutions lead to extraneous roots (this is not, however, ambiguity as the word is defined).

6. Speed; secondary—size, cost, reliability, less current, less heating.

7. John arrived at a swinging party. John caused a disagreeable display of himself in public.

8. Discussion might weigh public good against a person's right to privacy; i.e., to have information about him as a person kept out of public circulation. Possible subjects for examination are:

The data in the files of the Internal Revenue Service: the accusation has been made that the Service sells lists of names and addresses, even classified into income categories;

Credit status: errors by key-punch operators could long outlast the existence of any evidence in the situation, so that the harm done might be irreversible;

Health and illness information;

Any scheme that would produce for commercial exploitation lists of people supposed to have specialized interests and/or weaknesses.

9. In breaking a cipher, counts are made which show the frequency with which the various symbols appear; if the language is known this will generally reveal enough letters to make it possible to guess complete words (thus, in English *e* is by far the most frequent letter). When the Vigenère table is used, it turns out that even though a particular symbol may mean any letter and vice versa, when any given letter turns up in the message at intervals as long as the key word, it is represented by the same code symbol. Hence, with a good long message before him, a good analyst can break even a Vigenère code. But in the case described in the question there isn't any such way into the secret.

10. In CARDIAC and similar computers the second and third digits of an *instruction* word give the address of the cell where Control will find the *data* word to be operated on or to which the data word is to be transferred. The data word *does not include* any address. The *instruction* word, on the other hand, is fetched (at the proper time) from the cell of which the address is (at that time) indicated in the program counter. The addresses are taken, here, to be 00 through 07:

	0	1	2	3	4	5	6	7
0	101	102	103	104	105	106	107	108

11. Yes, it would. It reads as follows: Read the first card (A) into cell 11. Clear the accumulator and enter A into it. Read the second card (B) into cell 12. Add B to the contents of the accumulator. Store this sum in cell 13. Print the contents of cell 13. Stop.

Problems

1. The answer depends upon how many thumbs the student has, how skillfully he organizes the job, how slippery or sticky, stiff, flexible or perhaps broken the cards are, and how suits and numbers happen to be arranged after the shuffling. For a comparison the editor took 37 sec to sort into suits (0.71 sec/sort), another 57 to sort deuce to ace (1.1 sec/sort). He made no error in his one trial and so left well enough alone. There were 104 sorting actions (twice through the pack). The machine would take, at 1800/60 =30 actions/sec, 104/30 or 3.47 sec. It would be 94/3.47 = 27 times as fast. What "I" would take an hour to do, at \$2, the machine would finish in 60/27 = 2.2 min, costing 2.2/60 × 5 = \$0.185 or about 18.5¢, and this makes no allowance for boredom and tiredness slowing "me" down and causing errors. The advantages of the machine: much faster, much cheaper, errorless, tireless, and it doesn't take a coffee break.

2. a) $\dfrac{60 \text{ sec}}{10^{-7} \text{ sec}} = 6 \times 10^8$ decisions/min

b) $\dfrac{1}{10^{-7} \text{ sec/decision}} = 10^7$ decisions/sec

3. a) Each 0 of the message becomes 1, each 1 becomes 0. JOHN = 100001 100110 011000 100101 = 011110 011001 100111 011010 = < IP & or "Lessthanipand."

b) At first glance the message is concealed. If either 0 or 1 predominates, the message will be fairly easy to decode because large parts will be clear (from 0's) or inverted, so to speak, from 1's. This implies that the relative frequencies should be

1:1, but, as a necessary property, not just alternating but varying at a random rate.

4. If the product required is 2 × 1, then in the previous step we set P = 2; then here C = 1, at the next step we change the product to P = 4, and count to C = 2, which is not equal to smaller, so the looping continues indefinitely. This is avoided by the flow chart of Fig. 10-9 (T-1005) where the decision box goes to "Print" at the first pass.

5.

D | DEMONSTRATIONS, LABS, AND PROJECTS

I. Introduction to the CARDIAC

As already recommended in Part A of the Teacher's Manual, the student may find CARDIAC most useful if he completes Part A of the lab exercise and then tries the program on T-1012 just to drive the lesson home. This is not necessary, however, if he appears to be catching on to the system readily. Part

B contains material that is discussed on Chapter 11. This question then follows: Is it better to develop the new instruction codes 3 and 8 and to work out the Bootstrap Routine ahead of the text or after it? I do not venture to prescribe. Lab II, however, is complex enough so that it had really better be postponed to the next chapter.

Equipment for Each Student:

CARDIAC
Pencil
Cleansing tissue

A wax pencil is best because it causes less indentation when writing on the plastic surface. A lead pencil is useless unless it is very soft. Felt-tipped pens and Pentel pens work well if they contain water-soluble ink, but tend to leave a trace of the color when wiped off (the cleansing tissue may need to be slightly dampened, or you may breathe on the marks as if they were glasses).

If you decide to have your students become involved in Part B at this time, you will notice that when it is performed, the machine "stops" once the program has been loaded into memory. To restart, place the "bug" at cell 20 and push the starter button again. This procedure is equivalent to setting the counter at a predetermined point before starting operations again.

You will need to clarify several points about Bootstrap which are likely to seem fuzzy to students. Each should have CARDIAC before him as you lead the discussion. The last instruction in a program is normally 900: "set program counter to 00 and stop." It is possible to reset the program counter to any cell desired before turning the machine on, but to load a program we leave the counter at 00. Now point to cell 00 in which is printed +001. This instruction, "read the next card into cell 01," is permanently there and serves as a starter for loading. The first Bootstrap card is 002 which is read into cell 01 by that initial instruction. The program counter next fetches the instruction 002 from where it was just put in cell 01, and after the counter is updated, 002 is executed: the next card is read into cell 02. The next card is 800. This is the next instruction fetched, counter goes to 03, then 800 is read and executed: store counter's reading in cell 99, jump to 00 (i.e., reset counter to 00). The next card is now read into cell 01 (replacing the 002 already there), counter goes to 01, the card just read in says "read next card into cell so-and-so," which is done, then we get 800 again and around we go again. Cell 01 receives ever-changing contents. In the case illustrated here, they are 002, then 020, 021, 022, etc. In this loading routine there was actually no need to store the counter's reading at the instruction 800; but in general it *is* necessary at a jump because having that number in the memory tells the computer where to get back into a program after using a subroutine.

II. Double Precision Routines on a Digital Computer

As pointed out in connection with Lab I, this belongs with the next chapter, but it will be discussed here. By the time it is finished, all the op codes of the minimicro computer except 7 will have been used (and 7, Subtract, is managed here by adding a negative).

Equipment for Each Student:

Same as for Lab I

In this experiment the pupils use the CARDIAC, a 3-digit machine, to imitate a 6-digit machine. The experiment illustrates how clever programming (software) can be employed to extend the capability of a computer (hardware). Subroutines and calling sequences are illustrated.

PART A

Answers to Questions:

*1. The program to add 2 numbers is:

60	020
61	021
62	120
63	221
64	622
65	403
66	623
67	900

The numbers to be added are put on input cards 1 and 2. If card 3 is left blank, the instruction 67 is unnecessary. However, it is important that pupils develop the practice of terminating programs with a definite command.

*2. The program is independent of the signs of the numbers, because if both are negative the sum is numerically the same as if both were positive, but had a minus sign; if the signs are opposite, we add a negative and a positive, keeping the sign of the number with the greater magnitude.

*3. If the numbers to be added have opposite signs, overflow cannot occur because the sum will be less than the larger, and hence cannot have more digits.

PART B

The translation of the odd statement "call its position *a*, the jump step *xx*" is "when we reach step 54 we have a jump instruction, the updated counter will read 55 and this is the number to which it must be reset when we return to the main program."

Answers to Questions:

*1. The main program for finding the sum of 186324 and 241063 is:

50	095
51	096
52	097
53	098
54	886
55	659
56	559
57	598
58	900

The input cards for the above program should be:

#1	186
#2	324
#3	241
#4	063

As the program is executed, the pupil must follow the directions given by the control section of CARDIAC.

Points to observe are:

a) The clever manner in which the command 8(XX+1) stored in cell 94 is altered, to effect a return to the correct point in the main program.

b) While overflow does not occur when 324 and 063 are added, the command stored in cell 91 places the overflow in the proper position to be included in the next summing operation.

c) The efficient use of cell 98, for after the number originally stored there is processed, the cell is used for storing the first 3 sum digits.

*2. If the number to be summed were +123456 and −100457 the subroutine would fail, since the summing of +456 and −457 would require borrowing from digits which at that instant are in memory.

Signed numbers may be manipulated by treating $A - B$ as $A+(-B)$, and preparing the input cards accordingly.

*3. If the numbers to be summed were +816,324 and +241,063, overflow would occur when the most significant digits were added. This could be handled in a fashion similar to the command stored in cell 91. However, instead of allowing the overflow digit to remain in the extreme right column of the accumulator, it would have to be stored in memory so that a print-out command could be accomplished. Hence the subroutine would have to be shifted so that entry to the subroutine would be at instruction 83 rather than 86 while reserving cells 95 through 98 for data. The main program would also require some changes, since overflow requires print-out instructions.

The following program satisfies these requirements:

Main Program		Subroutine			
50	095	83	199	95	___
51	096	84	692	96	___
52	097	85	196	97	___
53	098	86	298	98	___
54	883	87	698	99	8__
55	596	88	403		
56	597	89	295		
57	598	90	297		
58	900	91	697		
		92	403		
		93	696		
		94	8(xx)		

III. Ciphers and Codes

The purpose of this activity is to provide students with the opportunity of working with a system of coding which is different from those discussed in the text. Student involvement in this activity should result in a better understanding of the process of encoding and decoding. The only equipment that is necessary are strips containing letters and other symbols (see following page for strips) and a coding chart as shown below.

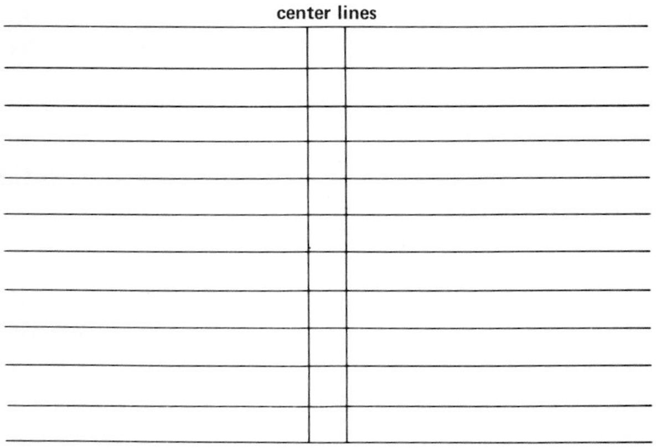

center lines

Suggestions for Smooth Operation:

1) Notice that a strip of symbols is made by cutting the strips from the following page and attaching one strip from the first page to another from the second page. (Letters *M* and *N* should be next to each other.)

2) If you want more than one set of strips, use the following page as masters for reproducing other pages.

3) The strips and coding charts can be made more permanent by pasting them to cardboard.

CIPHERS AND CODES

−	X	÷	,	.	&	1	2	3	4	5	A	B	C	D	E	F	G	H	I	J	K	L	M
−	X	÷	,	.	&	1	2	3	4	5	A	B	C	D	E	F	G	H	I	J	K	L	M
−	X	÷	,	.	&	1	2	3	4	5	A	B	C	D	E	F	G	H	I	J	K	L	M
−	X	÷	,	.	&	1	2	3	4	5	A	B	C	D	E	F	G	H	I	J	K	L	M
−	X	÷	,	.	&	1	2	3	4	5	A	B	C	D	E	F	G	H	I	J	K	L	M
−	X	÷	,	.	&	1	2	3	4	5	A	B	C	D	E	F	G	H	I	J	K	L	M
−	X	÷	,	.	&	1	2	3	4	5	A	B	C	D	E	F	G	H	I	J	K	L	M
−	X	÷	,	.	&	1	2	3	4	5	A	B	C	D	E	F	G	H	I	J	K	L	M
−	X	÷	,	.	&	1	2	3	4	5	A	B	C	D	E	F	G	H	I	J	K	L	M
−	X	÷	,	.	&	1	2	3	4	5	A	B	C	D	E	F	G	H	I	J	K	L	M
−	X	÷	,	.	&	1	2	3	4	5	A	B	C	D	E	F	G	H	I	J	K	L	M
−	X	÷	,	.	&	1	2	3	4	5	A	B	C	D	E	F	G	H	I	J	K	L	M

CIPHERS AND CODES

N	O	P	Q	R	S	T	U	V	W	X	Y	Z	6	7	8	9	0	%	(	)	$	?	+
N	O	P	Q	R	S	T	U	V	W	X	Y	Z	6	7	8	9	0	%	(	)	$	?	+
N	O	P	Q	R	S	T	U	V	W	X	Y	Z	6	7	8	9	0	%	(	)	$	?	+
N	O	P	Q	R	S	T	U	V	W	X	Y	Z	6	7	8	9	0	%	(	)	$	?	+
N	O	P	Q	R	S	T	U	V	W	X	Y	Z	6	7	8	9	0	%	(	)	$	?	+
N	O	P	Q	R	S	T	U	V	W	X	Y	Z	6	7	8	9	0	%	(	)	$	?	+
N	O	P	Q	R	S	T	U	V	W	X	Y	Z	6	7	8	9	0	%	(	)	$	?	+
N	O	P	Q	R	S	T	U	V	W	X	Y	Z	6	7	8	9	0	%	(	)	$	?	+
N	O	P	Q	R	S	T	U	V	W	X	Y	Z	6	7	8	9	0	%	(	)	$	?	+
N	O	P	Q	R	S	T	U	V	W	X	Y	Z	6	7	8	9	0	%	(	)	$	?	+
N	O	P	Q	R	S	T	U	V	W	X	Y	Z	6	7	8	9	0	%	(	)	$	?	+
N	O	P	Q	R	S	T	U	V	W	X	Y	Z	6	7	8	9	0	%	(	)	$	?	+

E | EVALUATION

The questions in this section are rated according to the chapter objectives and the performance levels stated in the introduction to the teacher's manual. This group of questions is not intended to be all inclusive, but just as a guide to possible questions. Zeros in the chapter objective column indicate no chapter objective for this question.

Chapter Objective	Performance Level	

Judged to be Relatively Easy (there is no "more difficult" test):

All of the following statements are true EXCEPT (check the exception):

1. A symbol
   a) can be used to stand for another symbol.
   b) can be understood whether or not it can be written.
   c) is a noisy instrument in a brass band.
   d) is the basis of most kinds of communication.
   e) may mean whatever we want it to mean.

Chapter Objective 3, Performance Level I

In the remaining questions, check the best answer:

2. Man's struggle for survival in the world
   a) was no longer necessary after he invented stone tools.
   b) is still going on today.
   c) has now been replaced by the development of education.
   d) was never encouraged by woman.
   e) has been taken over entirely by the computer.

Chapter Objective 2, Performance Level I

3. It is sometimes said that algebra is a language. This statement is
   a) true only in part.
   b) true only some of the time.
   c) false in the graphical part of algebra.
   d) certainly false.
   e) certainly true.

Chapter Objective 1, Performance Level I

4. A person who knows how to use a computer (and has access to one)
   a) no longer needs to do any thinking.
   b) can save himself much mental drudgery.
   c) might program the machine to take a blindfold test of the flavors of soft drinks.
   d) can use the computer to do the housework.
   e) must be able to use a typewriter to record the output.

Chapter Objective 5, Performance Level I

5. Computers are particularly important
   a) only to people who know how to program them.
   b) only to people who have enough money to buy one.
   c) only to people engaged in scientific research.
   d) to all people who live in a technological society.
   e) to all people who live on farms.

Chapter Objective 2, Performance Level I

6. In general, the people most capable of learning to use computers are
   a) young.
   b) old.
   c) foreigners.
   d) men.
   e) women.

Chapter Objective 2, Performance Level I

7. The part of a computer which arranges its automatic action is called
   a) the memory.
   b) the program decoder.
   c) the instruction counter.

Chapter Objective 7, Performance Level I

Chapter Objective	Performance Level	Judged to be Relatively Easy:

d) the control.
e) the instruction register.

8. An instruction to a computer consists of 2 parts called

<table>
<tr><td>1</td><td>I</td><td>

a) selector switch and memory.
b) arithmetic unit and processor.
c) input and output.
d) op code and address.
e) accumulator and register.

</td></tr>
</table>

9. Following is a list of several operation codes and their translations:

2 Transfer number from memory to accumulator and add it to the number already there.

<table>
<tr><td>6</td><td>I</td><td>

5 Transfer number from memory to output.
6 Transfer accumulator contents to memory.

The instruction 265 means

a) Transfer number in memory address 65 to accumulator and add it to number already there.
b) Transfer number from memory address 26 to output.
c) Transfer number from memory to accumulator and then to output.
d) Transfer number from accumulator contents to memory.
e) Transfer number from accumulator to memory and then to output.

</td></tr>
</table>

Answers to Evaluation Questions:

1. c	6. a
2. b	7. d
3. e	8. d
4. b	9. a
5. d	

F | FILMS

F-1001 DIGITAL COMPUTER TECH-NIQUES: INTRODUCTION

Recommendation: Highly recommended.
Application: Enrichment. As a preview to digital computers or alternatively just before Chapter 15.
Length and Type: 16 min, color, sound.
Source: #14 (No charge) Address requests well in advance. (Navy Film No. MN 8969A)
Summary: General introduction, reviewing history and indicating differences between analog and digital devices.

F-1002 UNIVERSE OF NUMBERS

Recommendation: Highly recommended.
Application: Enrichment. To stimulate interest or as introduction to programming.
Length and Type: 30 min, b & w, sound.
Source: #8
Summary: History from Pascal, then an explanation of how a computer solves a problem. Somewhat talky, but gives the student a chance to see such people as Eckert and Hamming.

F-1003 THE LIVING MACHINE

Recommendation: Part I is highly recommended. Part II is optional.

Application: Enrichment. In Part I an overview of computer applications. Part II is more philosophical and discusses the impact of the computer on society.

Length and Type: 27 min for each part, b & w, sound.

Source: #1 or #15. Apparently Part I cannot be rented without Part II.

Summary: Part I shows a checker game between a man and a computer, then numerous applications, of which few are familiar. Part II is Dr. McCulloch of MIT describing his research on frog's eye and man's brain.

F-1004 THE COMPUTER REVOLUTION, PART I

Recommendation: Optional.

Application: Enrichment, general introduction to computers.

Length and Type: 30 min, color, sound.

Source: #2 (No charge)

Summary: CBS "21st Century" series. In a very general way, shows some of computer's applications and touches lightly on their impact on society.

F-1005 COMPUTER SKETCHPAD

Recommendation: Good film to show development of use of CRO as an output device.

Application: Enrichment. Use with Section 5.

Length and Type: 30 min, b & w, sound.

Source: #8

Summary: NET "Science Reporter" series. Discussion of development illustrated by plenty of action shots, including some showing 3-dimensional applications.

F-1006 THE COMPUTER REVOLUTION, PART II

Recommendation: Good film to illustrate current applications of computers, and future possibilities.

Application: Enrichment.

Length and Type: 30 min, color, sound.

Source: #2 (No charge)

Summary: CBS "21st Century" series. Shows current uses much better than Part I, and touches on sociological aspects.

F-1007 COMPUTERS AND HUMAN BEHAVIOR

Recommendation: Optional film for limited application.

Application: Enrichment. Shows an application of computers in the social sciences.

Length and Type: 30 min, b & w, sound.

Source: #8

Summary: NET "Focus on Behavior" series. Efforts at Carnegie Tech to evolve new theories about human mental processes: motion and depth perception, memorizing, and human problem solving.

G | GENERAL

I. Bibliography

C. Cherry, *On Human Communication.* M.I.T. Press, 1966 (B) (paper)

> "Intended as a review, a survey, and a criticism — nothing more." "A series of simple essays, written in the simplest language that I am able to command." Nevertheless, the book is recommended with reservations, because most of us are likely to find it much more complete than we bargained for. It is reading for a long vacation, perhaps, when it will be found a remarkable and mind-stretching book.

E. A. Feigenbaum and J. Feldman, eds., *Computers and Thought.* McGraw-Hill, 1963 (C)

> Here are 20 research reports, nearly all reprinted from journals, by 28 authors, with a dividend of 3 useful introductory essays by the editors. The reports were collected to be used as readings in certain courses (as well as for reference) and no doubt are out of date (note the year of publication). Nevertheless, they are full of information that will be new to many. The book belongs with the last Section of Chapter 10 and is largely peripheral, but most valuable as background on computer intelligence: Can computers think? Do they? What is thought? What sort of tasks, perhaps showing intelligence, are computers being programmed for? (E.g., playing chess, proving geometry theorems, doing integration problems, recognizing patterns, understanding English.)

D. G. Fink, *Computers and the Human Mind.* Anchor-Doubleday S-43, 1966 (A) (paper)

Especially recommended: Chapters 1, 6, 10, and 12: "Why the Computer?" "Diodes, Transistors, Memory Cores"; "Intelligence"; "Can Machines Create?" All are thought-provoking and most of these topics are not in our text.

H. F. Gaines, *Cryptanalysis.* Dover reprint, 1956 (B) (soft cover)

A fine beginner's book, not as entertaining to read as Kahn (see below) but more complete.

D. S. Halacy, Jr., *The Robots Are Here!* W. W. Norton, 1965 (B)

Primarily for "enrichment" of students (though the teacher may be enriched too). Easy text with plenty of photographs on such things as How the Robot Works, Robot Spacemen, Electronic Brains, and Robots at Play.

C. Jacker, *Man, Memory, and Machines. An Introduction to Cybernetics.* Macmillan, 1964 (B)

The first half is repetitive of *The Man-Made World* on feedback, mostly, but the second half has much on automata, bionics, artificial intelligence, and the learning problem. It is pleasingly written and most interesting.

D. Kahn, *Codebreakers.* Macmillan 1967 (D)

Serious history of cryptography, over 1000 pages long, breezily written, lots of anecdotes. It discusses the decrypting of the Cretan written language called Linear B, and is fascinating.

A. Love and J. S. Childers, eds., *Listen to Leaders in Engineering.* McKay, 1965 (B)

Some pleasant and interesting essays; one with special relevance: Computing, an Alliance of Man and Machine.

Sir Geo. Thomson, *The Foreseeable Future.* Viking Press, 1960 (out of print)

Worth hunting for, in libraries or second-hand book stores. The author, a Nobel laureate and son of the celebrated "J. J." who discovered the electron, wrote a sober, practical, enjoyable book. Especially appropriate for *The Man-Made World* are: "Some Social Consequences"; "Thought, Artificial and Natural."

J. von Neumann, *The Computer and the Brain.* Yale University Press, 1958 (A) (paper)

Like almost all absolutely front-rank people, von Neumann knew how to make the complicated simple. His writing is pellucid, his material fascinating and entirely comprehensible to high school undergraduates. Not all he says is still true, of course: 10 years in computer life must be equivalent to at least a century in human history.

N. Wiener, *God and Golem, Inc.* M.I.T. Press, 1964 (A) (paper)

A golem, in Jewish legend, was a human image which was given life by human agency. In this book it symbolizes the computer. Wiener asks: Can a computer learn? Can a computer reproduce itself? He answers both "Yes." The book is a background-reading thought provoker, only tangentially applicable to *The Man-Made World.*

II. Error Detection and Error Correction

The subjects of error detection and error correction in transmitted messages are very broad. We have already studied one method of error correcting (the Hamming code), and in the following we consider this code somewhat more fully. First, however, let us examine some other schemes that are sometimes used.

Table 10-3 shows a method of coding using strings of 6 bits, 6 binary choices (0 or 1). The plan therefore allows for 2^6 = 64 symbols: 26 letters, 10 digits, and 28 other symbols used in ordinary printing.

One difficulty with codings such as that in Table 10-3 lies in the possibility of making errors. With a long string of 0's and 1's, it is all too easy for a person to substitute a 1 for a 0 when copying. Relay and switch contacts, too, can malfunction and be open when they are supposed to be closed or vice versa. One way of protecting against errors is to add to the binary string an extra digit whose value, 0 or 1, is arranged so that the total number of 1's in each 7-bit string is even; that is, 0, 2, 4, or 6. The table, which follows in the Manual, is the same as Table 10-3 with an additional bit appearing at the left end of the string. Note that all the 7-bit strings have an even number of 1's. Should a string appear with an odd number of 1's during a transmission, you can be sure that an error has occurred in the transcription of the original coding.

This 7-bit representation is an example of an *error-detecting* code, and such codes are often used where great amounts of data and symbols are to be handled. Computers are one example, and error detection is vital for them since their elements can fail, even though such failures are infrequent.

This particular error-detecting code always works when a single digit is in error. It may not work if 2 or more digits are wrong. For example, a 1 can be interchanged with a 0 in any of the 7-bit strings without violating the "even-number-of-1's conditions." However, single errors are the predominant kind in many situations and so our single

Seven-bit alphanumeric code

0	0000000	†	1100000
1	1000001	J	0100001
2	1000010	K	0100010
3	0000011	L	1100011
4	1000100	M	0100100
5	0000101	N	1100101
6	0000110	O	1100110
7	1000111	P	0100111
8	1001000	Q	0101000
9	0001001	R	1101001
[	0001010	-	1101010
#	1001011	$	0101011
@	0001100	*	1101100
:	1001101	)	0101101
>	1001110	;	0101110
?	0001111	'	1101111
b	1010000	+	0110000
A	0010001	/	1110001
B	0010010	S	1110010
C	1010011	T	0110011
D	0010100	U	1110100
E	1010101	V	0110101
F	1010110	W	0110110
G	0010111	X	1110111
H	0011000	Y	1111000
I	1011001	Z	0111001
&	1011010	←	0111010
.	0011011	,	1111011
]	1011100	%	0111100
(	0011101	=	1111101
<	0011110	"	1111110
\	1011111	!	0111111

"parity-check" error-detection code, as it is called, can be quite useful. Codes which can detect multiple errors and can also be used to correct them have been devised for applications where higher reliability is necessary. All such codes involve adding additional bits to the binary words so that certain prescribed relations exist among the bits making up the words.

REPETITION CODING

An efficient way to represent 16 different message signals (e.g., 16 letters) is to develop a distinctive code of 4 binary digits for each "message." For instance, the first message could be encoded 0000, the second 0001, and so on up to 1111. It is evident that with 5 digits we could encode 32 messages, or enough for the 10 Arabic numerals plus the alphabet, if such redundant letters as *c, q, x,* and *y* are eliminated. One method of transmitting these messages is to let each binary digit be associated with the operation of a switch which controls a light at a remote receiving location. As long as each light is on only when its associated switch is operated, and off when it is unoperated, this scheme is a satisfactory one. But if a light goes bad, or if the 2 wires which connect a switch to its light accidentally become shorted together, the message which the sender meant to send will not be the one which the pattern of lights indicates at the receiver. In that case, the receiver will mistakenly interpret one message for another. The same kind of difficulty plagues telegraphic transmission. It is possible to encode messages so that even though individual digits are received in error, the message itself will not be. Incidentally, this is not unlike Ampère's original electromagnetic telegraph (nearly 20 years before Morse), in which small compass needles were set in motion by current-carrying coils.

Suppose we repeat each digit of our encoded message so that, for example, instead of sending 0101 we send instead 00110011. Now when a single error is made, we cannot confuse one message with another. For instance, imagine that a message we know has been encoded in this way is actually received as 11010011. We know that an error was made because the third and fourth digits are different. But we still cannot tell from the received set of digits whether the transmitted message was 11000011 (with an error in the fourth position) or 11110011 (with an error in the third position). An encoding procedure of this type, in which single errors cannot transform one message code into another, is called a single-error *detecting* code.

If we repeat each digit of the original code twice, we get messages represented in such forms as 000111000111. If we know that at most a single error can be made in the transmission of this type of code, we can actually reconstruct the transmitted code because it will be evident which digit was changed. For instance, the received code 111010111000 must have been transmitted as 111000111000. This kind of encoding procedure leads to a single-error *correcting* code.

LIMITATION CODES

The repetition of a digit of a message 3 or more times is a simple way of getting codes which will detect and correct 2 or more errors. But this kind of encoding procedure leads to codes which are needlessly long for the protection they give against errors. The reason that any error-correcting encoding procedure works is that it gives message codes which are sufficiently different from each other. The degree of difference can be measured by seeing in how many positions the digits of 2 message codes are different. For example, each of the set of 4 codes, 000, 011, 101, and 110 is different from the others in 2 of its digits. This set is another example of a single-error detecting code. The set of 2 message codes 000 and 111, on the other hand, are different in each of the 3 positions and, as we have just seen, lead to the possibility of correcting (not merely detecting) single errors.

The pair of message codes 000 and 111 can be pictured as in diagram (a). The points in this diagram represent the 8 possible combinations of 3 binary digits. The system here adopted for numbering the cube vertices is as follows. If the first of the three digits is 1, the vertex is one of the top 4 on the cube; if the first digit is 0, the vertex is one of the bottom 4. Similarly, if the second digit is 1, the vertex is one of the 4 on the back, and if the third digit is 1, the vertex lies on the right side of the cube. The 2 points indicated by black dots are the

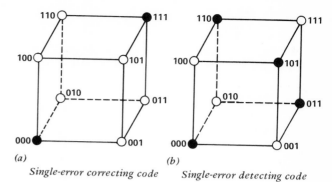

(a)   *(b)*

Single-error correcting code   *Single-error detecting code*

A visualization of 2 codes

message codes themselves. A single error has the effect of transforming a message code into one which is represented by an adjacent point on the diagram. But if only one error is made, we can always tell what the message was because the received code will always be closer to one black dot than the other. It is clear from the cube diagram that the message codes are separated by a *distance* of 3 units (measured along the edges).

The set of 4 message codes 000, 011, 101, and 110 are shown on the cube of diagram (b). It is clear that they are separated from each other by a distance of only 2. And when we receive 010 we cannot tell whether 000, 011, or 110 was sent since 010 is equally distant from all 3 of them.

The problem of designing good error-correcting and detecting codes is the same as the problem of finding on this type of cube diagram sets of points which are separated from each other by sufficiently large distances.

Even though it is difficult to draw such diagrams for more than 3 digits, the intuitive notion suggested by the simple cube diagram is correct. More errors can be corrected if the messages are more widely separated, but the more widely separated the messages are, the fewer message codes there can be.

HAMMING CODES

A set of codes which can correct errors is necessarily inefficient in the sense that it has more digits than would be necessary only to make the message codes different from each other. But among several possible encoding schemes, each of which will correct a given number of errors, one may be more efficient than another. This fact is illustrated by the Hamming code, which uses a total of only 7 digits, rather than the 12 which we would need if we used the simple digit-triplication method.

In the diagram (a), below, the 7 closed regions formed have been designated by numbers instead of letters. The advantage of doing so is illustrated by (b). If we associate circles A, B, and C with the numbers 1, 2, and 4 (or 2^0, 2^1, and 2^2), then the position affected by a single error can be identified by adding together the identification numbers of the circles which contain an odd number of 1's. In this case it is the "2" circle and the "4" circle which have odd numbers of 1's. By adding 2 to 4, we discover that position 6 contained the error. We can experiment with each of the 7 positions to verify that each region number can be found by adding together the numbers of the circles which contain that region.

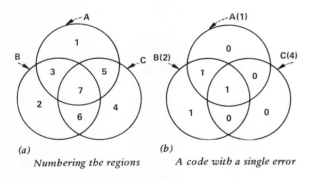

(a)
Numbering the regions

(b)
A code with a single error

Visualization of Hamming codes

Hamming codes can also be designed for other numbers of information and check digits. The next diagram of (a) has 4 loops and therefore can be used to describe a code with 4 check digits. Since there are a total of 15 closed regions, the remaining 11 positions are information positions. The region numbering system is similar to the earlier one. Diagram (b) shows one of the 2^{11} = 2048 possible message codes which can be designed with the aid of this diagram. If we had used the method of triplication to get single-error correction capabilities with

a total of 15 digits, then there would have been only 5 information digits (rather than 11) and 10 redundant digits (rather than 4).

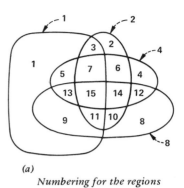

(a)
Numbering for the regions

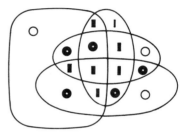

(b)
Example of a message code

Another Hamming code

The superior efficiency of the Hamming code can be attributed to the fact that it adds redundancy to all of the information digits simultaneously rather than, in effect, providing error protection to each information digit individually. In general, a Hamming code with r redundant (check) digits will contain a total of $2^r - 1$ digits and therefore, $2^r - r - 1$ information digits. As the total number of digits is increased, the efficiency of these codes becomes higher since the number of check digits becomes a small fraction of the total.

III. A Preview of Computers

Just before embarking upon the text of Chapter 10, it may be a good idea to take a quick look at the "big picture" of a computer. The first point is that a computer accepts information (both data and program). Then, having information in the computer, we want to process or *transform* this information in some way. For example, we may want to add a column of numbers to obtain their sum, or arrange (sort) numbers so that they are in descending order from largest to smallest. Computers perform such functions by taking input information and then processing it according to a program. After the job is completed, the results are given as output. This overall process can be described by the diagram. We say information is processed according to a plan to yield results.

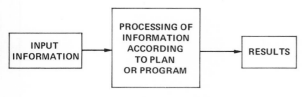

What any computer does

Let us look at a few examples of information processing:

Input information	Processing	Result
Binary number	Calculate decimal equivalent	Decimal number
Hours worked by employees during week	Calculate appropriate salaries	Payroll checks
Thrust sequence and mass of rocket	Calculate orbit	Prediction of satellite position
Geographical positions of cities to be visted	Calculate distances between cities	Route having minimum distance

We may carry these stages a step farther as follows:

1. Input Operations: transferring information ("data") and program into memory

2. Processing Operations: *encoding* from programming language (e.g., BASIC) into machine (binary) language

control, the action of internal circuits which determine the operations to take place and the parts of the computer which perform each of these

arithmetic, operations on numbers (adding, comparing, etc.), in the accumulator

logic, selection of alternative actions, and program modification

3. Output Operations: print-out, recording on magnetic tape, display on CRO, and the like.

These are all characteristic of general-purpose computers. There are innumerable special-purpose computers, like washing machines (input: clothes, water, detergent; processing: washing, rinsing, spinning; output: clean clothing and dirty water), and gasoline pumps (input: selection of gas grade, resetting counter to 0, number of gallons; processing: delivery of gasoline, counting gallonage, computing price; output: gasoline, display of gallons delivered and total cost).

A useful block diagram follows.

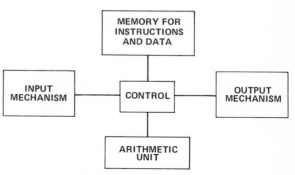

Block diagram of computer functions

In thinking of the control function, it may be helpful to liken it to the operation of a telephone switchboard. The switchboard and operator in the telephone application connect people who want to talk to each other. The control function in the computer connects input, output, memory, and arithmetic unit when they want to "talk" to each other; that is, when information is to be transferred from one to the other.

CHECKLIST FOR CHAPTER 11

COMMUNICATING TO COMPUTERS

APPROX. TIME: Text: 8 Days Lab: 2 Days

A. APPROACH	CLASS PERIODS	B. BLACK & WHITE TRANSPAR- ENCIES	C. CUES (k = key problems)				D. DEMON- STRATIONS, LABS & PROJECTS	E. EVALU- ATION	F. FILMS	G. GENERAL
			Discussion	Easy	Medium	Hard				
1. Introduction	1	1101 1110	1	1k,2k	3k, 5	6		1,3,4, 5	1101 1102 1103	
2. Loops, Loaders, and Bootstraps	4	1102 1103 1104 1105 1106a, b, c	2,4,5,6, 7		4k,11	7,8,9		2,7,8	1104	II
3. Building Blocks for Programs: Subroutines	1	1107 1108	3, Prob. 10			12		6,9,10		
4. Programs for Writing Programs	1	1109	8						1105	III, IV
5. Billiard-Table Simulation	1		9						1106	
6. Final Comment										

Communicating to Computers
11

A | APPROACH

I. Purpose and Organization of the Chapter

Chapter 10 was an essential preliminary, but it must be admitted that it was to some degree only *about* computers, while this chapter really gets down to cases. (The analogy in mind here is the course *about* music contrasted with the teaching *of* music.) Computers excite wonder and disbelief and sometimes rage in the general public, but only people who have worked with them are likely to have reasoned opinions about them. Here we have the elements of programming, which are an important phase of anybody's education for life in today's world. We will certainly have experience in making programming errors. The person who has made such errors knows how to interpret a remark such as, "This must be so; it was worked out by a computer."

Starting with flow diagrams similar to those already studied, we proceed to examine a few of the schemes which make programs shorter and programming easier. Those explored enough to make them usable by the student programmer are loops, jumps, both unconditional and conditional, shifting, loading programs, and subroutines. At the end there is a brief look at the hierarchy of languages, machine, assembler, and compiler, and reference to such programmer aids as diagnostic and debugging packages.

II. Objectives for Students

Upon completion of the activities, discussion, and reading in this chapter, students should be able to:

1. Recognize and identify the terms *debugging* and *index*.

2. Demonstrate an understanding of flow diagrams (a) by interpreting samples that include loops and tests; and (b) by writing samples for multiplying two numbers, or others of similar difficulty.

3. Describe the contents of a memory cell, both before and after an operation of storage in it.

4. Translate machine code programs into English and interpret what they do.

5. Explain the result of a "shifting operation."

6. Discriminate between conditional and unconditional jumps.

7. Illustrate the method of testing the accumulator and justify the test in specific cases.

8. Explain how and when to stop a loop (a) by testing the accumulator; and (b) by using a blank card.

9. Decide in specific cases whether or not a subroutine would be a helpful arrangement.

10. Write the portions of a machine code program which call for a subroutine, prepare an exit from it, and return to the main program.

11. Interpret the "bootstrap routine" and use it to develop a program for loading a computer.

269

12. Distinguish among machine code, assembler, and compiler languages. Justify the need for each.

> NOTE: It is not considered necessary for students to memorize the operating code numbers, but they should be able to use the numbers if given a list similar to that in T-1110.

III. Suggestions for Teaching

Planning this chapter will take careful thought. For instance, if in your philosophy the computer is indeed a notable and exceedingly useful gadget of contemporary culture, but only a gadget nonetheless, Chapter 11 has but one importance. That is, to give your pupils definite examples of some of the almost innumerable kinds of problems that a computer can handle. The details of the programming are then of little interest and require little attention. If, on the other hand, you believe that the ability to use computers is going to be of steadily increasing importance to educated people throughout the foreseeable future, you will give this material more extensive treatment.

Even if you have a terminal available, it is extremely desirable to trudge through most of the programs of the chapter with CARDIAC. There is no other way to understand, really understand, how the programs are executed by the computer. We can learn to use BASIC (a higher level language), for instance, but not understand how the computer solves the problem. Many of the questions and problems will go faster and more easily with CARDIAC's help. Another way in which CARDIAC can be very useful is in debugging programs. See Section G, Part II ("Debugging with CARDIAC"), for a sample. Discussion of programming via machine code or symbolic code is another example of man-machine interaction. The former is better matched to machines while the latter is better matched to people.

Section 1. Introduction. The section really is introductory and ought to be run through in enough detail so that later on you can remind your class of it when going more deeply into the topics presented. The solitary program here is the same as the one in Part A of Lab I, Chapter 10, and therefore no time should be spent on its details now. The flow diagram, however, may be worth lingering over a little. It is implemented in Fig. 10-16 (T-1010).

Section 2. Loops, Loaders, and Bootstraps. It should probably be pointed out again to your class (as it was in the last chapter) that none of the programs contains data words. Perhaps they will recall that it was the great invention of von Neumann and a few others to store the program in the computer's memory and feed in needed data only for each specific problem.

Loops and jumps. (1) The op code 8, which makes possible the looping of Fig. 11-3 (T-1103), produces an unconditional jump (contrasted with the conditional jump of op code 3). It should be noted that the instruction to write the bug's cell number in 99 is needless for this kind of jump; it will be essential, however, when we get to subroutines, in order to record the place in the main program to which to return after the subroutine has been performed. (2) In the description of instruction 0XY (Note: Zero XY), the last clause "advance the input stack" means the same as "advance the top card" did: the whole remaining stack of input cards is taken away. (3) When op code 3 is defined, the "next higher address in order" means just that: not higher up on the CARDIAC list; but if we are at address 36, for instance, we go next to address 37. In CARDIAC, however, notice that the instruction statement for op code 3 is incomplete: it ought to read "test accumulator contents; if 0 or + move bug to next cell, but if−, move bug to cell XB."

An example of Looping: Multiplication: (1) In Fig. 11-5 (T-1105) it should be pointed out that it is not usually necessary to clear a cell in memory to hold anything, because the act of storing automatically erases the previous contents. It is necessary here because at address 15 the data in cell 33 are transferred to the accumulator, and when this first happens the number must be 000, to which BC is later added as many times as necessary. The hint in the flow diagram, "Read A: to be used as index 'n,' " is worth following a little further. It is very common to use an index in this way, reducing it by 1 (or occasionally by another number) on each pass through a loop, in order to tell when to terminate the loop. A slightly different indexing scheme appears in Fig. 11-4 (T-1104). (2) Somebody is going to think that this program looks longer than that of Fig. 10-9, the "Idiot Multiplier." The latter, however, is a flow diagram, not a program, and conceals a lot of steps. Consider "Select the larger." The program for this might be translated as follows: Read A into the accumulator. Subtract B. Test accumulator contents. If negative, jump down to Set "product" equal to larger (which must be B). If + or 0, it means either that A is larger or that A = B; in either case, we may Set "product" equal to A. Then farther down, to find if Count equals the smaller, we must bring Smaller to accumulator, subtract Count, test accumulator contents. If they are + or 0 we have two possible actions: (a) subtract 1 (instruction 700) from the difference and test again; if the difference is now negative, the earlier difference was 0, so Smaller = Count; or (b) subtract Count − Smaller, knowing that if the test is again 0 or + it can only be 0 so we can proceed to print. (The reasoning was this: if $A - B \geqslant 0$, and $B - A \geqslant 0$, the only answer is 0.) A good exercise for class action at this point would be to write this program, and follow up by CARDIAC execution. To save time in the latter, let A = 3, B = 5.

Shifting. Note T-1110, which lists the CARDIAC instructions for reference.

Bootstraps and Loaders. Here is the proper place for Part B of Lab 1 for Chapter 10. This should be done at the seats in the classroom as part of the text period, and special attention be given to the way memory cell 001 holds the series of addresses for the program instructions, one after another. T-1106a-c may also help in putting this process across. It may not seem very important to understand the loading routine, but it really does help the student to feel that a computer is a tool, not a mystery and a threat.

Section 3. Building Blocks for Programs: Subroutines.

This again is most easily handled by using CARDIACs at the seats to do Lab II, Chapter 10, which is the program discussed in the text. The important and confusing part is the sequence for jumping (or "branching") to and from the subroutine. In T-1108 attention is concentrated on just this bit. Here at last is the reason for recording the number of the bug's current cell (i.e., the updated program count) in memory cell 99 as a temporary holding operation until it can be installed at the end of the subroutine. It may be asked: Why not put the number in the proper spot of the subroutine right away? The answer is that most subroutines are permanently kept in the machine's memory; they are not set up for just one program to use. The programmer therefore does not normally know what the address of the "proper spot" is: but the subroutine program permanently contains the two instructions 199, 6YR (or whatever the corresponding addresses happen to be in the computer actually being used), where YR is the address of that last subroutine cell. All the programmer must know is the address of the first subroutine instruction (199).

Section 4. Programs for Writing Programs.

As we see here, the programmer just mentioned need not in fact know even the first subroutine address. When he uses a compiler language, he just "calls up" the subroutine by a single operating instruction. In fact, he probably never even stops to think whether he is about to use a subroutine, but leaves it to the assembler program to take care of it. The task of program writing is indeed much simpler than one might guess from the earlier part of this chapter. It is conventional for a very large computer to contain a number of assembler programs in a portion of the memory set aside permanently for this purpose, each individual assembler being designed for a specific compiler language. The person using the machine starts by typing or punching in the name of the language he plans to employ, which calls up the appropriate assembler program to translate his remarks into machine language. Small computers may be connected to a still smaller satellite computer which is programmed to assemble one particular compiler language: but the programs for other languages may be at hand in the form of punched tape or the like, ready to be inserted if needed. It is also worth noting that professional programmers, unwilling to leave a good thing alone, seem to be forever tinkering with existing languages (as well as inventing new ones) to make them more powerful for particular uses. This has the unfortunate side effect, when approaching a strange computer, of having to check out in advance the particular language peculiarities that may exist in its assembler programs.

Sections 5 and 6. Billiard-Table Simulation and Final Comment.

No additional remarks are called for.

B | BLACK AND WHITE TRANSPARENCIES

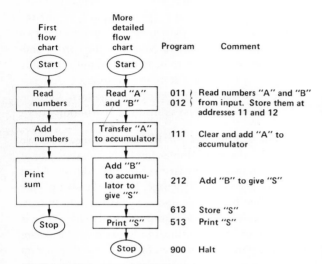

T-1101   FLOW DIAGRAMS FOR A + B

T-1102   TO TRIPLE NUMBERS WITHOUT LOOPING

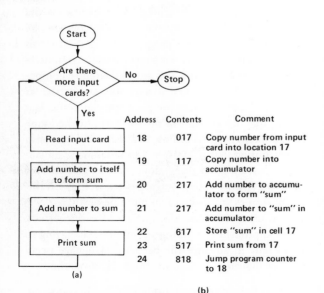

T-1103   TO TRIPLE NUMBERS, USING LOOP

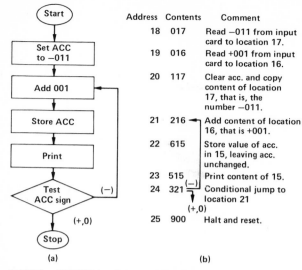

T-1104 AUTOMATIC COUNT-DOWN

Address	Contents	Comment
18	017	Read −011 from input card to location 17.
19	016	Read +001 from input card to location 16.
20	117	Clear acc. and copy content of location 17, that is, the number −011.
21	216	Add content of location 16, that is +001.
22	615	Store value of acc. in 15, leaving acc. unchanged.
23	515	Print content of 15.
24	321	Conditional jump to location 21
25	900	Halt and reset.

(a)   (b)

Card		Content of card
1	002	BOOTSTRAP
2	800	
3	018	Address
4	017	Instruction — 017 to be loaded into address 18
5	019	Address
6	016	Instruction — 016 to be loaded into 19
7	020	Address
8	117	Instruction — 117 to be loaded into 20
9	021	Address
10	216	Instruction — 216 into 21
11	022	Address
12	615	Instruction — 615 into 22
13	023	Address
14	515	Instruction — 515 into 23
15	024	Address
16	321	Instruction — 321 into 24
17	025	Address
18	900	Instruction — 900 into 25
19	Blank	Signals end of program to be loaded
20	818	Transfer Control to program just loaded
21	−011	Data to be read by program after loading
22	+001	

T-1106a CARDSTACK TO LOAD COUNT-DOWN

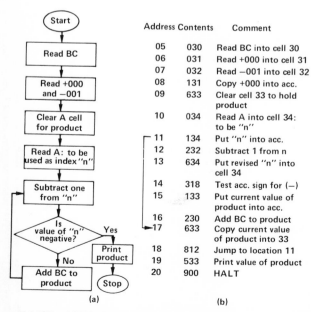

T-1105 MULTIPLY A X BC

Address	Contents	Comment
05	030	Read BC into cell 30
06	031	Read +000 into cell 31
07	032	Read −001 into cell 32
08	131	Copy +000 into acc.
09	633	Clear cell 33 to hold product
10	034	Read A into cell 34: to be "n"
11	134	Put "n" into acc.
12	232	Subtract 1 from n
13	634	Put revised "n" into cell 34
14	318	Test acc. sign for (−)
15	133	Put current value of product into acc.
16	230	Add BC to product
17	633	Copy current value of product into 33
18	812	Jump to location 11
19	533	Print value of product
20	900	HALT

(a)   (b)

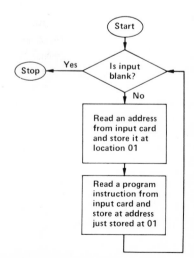

T-1106b BOOTSTRAP FOR *CARDIAC*

Program Step		Memory location	Instruction word	Action resulting
0	(wired into memory	00	001	Read top card into address 01 (Top card is 002)
1	the program	01	002	Read top card into address 02 (Top card is 800)
2		02	800	Jump back to address 00
3	2nd time through	00	001	Read top card into address 01 (Top card is 018)
4	the loop	01	018	Read top card into address 18 (Top card is 017)
5		02	800	Jump back to address 00
6	3rd time through the loop	00	001	Read top card into address 01 (Top card is 019)
7		01	019	Read top card into address 19 (Top card is 016)
8		02	800	Jump back to address 00
9	4th time through	00	001	Read top card into address 01 (Top card is 020)
10	the loop	01	020	Read top card into address 20 (Top card is 117)
11		02	800	Jump back to address 00

and so on for 9 passes through the loop.

T-1106c STEPS IN LOADING PROGRAM

DOUBLE PRECISION SUBROUTINE FOR A + B = SUM

MAIN PROGRAM

	Address	Contents		Address	Contents
Calling Sequence	50	082	Read first number	86	199	Prepare return jump
	51	083		87	694	
	52	084	Read second number	88	183	Add least sig. digits
	53	085		89	285	
	54	886	Jump to subroutine	90	695	Store result
	55	696	Store and print most sig. digits	91	403	Shift carry to right 3 places
	56	596				
	57	595	Print least sig. digits	92	282	Add most sig. digits
				93	284	
	58	900	Halt	94	855	Jump back to main program

T-1107 DOUBLE PRECISION SUBROUTINE

MAIN PROGRAM		SUBROUTINE	
ADDRESS	**INSTRUCTIONS**	**ADDRESS**	**INSTRUCTIONS**
.	.	.	.
.	.	.	.
.	.	.	.
XF	8YM (STORE XG AT 99 AS 8XG, JUMP TO SUB-ROUTINE AT LOCATION YM)		
		YM	199 (8XG TO ACCUMULATOR)
		YN	6YR (8XG TO YR)
		.	.
		.	.
		.	.
		YR	8XG (JUMP TO MAIN PROGRAM AT LOCATION XG)
XG	REST OF MAIN PROGRAM		
.	.		
.	.		

T-1108   SUBROUTINE PROGRAM SEQUENCE

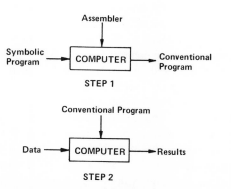

T-1109   USING AN ASSEMBLER

OP – CODE	OPERATION
0	INPUT
1	CLEAR AND ADD
2	ADD
3	TEST ACCUMULATOR CONTENTS
4	SHIFT
5	PUNCH
6	STORE
7	SUBTRACT
8	JUMP
9	HALT AND RESET

T-1110 LIST OF *CARDIAC* INSTRUCTIONS

C | CUES TO QUESTIONS AND PROBLEMS

Questions for Study and Discussion

1.0:Input, read in, usually from a card to a memory cell.

1: Clear the accumulator (reduce its contents to 0000) and add the contents of a memory cell.

2:Bring to the accumulator the contents of a memory cell and add to what is already there.

3:Test the contents of the accumulator; if 0 or +, go to next instruction; if −, jump to memory cell listed. Used as one way to terminate a loop.

4:Shift contents of accumulator, x places left, followed by y places right (instruction reads $4xy$).

5:Punch (a card), print, output.

6:Store the contents of the accumulator in a designated cell of memory.

7:Subtract the contents of a designated cell from the contents of the accumulator.

8:Store the number of the next instruction in cell 99, and jump to cell designated. Used for looping and for subroutines.

9:Stop. Reset program counter to designated number (normally 00).

2. The program prints out a series of cards such that each has a numerical value 5 larger than that of the corresponding input card.

3. When the desired sequence involves a frequently required routine operation—such as that of multiplying m by n or finding the area of a polygon—the programmer calls on a "subroutine," a program written by him or someone else and kept in a library of similar often-used programs. A program to solve the physics problems involved in precisely orbiting a satellite may call upon the assistance of scores of subroutines. Complex tasks are often broken down into sections to be programmed by different people as subroutines. Or one person may similarly divide his task into independent sections which he will program at different times. Because the subroutine occupies numbered cells, these may be designated in the usual way in the program. To transfer to a subroutine the instruction 8YM is fetched, where YM is the address of the first subroutine step. At the same time, the updated number in the program counter (say XG) is stored as digits 2 and 3 in cell 99 (CARDIAC, or a cell with an op Code 8 permanently wired as the first digit). The first subroutine instruction is 199, which brings 8XG to the accumulator. The second instruction is 6YR (where YR means the last address in the subroutine) and hence stores 8XG in that cell. When the subroutine program reaches cell YR, 8XG calls for a jump to XG in the main program, which thus takes control again.

4. The program prints out, at each pass through the program loop, the difference between the number on the most recently examined input card and the number on the card immediately preceding it. Note that the instructions 629, 821 result in the second card now occupying the memory cell originally designated for the first card, but the jump instruction makes the loop start at the instruction originally for the second card; therefore the third card, when it comes up, will indeed be subtracted from the second: A − B, B − C, etc.

5.a) Two tests are required because A may be equal to B.

b) Instructions stored at addresses 22 and 23 could be omitted.

c) The next instruction to be executed is located at address 24.

d) The top output card will read 000, indicating that A is not larger than B.

6. If a program requires the same set of operations to be performed repeatedly, a loop enables one to write the sequence of instructions for that set once only. Obviously, no steps are saved if there is no opportunity to use a loop.

7. The working of the bootstrap loader is made possible because memory cell 00 has a permanent instruction wired in: +001. The first card of the loading program reads 002. Since 001, when "fetched" to the instruction register, says "read top card into 01," this cell receives the 002 instruction. The second bootstrap card is 800, "jump to 00," and is read by the 002 instruction into cell 02. The next operation is that jump, and the loading program proper now follows, consisting of pairs of

cards. The second card of each pair is one instruction of the program, the first is 0 followed by the address where that instruction should go. Thus, when the next card (the address card) is read, it is steered by the 001 instruction in 00 into cell 01. The program counter at this stage reads 01, so the second card of the pair is read into the address which was shown on its mate. 800 follows again, and the cycle continues until the last pair of cards has been used, when a blank card terminates the process. (The answer to the second sentence in the question is included above: the pairs of cards, alternately 0XA, "read the next card into address XA," and whatever the program step may be that belongs at XA.)

8. The computer is programmed in machine code (long strings of binary numbers, incidentally, not the brief decimal numbers we use), and each instruction must be placed in an address which must be remembered for future reference. The programmer wishes to use something approaching English and to follow a procedure as much as possible like a flow diagram, where one step often means several instructions to the computer. The compiler is a language which matches these requirements. It can be "understood" by the intermediate assembler. This is a program to translate the abbreviated compiler instructions into the full sequences of machine steps that correspond, to put those steps into machine code, to decide (and remember) what memory cells to use, to call for subroutines when appropriate, and in general to act as an extremely knowledgeable and efficient private secretary to the programmer.

9. The errors are very seldom made by the computers, rarely by the programmers, nearly always by the keypunch operators: the people who enter the data on the input cards. GIGO (Garbage In, Garbage Out) applies to them, too.

Problems

1. a) 034
   b) 252
   c) 195
   d) 824
   e) 642
   f) 733
   g) 412
   h) 900
   i) 313
   j) 519

2. a) 042: Read the top input card and copy the contents in address 42, and advance the top input card.

b) 403: Shift contents of accumulator 0 places to left and 3 places to right (the result is 000).

c) 171: Clear the accumulator and bring to it a copy of the word found at address 71.

d) 440: Shift contents of accumulator 4 places to left and 0 to right.

e) 672: Store contents of accumulator at address 72.

f) 819: Jump to instruction found at address 19; in effect, this operation resets instruction counter to 19.

g) 713: Subtract the contents found at address 13 from the contents found in the accumulator at this time.

h) 215: Add to the contents of the accumulator the word found at address 15.

i) 341: Test the contents of the accumulator. If 0 or positive, go to the next instruction; if negative, go to the instruction to be found at address 41.

j) 516: Print on an output card the contents at address 16.

k) 900: Halt calculation and reset instruction counter to 000.

l) 309: Test contents of accumulator. If 0 or positive, go to next instruction; if negative, go to instruction found at address 09.

3. a) This program will add 473 to 052 and print out the sum.

b) This program will subtract 052 twice from 473 and print out the final difference.

Note two things: in (a) a place was set aside for the first card by 63   000. It would have been polite, no doubt, to insert also 64   000. In (b) observe the neat way in which a single memory cell, with the help of the accumulator, handles all the data.

4.

Memory address	Word stored	Contents of accumulator
55	162	008
56	263	011
57	324	011
58	440	000
59	664	000
60	564	000
61	900	000
62	008	000
63	003	000
64	000	—

(a)

Memory address	Word stored	Contents of accumulator
27	134	329
28	735	202
29	735	075
30	326	075
31	636	075
32	536	075
33	900	—
34	329	—
35	127	—
36	000	—

(b)

5.

	Version I			Version II
53	060		53	060
54	061		54	160
55	160		55	060
56	761		56	760
57	662		57	660
58	562		58	560
59	900		59	900
60	—		60	—
61	—			
62	—			

6.

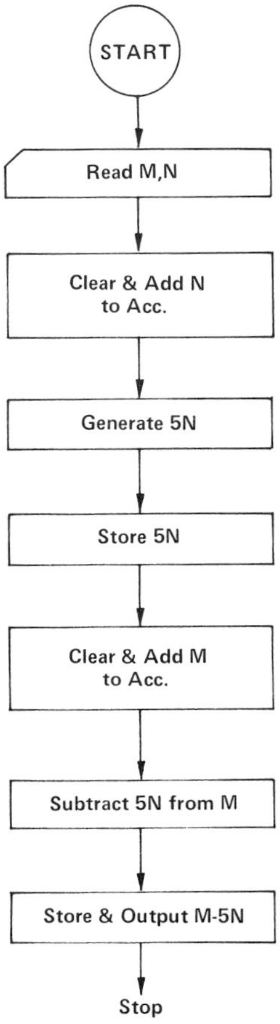

START

Read M,N

Clear & Add N to Acc.

Generate 5N

Store 5N

Clear & Add M to Acc.

Subtract 5N from M

Store & Output M-5N

Stop

The program:

23	036	32	738
24	037	33	639
25	137	34	539
26	237	35	900
27	237	36	—
28	237	37	—
29	237	38	—
30	638	39	—
31	136		

7. "Descending order" means "in terms of size." The scheme used here is to get the largest number into cell 53, the second into 54, the third into 55. If the test at 24 is +, then B>A and the next six steps get B into 53, A into 54. If test 24 is −, then A>B

and they are properly stored to begin with (until C can be tested). Addresses 31 to 39 are to find how C stacks up against A and to get them arranged; then 40 to 48 compare and arrange C and B.

Address	Word	Address	Word
19	053	38	156
20	054	39	655
21	055	40	154
22	154	41	753
23	753	42	349
24	331	43	153
25	153	44	656
26	656	45	154
27	154	46	653
28	653	47	156
29	156	48	654
30	654	49	553
31	155	50	554
32	754	51	555
33	340	52	819
34	154	53	—
35	656	54	—
36	155	55	—
37	654	56	—

8.

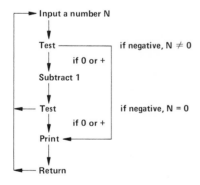

The program:

	20	027
	21	127
	22	325
	23	700
	24	320
	25	527
	26	820
	27	000

9.

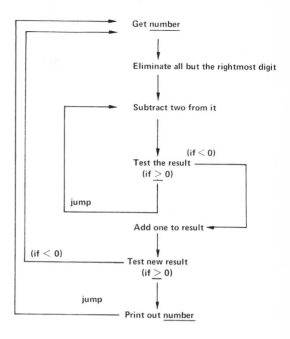

The program:

20	032	The rationale is that any
21	132	number, reduced (even
22	320	until negative) in steps
23	433	of 2, remains odd or
24	731	even as the case may
25	327	be; but then when in-
26	824	creased by 1 only the
27	200	odd number can be-
28	330	come 0. Thus it signals
29	532	that it is to be printed.
30	820	
31	002	
32	000	

10. This program is not plausible in light of the fact that a decimal code is used in this chapter. Multiplication by shifting is only possible when the number system being used is binary. However, this question can be assigned as a discussion question. The point is that multiplication by shifting is more efficient than multiplication by repeated addition.

11. This program reads the top input card and finally stores at address 36 the same number with its

digits reversed (the implicit assumption is that there are 3 digits, but the program will also work for 2). The program would be better if a print instruction were included, and also if 2 memory cells were set aside for storage purposes. Primarily, the problem is a drill in the use of the shift instruction.

12.

Main Program		Subroutine	
20	024	50	199
21	850	51	667
22	525	52	124
23	900	53	357
24	000 (Store)	54	268
25	000 (Total)	55	668
		56	820
		57	200
		58	367
		59	168
		60	225
		61	625
		62	568
		63	168
		64	404
		65	668
		66	820
		67	000 (Return)
		68	000 (Grade Count)

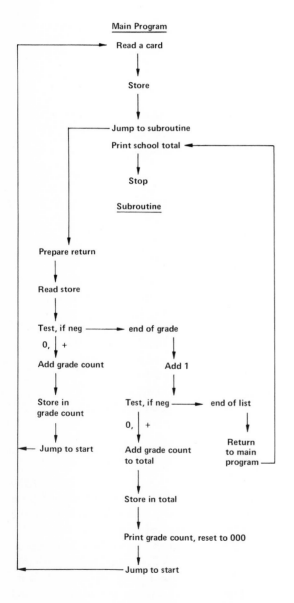

At first glance this difficult program looks like a fine example of technological overkill, especially since it is slightly easier to write the program without a subroutine. Suggest that the research committee was established by the state Board of Education to make a statistical study of all the schools in the state. Properly speaking, in that case, address 23 should be 820, and the program should be terminated by a blank card after the inclusion of all schools. The program is a good illustration of the fact that computers are our slaves, not the other way around. Naming part of the program a subroutine does not mean that it has to play all by itself; on the contrary, it may dip into the main program as often as necessary.

E | EVALUATION

The questions in this section are rated according to the chapter objectives and the performance levels stated in the introduction to the teacher's manual. This group of questions is not intended to be all inclusive, but just as a guide to possible questions. Zeros in the chapter objective column indicate no chapter objective for this question.

Chapter Objective	Performance Level	
		Judged to be Relatively Easy:
		In the first four questions, check the best answer.
2	I	1. The chart below represents a flow diagram of the process of making a telephone call.

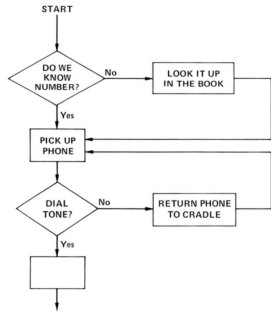

a) The empty box is needless because the call is complete.
b) The empty box should have been placed above the decision box.
c) One loop appears in the flow diagram.
d) The empty box should be filled with "WRONG NUMBER."
e) The empty box should be filled with "BELL RINGING."

OPERATION CODE:
0 Input
1 Clear accumulator and fetch to it
2 Add to accumulator contents
3 Test accumulator contents
4 Shift accumulator contents
5 Output
6 Store accumulator contents
7 Subtract from accumulator contents
8 Jump
9 Stop

Chapter Objective	Performance Level	

Judged to be Relatively Easy:

2. The accumulator contains the number 0456. The next instruction reads "411." After execution, the accumulator will contain

5   I
- a) 0456
- b) 0450
- c) 0045
- d) 0560
- e) 0050

3. Below is written a simple computer program.

4   I

Step	Address	Contents	
1	30	030	First card = 5
2	31	031	Second card = 20
3	32	130	
4	33	230	
5	34	230	
6	35	638	
7	36	538	
8	37	900	
9	38	----	

This program would print out
- a) 30
- b) 35
- c) 40
- d) 45
- e) 50

4. Before the program of Question 3 starts, address 38 will contain

3   I
- a) 000
- b) 111
- c) 101
- d) 010
- e) any combination of 0's and 1's

In the following question, mark the one incorrect sentence.

5. The following observations refer to the program of Question 3:

4   I
- a) If Step 8(900) were omitted, the program counter would not return to 00.
- b) Step 2 has no part to play in the program.
- c) The program is defective because the first step says to read address 30 into itself.
- d) A memory cell could be saved if steps 6 and 7 read 630 and 530 respectively.
- e) The program could be terminated by a blank card instead of 900.

Judged to be More Difficult:

The Operation Code should be provided here also.
In the following question, mark the one incorrect sentence.

6. Below is a very small fragment of a program:

4   II

Address	Contents
39	---
40	---
41	739
42	878
43	---
44	---
45	900

Judged to be More Difficult:

a) The program requires that address 43 be stored at address 78.

b) After the contents of address 42 have been fetched, address 99 will receive 43.

c) It is reasonable to assume that a subroutine is being called in this program.

d) The program will certainly require debugging, unless the subroutine arranges a return to address 43.

e) The instructions at address 41 call for the contents of cell 39 to be subtracted from the accumulator contents.

In the remaining four questions, check the best answer.

7. Following is a computer program:

Address	Contents	Address	Contents	
25	036	32	828	First card: 45
26	037	33	538	Second card: 3
27	038	34	900	Third card: 2
28	136	35	000	
29	237	36	000	
30	238	37	000	
31	638	38	000	

8

II

a) After the computer has gone through this sequence once, cell 38 will contain the number 50.

b) The program furnishes no way to terminate the loop.

c) The program will print out 45, 48, 51.

d) After the program prints out 49, it will stop and the counter will be reset to 00.

e) This program is defective because the computer will stop before it reaches the data.

8. A computer has been loaded with the following program. The starter button is pushed. After the test called for at location 28, the computer will

a) run through the loop twice and then stop.

b) run through the loop once and then stop.

c) run through the loop indefinitely.

d) proceed to a print-out and return to 25.

7

II

e) continue through 29 to a print-out and stop.

Address	Contents		Address	Contents
25	132		31	900
26	233		----------------	
27	734		32	014
28	325		33	007
29	635		34	020
30	535		35	000

9. A student programmer suggests that he can save memory space in a subroutine if he omits the initial steps which prepare a return, and simply ends the subroutine with 899.

10

II

a) Since address 99 contains the address in the main program to which the computer must return, this idea will work.

b) Since op code 8 requires that the number in the program counter be entered in cell 99, this will erase the return number, so the idea won't work.

c) The scheme sounds good but so many other steps would have to be used that more space would be wasted than saved.

d) Since the last cell in the memory already contains 899, this merely amounts to duplication.

e) The plan would work if the instruction 899 were placed in the main program, not the subroutine.

Chapter Objective	*Performance Level*	*Judged to be More Difficult:*
		10. Division can be performed with a computer by successive subtractions (the inverse of multiplication). Sometimes it is convenient to have a subroutine for division. Suppose such a subroutine has been prepared. A first card is punched with the number to be divided, and a second with the divisor.
10	II	a) The first step in the main program will be to read (input) the first card into the first memory cell of the subroutine.
		b) The first step in the main program will be 899.
		c) The first step in the subroutine will be 199.
		d) After the exit from the subroutine is prepared, the next step will call the second card to the accumulator.
		e) The subroutine will use the contents of the first card as an index to decide when to stop subtracting.

Answers to Evaluation Questions:

1. c

2. a

3. d

4. e

5. c

6. a

7. b

8. e

9. b

10. c

F | FILMS

F-1101   DIGITAL COMPUTER TECHNIQUES: COMPUTER UNITS

Recommendation: This film is good for clarification of computer organization.

Application: Concept development. Best used for review after class discussion of the overall plan for a computer.

Length and Type: 24 min, color, sound.

Source: #14 (Navy Film No. MN 8969D)

Summary: Describes in a general way the functioning of the major units of a computer, and also shows the purposes of clocking and sequencing.

F-1102   MEMORY DEVICES

Recommendation: Optional. Use only if additional emphasis on memory hardware is needed.

Application: Enrichment. Illustrates the wide variety of devices which can be used for a computer's memory.

Length and Type: 28 min, color, sound.

Source: #16

Summary: Very brief discussion of binary nature of memory devices, followed by punched cards and tape, relays, magnetic tape, and magnetic cores.

F-1103   "THINKING" MACHINES

Recommendation: Limited application (see Summary).

Application: Enrichment, to illustrate machine memory.

Length and Type: 20 min, color, sound

Source: #11

Summary: Experiments in machine "intelligence," such as a mechanical mouse that learns by trial and error, a chess-playing computer, a machine that recognizes visual patterns.

F-1104 DIGITAL COMPUTER TECHNIQUES: PROGRAMMING

Recommendation: Good film to illustrate programming.

Application: Concept development.

Length and Type: 14 min, color, sound.

Source: #14 (Navy Film No. MN 8969F)

Summary: Defines programming, shows preparation of flow diagrams, and how instructions are encoded into machine language.

F-1105 UNIVERSAL MACHINE

Recommendation: Optional film, limited application.

Application: Enrichment, on the "computer revolution." Somewhat "talky," but the talkers are important people.

Length and Type: 30 min, b & w, sound.

Source: #8

Summary: The title refers, of course, to the computer. This NET "Computer and the Mind of Man" series film remarks that a computer can do whatever we can instruct it to. A fundamental advance because of its speed. GIGO and the lack of a single language delay it.

F-1106 A COMPUTER GLOSSARY

Recommendation: Short, imaginative animation, a "fantastic voyage" into a computer.

Application: To wind up the general discussion of computers and programming, set the stage for the study of circuitry.

Length and Type: 10 min, color, sound.

Source: IBM, Dept. 10-802, Armonk, New York 10504, where teachers may also obtain an interesting wall chart derived from the film.

Summary: Microcircuitry of a computer, also definitions of Boolean logic, nanosecond, etc.

G | GENERAL

I. Bibliography

V. S. Darnowski, *A Teacher's Guide to "Computers: Theory and Uses."* N.S.T.A., 1964 (A)

There are lesson plans, flow sheets, a "game" of computers, computer toys, a 50-question multiple-choice test, and a very extensive bibliography, including *Scientific American* articles

and relevant films. The text to which this is a guide will be found much less helpful, though it explains one way to handle decimals (as binary numbers), and contrasts analog and digital computers very clearly.

J. G. Kemeny and T. E. Kurtz, *BASIC Programming.* Wiley 1967 (B)

The authors have been closely associated with BASIC from its inception. The book seems to be an ideal way to teach yourself to program in this language. Numerous examples, those which illustrate troubles being especially helpful.

H. D. Leeds and G. M. Weinberg, *Computer Programming Fundamentals.* McGraw-Hill, 1966 (B)

Good and quite complete. It is based on FORTRAN, but of course the fundamentals are nearly independent of language.

A. H. Lytel, *The ABC's of Computers.* Bobbs-Merrill, 1961. (B) (paper)

Good for ready reference, especially for topics omitted in our text; e.g., use of octal-based numbers; gate circuits; other kinds of memory; subtraction by adding the complement. As is characteristic of books published by Sams (now a division of Bobbs-Merrill), this is extremely clear.

National Council of Teachers of Mathematics, *Computer-Oriented Mathematics: Introduction for Teachers.* (A)

A mine of practical suggestions.

E. R. Sage, *Problem-Solving with the Computer.* ENTELEK, Inc., 42 Pleasant St., Newburyport, Mass. 01950, 1969 (B) (soft cover)

Written by a high school teacher for use in his own BASIC course, the book is oriented toward mathematics classes but is so clear that it belongs on the reference shelf beside any computer terminal.

W. F. Sharpe, *BASIC: Introduction to Computer Programming Using the BASIC Language.* Free Press (Macmillan), 1967 (B) (paper)

Though designed to go with a particular time-sharing scheme, it may be as good a book as

Kemeney's for learning purposes. Very well written.

"BASIC Language Programming: Instructor's Guide." General Electric Co., 1967

"General Information Manual: Introduction to IBM Data-Processing Systems." (Obtainable from any IBM branch office)

"How the Computer Gets the Answer," Life Educational Reprint #33 (from issue of November 27, 1967)

"Introduction to IBM Punched Card Data Processing." (Obtainable from any IBM branch office)

"You and the Computer, A Student's Guide." Educational Relations, General Electric Co., Schenectady, N.Y. 12305

II. Debugging with CARDIAC

(Excerpted from E. R. Sage reference in the Bibliography by permission of the publisher and rewritten in machine code.)

Students should be reminded that no memory cell is ever "blank," and when they are using CARDIAC the contents of a memory cell should never be erased except to enter other information (including 000).

Problem: Write a program that will find the number of items and the sum of the numbers in each of two (or more) lists. List A: 2, 3, 8; List B: 4, 5. Terminate each list by a card reading −10, and terminate the program by a blank card.

Flow Diagram	Machine Program	
┌─►Start	25	039
Read a number into Store	26	139
Bring number to accumulator	27	334
Test number; if neg., go to	28	238
↓ if 0 or +	29	638
Add Sum	30	137
Store in Sum	31	200
Bring Count to accumulator	32	637
Add 1	33	825
Store in Count	34	538
◄─Jump to Start	35	537
Print Sum ◄──	36	825
Print Count	37	000 (Count)
◄─Jump to Start	38	000 (Sum)
	39	000 (Store)

The expected print-out is (1) Sum 13, Count 3; (2) Sum 9, Count 2. The actual print-out is 13, 3, 22, 5.

When the program is set up on CARDIAC, all goes well for the first three passes, including the print-outs. But on the fourth pass we find that address 37 still contains 3 and address 38 still contains 13, and the numbers in List 2 are simply added to these. The trouble lies in the failure to restore these to 000 after the print-outs. The remedy is found in three more instructions: 440, 637, 638. These can be inserted after address 35 (pushing the contents of the following addresses down three spaces, and making appropriate address changes in the instructions at 25, 26, 28, 29, 30, 32, 34, and 35). It is easier to put them first, at addresses 22, 23, 24, and change the contents of address 36 to 822.

This is a rather good example of a program so simple that it just cannot go wrong, but does. The user of CARDIAC, being continually aware of the contents of every memory cell, is able (if he keeps alert) to catch his "bug" immediately.

III. Symbolic Programming

There is an intermediate stage between programming in machine code and programming in a simple compiler language: that occupied by the assembler. For many purposes (especially those of inexperienced programmers), one may insert yet another step between compiler and assembler. This is the use of symbolic code. In this language all the steps of machine code exist, but the rather tiresome numbers are eliminated. Many teachers of *The Man-Made World* have found symbolic programming a useful way to wean their students from machine code; in the expectation that others may do so too, we reprint a general consideration of it and display two programs written in it.

The writing of a program for a computer involves much more than knowing a convenient language, just as writing a French novel requires more than a knowledge of grammatical rules of that language. In either situation one must have something to say. In the case of the computer the "something to say" is usually a set of instructions about how to do a comparatively tedious and prosaic job. The programmer wants the computer to act like an obedient slave. Before this is possible the programmer must himself think out, step by step, how he wishes his totally unimaginative slave to accomplish the job. He must remember that the computer will be completely obedient even when this obedience leads it to do things which are, to the programmer, obviously not what was intended. It may seem that the computer is being perverse, but the programmer is master of the situation and must take the responsibility for his own errors. Now let us, without further preface, examine a program or two in which symbolic code has been used.

A PROGRAM TO DETERMINE THE LARGEST OF A SET OF INTEGERS

As a first example, consider the problem of determining the largest of an indefinitely large set of positive integers written on input cards. We shall assume that in the input card stack immediately below the cards which contain the set of positive integers is a card with some negative number. The first thing to do is to imagine how the job might be done without a computer available. The first number (on the top input card) may be the largest; therefore, put it aside as a tentative largest number. Now get the next card and examine its sign. If the number is negative, that is a signal that the first number was the only one in the set and it was of course the largest. If the second number was not negative, it should be compared with the largest one found so far. If the largest one found so far is the smaller of the two, it should be replaced by the new one (or even if they are the same size: it simplifies the programming). This procedure should be repeated again beginning with the selection of a new number from an input card.

In the flow chart, opposite, LARGEST and NEXT are our names for the addresses in memory at which are stored, respectively, the largest number found up to a given time in the process and the next number being considered. The chart is for the most part self-explanatory. Each new number is examined. If it is negative, this is an indication that we have reached the end of the set of nonnegative numbers of the set, and we print out the largest number already found.

Another test is performed when we subtract the largest number already found from the new number we are examining. If the result is negative we know that the new number is no larger than the one we have already found, and we get the next number. If the result is nonnegative we replace the previously found largest number by the new one. These two tests each have two possible outcomes and these are indicated by lines with arrows. (The operation code $X = 3$ will be used in the final program we are in the process of writing to allow the computer to take either the next sequential instruction or jump to another one, depending upon the result of the test.)

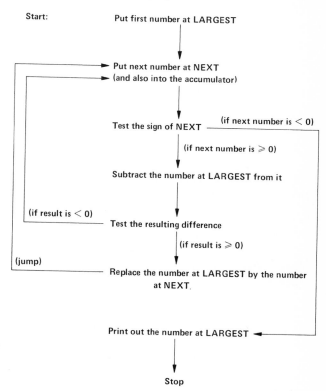

Flow chart for finding the largest number of a set

The next step is to rewrite the information which is contained in the flow chart in the form of a program in *symbolic code*. The program written in this symbolic code (next page) has two features which distinguish it from the final program written in *machine code*. First, *mnemonics* are used instead of decimal numbers to represent the various possible machine operations. For example, the mnemonic

STO is used instead of "6" for the operation which stores the contents of the accumulator at the designated storage location. Thus, a mnemonic is a shorthand form for an operation code. This form is concise and yet it reminds us of the English words describing the operation so that we need not always refer to the computer manual to see its meaning. Next we see a table listing the 10 mnemonics which we shall use.

Table of correspondence between operation codes and mnemonics

Operation code	Mnemonic	Meaning
0	INP	input
1	CLA	clear and add
2	ADD	add
3	TAC	test accumulator contents
4	SFT	shift
5	OUT	output
6	STO	store
7	SUB	subtract
8	JMP	jump
9	HRS	halt and reset

The second feature of symbolic code is that *symbolic location names* (such as ABOVE and LARGEST) are used to identify certain lines of the program. These names can be chosen arbitrarily and are used so that the programmer need not concern himself about the identity of the exact locations at which his program will finally be stored. For instance, the instruction "SUB LARGEST" means "Subtract from the contents of the accumulator the contents of the memory location at which we have stored the largest number which we have found so far; we have agreed to give this location the symbolic name LARGEST." As another example the instruction "JMP ABOVE" means "Jump to the line of the program which we have given the name ABOVE; that is, the second line of the program."

Symbolic coding is clearly much easier than machine coding. It relieves the programmer of the job of assigning actual memory addresses to the lines of his program and it allows him to think in terms of the convenient-to-remember mnemonics instead of the numerical operation codes. Before the symbolic program can be stored in the computer memory, however, it must be translated into machine code. This translation process is a form of

assembly. It is not usually carried out by hand, although here we shall do it that way. We want to illustrate that this assembly process is an orderly one, and therefore one which itself could be (and now usually is) carried out by a properly written computer program.

Assembly customarily is accomplished in two steps, or *passes*. Each pass is a single sequential processing of the symbolic program. In the first pass memory locations are assigned to the lines of the program and consequently a correspondence between symbolic locations and memory locations can be established. These correspondences are listed in a *symbol table*. In the second pass the various instructions are assembled. That is, each mnemonic is replaced by its associated operation code and each symbolic location is replaced by the appropriate memory location listed in the symbol table.

A program in symbolic code

10		INP	LARGEST
11	ABOVE	INP	NEXT
12		CLA	NEXT
13		TAC	BELOW
14		SUB	LARGEST
15		TAC	ABOVE
16		CLA	NEXT
17		STO	LARGEST
18		JMP	ABOVE
19	BELOW	OUT	LARGEST
20		HRS	00
21	LARGEST		
22	NEXT		

For our problem, we assume that the first pass assigns addresses 10 through 22 to the lines of the symbolic program, as shown at the left edge (above). After this pass we can write the symbol table shown below. On the second pass each line of

A symbol table

Symbol	Location
ABOVE	11
BELOW	19
LARGEST	21
NEXT	22

the symbolic program is examined, mnemonics are replaced by operation codes (from table, opposite) and symbolic names by memory addresses (from table, above). The resulting program in machine code is given below. The words at addresses 21 and 22 have been assembled as *zeros*. However, it is actually unimportant what the initial contents are at these locations because when the program is executed they will be erased before new information replaces them.

An assembled program in machine code

Memory address	Stored Word
	(X YZ)
10	0 21
11	0 22
12	1 22
13	3 19
14	7 21
15	3 11
16	1 22
17	6 21
18	8 11
19	5 21
20	9 00
21	(0 00)
22	(0 00)

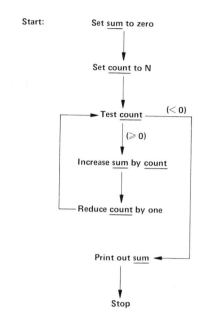

Flow chart for summing the first N integers

COMPUTING THE SUM OF THE FIRST N POSITIVE INTEGERS

As another example, consider writing a program to compute the sum of the first N positive integers ($sum = N + \ldots + 2 + 1$). The program is to work for all integers N for which the sum can be stored as one word in the computer memory. This means that N must be in the range from 1 to 44 (the sum of which is 990 and will fit in memory). The value of N is punched in and read from an input card; the resulting value of *sum* is to be punched in an output card.

A flow chart for our problem is given next. There are two quantities, *sum* and *count*, which are changed during the computation. (We shall use lower-case italicized type to denote the *contents* at a particular address with the same symbolic location name. For instance, *sum* is the number contained at the machine address which has been assigned the name SUM.) The quantity *sum* at a given time has a value which is the partial sum of all the integers, from N downward, which have so far been added together. The quantity *count* is the largest integer which has not, up to that time, been added to the partial sum. The initial values of *sum* and *count* are set to zero and N, respectively. The updated value of *count* is tested immediately after it is decreased by one in order to detect when it first becomes negative. At that point the summing is stopped and the answer, *sum*, is printed out. Until then the procedure alternately causes (1) the partial sum to be increased by the largest integer (*count*) yet to be added and (2) this integer to be reduced by one.

The flow chart given above is about as complex as any that an experienced programmer would actually ever write for our problem. He would next write the program in symbolic code. For us it is valuable to write a slightly more detailed flow chart (next page, top) in which the terminology is quite close to that of symbolic code. We shall not discuss this new flow chart but shall leave it to the reader to verify that it is equivalent to the earlier one.

The symbolic program (next page, bottom) is, for the most part, self-explanatory. The comments are not themselves a part of the symbolic program and no use of them is made in the assembly process. These comments are similar to those an experienced programmer would write to help him (and others)

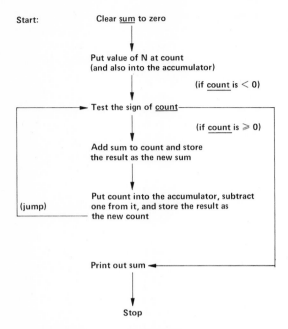

Start: Clear <u>sum</u> to zero

Put value of N at count
(and also into the accumulator)

(if <u>count</u> is < 0)

Test the sign of <u>count</u>

(if <u>count</u> is ≥ 0)

Add sum to count and store
the result as the new sum

(jump) Put count into the accumulator, subtract
one from it, and store the result as
the new count

Print out sum

Stop

A more detailed flow chart for summing the first N integers

of several possible ways of clearing the accumulator contents to zero. The instruction "SUB ONE" subtracts from the contents of the accumulator the contents of the memory address which has been given the symbolic name ONE. (The computer does *not* automatically understand the English word ONE. It is only because we have explicitly specified the contents at location ONE to be 0 01 that the effect is the one we want.) Following is a corresponding program in machine code with the initial address arbitrarily chosen to be "25."

Assembled program in machine code

Memory address	Stored word	
	(X	YZ)
25	4	03
26	6	38
27	0	39
28	1	39
29	3	36
30	2	38
31	6	38
32	1	39
33	7	40
34	6	39
35	8	29
36	5	38
37	9	00
38	(0	00)
39	(0	00)
40	0	01

understand what each step of the program is to do. Even a simple program tends to look somewhat cryptic after the passage of time not only to others but also to the programmer who wrote it unless comments accompany the program.

The "SFT 03" instruction shifts the initial accumulator contents 3 digits to the right and is one

A symbolic program corresponding to the preceding flow chart

	Operation	Address	Comment
	SFT	03	Clear accumulator to zero
	STO	SUM	and store this zero at SUM.
	INP	COUNT	Copy value of *N* from input card into COUNT
	CLA	COUNT	and bring this same value to accumulator.
UP	TAC	DOWN	Test negativeness of the number at COUNT.
	ADD	SUM	If *count* is nonnegative, add *sum* to it
	STO	SUM	and store the result as the new *sum*.
	CLA	COUNT	Get *count* again,
	SUB	ONE	subtract one from it,
	STO	COUNT	store as the new *count* and
	JMP	UP	go back to earlier instruction.
DOWN	OUT	SUM	If *count* is negative, print out *sum*
	HRS	00	and stop.
SUM			
COUNT			
ONE		01	

IV. Compiler Languages

For computers to be useful we must be able to communicate with them easily. If the exploitation of computers is not to be confined to specialists, communication with them must be by language much more like natural languages than are machine or symbolic languages. This need creates a problem because a natural language such as English is too full of ambiguities to be appropriate. Computer languages must contain only expressions and statements which have only one meaning, and yet they must resemble English enough so that they are easy to understand.

It may be surprising to learn that hundreds of these languages have been developed, most of them still somewhat bewildering except to the initiated, and there are certain to be many more. Many are designed to have an advantage for some special class of problems. Others are meant to have more general applicability. Notable examples of these latter languages are ALGOL, MAD, and FORTRAN.

Commonly, when a novice "learns to program" he learns how to express his algorithms and flow charts in one of these languages. Examples of instructions in these are:

1) ;LST:=0;for K:=1 step 1 until 50 do if LST $<$N(K) then LST:=N(K); stop: —— (ALGOL)

2) THROUGH END, FOR Y=N/2, (N/Y−Y)/2, .ABS. (N/Y−Y) .L. EPS —— (MAD)

3) IF (ABSF(ARCCOSF(−A/(5.*SQRTF(−A**4)))) − EPS) 85, 84, 84 —— (FORTRAN)

There are newer languages which are much more like English than these. It is possible to learn to write programs in one of these "higher-level" languages without having the slightest understanding of what happens to it inside the computer.

Each statement in languages such as the three given above is the equivalent of many lines of instruction in machine or symbolic code—and ultimately it must be translated into the machine code which computers understand. The process of translating expressions of these types into sequences of instructions in machine code is an orderly one which is accomplished by executing a computer program. This translation program is called a *compiler*. The language which requires the translation is itself often known as a *compiler language*.

High-level languages which are suited to other than algebraic problems also exist, and each requires its own compiler. For instance, LISP and SLIP are languages which are particularly effective in handling lists. COMIT and SNOBOL are especially useful for language translation while COBOL applies best in business-oriented, data-processing problems.

Compiler languages differ from, and have advantages over, symbolic languages. The number of lines of instruction necessary in a symbolic program is essentially the same as if it were written in machine code. Programming in symbolic code demands a detailed knowledge of the operations that the computer is capable of performing. On the other hand, it is not necessary for a programmer who uses a compiler language to know about the logical structure of the computer within which the program is finally executed. A program written in compiler language can be executed on any computer for which a corresponding compiler (translation) program has been written. However, the writing of compiler programs is a task which requires the efforts of highly skilled professional programmers.

In general, the easier it is to learn a computer language the harder it is to translate it into machine code. At one extreme are symbolic languages which require only the simple assembly procedure for translation. At the other extreme are languages which approach English in the ease with which they can be learned and used but which require elaborate procedures for their compilation. To be thoroughly competent a programming expert must be familiar with an entire spectrum of languages.

Learning computer languages is analogous to learning to drive a car. We know that it is possible to learn enough about a car in just a few hours to drive it around town. Similarly it is possible to learn enough about a high-level language to solve a few common algebraic problems in an equally short time. But we know too that a professional driver has some big advantages; he has a "feel" for fuel mixtures, brake drums, the ignition system and the transmission, and he is not content merely to sit on his side of the dashboard and manipulate chromium-plated levers. In the same way a professional programmer has a "feel" for shift registers, addressable memories, counters, and machine code and how he can put them to use for best results.

CHECK LIST FOR CHAPTER 12

LOGICAL THOUGHT AND LOGIC CIRCUITS

APPROX. TIME: Text: 8 days Lab: 3 days

A. APPROACH	CLASS PERIODS	B. BLACK & WHITE TRANSPARENCIES	C. CUES (k = key problems) Discussion Questions	Problems Easy	Problems Medium	Problems Hard	D. DEMONSTRATIONS, LABS & PROJECTS	E. EVALUATION	F. FILMS	G. GENERAL
1. Introduction	2	1201 1202						12	1201 1202	
2. How to Make Electric Circuits Say "And" and "Or"	2	1203 1204 1205 1213 1214	1, 3, 4	4k,5k, 6k		10	I	2, 4, 8, 9		II IV
3. The Majority-Vote Problem	1	1206	6		9,11	1, 2	IIa	3, 7, 13		III
4. How to Make an Electric Circuit Say "Not"	1	1207 1208 1209	2					1, 6, 10, 11		
5. Analysis vs Synthesis	1	1210 1211	5	8	3, 7k		IIb	5		V
6. Additional Topics on Logical Thought and Circuit Models	1	1212	7				III			
7. Final Comment										

Logical Thought and Logic Circuits

12

A | APPROACH

I. Purpose and Organization of the Chapter

Chapter 12 begins the final unit of the course. The course started with a look at the interaction of man and machine on a personal basis, and society and technology on a wider basis. This was followed by a look at some uses of technological concepts in decision making. The engineering approach to the analysis of systems followed with a section on man-man communication and man-machine communication.

The one machine with which most people in technological societies will communicate is the computer. This final unit looks at the digital computer in detail. Having seen in Chapters 10 and 11 how man can communicate with the computer, students are now quite motivated to look into the computer to see how it works.

Chapter 12 begins with rather simple logical statements, discusses how these are simulated by electric circuits, and goes on to more complex logic and shows how these can be simulated by combinations of the simple logic circuits learned at the beginning of the chapter. The emphasis during this and all succeeding chapters must be on the Logic Circuit Boards and all work should be centered in the laboratory setting. After just a day or two, students should be designing their own logic circuits to an-

swer many of the questions and problems which come up in class, as well as those at the end of the chapter. This work should be encouraged. If school policy permits, the students should be encouraged to take the LCB's home to work on them. Many schools have assigned one or two LCB's to the school library for *The Man-Made World* students to use in study carrels during their unassigned periods.

II. Objectives for Students

Upon completion of the reading, activities, and discussions of this chapter, the student should be able to:

1. Identify the following terms: *"and" circuit, binary element, "exclusive or," hierarchical, "inclusive or," logic circuit, logical design, make and break contacts,* and *odd parity.*

2. Design and wire a simple on-off logic circuit, an "and" circuit, an "or" circuit, and a "not" circuit.

3. Develop and use truth tables to verify simple logic statements and tables of combinations to verify the corresponding circuits.

4. Design and wire a compound logic circuit from combinations of simple logic circuits; break down a compound circuit into its logic elements.

5. Relate logic circuits to devices and situations which he normally interacts with or reads about,

such as coin telephones, astronaut escape mechanisms, majority-vote indications, photographic dark room warning lights, hall light with two switches, etc.

6. Synthesize and analyze logic circuits involving up to three inputs.

7. Analyze and determine the credibility of compound statements.

8. Relate Boolean Algebra connectives to logic circuits.

III. Suggestions for Teaching

Section 1. Introduction. The major point in the introductory section of this chapter is to bridge the gap from the look at communicating with computers in Chapters 10 and 11, to what actually goes on inside the digital computer as discussed in Chapters 12-15.

People are often impressed with hierarchical situations in printing. The students might be interested in looking at the color of pictures in a magazine with a magnifying glass to see the dots which are the lowest visible level of that situation. Further steps would, of course, be the molecules of which the ink pigment is made, then atoms, then nuclei, and finally nuclear particles.

Spending a bit of time on this section will be helpful in trying to keep perspective as you move from the simple circuits of the Logic Circuit Board back up to the computer itself. Many teachers have found it useful to set up the Logic Circuit Board to demonstrate the logic AND and OR statements related to going to the beach, then discussing Question 2 on page 524.

Section 2. How to Make Electric Circuits Say "And" and "Or." This section is most effectively taught by presenting the problem of the jet pilot first as a demonstration by wiring the board as the problem is described and then having the students do Lab I.

This is the first step in the hierarchical development which should proceed through to the development of the minimicro computer in Chapter 15.

Section 3. The Majority-Vote Problem. This section builds directly on the previous one by adding additional switches and more complex networks. It is important to have the students understand that there may be many different designs of network of switches for a particular logical situation, but it is possible to optimize among these designs for fewest number of wires, etc. Simplifying a Boolean algebraic expression for a logic situation often helps in simplifying the logical design of the circuit.

Section 4. How to Make an Electric Circuit say "Not." This discussion of the "Not" logic of the break side of a switch should be demonstrated with the Logic Circuit Board after first posing the question of how the switches which operate the hall light work to control the same light from either end of the hall. This leads directly into Inclusive OR and Exclusive OR discussions.

Section 5. Analysis vs Synthesis. The important points to consider in this section are:

1. To understand the capabilities of a circuit, we analyze it, but the design of a circuit which will function as we want it to is synthesis.

2. Circuits can be simplified by using fewer contacts if the same logic is still true.

3. The logical way to verify circuits is by the use of a truth table or table of combinations.

Section 6. Additional Topics on Logical Thought and Circuit Models. At this point the review of logical thought in the opening paragraphs of this section should be discussed thoroughly, and then the model for the river-crossing problem should be given by demonstrating the completed circuit on the LCB. After the demonstration, have the students start Lab III, Part A.

During the laboratory period it will be helpful to discuss individual problems with students. A full discussion of the text should *follow* the lab. Discussion of the fact that there is more than one series of operations which will successfully complete the crossing is helpful to again emphasize that there is often more than one "correct" answer to a problem.

Section 7. Final Comment. The summary is self-explanatory. We have gone from simple ON-OFF circuits to AND, OR, and NOT circuits and then to the hierarchy of circuits which can model more complex logical situations.

B | BLACK AND WHITE TRANSPARENCIES

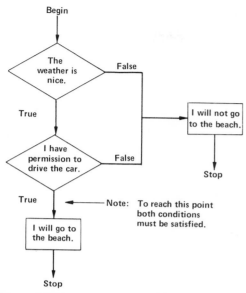

T-1201   DIAGRAM AND FLOW CHART FOR LOGICAL <u>AND</u>

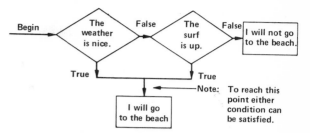

T-1202   DIAGRAM AND FLOW CHART FOR LOGICAL <u>OR</u>

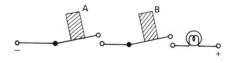

Switch A	Switch B	Light
Released	Released	Off
Released	Operated	Off
Operated	Released	Off
Operated	Operated	On

Path through contact on switch A	Path through contact on switch B	Path through the contacts in series
0	0	0
0	1	0
1	0	0
1	1	1

Condition 1 (C1)	Condition 2 (C2)	(C1 AND C2)
FALSE	FALSE	FALSE
FALSE	TRUE	FALSE
TRUE	FALSE	FALSE
TRUE	TRUE	TRUE

T-1203   <u>AND</u> (SERIES) CIRCUIT

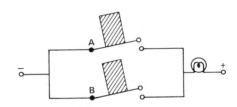

Switch A	Switch B	Lamp
Released	Released	Off
Released	Operated	On
Operated	Released	On
Operated	Operated	On

Path through contact on switch A	Path through contact on switch B	Path through the contacts in parallel
0	0	0
0	1	1
1	0	1
1	1	1

C1	C2	C1 OR C2
FALSE	FALSE	FALSE
FALSE	TRUE	TRUE
TRUE	FALSE	TRUE
TRUE	TRUE	TRUE

T-1204   <u>OR</u> (PARALLEL) CIRCUIT

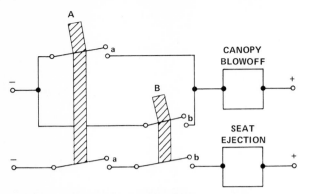

T-1205   COMBINED <u>AND</u> AND <u>OR</u> CIRCUIT

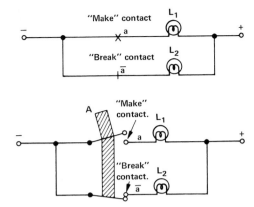

T-1207   COMPLEMENTARY CONTACTS

A	B	C	Desired Logical Conditions	State of Network
0	0	0	0	0
0	0	1	0	0
0	1	0	0	0
0	1	1	1	1
1	0	0	0	0
1	1	0	1	1
1	1	0	1	1
1	1	1	1	1

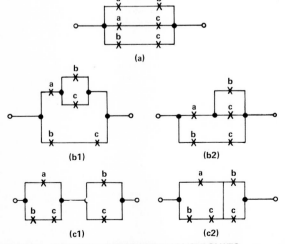

T-1206   EQUIVALENT MAJORITY CIRCUITS

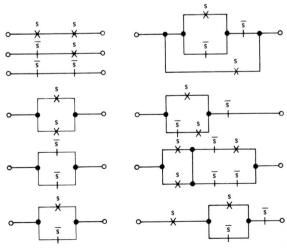

T-1208   CIRCUITS FOR ANALYSIS

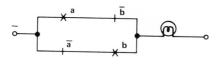

(a)

Switch A	Switch B	Path	(Light)
Released	Released	Open	(Off)
Released	Operated	Closed	(On)
Operated	Released	Closed	(On)
Operated	Operated	Open	(Off)

(b)

a	b	Light
0	0	0
0	1	1
1	0	1
1	1	0

(c)

T-1209   HALL LIGHT CIRCUIT

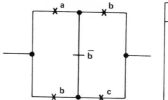

A	B	C	path
0	0	0	
0	0	1	
0	1	0	
0	1	1	
1	0	0	
1	0	1	
1	1	0	
1	1	1	

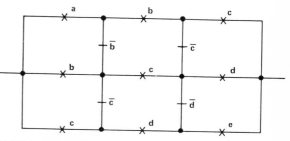

T-1211   MAJORITY CIRCUITS

A	B	C	Path
0	0	0	0
0	0	1	1
0	1	0	1
0	1	1	0
1	0	0	1
1	0	1	0
1	1	0	0
1	1	1	1

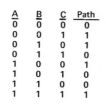

T-1210   THREE VARIABLE ODD-PARITY CIRCUIT

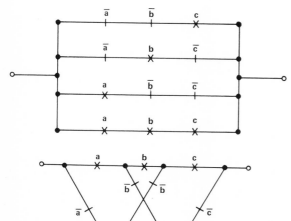

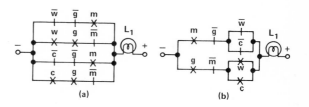

(a)   (b)

W	C	G	M	light
0	0	0	0	0
0	0	0	1	1
0	0	1	0	0
0	0	1	1	0
0	1	0	0	0
0	1	0	1	1
0	1	1	0	1
0	1	1	1	0
1	0	0	0	0
1	0	0	1	1
1	0	1	0	1
1	0	1	1	0
1	1	0	0	0
1	1	0	1	0
1	1	1	0	1
1	1	1	1	0

(c)

T-1212   RIVER CROSSING PROBLEM

298

Network   Combinations

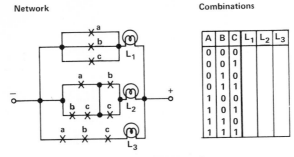

A	B	C	L_1	L_2	L_3
0	0	0			
0	0	1			
0	1	0			
0	1	1			
1	0	0			
1	0	1			
1	1	0			
1	1	1			

T-1213   PROBLEM 10

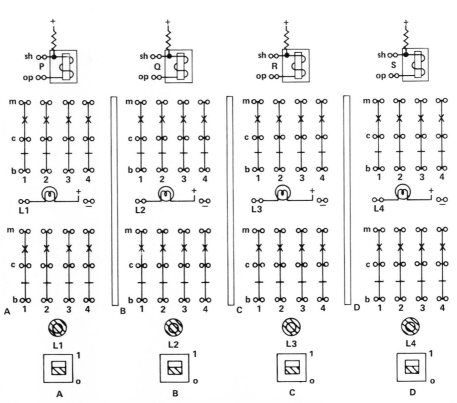

T-1214   LOGIC CIRCUIT BOARD WIRING PANEL

C | CUES TO QUESTIONS AND PROBLEMS

Questions for Study and Discussion

1. The 3 operators must agree that the firing should take place and their switches should be in series:

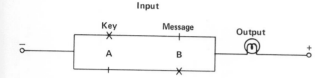

2. This is the hall light or odd-parity circuit.

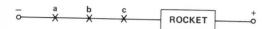

The lamp will light if A or B is operated (but not for both); i.e., if the key is 0 the lamp must light if the message is 1, and if the key is 1 the lamp must light if the message is 0. So we define 0 to mean "switch is released," and 1 to mean "switch is operated."

3. Unanimous voting circuit
   Burglar alarm
   Making a call by dial phone

4. Any 1 out of 3 voting circuit
   Burglar alarm
   House with 3 doorbells

5. a) The circuit is closed whenever any odd number of switches is operated.

   b) The circuit is closed whenever any even number of switches is operated.

6. Majority voting
   2 or 3 out of 3
   3, 4, or 5 out of 5, etc.
   Mixing dangerous ingredients
   Fatal symptoms in an intensive-care patient

7. Try both cases:

If T is a truth-teller, his answer to the question must be "yes." But then S has to be the liar, so when he says "he says yes" he is not lying, though when he says "he's a liar" he *is* lying.

But if T is a liar, "Groom" must mean "yes" (since that would be a lie). And if T is of the lying tribe, S is a truth teller, and both of his statements are indeed true.

∴ The tall tribesman is the liar, and the short tribesman is truthful.

Problems

1. a)

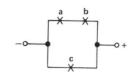

b)

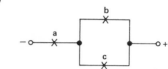

c)

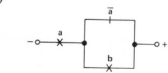

d)

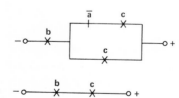

e)

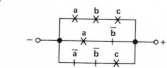

f)

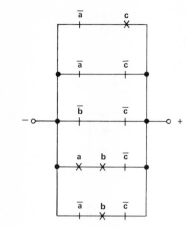

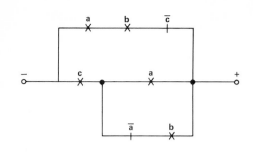

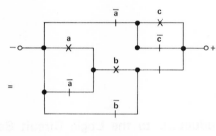

=

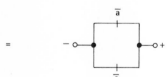

=

2.

$\bar{a}bc + \bar{a}\bar{b}c + ab\bar{c} + abc$
$= \bar{a}bc + a(\bar{b}c + b\bar{c} + bc)$
$= \bar{a}bc + a[c(\bar{b} + b) + b\bar{c}]$
$= \bar{a}bc + a(c + b\bar{c})$

$\bar{a}bc + a\bar{b}c + ab\bar{c} + abc$
$= \bar{a}bc + c(ab + ab + ab)$
$= ab\bar{c} + c[a(b + b) + ab]$
$= ab\bar{c} + c(a + \bar{a}b)$

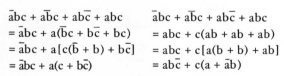

3.

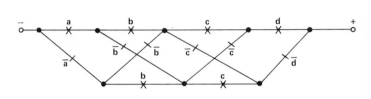

4.

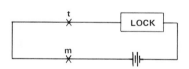

5.

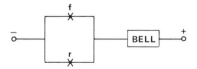

6.

A	B	Canopy blowoff charge	Seat ejection
0	0	0	0
0	1	1	0
1	0	1	0
1	1	1	1

7.a)

A	B	
0	0	0
0	1	1
1	0	1
1	1	0

b) The tables are identical.

c) This is an odd-parity circuit.

8.

A	B	C	
0	0	0	0
0	0	1	1
0	1	0	1
0	1	1	0
1	0	0	1
1	0	1	0
1	1	0	0
1	1	1	1

9.a) Contacts "b," "c," and "d"

b) No

c)

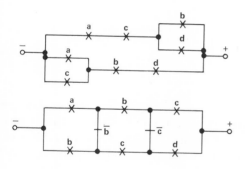

10.a)

A	B	C	L_1	L_2	L_3
0	0	0	0	0	0
0	0	1	1	0	0
0	1	0	1	0	0
0	1	1	1	1	0
1	0	0	1	0	0
1	0	1	1	1	0
1	1	0	1	1	0
1	1	1	1	1	1

b) One

c) Two

d) Three

e) No

f) Any counting circuit (up to 3). Any situation in which the desired outcome is independent of the sequence of operations, as in the case of the seat-ejection problem.

11.

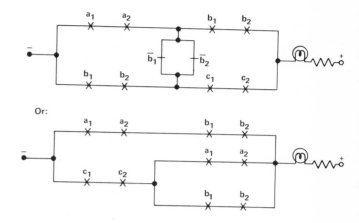

D | DEMONSTRATIONS, LABS, AND PROJECTS

I. Introduction to the Logic Circuit Board

Although the title implies introduction to the whole LCB, you should only introduce the students to the lower half of the LCB. The main purpose of this activity is to teach the operation of the manual switches and how they can be used to model simple logic statements or situations. Discussion of the operation of a relay will cause confusion, so wait until Chapter 13 to explain its operation.

In introducing the experiment, a large single-pole double-throw switch may be used to demonstrate switching action. The idea of "breaking" a conducting path when the switch handle is operated is a new concept to the student, even though he has done this very thing at home and in school.

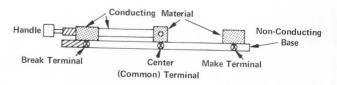

Single Pole Double Throw Switch

An LCB switch demonstrator can also be used to explain the operation of the slide switch. It is made for use with an overhead projector and can be purchased from American Machinery and Foundry for $4. It is very useful for explaining the meaning of "make" and "break" contacts.

Equipment:

   One LCB and an A.C. outlet for each laboratory group

Answers to Questions:

*1.

A	L1	L2
0	0	1
1	1	0

*2.

*3.

A	B	L1
0	0	0
0	1	0
1	0	0
1	1	1

The circuit in Fig. 10 is called an AND circuit because only the operation of both switches, A and B, will cause L_1 to light. As indicated, only one "1" is in the output column of the table.

*4. Again, only one "1" would be found in the output column of the table.

*5. The diagram for the phone booth problem is:

Receiver Activated   Coin Activated

(−)   Telephone Exchange

*6.

A	B	L1
0	0	0
0	1	1
1	0	1
1	1	1

The circuit in Fig. 12 is called an OR circuit because the operation of either switches A or B or both will cause L_1 to light. Actually, this is an inclusive OR circuit as contrasted to the exclusive OR circuit which is studied later. As indicated above, three "1's" are in the output column of the table.

*7. For the situation A OR B OR C, seven "1's" would be found in the output column of the table.

*8. The diagram for the school fire-alarm system is:

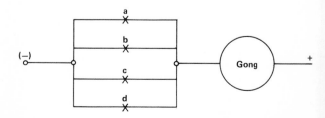

Answer to Problem:

*1. The diagram for the canopy-seat ejection system is:

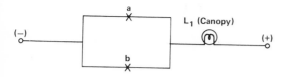

II. The Odd-Parity and Majority Circuits

To minimize confusion, this experiment is best done as two separate experiments. They can be used to introduce the concepts of odd-parity and majority circuits, followed by a reading assignment from the body of the text.

Equipment:

One LCB and an A.C. outlet for each laboratory group

Answers to Questions:

*1. Connect terminal $1b$ of switch A to terminal $1m$ of switch B.

Connect a terminal of L_1 to terminal $1c$ of switch B.

A	B	a	$\bar{a}$	b	$\bar{b}$	$a \cdot \bar{b}$	$\bar{a} \circ b$	L_1
0	0	0	1	0	1	0	0	0
0	1	0	1	1	0	0	1	1
1	0	1	0	0	1	1	0	1
1	1	1	0	1	0	0	0	0

*2. The running list for the 3-variable, odd-parity circuit is: $C1c, L1; B1b, B2m, C1b; B1m, B2b, C1m; A1b, B2c; A1m, B1c;$ Neg, $A1c;$

A	B	C	L_1
0	0	0	0
0	0	1	1
0	1	0	1
0	1	1	0
1	0	0	1
1	0	1	0
1	1	0	0
1	1	1	1

*3. The running list for the majority circuit is: $L1, B1c, C1c, C2c; B2m, C2m; A2m, C1m; A1m, B1m;$ Neg, $A1c, A2c, B2c;$

A	B	C	L_1
0	0	0	0
0	0	1	0
0	1	0	0
0	1	1	1
1	0	0	0
1	0	1	1
1	1	0	1
1	1	1	1

III. Circuits Which Model Logic Problems

This experiment is an excellent example of the use of functional models as tools for solving problems. Students should be reminded of previous uses of functional models in making decisions (i.e., analog computer simulations). For some students this experiment may require two laboratory periods. Better students might be asked to model a river-crossing problem involving 3 married couples and a boat which can only hold 2 people at a time. The object is to get everybody across the river under the condition that no husband or wife is ever left alone with another person's mate.

Students who work faster in the laboratory can also be asked to "improve" their LCB model by using a buzzer (unstable relay circuit) as an indicator of error and the lights as an indicator that an object has crossed the river.

Equipment:

One LCB and an A.C. outlet for each laboratory group

PART A

Answers to Questions:

*1.

	A Boatman	B Cabbage	C Wolf	D Goat	Warning Light
a.	0	0	0	0	0
b.	0	0	0	1	0
c.	0	0	1	0	0
d.	0	0	1	1	1(light on)
e.	0	1	0	0	0
f.	0	1	0	1	1
g.	0	1	1	0	0
h.	0	1	1	1	1
i.	1	0	0	0	1
j.	1	0	0	1	0
k.	1	0	1	0	1
l.	1	0	1	1	0
m.	1	1	0	0	1
n.	1	1	0	1	0
o.	1	1	1	0	0
p.	1	1	1	1	0

The laboratory manual describes a procedure for coding the position of the man, the cabbage, the wolf, and the goat on switches *A, B, C,* and *D* respectively. The pupils should be advised to attach a small strip of suitably labeled masking tape adjacent to each switch which associates the switch with the man, cabbage, wolf, or goat.

*2.The circuit for the remaining conditions is:

line i $\quad a \cdot \overline{b} \cdot \overline{c} \cdot d = 1$
line k $\quad a \cdot \overline{b} \cdot c \cdot \overline{d} = 1$
line m $\quad a \cdot b \cdot \overline{c} \cdot \overline{d} = 1$

*3.These are translated into a network as:

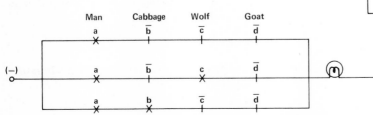

PART B

*1.The Boolean Algebra expression for the designed circuit is:

$$a \cdot \overline{b} \cdot \overline{c} \cdot \overline{d} + a \cdot \overline{b} \cdot c \cdot \overline{d} + a \cdot b \cdot \overline{c} \cdot \overline{d} = 1$$

This can be factored to give:

$$a \cdot \overline{d} \, [\overline{b} \cdot \overline{c} + \overline{b} \cdot c + b \cdot \overline{c}] = 1$$

or

$$a \cdot \overline{d} \, [\overline{b}(\overline{c} + c) + b \cdot \overline{c}] = 1$$

and by setting $(\overline{c} + c)$ equal to 1

$$a \cdot \overline{d} [\overline{b} + b \cdot \overline{c}] = 1$$

The circuit for this expression is:

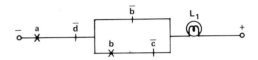

The complete circuit then is:

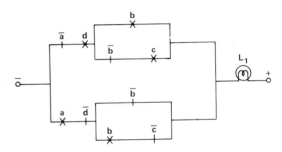

Further simplification gives a final circuit of:

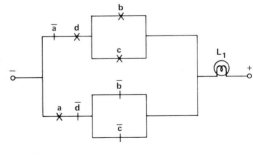

The final form is suggested by an inspection of the lower branches of the two parallel circuits where the switches representing the cabbage and the wolf are in series. The wolf represents no threat to the cabbage or vice versa. Therefore it is unessential to have $\bar{b}$ in series with c or b in series with $\bar{c}$.

This line of reasoning will be objected to by some pupils, as it should. Therefore, further recourse to Boolean Algebra is necessary.

Five postulates are sufficient to develop all the theorems required for the analysis or the synthesis of circuits containing series and parallel connections of switching elements, regardless of the complexity of the network.

The postulates are:

a) $Z = 0$ if $Z \neq 1$
 $\quad Z = 1$ if $Z \neq 0$
b) $0 \cdot 0 = 0$
 $\quad 1 + 1 = 1$
c) $1 \cdot 1 = 1$
 $\quad 0 + 0 = 0$

d) $1 \cdot 0 = 0 \cdot 1 = 0$
 $\quad 0 + 1 = 1 + 0 = 1$
e) $\bar{0} = 1$
 $\quad \bar{1} = 0$

These postulates may be demonstrated on the LCB, and may be used to show that

is equivalent to

for by developing a table of combinations and assigning values of 0 or 1 to b and c, the equivalence of these circuits can be established.

b	$\bar{b}$	c	$b + \bar{b} \cdot c$	$b + c$	Total value
0	1	0	$0 + 1 \cdot 0$	$0 + 0$	0
0	1	1	$0 + 1 \cdot 1$	$0 + 1$	1
1	0	0	$1 + 0 \cdot 0$	$1 + 0$	1
1	0	1	$1 + 0 \cdot 1$	$1 + 1$	1

*2. The running list for the river-crossing problem is: Neg, $A1c$; $A1b$, $D1c$; $D1m$, $B1c$; $B1m$, $L1$; $D1m$, $C1c$; $C1m$, L_1; $A1m$, $D2c$; $D2b$, $B2c$; $B2b$, $B1m$; $D2b$, $C2c$; $C2b$, $C1m$;

*3. The sequence of safe moves which leads to all switches in the 1 position (North Shore) can be found in Section 6.

E | EVALUATION

The questions in this section are rated according to the chapter objectives and the performance levels stated in the introduction to the teacher's manual. This group of questions is not intended to be all inclusive, but just as a guide to possible questions. Zeros in the chapter objective column indicate no chapter objective for this question.

Judged to be Relatively Easy:

The first five questions refer to the following diagrams:

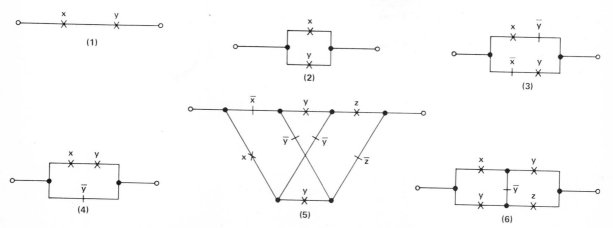

Chapter Objective	Performance Level	Judged to be Relatively Easy:

1   I

1. A circuit which can properly be described as an exclusive OR circuit is
   a) 1.
   b) 2.
   c) 3.
   d) 4.
   e) 5.

1   I

2. A circuit which can properly be described as an inclusive OR circuit is
   a) 1.
   b) 2.
   c) 3.
   d) 4.
   e) 6.

5   I

3. A circuit which can properly be described as a majority-vote circuit is
   a) 2.
   b) 3.
   c) 4.
   d) 5.
   e) 6.

1   I

4. A circuit which can properly be described as an AND circuit is
   a) 1.
   b) 2.
   c) 3.
   d) 4.
   e) 5.

4   I

5. A circuit which can properly be described as a 3-switch even-parity circuit is
   a) 2.
   b) 3.
   c) 4.
   d) 5.
   e) 6.

6.

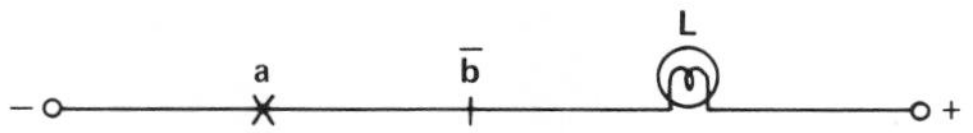

6   II

Lamp L in this circuit will light if
   a) switches A and B are operated.
   b) switches A or B or both are operated.
   c) switches A or B but not both are operated.
   d) switch A and not switch B is operated.
   e) switch B and not switch A is operated.

7.

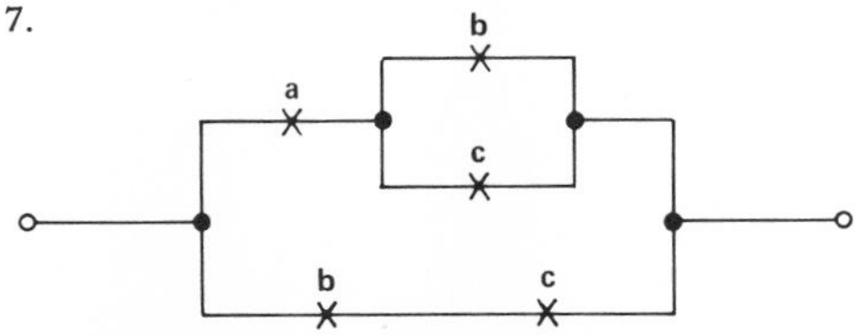

Chapter Objective	Performance Level	

Judged to be Relatively Easy:

5 II

The diagram shown at the bottom of the preceding page represents
a) a NOT circuit.
b) a hall-light circuit.
c) an odd-parity circuit.
d) a majority-vote circuit.
e) a canopy blowoff circuit.

5 I

8. Of the following diagrams, the one which represents the best way to connect switches for the canopy-blowoff, pilot-ejection, circuit is

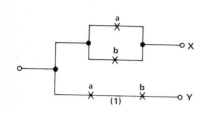
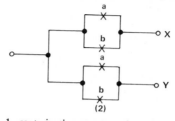
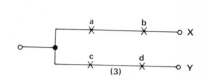

a) 1, seat ejection connected at *X*.
b) 1, seat ejection connected at *Y*.
c) 2, seat ejection connected at either *X* or *Y*.
d) 3, seat ejection connected at *X*.
e) 3, seat ejection connected at *Y*.

3 II

9. A table of combinations for this circuit has been started.

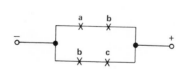

Row	A	B	C	Circuit
1	0	0	0	
2	0	0	1	
3	0	1	0	
4	0	1	1	
5	1	0	0	
6	1	0	1	
7	1	1	0	
8	1	1	1	

A proper number to place in the column labeled "Circuit" is 1 in row
a) 2.   d) 5.
b) 3.   e) 6.
c) 4.

Judged to be More Difficult:

6 II

10. This diagram represents a switching circuit with four lamps, *L*1, *L*2, *L*3, and *L*4.

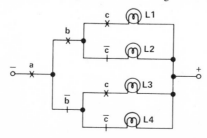

Chapter Objective	*Performance Level*	*Judged to be More Difficult:*

a) If switches A, B, and C are operated, $L1$ and $L2$ will light.

b) If switch A is operated but neither B nor C, $L4$ will light.

c) If switch B is operated but not C, $L2$ will light.

d) In order to light $L3$ only, operate switch C and no others.

e) To turn on all the lights at once, operate all the switches.

| 4 | II | 11. In order to turn on lamp L in this diagram, |

a) the only way is to operate switch A.

b) the only way is to operate switch B.

c) the only way is to operate switches A and B.

d) one may operate switch A or switch B, but not both.

e) no operation of the switches will be successful.

| 8 | II | 12. According to the laws of a certain state, an income tax return must |

be filed by each person who

1) is a resident of the state.

2) has a total taxable income of $2000 or more.

3) has dividends and interest subject to taxation.

4) is a nonresident who received income of the above classifications from within the state.

In stating these requirements as an exercise in logic, the proper connectives are

a) (1) AND (2) AND (3) AND (4).

b) (1) OR (2) OR (3) OR (4).

c) (1) AND (2) OR (3) OR (4).

d) (1) AND (4) OR (2) OR (3).

e) (1) OR (4) AND (2) OR (3).

| 8 | II | 13. |

This circuit can be expressed in Boolean symbols in the following way:

a) $a + (\bar{b} + c)(b + \bar{c}) + \bar{d}$

b) $a + (\bar{b}c + b\bar{c}) + \bar{d}$

c) $a(\bar{b}c + b\bar{c})\bar{d}$

d) $a + (\bar{b}c)(b\bar{c}) + \bar{d}$

e) $a\bar{b}c + \overline{bc}d$

Answers to Evaluation Questions:

1. c	6. d	10. b
2. b	7. d	11. e
3. e	8. b	12. e
4. a	9. c	13. c
5. d		

F | FILMS

F-1201 THE THINKING ??? MACHINE

Recommendation: Highly recommended.
Application: Excellent way to motivate class discussion of the question: Can computers think? Can be used anytime during the study of logic circuits.
Length and Type: 15 min, color, sound.
Source: #6 (no charge), or contact local Bell Telephone business office.
Summary: An extremely entertaining analysis of the computer's capabilities and limitations as a thinking machine. Using the device of computer *vs* human thinking abilities, this breezy yet informative film is intended to spark interest and lively discussion.

F-1202 MAN AND COMPUTER. . .A PERSPECTIVE

Recommendation: Good film for reinforcing concepts studied in Chapters 10 and 11.
Application: Can be used as a bridge in the transition from the study of software (Chapters 10 and 11) to the study of hardware (Chapters 12-15).
Length and Type: 20 min, color, sound.
Source: IBM motion picture Library c/o (2) (no charge).
Summary: A primer on some of the basic elements in data processing, such as input, output, storage control. These are explained in detail (both in live action and animation), with examples shown as to just how they work and what functions they perform. In addition, the binary system is illustrated in an understandable and graphic manner.

G | GENERAL

I. Bibliography

I. Adler, *Thinking Machines.* John Day, 1961 (B)

> There may be some items here of use in introducing such topics as simple logic, Boolean algebra, and the like. There are some amusing examples (for example, from Lewis Carroll, but not very convincing), and a description at a low level of the Turing machine.

G. Boole, *An Investigation of the Laws of Thought.* Dover Reprint S-28, 1953 (B) (soft cover)

> Reprint of the American edition of 1854. Boole's final statement, at least parts of it are easily readable. Very interesting as the basic book for so much subsequent mathematical development, but not essential reading.

S. H. Caldwell, *Switching Circuits and Logical Design.* Wiley, 1958 (C)

> Expensive and much more comprehensive than the teacher of *The Man-Made World* needs, but extremely clear on Boolean algebra and its application to this topic.

G. Hoernes and M. Heilweil, *Introduction to Boolean Algebra and Logic Design.* McGraw-Hill, 1964 (B) (soft cover)

F. E. Hohn, *Applied Boolean Algebra.* Macmillan, 1966 (2nd edition) (B)

> An interesting book to compare with Caldwell's. The latter is an engineer, Hohn a mathematician, who includes also formal logic and (perhaps surprisingly) a review of diode and transistor applications in logic circuits.

A. H. Lytel, *The ABC's of Boolean Algebra.* Bobbs-Merrill, 1963 (2nd edition) (B) (paper)

> If the present chapter has fired you with zeal for Boole, get this very clear book and go a stage or two further.

II. A Brief Review of Formal Logic

1. Relational Symbols Used
   1. $\rightarrow$: if . . ., then . . .; or . . .implies . . .
   2. $\leftrightarrow$: . . . if, and only if . . .; or IFF
   3. $^{-}$: not (as in $\overline{X}$ = not - X)
2. Definitions and Basic Rules

1) X and Y	Conjunction
2) X or Y	Disjunction
3) $\overline{X} \leftrightarrow$ not X	Negation
4) $X \rightarrow Y$	Conditional

5) if $X \to Y$ and $Y \to Z$, then $X \to Z$ Transitive property

6) $(X \leftrightarrow Y) \leftrightarrow (X \to Y$ and $Y \to X)$ Biconditional

7) $(X \to Y) \leftrightarrow (Y \to \overline{X})$ Contrapositive

8) $\overline{(X \text{ and } Y)} \leftrightarrow (\overline{X} \text{ or } \overline{Y})$ Negative of conjunction

9) $\overline{(X \text{ or } Y)} \leftrightarrow (\overline{X} \text{ and } \overline{Y})$ Negative of disjunction

10*) $(X \to Y) \leftrightarrow (\overline{X} \text{ or } Y)$ Conditional equivalency

*This permits us to represent a conditional by means of a switching circuit.

3. Truth Tables for (2)

1	2	3	4	5	6	7	8	9
X	Y	$\overline{X}$	$\overline{Y}$	X and Y	X or Y	$\overline{X}$ and $\overline{Y}$	$\overline{X}$ or $\overline{Y}$	$\overline{X \text{ and } Y}$
T	T	F	F	T	T	F	F	F
T	F	F	T	F	T	F	T	T
F	T	T	F	F	T	F	T	T
F	F	T	T	F	F	T	T	T

10	11	12	13	14	15
$\overline{X \text{ or } Y}$	$\overline{X}$ or Y	$X \to Y$	$Y \to X$	$X \leftrightarrow Y$	$\overline{Y} \to \overline{X}$
F	T	T	T	T	T
F	F	F	T	F	F
F	T	T	F	F	T
T	T	T	T	T	T

The first four statements of (2) are expressed in the columns of (3) noted below. The last five statements of (2) are exemplified by comparing two (in one case three) columns of (3):

Statement	Columns
1	5
2	6
3	1 and 3
4	12
5	——
6	14 and (12 and 13)
7	12 and 15
8	9 and 8
9	10 and 7
10	12 and 11

It will be recalled that the third and fourth lines of column 12 (also 15), or the first and second of column 13, result from an arbitrary definition: when the antecedent clause of the "if . . ., then . . ." statement is false, the nature of the conclusion is a matter of indifference. It may as well be deemed "true," especially since this convention enables us to have a completed truth table, and also leads to the important conditional equivalency of (2), statement 10. The apparent paradoxes that often result from this definition usually turn out to stem from a lack of any real connection between statements X and Y. Consider "if that is so, then I'm a monkey's uncle." I may or may not possess such a nephew, even if "that" is *not* so, and the statement can be called "true" since there is no apparent logical connection between its clauses.

III. Elements of Boolean Algebra

INTRODUCTION

Boolean algebra is a symbolic treatment of logical inference. (See the G. Boole and Shannon references in the bibliography for this chapter.) That portion of it which has proved fundamental to switching theory (C. E. Shannon, 1938) is often called switching algebra.

Switching algebra uses only a few modifications of familiar algebra. The most puzzling of these modifications, to beginners, are three in number: the sign "+" (often written "V") means "or"; the dot sign of multiplication, "·", means "and"; and $1 + 1 = 1$. These apparently arbitrary and capricious conventions were in fact a stroke of genius by Boole; they are what makes it possible to use the other rules of ordinary algebra to manipulate logical relationships. A fourth convention to remember is that the symbols "0" and "1" are *not* numbers, not even binary numbers. In switching algebra they are merely shorthand for "off" and "on," or "open" and "closed," or "not operated" and "operated." The third convention quoted above loses much of its mystery if it is read "operated *or* operated means operated," which is obviously a description of two switch contacts in parallel. The power of binary numbers in the field of computers stems from the double meaning of the two digit symbols. In the input of a computer they are numbers, but once they have entered the machine they become Boolean symbols for the state of switching contacts or solid-state devices; then, when the states of the final contacts are reported to the output apparatus, they resume their role as actual numbers.

POSTULATES

The postulates of switching algebra may be conveniently stated as follows:

1) There are only two variables, 0 and 1
2) $\overline{0} = 1$, $\overline{1} = 0$ (these pairs are called "complements")

3)

·	0	1
0	0	0
1	0	1

4)

+	0	1
0	0	1
1	1	1

(the operations · and + are also deemed complementary)

The matrixlike patterns of (3) and (4) are to be understood as giving the results of combining a quantity in the row at the top with a quantity in the column at the left. Thus $0 \cdot 0 = 0$, or 0 and $0 = 0$; also [in the upper right and lower left of the matrix (3)], 0 and $1 = 0$. Just as in the case of $1 + 1 = 1$, we can understand this easily in terms of electric currents. 0 means a break in the circuit. Adding on an operated switch does not make the circuit conduct.

PRELIMINARY THEOREMS

From these postulates we can derive a series of theorems which involve the unknown variable X (which may be either 0 or 1 when it becomes known). These can easily be proved by substituting first 0, then 1, for X and referring to the postulates.

5) $X + 0 = X$
5') $X \cdot 1 = X$
6) $1 + X = 1$
6') $0 \cdot X = 0$
7) $X + X = X$
7') $X \cdot X = X$
8) $(\overline{\overline{X}}) = \overline{X}$
8') $(\overline{\overline{X}}) = X$
9) $X + \overline{X} = 1$
9') $\overline{X} \cdot X = 0$

These theorems, and also those that follow, are stated in pairs in order to bring out a relation called "duality." Given a theorem, one can write its dual immediately by substituting for each symbol its complement. Thus, starting with (5), one writes (5') by substituting "·" for "+" and "1" for "0." Actually, these two theorems are only partial duals, since we have not written "$\overline{X}$" for "X"; the last two pairs exhibit full duality.

THEOREMS IN TWO OR THREE VARIABLES

The preliminary theorems are chiefly useful in helping to prove the later ones that follow. Most of these have immediate application in simple switching circuits.

10) $X + Y = Y + X$ Commuta-
10') $X \cdot Y = Y \cdot X$ (or $XY = YX$)   tive laws
Self-evident, but easily proved by constructing tables of combinations for the two sides with the aid of (3) and (4).

11) $X + XY = X$
11') $X(X + Y) = X$
The left side of (11) becomes $X(1 + Y)$, which is X by (6). The left side of (11') becomes $X + XY$, because $X \cdot X = X$ by (7'); thus (11') has been reduced to (11), already proved.

12) $\overline{X\,Y} = \overline{X} + \overline{Y}$ De Mor-
12') $\overline{X + Y} = \overline{X}\,\overline{Y}$ gan's laws
Note that these say "the complement of a product (or disjunction) of two terms is the sum (or conjunction) of the complements of the terms," and "the complement of a sum (or conjunction) of two terms is the product (or disjunction) of the complements of the terms." They are identical to statements (8) and (9) in Part II.

13) $(X + \overline{Y}) Y = X Y$

13') $X \overline{Y} + Y = X + Y$

(13) multiplies out to $XY + Y\overline{Y}$ which equals XY by (9'). It is readily possible to prove (13') by tables of combinations, but the following proof illustrates a method which is often useful. Remembering (9) one can write $X\overline{Y} + Y = X\overline{Y} + Y(X + \overline{X}) = X\overline{Y} + XY + \overline{X}Y$; and since $X + X = X$ (by 7'), it follows that $XY + XY = XY$, so the middle term of $X\overline{Y} + XY + \overline{X}Y$ can be expanded to give $X\overline{Y} + XY + XY + \overline{X}Y$, which factors to $X(Y + \overline{Y}) + Y(X + \overline{X}) = X + Y$ (by 9).

Switching implementations are, respectively:

14) $X + Y + Z = (X + Y) + Z$ Associative
                $= X + (Y + Z)$ laws

14') $XYZ = (XY) Z = X (YZ)$

15) $XY + XZ = X (Y + Z)$ Distributive
                law

15') $(X + Y) (X + Z) = X + YZ$ Absorptive
                law

Prove (15) by tables of combinations. For (15'), multiply out the left side to give $X + XY + XZ + YZ$; but $X + XY = X$ (see 11), so this reduces to $X + XZ + YZ$, and again $X + XZ = X$, yielding $X + YZ$, and the theorem is proved.

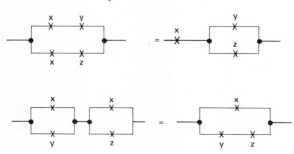

16) $(X + Y) (Y + Z) (Z + \overline{X}) = (X + Y) (Z + \overline{X})$

16') $X Y + Y Z + Z \overline{X} = X Y + Z \overline{X}$

To prove (16) we first use (15') to replace the product of the first two parentheses by $Y + XZ$. Then multiply out $(Y + XZ) (Z + \overline{X}) = YZ + Y\overline{X} + XZ$, remembering that $X\overline{X} = 0$, so the fourth term disappears. Now add $X\overline{X}$, giving $YZ + Y\overline{X} + XZ + X\overline{X}$, and factor: $Y(Z + \overline{X}) + X(Z + \overline{X}) = (Y + X) (Z + \overline{X})$. For (16'), one method of proof is to multiply the middle term by $(X + \overline{X})$, from (9). Thus we have $XY + YZ (X + \overline{X}) + Z\overline{X}$, which equals $XY + XYZ + \overline{X}YZ + Z\overline{X}$; this in turn becomes $XY (1 + Z) + \overline{X}Z (1 + Y)$, but the terms in parentheses each equal 1 (by 6), and the theorem is proved.

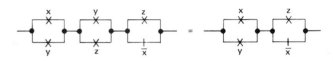

The way in which switching algebra is used to simplify switching circuits has been suggested in the theorems quoted and their proofs. Of course many additional theorems can be developed. To carry your appreciation of these powerful and fascinating methods further, consult one or more of the books listed in the Bibliography of this chapter.

IV. Trouble-Shooting the LCB, Model II

The following report by R. R. Rissler of Hinkley High School, Aurora, Colorado, is copied from the *Newsletter* of October 3, 1967.

> 1. If sections of the switches don't seem to work right, you will probably find that parts of the printed circuit have been shorted together by solder. This is easily removed by cutting out the unwanted section with a sharp single-edged razor blade.

2. If the board is plugged in but none of the lights will go on, check the connections from the transformer to the rectifier (small black cube). In two cases R. R. R. found no solder connections where there should have been.

3. The most mystifying case. During one period the LCB worked fine. In the next period, one relay appeared to function, but the associated circuit would not. When the case was removed, everything still looked fine; but on close inspection the relay solder connections on the bottom of the printed circuit board did not look right. It seems that some of the relay contacts were cut too short before the dip soldering was done and as a result the contacts just touched. After one period of work and associated vibration, all contacts on the switch section broke loose. You can easily spot the potential trouble by inspection of the contacts of all terminals. Each should protrude about 1/32 in or more. If not, it is a good idea to resolder each. An Ungar soldering pencil of 24 watts and Kester "44" solder do a good job.

V. LCB Circuits and Algebraic Functions

It is a truism that students enjoy playing with the LCB. Some of the possibilities of this device are not immediately apparent, however. We describe here two unusual applications, though they are admittedly too "intellectual" to appeal to all students. One of them is the design of a circuit which will evaluate a function (called F) of one variable (called N); i.e., if a binary numerical value of N is set on the switches, then the lamps will indicate the binary value of F. The other application is a sort of inside-out aspect of the first. The board is presented ready wired, and the problem is to discover the function F which is represented; one does this by examining the output numbers produced when all possible input numbers (values of N) are tried. The third circuit is similar to the second, but very much more difficult.

Because of the size limitations of the LCB, it is not as easy as one might suppose, however, to find suitable functions to work with. Since one board has only four switches and four lamps, the maximum value either of N or of F is 15. One could raise this maximum by wiring two or more boards in parallel, but the complexity increases faster than the fun.

A CIRCUIT WHICH EVALUATES A FUNCTION

It is often convenient to have a logic circuit which solves a numerical problem of a very specialized type, even though in theory this could be done by more general circuits. The advantage of building the specialized circuit is usually that it gives its answer very quickly. The advantage of more general circuits is that they can be interconnected in various ways to solve a variety of problems.

Tables for circuit which evaluates a function

N	$\frac{N^2 - 3N + 2}{2}$		A	B	C		L1	L2	L3	L4
0	1		0	0	0		0	0	0	1
1	0		0	0	1		0	0	0	0
2	0		0	1	0		0	0	0	0
3	1		0	1	1		0	0	0	1
4	3		1	0	0		0	0	1	1
5	6		1	0	1		0	1	1	0
6	10		1	1	0		1	0	1	0
7	15		1	1	1		1	1	1	1

(a) values of the function $\frac{N^2 - 3N + 2}{2}$ (b) table of combinations

The table above, (a), shows the value F of the expression $(N^2 - 3N + 2)/2$ for the eight integer values of N lying between 0 and 7 inclusive. Table (b) shows these same numbers in binary, rather than decimal, form, together with a table of combinations to be used to design a circuit with three input switches (A, B, C) to represent the number N, and four lamps ($L1$, $L2$, $L3$, $L4$) to represent the value of F. One can then write the Boolean formulas for the switching networks for the different lamps. For instance, lamp $L1$ is served by $a\,b\,\bar{c} + a\,b\,c$, which simplifies to $a\,b$. The other lamps are managed equally easily. The following diagram shows the resulting circuit. A student who successfully designs this circuit from the data of (a) and (b) should be urged to sketch a rough graph of the equation $F = (N^2 - 3N + 2)/2$ on F, N axes. In this way he would discover not only that adding just one more switch would raise the maximum value of N to a point where it would take seven lamps to show F, but also that he has no way to handle the part of the parabola representing negative N. This would give the teacher an opening for a preliminary discussion of sign bits (if not already covered in class), and a chance for the student to try his hand at modifying his design in such a way as to use another switch and another lamp (they might both be on an LCB wired in parallel) to accept and indicate sign bits.

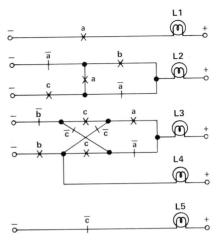

Circuit for a function to be determined

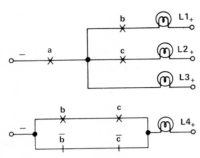

A circuit which evaluates a function

A CIRCUIT FOR AN UNKNOWN FUNCTION

Following is the circuit diagram, which can be wired readily from the following running list:

Neg, A1c; A1m, L1; A1b, A2m, B2m; B2c, A2b, L2; Neg, C1c; C1m, A2c; Neg,B1c;B1b, C2c; B1m, C3c, L4; C3b, C2m, A3m; C3m, C2b, A3b; A3c, L3; C1b, L5. (Notice that L5 must be borrowed from another LCB, in parallel.)

The pupil should construct a table of values and a table of combinations similar to (a) and (b) (of course with an extra column for the extra lamp). He should start with the set of numbers N, translate into the binary values, and set these down for switches A, B, C; then by experiment he finds and fills in the numbers for the lamps, and as a last step translates the resulting binary expressions back into decimal values of F. The chances are that he will see fairly quickly the simple formula for F in terms of N; if not (or perhaps in any case), he will find what he is seeking by plotting on F, N axes the values read from the tables. Another advantage of the graph is that it reveals immediately any errors in filling in the table of combinations, because one or more points will be wildly out of place. To save you time, $F = 3N + 5$.

DIFFICULT CIRCUIT FOR AN UNKNOWN FUNCTION

The solution is accomplished as usual by drawing up a table of combinations. A graph of F against N quickly reveals, however, an unsymmetrical curve (F is in fact a cubic). If $N = 0$, then $F = 19$, which shows one fact: the equation contains the constant term 19. One may hazard the guess (not being sure, however, that the equation *is* a cubic) that the function has the form $F = aN^3 + bN^2 + cN + 19$, or for convenience in the next step, $F - 19 = aN^3 + bN^2 + cN$.

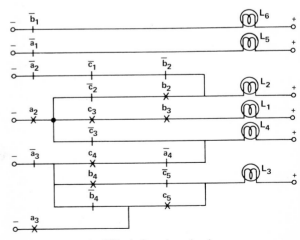

A difficult function circuit

Table of combinations

A	B	C	N	L_1	L_2	L_3	L_4	L_5	L_6	F	F − 19
0	0	0	0	0	1	0	0	1	1	19	0
0	0	1	1	0	0	1	1	1	1	15	− 4
0	1	0	2	0	1	0	1	0		10	− 9
0	1	1	3	0	0	0	1	1	0	6	− 13
1	0	0	4	0	0	0	1	0	1	5	− 14
1	0	1	5	0	0	1	0	0	1	9	− 10
1	1	0	6	0	1	0	1	0	0	20	1
1	1	1	7	1	0	1	0	0	0	40	21

The table above is provided with an extra column for the results of subtracting 19 from F in each case. Then one can write a series of equations in a, b, and c by substituting $N = 1$ in the equation $F - 19 = aN^3 + bN^2 + cN$ above, then $N = 2$, etc. The first of these gives $a + b + c = -4$; the second $8a + 4b + 2C = -9$. If $N = 3$, we have $27a + 9b + 3c = -13$, etc. Any three of these can be solved as a simultaneous group and the upshot is that the original function is

$$F = \frac{x^3}{3} - \frac{3x^2}{2} - \frac{17x}{6} + 19.$$

Clearly, this is suitable only for the beaver so eager that he should have Early Admission to C.I.T.

CHECK LIST FOR CHAPTER 13

LOGIC CIRCUITS AS BUILDING BLOCKS

APPROX. TIME: Text: 7 days   Lab: 3–4 days

A. APPROACH	CLASS PERIODS	B. BLACK & WHITE TRANSPARENCIES	C. CUES (k = key problem) Discussion Questions	Easy	Medium	Hard	D. DEMONSTRATIONS, LABS & PROJECTS	E. EVALUATION	F. FILMS	G. GENERAL
1. Introduction	2	1301 1302 1303 1304 1305		1k,2k 3k,8k		4,5 10		1, 2, 3, 4, 8, 9	1301	II, VIII
2. The Decimal and the Binary Number Systems										
3. An Automatic Parallel Binary Adder	2	1306 1307a, b, c	2, 5				I,II	5, 6, 10, 11		
4. Numbers with a Sign	1	1308	6			11	III	12		III,IV
5. A Circuit Which Compares the Magnitude of Two Numbers	1	1309	1, 3, 4, 7	6k,9	7		IV	7,13		VI
6. A "Tree" Circuit	1	1310					V, VI	8, 14	1302	V, VII
7. Final Comment										

Logic Circuits as Building Blocks
13

A | APPROACH

I. Purpose and Organization of the Chapter

We have just studied how switch contacts can simulate the primary connectives of logic, and have combined these connectives in a few simple ways. Now we see how the representation of "closed" or "open" contacts by 1 or 0 leads directly to the binary number system for computer use, and this system in turn suggests simple kinds of number manipulation such as addition and comparison of size, still building on logic elements. A circuit for addition turns out to require a method of throwing switches automatically (the relay), which will be put to another very important use (machine memory) in Chapter 14. When that chapter has been completed, we shall be ready to describe the structure of a simple computer which can be used in the ways already studied in Chapter 11.

After a brief introduction, the chapter reviews the binary number system. Addition of binaries is found to follow rules which can be implemented by circuits already developed. The need for automatic transfer of the state (open or closed) of one circuit to the state of contacts in another becomes apparent, and the need is met with relays, the structure of which is described. A comparator circuit follows, and a "tree" circuit which will be necessary to provide access to specific memory cells in a computer.

II. Objectives for Students

Upon completion of the activities, discussion, and reading in this chapter, students should be able to:

1. Recognize and identify such terms as *armature, carry digit, most* (and *least*) *significant digit, position value, sum digit.*

2. Translate decimal numbers to binary notation and vice versa.

3. Add two binary numbers, and compare the process with the addition of decimal numbers.

4. By reference to examples with decimal numbers, derive the rules for addition of signed numbers, whether of the same magnitude or different.

5. Describe the operation of a relay, including its action as a switch.

6. Interpret the construction of a parallel binary adder in terms of the rules for binary addition and the logic circuits for odd parity and majority.

7. Trace the signal flow in a circuit for comparing the magnitudes of two binary numbers.

8. Demonstrate the use of a "tree" circuit, and calculate the number of switches needed to build such a circuit of stated size.

9. Construct tree, adder, and comparison circuits (the last two for 2-digit numbers only) on the LCB.

10. Identify at least one use in a computer for each of the circuits listed in the nine items directly above.

317

III. Suggestions for Teaching

Since so much of this chapter depends on the binary number system, the teacher must have the answer to one question in his hands before starting: Have all, some, or none of the class met the idea of number bases other than 10 in their previous math? Even if the answer is "all," a certain amount of review drilling is called for. An interesting way of starting a discussion of binary numbers is to use "binary baffle" (Section D, Lab II). Also, it helps to use tables of combinations for the addition process (T-1303).

Section 1. Introduction. At first it may surprise some students to have the terms *open* or *closed* applied to an entire network, though the possibility is plain enough when pointed out (e.g., Fig. 12-10 has a lamp in series with the network), and tables of combinations often indicate it. So many times hereafter the state of a relay is dependent (at least initially, before a holding contact takes charge) on the state of a controlling network that the concept must be made really obvious to everybody.

Section 2. The Decimal and the Binary Number Systems. For the convenience of teachers who must cover the whole ground on binaries, T-1301 reproduces the conversion exercise in the chapter, and T-1302 copies the two addition examples. Since the text makes no comment about changing decimal to binary, a discussion of two approaches to the process appears in Section G, Part VIII. If interest appears, Section G, Part II describes "binary" fractions (not "decimal"). T-1303 displays the tables of combinations for addition. The "Delay" block in Fig. 13-1 (T-1304) is included because the carry digit, though generated when each pair of digits is fed in, is not used until the next pair is entered. The design of delay lines is a task for electrical engineers and the block should be treated as a typical black box: what comes out is a later copy of what went in, but how it works does not concern us. In T-1305 (Fig. 13-2) it may be worth a moment to point out that some delay still exists: the action "ripples" from least toward most significant digit, each one being added up only when the carry reaches it from "downstream." The delay is not very significant, however.

Section 3. An Automatic Binary Parallel Adder. Presumably you have a large model relay in your *Man-Made World* equipment. The textbook diagrams (Fig. 13-3, T-1306) are greatly clarified by a look at the real thing. Do emphasize the fact that the armature can close many contacts and open many others simultaneously, because this concept is essential to the complete computer. Lab I should be done next. Now is the time to show that the adder is the fundamental circuit in an accumulator. Of course, commercial computers have accumulators which can do various arithmetical operations, but the minimicro computer of Chapter 15 uses only addition, to avoid putting in details which complicate without clarifying the basic ideas. T-1307a, b, and c are offered to help emphasize the hierarchical development of Figs. 13-5, 6, and 7 by the use of overlays (it was necessary to show a relay, not a lamp, for the carry circuit of Fig. 13-5). Notice that columns in the addition are numbered from right to left, from least to most significant digit, as they will be in the minimicro computer. Lab II should clear up any lingering difficulties.

Section 4. Numbers with a Sign. The sign-bit idea is not new (it was presented in Chapter 11, where the point was also made that a blank card represents −000, or minus as many zeros as are needed to fill out the bits in the numbers used by a particular computer). The rules for adding signed numbers look a little sticky, but are easy if approached from the rear: start with the numerical examples (T-1308) and then generalize. When this level is reached, see Section G, Part IV for a flow diagram; also see Section G, Part III if there is interest in the actual subtraction process.

Section 5. A Circuit Which Compares the Magnitudes of Two Numbers. It is clear that this is needed to implement the addition of signed numbers. Remind the class that op code 3 requires the same comparison. The footnote about filling out the shorter of two numbers with zeros may be compared to the fact already known: there are no blanks in a computer, but every digit is either 0 or 1. So the 0's were automatically inserted when the number was stored in a (previously cleared) memory cell. See T-1309, and Lab III may be done in place of class discussion, or the design and construction on the LCB of a 2-digit comparator makes a good closed-book exercise.

Section 6. A "Tree" Circuit. Again, most classroom discussion can be skipped in favor of Lab IV. However, students should make a careful comparison of the "partial" tree of the lab exercise with the complete one of Fig. 13-10 (T-1310); and do not fail to emphasize that n switches give us access to 2^n terminals. It may be a good idea to lay the groundwork for an addressable memory (Chapter 14), which

needs two identical trees, one accessing the 1 side, the other the 0 side, of each memory cell. This doubles the number of contacts needed on each switch (or relay), but not the number of switches.

Section 7. Final Comment. Lab V is listed for this section, but it can be used whenever you want to emphasize the input portion of the computer. Section D, Lab VI contains a discussion of computer toys which can be used to summarize some of the ideas of this chapter and introduce other ideas from the next chapter.

B | BLACK AND WHITE TRANSPARENCIES

Binary representation	Decimal representation
$1 \cdot 2^4 + 1 \cdot 2^2 + 1 \cdot 2^0 = 10101$	$2 \cdot 10^1 + 1 \cdot 10^0 = 21$
111001	57
1001101	77
1110111	119
1111111	127
11111000000	1984
1010	10
1100100	100
1111101000	1000
11110100001001000000	1000000

T-1301 BINARY AND DECIMAL CONVERSIONS

Least Significant Digit:

X	Y	SUM	CARRY
0	0	0	0
0	1	1	0
1	0	1	0
1	1	0	1

```
CARRY DIGITS ——►  11110
                  56750  ◄—— FIRST NUMBER
                  67359  ◄—— SECOND NUMBER
                 124109  ◄—— SUM
```

(a)

```
CARRY DIGITS ——►  1 1 1 1 0 0 0 1
                  1 1 0 1 1 0 0 1  ◄—FIRST NUMBER
                  1 1 1 1 0 1 0 1  ◄—SECOND NUMBER
                1 1 1 0 0 1 1 1 0  ◄—SUM
```

(b)

T-1302 DECIMAL (a) AND BINARY (b) ADDITION

All Other Digits:

CARRY	X	Y	SUM	CARRY
0	0	0	0	0
0	0	1	1	0
0	1	0	1	0
0	1	1	0	1
1	0	0	1	0
1	0	1	0	1
1	1	0	0	1
1	1	1	1	1

T-1303 ADDITION, TABLES OF COMBINATION

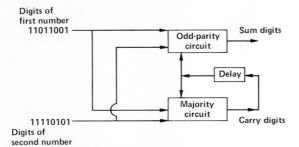

T-1304 SERIAL BINARY ADDER, BLOCK DIAGRAM

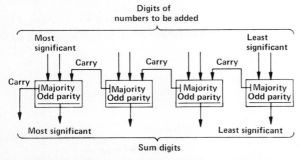

T-1305 PARALLEL BINARY ADDER, BLOCK DIA-GRAM

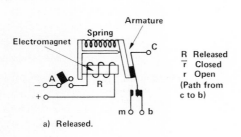

a) Released.

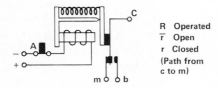

b) Operated.

T-1306 DIAGRAM OF RELAY, a) RELEASED, b) OPERATED

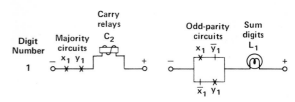

T-1307a ADDER FOR $X + Y$

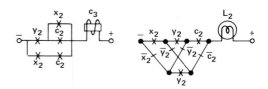

T-1307b OVERLAY FOR TWO-DIGIT ADDER

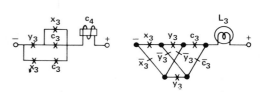

T-1307c OVERLAY FOR THREE-DIGIT ADDER

(1) Compare signs. If same, add $X + Y$, use sign of X.
   If different, compare magnitudes.

(2) If same, sum = 0

(3) If different, subtract smaller from larger. Use sign of larger.

Examples:

(1a) $X = 5$, $Y = 5$; $5 + 5 = 10$, sign +; Sum = +10
   Check: $(+5) + (+5) = +10$

(1b) $X = -5$, $Y = -5$; $5 + 5 = 10$, sign −; Sum = −10
   Check: $(-5) + (-5) = -10$

(2) $X = +5$, $Y = -5$; Sum = 0
   Check: $(+5) + (-5) = 0$

(3a) $X = -6$, $Y = +4$; $6 - 4 = 2$, sign −; Sum = −2
   Check: $(-6) + (+4) = -2$

(3b) $X = -4$, $Y = +6$; $6 - 4 = 2$, sign +; Sum = +2
   Check: $(-4) + (+6) = +2$

T-1308 ADDITION OF SIGNED NUMBERS

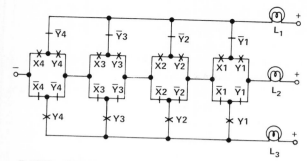

T-1309 COMPARISON CIRCUIT

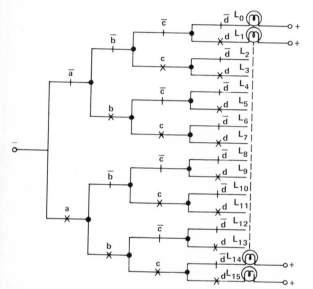

T-1310 TREE CIRCUIT

C | CUES TO QUESTIONS AND PROBLEMS

Questions for Study and Discussion

1.6 (Use, e.g., $<32, <16, <8, <4, <2, <1$)

2.a)Circuit to find the first carry digit (from the sum of X_1 and Y_1)

b)Circuit to find whether the sum of X_1 and Y_1 is 1 or 10 (i.e., is represented as 0)

3.To give access to the addressed memory cells of a computer. Each individual cell can be uniquely selected and connected to the root of the tree. The latter, in turn, can be connected at the proper time with the accumulator. Thus the contents of a given cell can be copied into the accumulator, or the contents of the accumulator copied into a desired cell.

4.a)No

b)No

5.Because if the addition of any pair of digits leads to 10 or 11 in the sum, the left-hand "1" must be carried to the next column. A majority circuit energizes a relay which operates contacts in both the odd-parity and the majority circuits of that column, thus accomplishing the carry.

6.Since + is represented by 1, − by 0, it is sufficient to operate a switch which is assigned to a positive number, release one assigned to a negative. Thus the output contact which is energized shows which number is +, which is −, if that is the situation; or that the signs are the same (but not whether they are + or −).

7.The twigs of the tree might each terminate in a lamp to illuminate one alphanumeric character. (It could be marked on a ground-glass cover over the lamp.) Then, if the switches of the tree were operated or left released in the order of the code binary number to be translated, the proper alphanumeric would light up.

Problems

1.

11 ⟶ 3		10000 ⟶ 16	
101 ⟶ 5		110010 ⟶ 50	
110 ⟶ 6		11010 ⟶ 26	
1011 ⟶ 11		1100100 ⟶ 100	
1010 ⟶ 10		1111101000 ⟶ 1000	

2.

1 ⟶ 1		15 ⟶ 1111	
8 ⟶ 1000		16 ⟶ 10000	
4 ⟶ 100		31 ⟶ 11111	
2 ⟶ 10		32 ⟶ 100000	
9 ⟶ 1001		27 ⟶ 11011	

3.$1010 + 110010 = 111100$ $\quad\left(\begin{array}{l}10 + 50 = 60\\ 11 + 26 = 37\end{array}\right)$

$1011 + 11010 = 100101$

4.$100 − 11 = 01$ $\qquad\qquad 4 − 3 = 1$

$1010 − 101 = 101$ $\qquad\quad 10 − 5 = 5$

$110011 − 11010 = 11001$ $\quad 51 − 26 = 25$

5.

$$\begin{array}{cc} 1100100 & 100 \\ -\ \ 11010 & \text{or} -26 \\ \hline 1001010 & 74 \end{array}$$

$$\begin{array}{cc} -110100 & -52 \\ \underline{11010} & \text{or} \ \underline{26} \\ 11010 & -26 \end{array}$$

6.

L1 A > B, because the first digit of A is 1, that of B is 0.

L3 A < B, because the second digit of B is 1, that of A is 0.

L2 A = B, because the digits are equal, pair by pair.

7. a) 6

b) 5

c) Number of guesses N is the power of 2 equal to or greater than the total range.

8. a) 15

b) 5

c) 8, 4, 2, 1.

9. In the ideal situation each player is of equal ability but actually, on any one day, one player is superior to his opponent. In the selection-tree process (elimination ladder) the best player in each pair wins the right to continue to work his way up to champion. Alternate answer: The tournament uses a selection tree in reverse.

10. Reduce 65,000 to binary:

65,000 = 1111110111101000—count 'em (16 bits). See Section G, Part VIII, for the method of solution.

11. If this difficult problem is to be assigned, remind the students that relays are fully described in this chapter.

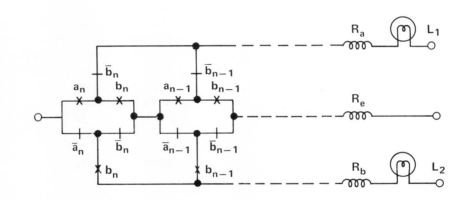

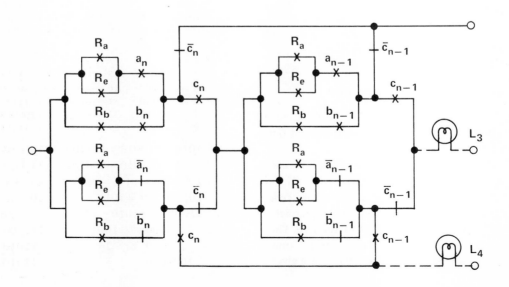

In the suggested solution, two lamps are omitted purposely since they add no information not otherwise available. The system adopted is to compare two of the numbers, and then to compare the larger of these with the third, using relays to activate the proper branch of the second comparator. If the first two turn out to be equal, "A" is arbitrarily chosen to compare with "C". The interpretation of the read-out lamps is as follows:

L_1 alone:	A largest
L_2 alone:	B largest
L_4 alone:	C largest
L_3 alone:	A = B = C
$L_3 + L_1$:	A = C (B least)
$L_3 + L_2$:	B = C (A least)
No lights :	A = B (C least)

D | DEMONSTRATIONS, LABS, AND PROJECTS

I. Extending Our Senses Using the Logic Circuit Board

The main purpose of this experiment is to familiarize students with the operation of the relay on the LCB. The need for studying the operation of relays can be emphasized by prewiring a binary adder and demonstrating its operation in class. In this application, the relay is being used as a control mechanism. Its use as a memory device is discussed in the next chapter.

Equipment:

One LCB and an A.C. outlet for each lab group

Answers to Questions:

*1.

A	L_1	L_2
0	0	1
1	1	0

*2.

B	L_3	L_4
0	1	0
1	0	1

*3. The method of Fig. 2 keeps battery drain as small as possible, permitting the use of smaller batteries with less frequent replacement. In general, when dry batteries furnish the power, the circuit of Fig. 2 is likely to be preferred.

Additional Question:

What advantages result from relay operation of contacts?

Answer:

Some advantages of relay operation are:
1. Switches may be located in hazardous areas such as high voltage lines, hence these are generally relay-controlled.
2. A relay may be activated when excessive current is in a line. Thus the relay-controlled switch acts as a protective device.
3. Some relays may be activated by very weak currents, such as photo cells generate. These relays can control other relays which turn on lights, open doors, and sound alarms.

II. Binary Numbers and the Binary Adder

The purpose of this experiment is to show students that the combination of 2 simple logic circuits (majority and odd-parity circuits) result in a circuit that can add binary numbers. Students should be very familiar with the binary number system before doing this experiment. One way of having an interesting review of binary numbers is playing a "binary baffle" game.

BINARY BAFFLE

Reproduce the following information (Magic Number Baffle) for each student. Each of the tables in the baffle contains decimal numbers and each table represents a position of a binary number. For example, table E is the least significant position

($2°$), and all the odd decimal numbers between 1 and 31 are in this table because a binary 1 exists in this position.

MAGIC NUMBER BAFFLE

Some of you must know that chess masters often play several games at once against many players. Today I will play a game against every member of the class called "The Magic Number Baffle."

Pick a number from 1 to 31. Write it down somewhere—your notebook or the back of this paper. You each have a series of 5 tables. Your number may appear in several tables. Carefully look through each table; if your number appears in a given table, write the table letter in the space provided.

NUMBER

A
16 17 18 19
20 21 22 23
24 25 26 27
28 29 30 31

B
8 9 10 11
12 13 14 15
24 25 26 27
28 29 30 31

C
4 5 6 7
12 13 14 15
20 21 22 23
28 29 30 31

D
2 3 6 7
10 11 14 15
18 19 22 23
26 27 30 31

E
1 3 5 7
9 11 13 15
17 19 21 23
25 27 29 31

BAFFLE

My number appears in:

Table _____

Table _____

Table _____

Table _____

Table _____

Check carefully.

As the teacher arrives at your desk, let him see your paper. He will tell you the number you picked.

You should try to figure out how the teacher is able to determine your number.

If you wish to see it again, ask your teacher if he will play another round.

If you are not familiar with this activity, an easy way of obtaining the number selected by the student is to add the numbers in the left-hand corner of the tables in which the student says his number appears. These numbers, namely 1, 2, 4, 8, 16, represent the binary progression.

PART A

Equipment:

One LCB and one A.C. outlet for each lab group

Answers to Questions:

*1. *Majority Circuits* (*Carry Digits*): Neg, B2c; B2m, D2c; D2m, Rop; Neg, A1c, C2c; A1m, R1m, C1m; R1c, C1c, R2c, Qop; C2m, R2m.

Odd Parity Circuits (*Sum Digits*): Neg, B1c; B1m, D1b; D1c, L4; B1b, D1m; Neg, A2c; A2m, C3c; C3m, C4b, R3m; R3c, L3; A2b, C4c; C4m, C3b, R3b; Neg, Q1c; Q1m, L2;

*2.

$$\begin{array}{r} 10 \\ +10 \\ \hline 100 \end{array} \qquad \begin{array}{r} 01 \\ +11 \\ \hline 100 \end{array} \qquad \begin{array}{r} 11 \\ +10 \\ \hline 101 \end{array}$$

This two digit binary adder can add 16 different pairs of numbers.

PART B

Equipment:

Two LCB's and two A.C. outlets for each lab group

The 4-stage binary adder should be built combining 2 laboratory groups who have finished Part A of this experiment before the rest of the class. It does not require any new understandings but does require patient and careful students. Notice that the contacts, relays, and lights have an x or y notation which refers to the X or Y LCB.

Running List for 4-Stage Binary Adder

Stage	Majority Circuits	Odd parity circuits
1st (2⁰ column)	Neg, D1xc; D1xm, D1yc; D1ym, Syop;	Neg, D2xc; D2xm, D2yb; D2xb, D2ym; D2yc, L4y;
2nd (2¹ column)	Neg, C1xc, S2yc; C1xm, C1yc, S1yc; C1ym, S1ym, Ryop; S2ym, C2yc; C2ym, Ryop	Neg, C2xc; C2xm, C3yc; C3ym, S3ym; C3yb, S3yb; S3yc, L3y; C2xb, C4yc; C4yb, S3ym; C4ym, S3yb;
3rd (2² column)	Neg, B1xc, R2yc; B1xm, B1yc, R1yc; B1ym, R1ym, Qyop; R2ym, B2yc; B2ym, Qyop;	Neg, B2xc; B2xm, B3yc; B3ym, R3ym; B3yb, R3yb; R3yc, L2y; B2xb, B4yc; B4yb, R3ym; R4ym, R3yb;
4th (2³ column)	Neg, A1xc, Q2yc; A1xm, A1yc, Q1yc; A1ym, Q1ym, Pyop; Q2ym, A2yc; A2ym, Pyop;	Neg, A2xc; A2xm, A3yc; A3ym, Q3ym; A3yb, Q3yb; Q3yc, L1y; A2xb, A4yc; A4yb, Q3ym; A4ym, Q3yb
Overflow (2⁴ column)	Neg x, Neg y;	Neg, P1yc; P1ym, L4x;

III. A Comparator Circuit for Two 4-digit Binary Numbers

The main purpose of this experiment is to demonstrate that logic circuits can be designed for comparing numbers. The concept of comparison of binary digits is straightforward and the whole class does not actually have to wire up LCB's. This circuit can be assigned as an extra project for a group of students who can then demonstrate its operation to the rest of the class.

Equipment:

Two LCB's and two A.C. outlets for each lab group

Answers to Questions:

*1. $A > B(L_1)$; $A = B(L_2)$; $A < B(L_3)$; $A = B(L_2)$; $A = B(L_2)$; $A > B(L_1)$; $A > B(L_1)$.

*2. This circuit can compare 225 (15^2) different pairs of numbers.

IV. Tree Circuits

Information flows in and out of the memory section of a computer via tree circuits. In this experiment, the student is introduced to a simple tree circuit which can translate binary numbers to their decimal equivalents.

Equipment:

One LCB and one A.C. output for each lab group

Answers to Questions:

*1. The running list for the 2-stage tree is: Neg, A1c; A1b, B1c; B1b, L1; B1m, L2; A1m, B2c; B2b, L3; B2m, L4.

*2. *Table of Combinations for 2-Stage Tree*

A	B	L1	L2	L3	L4
0	0	1	0	0	0
0	1	0	1	0	0
1	0	0	0	1	0
1	1	0	0	0	1

*3. There is never a continuous path between any two lamps for any path will involve a series arrangement of the make and break of the same switch section, i.e.

which may be expressed as a · ā whose value is always zero.

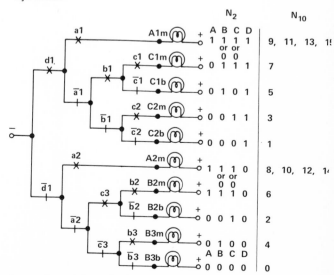

A partial tree for binary-to-decimal translation

Reproduction of Figure 13 from the text is modified (see page 325). The binary and decimal values associated with each lamp are given on this reproduction. The logic arrangement of the circuit has the lamps out of sequence. The physical arrangement may be whatever the builder desires.

*4. Neg, D1c; D1b, A2c; A2b, C3c; C3b, B3c; B3b, L1 (for 0)

Neg, D1c; D1b, A2c; A2b, C3c; C3m, B2c; B2b, L3 (for 2)

Neg, D1c; D1m, A1c; A1b, B1c; B1b, C2c; C2b, L2 (for 1)

Neg, D1c; D1m, A1c; A1b, B1c; B1b, C2c; C2m, L4 (for 3)

*5.

Table of Combinations for Tree Circuit of Figure 13

N_{10}	A	B	C	D	L0	L1	L2	L3	L4	L5	L6	L7	L8	L9
0	0	0	0	0	1	0	0	0	-	-	-	-	-	-
1	0	0	0	1	0	1	0	0	-	-	-	-	-	-
2	0	0	1	0	0	0	1	0	-	-	-	-	-	-
3	0	0	1	1	0	0	0	1	-	-	-	-	-	-
4	0	1	0	0	-	-	-	-	1	0	0	0	-	-
5	0	1	0	1	-	-	-	-	0	1	0	0	-	-
6	0	1	1	0	-	-	-	-	0	0	1	0	-	-
7	0	1	1	1	-	-	-	-	0	0	0	1	-	-
8	1	0	0	0	-	-	-	-	-	-	-	-	1	0
9	1	0	0	1	-	-	-	-	-	-	-	-	0	1
10	1	0	1	0										
11	1	0	1	1										
12	1	1	0	0										
13	1	1	0	1										
14	1	1	1	0										
15	1	1	1	1										

*6. Neg, D1c; D1b, A2c; A2b, C3c; C3b, B3c; B3m, L1 (for 4)

Neg, D1c; D1b, A2c; A2b, C3c; C3m, B2c; B2m, L3 (for 6)

Neg, D1c; D1m, A1c; A1b, B1c; B1m, C1c; C1b, L2 (for 5)

Neg, D1c; D1m, A1c; A1b, B1c; B1m, C1c; C1m, L4 (for 7)

*7. Neg; D1c; D1b, A2c; A2m, L4 (for 8)

Neg; D1c; D1m, A1c; A1m, L3 (for 9)

*8. Folding is important in the design of tree circuits to avoid excessive requirements for sets or pairs of contacts. Reference to the figure of a selection tree shown on page 549 of *The Man-Made World* shows that switch D must have 8 sets of contacts. This is cumbersome and expensive.

*9. a) To extend the tree to include 16 combinations requires 16 switch sections. The diagram as shown uses only 9 switch sections but it is impossible to distribute the remaining 7 sections to provide the required paths.

(Also, the original model of the LCB had switches with only 3 sections. This imposed further limitations.)

Section G, Part VI shows an arrangement for modifying Figure 13-10 of *The Man-Made World* so that switch D controls relays R and S. The 4 sections on these relays then provide the necessary contacts.

b) The circuit can be made inoperative for binary numbers 1011 through 1111 by adding $\bar{b}$ and $\bar{c}$ contacts in series with the ambiguous read-out lamps for these numbers.

Additional Question:

Other than in computers, where are tree circuits used?

Answer:

Every student will have experienced numerous applications of tree circuits. Whenever he uses the telephone he is involved with the world's largest tree circuit. A glance at the scoreboard at athletic contests like golf, tennis, and skiing reveals another use of a tree circuit.

V. Simple Card Reader For the LCB

Use this demonstration to provide students with a concrete example of inputting binary-coded information via punched cards. When wiring the circuit before class, notice that the negative terminal of the card reader is labeled COM. There are seven terminals on the card reader so that each transmitted word can only contain a maximum of 7 bits of information. After the demonstration, this device should be made available to interested students who can use it to input information to the adder circuit (this chapter) or the addressable memory circuit (next chapter).

VI. Computer Toys

There are 3 educational toys made by Educational Science Research (E.S.R.) Inc., 34 Label Street, Montclair, New Jersey 07042, which teachers might find useful in the classroom. They are:

1. Think-A-Dot
2. Dr. Nim
3. Digi-Comp 1

The first 2 are games which come ready for use, while the third has to be put together and is essentially a plastic model of a simple digital computer. Although intended as toys, they illustrate many of the basic ideas related to the operation of digital computers. These computer toys are available in most stores that sell toys and teachers are encouraged to evaluate them for possible use with their students. The following is a brief description of how Think-A-Dot might be used to supplement the computer section of *The Man-Made World* text.

THINK-A-DOT

This toy can be used with students in 3 ways:
1. As a game
2. As a vehicle for reinforcing the learning of computer concepts
3. As an exercise in developing models of logic systems

1. Students can be given Think-A-Dot to play with and can be asked to develop winning strategies for the game. After students have played the game for awhile (about 20 min), they should be asked to write down the computer concepts which they feel would be helpful in developing winning strategies.

2. Specifically, Think-A-Dot makes use of 3 computer concepts, namely, logical operations, machine memory, and sequencing of circuit. These ideas can be demonstrated with this toy. There are

Reproduced with permission of Electrical Science Research, Incorporated

eight flip-flops which are essentially OR gates and these flip-flops are connected together by AND logic. The color pattern (blues and yellows) on the face of Think-A-Dot is analogous to a bit in the memory of a computer and is changed whenever a marble goes through the system. Finally, dropping a marble in the same hole 8 times results in a sequence of patterns which is analogous to the counter of a computer.

3. Students can be asked to work out a flow chart (pictorial model) for predicting the change in the color pattern when a marble is dropped into the system. Basically, the flow chart will allow the student to predict the output of varying inputs, and show him that winning strategies are based on logic and not luck.

E ǀ EVALUATION

The questions in this section are rated according to the chapter objectives and the performance levels stated in the introduction to the teacher's manual. This group of questions is not intended to be all inclusive, but just as a guide to possible questions. Zeros in the chapter objective column indicate no chapter objective for this question.

Chapter Objective	Performance Level	

Judged to be Relatively Easy:

In each of the following questions, check the best answer.

1. In decimal notation, the binary number 1111 is
    a) 7.
    b) 15.
    c) 27.
    d) 30.
    e) none of these.

(Chapter Objective 2, Performance Level I)

2. When expressed in binary notation, the decimal numbers 30, 31, and 33 are alike in that
    a) all end in 0.
    b) all end in 1.
    c) all have the same number of digits.
    d) all include a 1 in the second place.
    e) in every case the first digit is 1.

(Chapter Objective 2, Performance Level I)

3. If an LCB were built with 6 switches, 6 relays, and 6 lamps, the largest number which could be represented by the lamps would be (in decimal)
    a) 60.
    b) 63.
    c) 64.
    d) 127.
    e) 128.

(Chapter Objective 2, Performance Level II)

4. The sum of 1100111
          + 110011   is
    a) 1011000.
    b) 10010110.
    c) 10011010.
    d) 10110100.
    e) 1010110.

(Chapter Objective 3, Performance Level I)

5. When the coil of a relay becomes energized,
    a) the spring overcomes the opposition offered by the magnetic field.
    b) all contacts carried by the armature must be closed.
    c) all contacts carried by the armature must be open.
    d) the controlling network must be closed.
    e) the controlling network must be open.

(Chapter Objective 5, Performance Level I)

6. An important reason for mounting relays on Logic Circuit Boards is that
    a) relays offer more switching contacts than hand-operated switches.
    b) the presence of the relays makes the boards look more impressive.
    c) without relays one could not build odd-parity switching circuits.
    d) relays make automatic operation of adding circuits possible.
    e) relay switching protects the operator from electric shock in some circuits.

(Chapter Objective 5, Performance Level II)

7. One important use of a comparison circuit is to determine
    a) whether the sum of 2 digits is to be taken as 0 or 1.
    b) whether 2 equal numbers have the same sign or not.

(Chapter Objective 7, Performance Level II)

Chapter Objective	Performance Level	

Judged to be Relatively Easy:

c) whether op code 8 ("jump") is to be followed.
d) whether switches have been connected in series or in parallel.
e) whether an addition produces an overflow.

8. Tree circuits are
 a) used in pairs to access the cells of a memory.
 b) capable of selecting one of 2^{N-1} lamps, where N is the number of switches used.
 c) of limited usefulness since they grow so complex as many switches are employed.
 d) commonly so-called because they allowed computers to move out of the bush leagues.
 e) always relay-operated.

(Chapter Objective 8, Performance Level I)

Judged to be More Difficult:

9. In order to assign each of 800 students in a school to a cell in a computer memory, each cell would need an address (in binary notation) consisting of not less than
 a) 6 bits.
 b) 7 bits.
 c) 8 bits.
 d) 9 bits.
 e) 10 bits.

(Chapter Objective 2, Performance Level II)

10. Below is a partial representation of the addition of two binary numbers.

$$\begin{array}{r} 1\ 1\ 1\ 1 \\ +\ \ 0\ 1\ 1\ 0 \\ \hline A\ B\ C\ D\ E \end{array}$$

a) The digit for which A stands is 0.
b) The digit for which B stands is 1.
c) The digit for which C stands was found with the aid of a carry digit of 1.
d) The digit for which D stands is 1.
e) The digit for which E stands is 1 with 1 to carry.

(Chapter Objective 3, Performance Level I)

11. A 3-digit parallel adder
 a) is designed to find the sum of 3 numbers, A, B, and C.
 b) may produce a 4-digit sum.
 c) uses odd-parity circuits to calculate the carry digits.
 d) uses inclusive-OR circuits to find the carry digits.
 e) uses circuits which are just alike for every digit.

(Chapter Objective 6, Performance Level I)

12. When adding $(-X)$ and $(+Y)$, (if unequal in size), the rule is to
 a) find $Y - X$ and use the sign of Y.
 b) find $X - Y$ and use the sign of X.
 c) subtract the smaller and use the sign of the larger, whichever it is.
 d) add X and Y and write the negative of the sum.
 e) express "minus" by 0 and "plus" by 1, and add the resulting binaries.

(Chapter Objective 4, Performance Level I)

13. The circuit to compare the magnitudes of 2 numbers is
 a) limited to 4-digit numbers when wired on LCB's because the switches have only 4 sets of contacts.
 b) an exclusive-OR circuit.
 c) a kind of majority-vote circuit.
 d) applied to the digits pair by pair from left to right.
 e) much more convenient when relays are used than with hand-operated switches only.

(Chapter Objective 7, Performance Level I)

330

Judged to be More Difficult:

14.

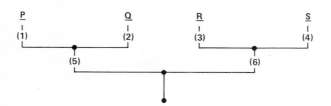

8   II

This diagram of a tree circuit has the positions of its contacts numbered, but not whether they are make or break, or what letters to attach to them. If the circuit were to be constructed,

a) (1) and (2) would have to be controlled by different switches.
b) (2) and (5) would both have to be break contacts.
c) only 2 switches in all would be needed.
d) (1) and (5) would necessarily be both make or else both break.
e) (5) and (6) would both be make or both be break contacts.

Answers to Evaluation Questions:

1.	b	8.	a
2.	e	9.	e
3.	b	10.	c
4.	c	11.	b
5.	d	12.	c
6.	d	13.	d
7.	b	14.	c

F | FILMS

F-1301 DIGITAL COMPUTER TECHNIQUES: COMPUTER LOGIC, BINARY NUMBERS

Recommendation: Good for limited application.
Application: Concept development. Use as an introduction or review for binary numbers, but don't rely entirely on the film to teach the topic.
Length and Type: 12 min, color, sound.
Source: #14 (No charge) (Navy Film No. MN 8969B)
Summary: Defines logic as applied to digital computers. Explains binary number system and binary addition. Cites examples of code variations of the binary system.

F-1302 ELECTRONIC COMPUTERS AND APPLIED MATHEMATICS

Recommendation: Not quite as good as F-1301.
Application: Enrichment and concept development (introduction to binary number system).
Length and Type: 23 min, b & w, sound
Source: #1
Summary: This film shows the basic units of electronic computers (rather superficially) and mentions some of their applications. The binary number system is discussed in some detail, and a few historical references are included.

G | GENERAL

I. Bibliography

Association of Teachers of Mathematics, *Some Lessons in Mathematics*. Cambridge University Press, 1964 (B) (paper)

> Models of lessons in many topics, such as binary arithmetic, flow diagrams, and simple logic. The age range of the expected students is considerable. Even nonmathematicians will gain tremendously from it, and everyone will wish he could teach as well as the simulated instructor.

C. C. C. T. Baker, *Introduction to Mathematics*. ARCO Publishing Co., 1966 (A) (paper)

> A small book, but it contains all the mathematics (or practically so) of this text and a lot more. Quite useful as a reference and reminder, probably too thin to offer an eager student.

S. H. Caldwell, G. Hoernes, M. Heilweil, and F. E. Hohn, all listed in the Bibliography for Chapter 12, are equally pertinent to this one.

II. Fractional Numbers in Binary Notation

In the text we represent only integers in the computer which is developed conceptually in Chapter 15. This is done for purposes of simplicity. You should realize, however, that fractional numbers can be represented in the binary system just as they can be in the decimal system. A "binary point" is used in a manner similar to the way in which we use the common decimal point. In the decimal system, digits to the right of the point have weights which are negative powers of 10. For example,

10^3	=	1000	which equals	1000.0000 (base 10)
10^2	=	100	which equals	100.0000
10^1	=	10	which equals	10.0000
10^0	=	1	which equals	1.0000
10^{-1}	=	$\frac{1}{10}$	which equals	0.1000
10^{-2}	=	$\frac{1}{100}$	which equals	0.0100
10^{-3}	=	$\frac{1}{1000}$	which equals	0.0010
10^{-4}	=	$\frac{1}{10000}$	which equals	0.0001

In the binary system, digits to the right of the point have weights which are negative powers of 2. For example,

2^3	=	8	which equals	1000.0000 (base 2)
2^2	=	4	which equals	100.0000
2^1	=	2	which equals	10.0000
2^0	=	1	which equals	1.0000
2^{-1}	=	$\frac{1}{2}$	which equals	0.1000
2^{-2}	=	$\frac{1}{4}$	which equals	0.0100
2^{-3}	=	$\frac{1}{8}$	which equals	0.0010
2^{-4}	=	$\frac{1}{16}$	which equals	0.0001

Thus 1011.101 (binary) = 11 5/8 = 11.625 (decimal).

Translation of decimal fractions into binary must be done separately from the translation of any part of the number which lies to the left of the decimal point. Then the method is to carry out successive subtractions of negative powers of 2. Thus, given decimal

	0.781	(Binary digit)
Subtract 2^{-1} =	$\dfrac{0.500}{0.281}$	1
Subtract 2^{-2} =	$\dfrac{0.250}{0.031}$	1
Subtract 2^{-3} =	0.125 (too large)	0
Subtract 2^{-4} =	0.062 (too large)	0
Subtract 2^{-5} =	$\dfrac{0.031}{0.000}$	1

Therefore decimal 0.781 = binary 0.11001. Unfortunately, this scheme leads to a pretty inconvenient process if the original decimal has many figures. Incidentally, the same device can also be used for decimal numbers larger than 0, starting with the largest power of 2 which is smaller than the original number and subtracting every smaller power of 2, one after another. Naturally, it helps if you know the values of the powers of 2 to start with, so you can tell where to begin.

III. Subtraction of Binary Numbers

The logic of binary subtraction is rather similar to the logic of addition. We consider two positive numbers where the smaller number (Y) is to be subtracted from the larger number (X). The usual method of subtraction with decimal numbers is illustrated here for comparison.

	10	1	Weights
	1	(0)	Borrowed digit
	6̸	5̸	First number, X
65 is the same as	5	15	New Form of X
−37	− 3	7	Second number, Y
28	2	8	Difference

As long as a digit of Y is smaller than or equal to the corresponding digit of X, no problem arises. When the Y digit is larger than its corresponding X digit, a special process called borrowing (actually the reverse of carrying) must be used to determine the difference digit. In this process, we borrow a "1" from the X digit immediately to the left and add a "10" to the X digit which was originally too small. Since the order of magnitude of any decimal digit is 10 times that of the digit to its right, borrowing "1" from a digit in any column and adding "10" to the digit immediately to the right makes no overall change in the value of X.

Likewise, in the binary system of numbers the normal procedure can be used when the Y digit is equal to or smaller than the X digit. Otherwise we must resort to borrowing. In the binary system, however, a shift of a borrowed "1" by one column to the right represents a multiplication of the borrowed digit by binary "10" ("one oh," decimal "2") rather than by the "10" of the decimal system. Thus, the borrow of a "1" from a digit in any column of a binary number must be balanced by the addition of a binary "10" to the digit in the next column to the right.

We can illustrate this process by examining the subtraction of the binary 1010 from 10011:

16	8	4	2	1		Weights
1	0	0	0	(0)		Borrowed digit
1	0	0	1	1	= 19	First number, X
0	10	0	1	1		New form of X
	− 1	0	1	0	= 10	Second number, Y
0	1	0	0	1	= 9	Difference

This process is somewhat more complex in such a case as this:

(1)	(2)	(3)	Column
1	0	0	X
0	1	1	Y
A	B	C	Difference

Here the difference digit C requires a borrow from column (2) where there is nothing to borrow from. To see how this is managed, we turn again to decimal numbers:

(1)	(2)	(3)	(4)	Column
1	0	0	0	X
		− 1	2	Y

The same difficulty confronts us, and of course is easily enough solved. We borrow from column (3) to build up column (4) just as though (3) really had something to lend. If it had, it would have been a "10," and after lending would have become "9." The only way it could have been a "10," however, would have been a result of a further borrow in its turn, from column (2), and so on. We are so used to saying "2 from 10, 1 from 9, 0 from 9" (or equivalent terms) that we are hardly conscious of the really rather complex "bank check" process that goes on. Column (3) issues a check to column (4) and, before it can bounce, gets column (2) to issue a check to it, and so on. Thus we mentally change the "First number, X" to the "New form of X" as shown here:

1	1	1	(0)	Borrowed
1	0	0	0	First number, X
9	9	10		New form of X
		− 1	2	Second number, Y
9	8	8		Difference

At this point we can return to the source of our troubles: the binary subtraction 100 − 011. We change column (3) to "10," borrowing from (2) to do so. Column (2) is thus reduced to "1," which we keep in mind until we get to it. When we do reach it, we see that column (2) had in turn borrowed from column (1), which, like a banker with hard cash, actually had a digit to lend. Written out in detail, the subtraction is:

Weights:	4	2	1	
X:	1	0	0	$= 1 \cdot 2^2 + 0 \cdot 2^1 + 0 \cdot 2^0$
Borrowed:	1	1	(0)	
New form of X:	0	1	10	$= 0 \cdot 2^2 + 1 \cdot 2^1 + 2 \cdot 2^0$
Y:	0	1	1	
Difference:	0	0	1	

This looks a bit complicated, though in fact it is not, after a little practice. To build a subtractor, however, a table of combinations is needed. It looks like this (shifting X and Y to x and y, and calling the borrow digit b):

Row	b	x	y	Borrow digit	Difference digit
1	0	0	0	0	0
2	0	0	1	1	1
3	0	1	0	0	1
4	0	1	1	0	0
5	1	0	0	1	1
6	1	0	1	1	0
7	1	1	0	0	0
8	1	1	1	1	1

To show the use of the table, we consider the following example of subtraction:

Weights:	64	32	16	8	4	2	1
Borrow digits, b:	1	1	0	1	1	1	(0)
First number, x:	1	0	0	1	0	1	0
Second number, y:	0	0	1	0	1	1	1
Difference, d:	0	1	1	0	0	1	1

The right-hand column has, as always, a borrow digit 0. The table shows that since the 3 digits in this column are 0, 0, 1, the difference is 1 and the borrow digit 1 (see row 2 of the table of combinations). The borrow digit must be set over the next column, which now contains 1, 1, 1. The bottom row of the table tells us that the difference is again 1 and the borrow digit 1. Continuing in this manner, we complete the example.

Section 3 of this chapter discusses the general task of designing an adder. Curiously enough, a subtractor circuit has only small differences. The logic can be described conveniently by the use of the Boolean notation. For example, we can write row 1 of the table as $\overline{b}\overline{x}\overline{y} = 0$ (true in this case whether we are interested in the resulting difference digit or the borrow digit). Or we can describe all cases where the difference digit is 1 by writing $\overline{b}\overline{x}y + \overline{b}x\overline{y} + b\overline{x}\overline{y} + bxy = 1$, from rows 2, 3, 5, and 8.

Turning now to the actual design problem, we recall first that (as with adding) the right-hand digit has especially simple rules: its borrow digit is always 0, and so can be ignored in designing; we want to turn on a light when the difference digit is 1. These requirements are met only in rows 2 and 3, which can be written $\overline{x}y + x\overline{y} = 1$ (the "1" standing, of course, for the difference digit). This is the same odd-parity or exclusive OR circuit as is used in adding. We must borrow from the second column if the subtrahend is larger than the minuend, or $\overline{x}y = 1$ (this "1" meaning the borrow digit), not a majority but an AND circuit. The circuits for this column are, then:

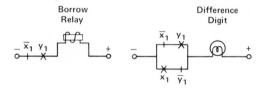

Borrow Relay   Difference Digit

In the remaining columns we find $d = 1$ (rows 2, 3, 5, 8) if $\overline{b}\overline{x}y + \overline{b}x\overline{y} + b\overline{x}\overline{y} + bxy = 1$. This is the same odd-parity circuit used for addition. For the borrow digit, $b = 1$ (rows 2, 5, 6, 8) if $\overline{b}\overline{x}y + b\overline{x}\overline{y} + b\overline{x}y + bxy = 1$. This can be simplified in various ways. For example, let us add two more copies of $b\overline{x}y$ (which, since it repeats a term already present, makes no change in the overall circuit). Thus, $\overline{b}\overline{x}y + b\overline{x}\overline{y} + b\overline{x}y + bxy + b\overline{x}y + b\overline{x}y = 1$ (where the added terms are underlined). These may now be factored in pairs to yield

$$\overline{x}y(b + \overline{b}) + b\overline{x}(\overline{y} + y) + by(x + \overline{x}) = 1$$

and all the terms in parentheses equal 1 and may be dropped. The equation has now become

$$\overline{x}y + b\overline{x} + by = 1$$

which can be simplified one step further by factoring any two terms. One of the resulting circuits is

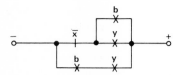

which reduces the original 12 contacts to 5, and seems to be as far as we can go. Thus these columns are handled in each case by such circuits as these, drawn here for column 2:

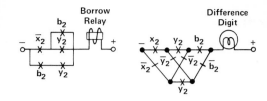

The leftmost column of a subtraction cannot generate a borrow digit (because $x = y$, rows 3, 4, 7 of the table; row 8 is excluded because, as a test or two will show, b is never 1 in this column if $x \geqslant y$). Therefore no borrow-digit circuit need be built for the extreme left column of a subtractor, and of course there cannot be an overflow digit when subtracting.

IV. Flow Diagrams for Sum or Difference of Binary Numbers

(For "sgnS" read "sign of S", etc.)

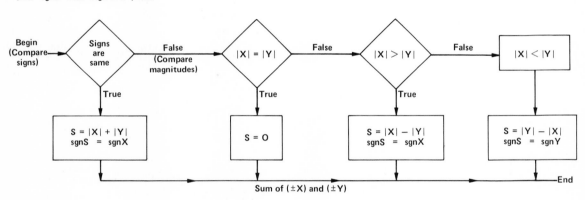

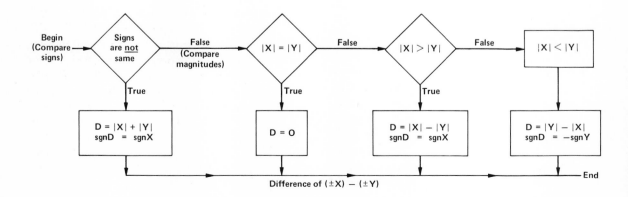

V. Decimal Number Display Circuit

Most of the circuit-design problems thus far considered in the text (for example, the majority circuit, the adder circuit, the number-comparing circuit, and the tree circuit) could be extended to include a large number of controlling switches without any further thought since they were solved by repeating a simple basic pattern. There are many problems, however, to which this technique cannot be applied. As an example of such a problem, we consider the conversion of a 4-place binary number to a visual display. This display will use a set of 7 elongated lamps (like showcase lamps) which are controlled by a contact network. A typical desired conversion is shown below. The number "5" in the binary system is 0101 and is associated with positions of 4 switches A, B, C, and D so that B and D are operated and A and C are released. By turning on all of the lights except L_2 and L_6, we get the desired visual pattern.

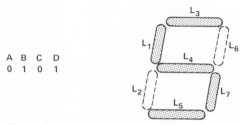

```
A  B  C  D
0  1  0  1
```

Conversion from binary number to visual display

The reason for considering this problem is that it is typical of the complexity of many actual design problems. It also demonstrates one method by which the results of a computer computation can be made available to human beings in an easily recognized form. It illustrates again a table of combinations. The table for our problem, in next column, shows for every possible combination of states of the 4 input switches whether each of the 7 lights should be on (1) or off (0). In our problem, we have arbitrarily decided to represent visually only the numbers 0 through 9. All other combinations are to cause only the lamp L_4 to be on. In complicated

situations such as this one, a table of combinations is a way for the designer to be sure that he has considered every possible situation that may arise.

Table of combinations for the decimal number of display circuit

Decimal number	Binary form				Desired visual output	Display lamp combinations L_1 L_2 L_3 L_4 L_5 L_6 L_7						
0	0	0	0	0	$\square$	1	1	1	0	1	1	1
1	0	0	0	1	/	0	0	0	0	0	1	1
2	0	0	1	0	2	0	1	1	1	1	1	0
3	0	0	1	1	3	0	0	1	1	1	1	1
4	0	1	0	0	4	1	0	0	1	0	1	1
5	0	1	0	1	5	1	0	1	1	1	0	1
6	0	1	1	0	6	1	1	0	1	1	0	1
7	0	1	1	1	7	0	0	1	0	0	1	1
8	1	0	0	0	8	1	1	1	1	1	1	1
9	1	0	0	1	9	1	0	1	1	0	1	1
10	1	0	1	0	—	0	0	0	1	0	0	0
11	1	0	1	1	—	0	0	0	1	0	0	0
12	1	1	0	0	—	0	0	0	1	0	0	0
13	1	1	0	1	—	0	0	0	1	0	0	0
14	1	1	1	0	—	0	0	0	1	0	0	0
15	1	1	1	1	—	0	0	0	1	0	0	0

The next problem the designer has is to convert the requirements given in the table of combinations into circuit form. We do not intend to show all the techniques which can be used. A circuit diagram is given, next page, which leads to the desired results. This fact can be verified by examining each of the 16 rows of the table and determining whether or not a path exists from the left-hand terminal to each of the 7 right-hand terminals. For example, when the 4 input switches are operated so that they represent the number "5," the "b" and "d" contacts are closed (therefore, the "$\bar{b}$" and "$\bar{d}$" contacts are open) and the "a" and "c" contacts are open (therefore the "$\bar{a}$" and "$\bar{c}$" contacts are closed). Under these conditions there is a path to Lamp L_7 through the "$\bar{a}$" and "d" contacts. This path is indicated by the dashed line in the circuit diagram. Under these same conditions there can be no path to the L_2 terminal since the rightmost contact "$\overline{d}$" is open. Since any path to L_2 would have to go through that contact, there can be no such path.

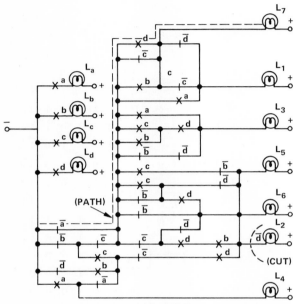

A circuit which displays numbers in decimal form

We have illustrated that the two entries which are shown checked in the table of combinations actually correspond to the circuit diagram we have drawn. A complete analysis would demonstrate at least one path such as the one given by the dashed line for each "1" entry in the table and at least one "cut" such as the one given by the dotted line for each "0" entry. (It is helpful to notice that if there is a path, there cannot be a cut; and if there is a cut, there cannot be a path.) A special rule which assists in the analysis is that there cannot be a path through two series contacts of opposite types (make and break) associated with a given switch since they cannot both be closed at the same time. In the same way there cannot be a cut through two parallel contacts of opposite types associated with a given switch since both cannot be open at the same time.

The preceding development is clearly not suitable for general class use except in unusual cases. Very able students, however (and the teacher too), may find it interesting to draw up the Boolean expressions for the switch network required by each lamp, simplify them as far as possible, and then check against the circuit. It is astonishing to see how skillfully the circuit designer has saved switch contacts by making one contact do multiple duty. Often this has been made possible by ingeniously inserting an extra contact of opposite type to prevent the formation of an unwanted path. For one example, $\overline{a}\,\overline{b}$ lights $L6$ (whether C and D are operated or not), and $\overline{a}\,\overline{b}\,\overline{d}$ lights $L5$; but $\overline{a}\,\overline{b}\,d$ is blocked from $L5$ by the fact that d and $\overline{d}$ are in series in that line. (But $\overline{a}\,\overline{b}\,c$ works $L5$ whether or not switch D is operated.)

One remark should be made: it is frequently possible, of course, to simplify a Boolean expression in more than one way. For this reason one's attempts to justify the wiring of the circuit may go astray. The secret of success, in such a case, is to write out the formulae for every path that actually exists in the wiring diagram, and see whether those which do not appear in the simplified version are perhaps to be found higher up on the page, among the expressions that have been eliminated or combined during the simplification.

VI. Unusual Uses of Tree Circuits, and a 4-Stage Tree

Very good multi-scale voltmeters are readily available commercially at quite modest prices. They use a rotary switch to connect the proper multiplier for a given meter scale in series with the microammeter which is usually provided to indicate the voltage. For a home-made voltmeter at a rock-bottom price, the rotary switch could be replaced by an assembly of a single-pole double-throw and a double-pole double-throw switch as in the following diagram. The number of multipliers could readily be doubled by adding another stage to the tree, though at a distinct loss in convenience.

Obviously, a conventional tree circuit would serve as well. The chief point in this note is to direct

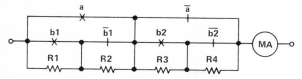

VM multipliers in a "dual tree"

attention to the unfamiliar "dual tree." Incidentally, the same scheme might be a convenient way to arrange the common lamp-board rheostat for some purposes.

For the sake of balance, we include the diagram below, which depicts a standard form of tree in the unusual guise of a selector of ammeter shunts. Be-

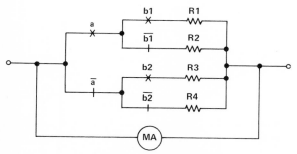

A tree to choose ammeter shunts

cause of the variable amount of contact resistance in the switches, this arrangement cannot be recommended, however.

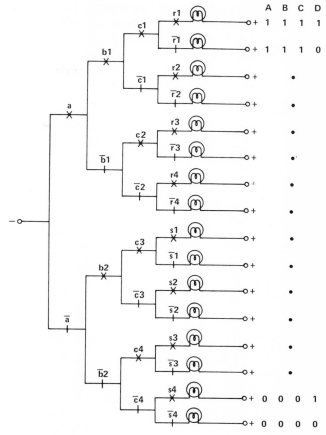

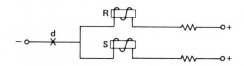

4-STAGE TREE

We all are aware of the frustration caused by running out of switch contacts when developing elaborate circuits on the LCB. The following circuit, which illustrates a strategy for bypassing the problem, appeared in the Teachers' Manual for 1966–67, and was "rediscovered" by a teacher and reported in the *Newsletter* the next fall.

Because the last stage of a 4-stage tree requires 8 switch sections and we have no such switches, the idea is to use the fourth switch to control 2 relays, each of which takes care of half the final addresses.

VII. Hamming Encoder, Decoder, Error-Correcting Circuit

This circuit should not be demonstrated until the Hamming error-correcting code has been studied in Chapter 9, Section 3, or Chapter 10, Section GII. It is not difficult to show that only odd-parity, tree, and exclusive-OR circuits are needed to implement the simplest "3-circle" form of the code. By implication, the circuits for patterns with 4 or 5 redundant digits could be equally easily developed.

Five new-model LCB's are needed. Teachers with the old-model boards can wire the circuit with suitable modifications to obtain enough contacts.

The error-correction bits for the Hamming code can be selected by reference to the diagram of Fig. 9-17, or without the diagram by the use of 3 rules, listed below and summarized in table below.

Rule X: The bit in position c is so chosen that there will be an even number of 1's in positions c, e, f, and g.

Rule Y: The bit in position b is so chosen that there will be an even number of 1's in positions b, d, e, and g.

Rule Z: The bit in position a is so chosen that there will be an even number of 1's in positions a, d, f, and g.

Position	a	b	c	d	e	f	g
Rule X			x		x	x	x
Rule Y		x		x	x		x
Rule Z	x			x		x	x

DEVELOPMENT OF CIRCUITS

We first need 4 switches (D, E, F, and G) on which to set the 4 information bits. Then we need circuits to generate the 3 additional bits (a, b, and c) according to the given rules. Examination of the rules shows that we wish to generate a "1" whenever there is an odd number of 1's in 3 given information positions. A 3-variable odd-parity circuit will perform this function. Three of these are shown as the "coding circuit" in following diagram. It is essential not to use more than 4 sets of contacts with any switch. If the encoding-circuit diagrams are first lettered in alphabetical order, students will discover the need to optimize. With the old-model LCB's, having only 3 sets of contacts per switch, the need is drastic.

The "transmitting circuits" (following) are simply to isolate the "transmission lines" from the indicator lights so that at the transmitter there will be no indication of errors which may be introduced farther along.

Coding Circuits

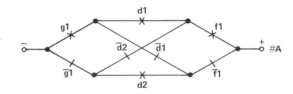

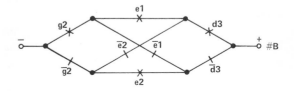

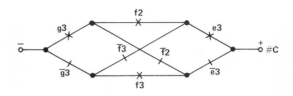

Transmitting Circuits

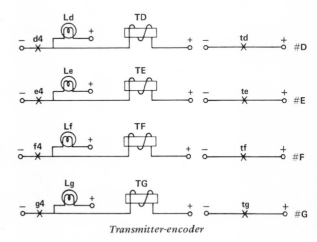

Transmitter-encoder

At the receiving end we need 7 relays, one for each strand of the transmission cable, and hence for each bit of the message. In a real application of the system some other scheme would have to be used to segregate the 7 bits from each other, since they would all be sent over a single "channel." Some pupils very likely have heard of multiplex telegraphy, which would offer one method. The 7 relays are indicated below, which also shows the error-detecting circuits. Here we need 3 relays (X, Y, and Z) whose operation will correspond to violations of the 3 corresponding rules. Since each rule is concerned with 4 positions, a 4-variable circuit is called for. The error relay should be energized if (and only if) an odd number of 1's is transmitted, so the circuit must be arranged for odd-parity.

here, and is shown below. Since we wish to correct only the information positions, the portions of the tree corresponding to zero errors, or an error in positions a, b, or c, have been omitted.

For the error-correcting circuit, we wish simply to reverse the signal at the information position found to be in error. A 2-variable odd-parity circuit (exclusive-OR) will accomplish this, and 4 of these are also shown below.

Receiving Relays

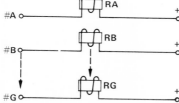

Correction Tree   **Error**

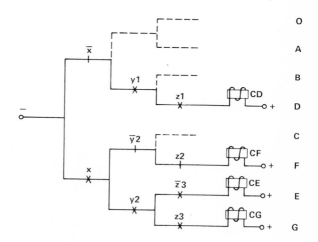

Error Detectors

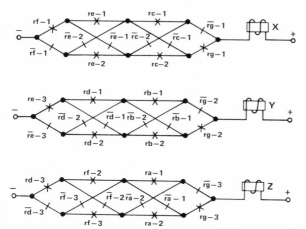

Receivers and error detectors

Error Corrected Output

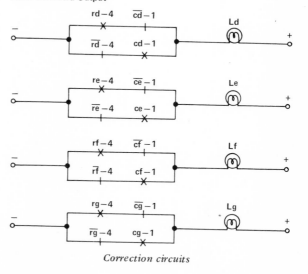

Correction circuits

We now need a circuit to tell us which position is in error because of a particular combination of rule violations. A tree circuit is clearly the solution

WIRING THE CIRCUIT

You may prefer to do this yourself or you can assign it to superior students.

Five LCB's are required. Board 1 will be the encoder and should be separated by at least several feet from Boards 2 through 5. It is suggested that masking tape be used to relabel the boards to correspond to the symbols used in the circuit:

Board 1: Label switches *A, B, C,* and *D* as *D, E, F,* and *G.*
Label relays *P, Q, R,* and *S* as *TD, TE, TF,* and *TG.*
Label lamps *L1* through *L4* as *Ld* through *Lg.*

Board 2: Label relays *P* through *S* as *RA, RB, RC,* and *RD.*

Board 3: Label relays *P* through *R* as *RE, RF,* and *RG.*

Board 4: Label relays *P, Q* and *R* as *X, Y,* and *Z.*

Board 5: Label relays *P, Q, R,* and *S* as *CD, CE, CF,* and *CG.*
Label lamps *L1* through *L4* as *Ld* through *Lg.*

The running lists are given below. You will need quite a few 18-in connecting wires (not supplied with new model LCB's but available from AMF; or make your own from solid 20-, 22-, or 24-gauge hookup wire and Vector T9.4 clips, available by the 100 from Allied Radio or Lafayette Radio Electronics Corp., or other electronics supply houses). It is recommended that you wire the circuit in sections and test it as you proceed.

Encoding and transmitting circuit:
Board 1:
    Neg, G1c, D4c, TD-1c; G1m, D1c; G1b, D2c; D1m, D2b, F1m; D2m, D1b, F1b; F1c, wire A. Neg, G2c, E4c, TE-1c; G2m, E1c; G2b, E2c; E1m, E2b, D3m; E2m, E1b, D3b; D3c, wire B. Neg, G3c, F4c, TF-1c; G3m, F2c; G3b, F3c; F2m, F3b, E3m; F2b, F3m, E3b; E3c, wire C. D4m, Ld, TD-op; TD-1m, wire D. E4m, Le, TE-op; TE-1m, wire E. F4m, Lf, TF-op; TF-1m, wire F.

G4m, Lg, TG-op; TF-1m, wire G.
    Neg, G4c, TG-1c.

Test at this point by operating switches *D, E, F,* and *G* in various combinations to be sure the proper signals appear on wires *A* through *G.* All remaining wiring is the same for both types of LCB.

ADDITIONAL WIRING NOTES

1. Wires A through G from Board 1 may be connected to the wires with the same designation on Boards 2 and 3 by clip leads and other longer wires. Errors may be introduced by removing one of these connections or by shorting a wire carrying a "1" to one carrying a "0."

2. If you wish to display the signals on wires A, B, and C, connect L1, L2, and L3 on Board 2 to the "op" terminals of RA, RB, and RC respectively.

Receiving and error-detecting circuits:
Boards 2, 3, and 4:
    Neg, RF-1c, RE-3c; RF-1m, RE-1c; RF-1b, RE-2c; RE-1m, RE-2b, RC-1c; RE-2m, RE-1b, RC-2c; RC-1m, RC-2b, RG-1b; RC-2m, RC-1b, RG-1m; RG-1c, RX-op; RE-3m, RD-1c; RE-3b, RD-2c; RD-1m, RD-2b, RB-1c; RD-2m, RD-1b, RB-2c; RB-1m, RB-2b, RG-2b; RB-2m, RB-1b, RG-2m; RG-2c, RY-op; Neg, RD-3c; RD-3m, RF-2c; RD-3b, RF-3c; RF-2m, RF-3b, RA-1c; RF-3m, RF-2b, RA-2c; RA-1m, RA-2b, RG-3b; RA-2m, RA-1b, RG-3m; RG-3c, RZ-op.
    RA-op, wire A; RB-op, wire B; RC-op, wire C; RD-op, wire D; RE-op, wire E; RF-op, wire F; RG-op, wire G. Connect all 5 boards by wires from Neg to Neg unless your boards have 3-wire grounded outlets (with the grounds connected!)

Test at this point by operating relays RA to RG in various combinations to be sure of the proper operation of relays X, Y, and Z.

Correction tree:
Boards 4 and 5:
    Neg, X1c; X1b, Y1c; Y1m, Y2c; Y1m, Z1c; Y2b, Z2c; Y2m, Z3c; Z1m, CD-op; Z2m, CF-op; Z3b, CE-op; Z3m, CG-op.

Test the tree by operating relays X, Y, and Z in various combinations to be sure of the proper operation of relays CD, CE, CF, and CG.

Correction circuit:

Boards 2, 3, and 5:

Neg, RD-4c, RE-4c; RD-4m, CD-1b; RD-4b,
CD-1m; CD-1c, Ld; RE-4m, CE-1b; RE-4b,
CE-1m; CE-1c, Le; Neg, RF-4c, RG-4c; RF-4m,
CF-1b; RF-4b, CF-1m; CF-1c, Lf; RG-4m,
CG-1b; RG-4b, CG-1m; CG-1c, Lg.

VIII. Converting Decimal Numbers to Binary Notation

A few preliminary comments must be made. A number written in decimal notation can be multiplied by 10 by shifting every digit one place to the left and appending 0. Similarly, a number in the binary system can be multiplied by 2 by shifting every digit one place to the left and appending 0. Hence, 101110 is twice 10111. Conversely, if a binary number ends in 0, striking off the 0 (and moving each digit one place to the right) is equivalent to division by 2.

To determine whether a binary number is even or odd, it is therefore enough to look at the right-hand or least significant digit. If that digit is 0, the number is exactly twice the value of some other number, and so must be even; and if the least significant digit is 1, the number is odd. In this case, it can be made even, and therefore divisible by 2, by subtracting 1 from it.

We use these facts to convert decimal numbers to binary. The procedure determines the digits in the binary number, one at a time, starting with the least significant digit and working to the left. For an example, let us convert decimal 117 to binary. We know the number we want will be of the form

$$B_n \quad \cdots \cdots \quad B_2 \, B_1 \, B_0,$$

where each B represents one of the binary digits, but of course we do not know the magnitude of the subscript "n." Since 117 is an odd number, so must the binary number be, and its final digit is 1

$$B_n \quad \cdots \cdots \quad B_2 \, B_1 \quad 1 \; = \; 117$$
$$1 \; = \; 1$$

Subtracting 1 from each side of the equation we have

$$B_n \quad \cdots \cdots \quad B_2 \, B_1 \; 0 \; = \; 116$$

Since both numbers are now even, we can divide by

$$2) \, B_n \quad \cdots \cdots \quad B_2 \, B_1 \; 0 \; = \; 116$$
$$B_n \quad \cdots \cdots \quad B_2 \, B_1 \quad \; = \; 58$$

Now since 58 is even, B_1 must be 0, and division of the equation again by 2 leaves

$$B_n \quad \cdots \cdots \quad B_2 \quad \; = \; 29, \text{again odd so}$$
B_2 is 1, etc.

This long-winded process can be made quicker and easier by successive divisions of the original decimal number by 2, noting in each case whether the remainder is 0 or 1, as follows:

2)117		
2)58	and remainder	1
2)29		0
2)14		1
2)7		0
2)3		1
2)1		1
0		1

Now we read the remainders from bottom to top, and this gives the desired binary form of 117: 1110101.

APPROX. TIME: Text: 9 days Lab: 3—4 days

A. APPROACH	CLASS PERIODS	B. BLACK & WHITE TRANSPARENCIES	C. CUES (k=key problem) Discussion Questions	C. CUES Problems Easy	C. CUES Problems Medium	C. CUES Problems Hard	D. DEMONSTRATIONS, LABS & PROJECTS	E. EVALUATION	F. FILMS	G. GENERAL
1. Introduction	1		1, 7, 8							
2. The Basic Relay Memory Element	1	1401 1402 1403 1404 1405 1406 1407 1408	5, 9, 10, 11	5	1, 2, 3 4	6	I	1a, b, c, d, e, 2 1f, h, i, j, k, l, 4, 5	1401, 1402	II, V VI
3. An Addressable Memory	1	1409a, b, c, d	2, 3, 6					1m, 6		
4. Shifting and Shift Registers	2	1410 1411a, b, c, d 1412	4				II	1n, o, p 3,8		I, III
5. Circuits That Count	2	1413a, b, c, d, e 1414 1415 1416 1417	12			7	III	1q, 7, 9		IV
6. Turning a Number into Action	2	1418 1419 1420a, b 1421					IV	1g, r, s, 9	1403	
7. Final Comment										

Machine Memory

14

A | APPROACH

I. Purpose and Organization of the Chapter

What makes a digital computer different from a desk top calculator? What is the major advantage of a digital computer over the analog computer? What is a major advantage of the digital computer over the human for record keeping? In all cases, the answer is memory.

The purpose of this chapter is to study the memory unit and to show its place in the memory bank, the instruction register, the program counter, and the accumulator. As with the previous two chapters, the time spent will depend on the interest and ability of the students and, of course, the time available. Chapter 15 is quite short and should take only a few days. This might help in your planning.

Starting with the use of memory circuits in everyday devices such as telephones, elevators, and traffic lights, the chapter proceeds to the specifics of the relay as a memory unit, looking at a 1-bit memory, the 4-cell memory units, and then going on to shifting and the shift register. This brings the student to counting circuits and finally into the transfer of information from one part of the "computer" to another as exemplified in the automatic Morse Code Transmitter. Many teachers have found that while a number of students really are turned on

by the detailed look at these items, an equal number seem to be turned off. Here is an ideal opportunity for individualized instruction in which some students will design and build the circuits studied while others will be content to build them from running lists. All students should be involved in the activities, and at differing levels of understanding will be impressed with the concept of building complex circuits from the simpler circuits studied in Chapters 12 and 13. It is not important that every student actually build the shift register, binary counter and Morse Code Transmitter. Understanding of the operation of these circuits is what should be stressed.

II. Objectives for Students

Upon completion of the activities, discussion, and reading in this chapter, students should be able to:

1. Recognize and identify such terms as *addressable storage, memory circuit, memory element,* and *shift register.*

2. Describe the difference between the use of a relay in its own logic circuit and the use of the relay to control switch contacts in another circuit.

3. Explain how memory circuits are used in some common devices as well as in computers.

4. Trace the circuit which is used in a simple memory element.

5. Demonstrate the operation of a 4-cell memory circuit.

6. Demonstrate the operation of a shift register and a binary counter.

7. Trace the transfer of information in a device such as the Morse Code Transmitter.

III. Suggestions for Teaching

Section 1. Introduction. The first day of this section might well be spent not only in the discussion and demonstration of simple memory elements which are used in devices other than computers, but also in the demonstration of some of the devices which the students will later build during the laboratory sessions. These demonstrations should be without any detailed explanation of the circuits, but rather with explanation of the need for memory elements in their operation. Section D of this chapter has the diagrams and demonstrations of the use of memory elements in the automatic opening of supermarket doors as well as the high beam switch for automobiles in both U.S. and foreign cars. Again, having these wired in advance for student operation is an important part of the demonstration because explanation of the operation of the memory elements should be deferred until later in the study of the chapter.

Section 2. The Basic Relay Memory Element. At this point in the course, many of the students are interested in finding out the workings of some of the devices which they have used. If your students show interest, this is a good time to have them go through the operation of the relay in detail. For those who are not so interested, it is sufficient to stick to the description of the relay as a memory element as described in the text. While there are many other devices used as memory elements, the relay is particularly useful at this level because the students can see it move and hear it click.

Section 3. An Addressable Memory. This section, along with the next two, are best understood if they are discussed in a classroom laboratory setting in which the students have the logic circuit boards at their desks and are working on the labs associated with the section. Students should work in pairs. Demonstration of more complex situations as described in Section D of this chapter should precede the laboratory sessions.

The important details in this section are: How to read the state of a relay, the use of the tree circuit studied earlier and the memory element to make the addressable memory possible, and finally, the "reading" of the contents of the memory element.

Section 4. Shifting and Shift Registers. As mentioned earlier, for some students it will be sufficient to know *that* the simpler circuits learned earlier can be combined to form a shift register. For other students who desire it, it is important to know *how* these simpler circuits are combined. Again, the lab should be the major emphasis of this section, with individuals going as far as they can grasp. For the use of the shift register in multiplication, see Section G, Part III.

Section 5. Circuits That Count. A demonstration of a 4-stage counter prior to the study of this section is extremely motivating to almost all students. Follow this with Lab III, "The Counter Circuit," in order to build a 1-stage counter which then becomes a part of the hierarchy of the computer development, which is the major concept to be taught. The students should discover the close similarity between the counting circuit and the shifting circuit, the need for the control unit to be able to count, and the method of resetting a counter.

Section 6. Turning a Number into Action. The major purpose of this section is to show the function of the control unit in determining what instruction is to be executed and how the execution is performed. The Morse Code Transmitter is used as a demonstration of how a static code is converted to a dynamic sequence of actions.

The wiring of the Morse Code Transmitter should be left to the more LCB-oriented students. The important points are its operation as a simulation of how the control unit operates. If all students are required to wire the transmitter, many will lose sight of the main function in the maze of wiring. On the other hand, each of the simple circuits which go to make up this control unit should be pointed out as further reinforcement of the hierarchy development of the digital computer.

Section 7. Final Comment. We have none.

B | BLACK AND WHITE TRANSPARENCIES

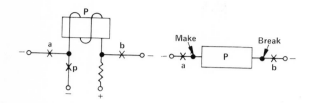

T-1401   BASIC MEMORY CIRCUIT

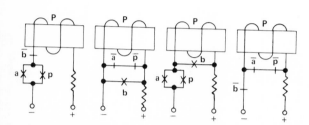

T-1402   EQUIVALENT MEMORY CIRCUITS

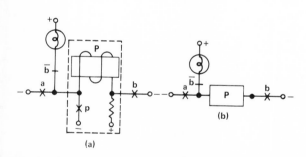

T-1403   ONE-BIT MEMORY WITH READOUT   (a) DE-TAILED CIRCUIT, (b) SYMBOLIC DIAGRAM

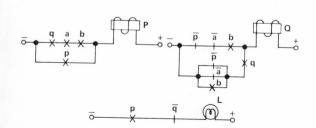

T-1404   DISCUSSION QUESTION 9

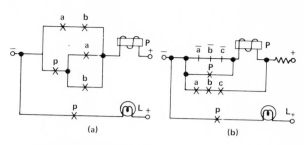

T-1405   DISCUSSION QUESTION 10

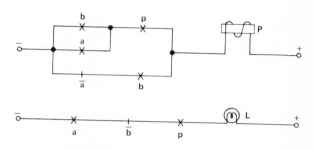

T-1406   DISCUSSION QUESTION 11

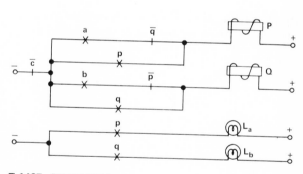

T-1407   PROBLEM 5

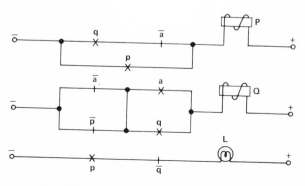

T-1408   PROBLEM 6

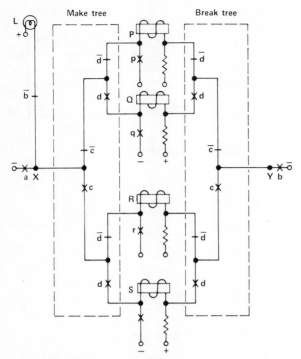

T-1409a FOUR-CELL MEMORY

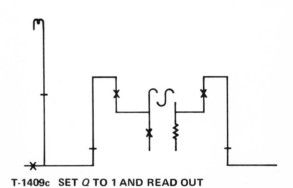

T-1409c SET *Q* TO 1 AND READ OUT

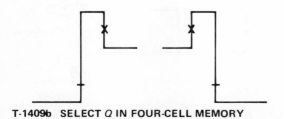

T-1409b SELECT *Q* IN FOUR-CELL MEMORY

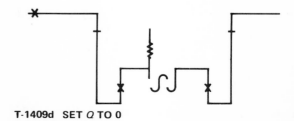

T-1409d SET *Q* TO 0

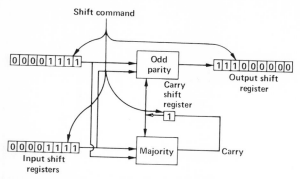

T-1410 SERIAL ADDER WITH SHIFT REGISTERS

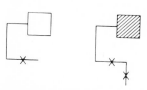

T-1411b *S* OPERATED, *P* BECOMES 1

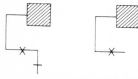

T-1411c *S* RELEASED, *Q* ASSUMES STATE OF *A*(1)

T-1411d *A* RESET TO 0, HOLDING CONTACT ON *P*

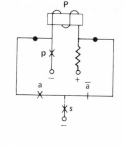

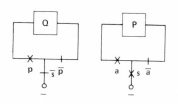

T-1411a BASIC SHIFT REGISTER CIRCUIT

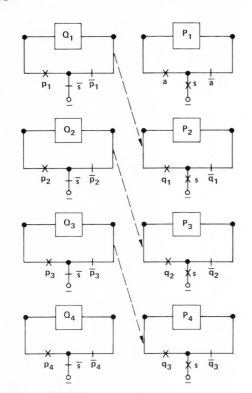

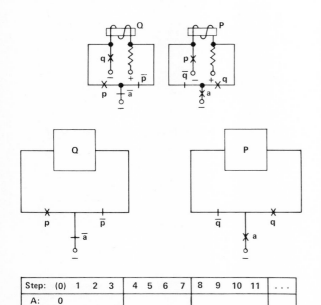

T-1412 FOUR-STAGE SHIFT REGISTER

Step:	(0)	1	2	3		4	5	6	7		8	9	10	11		...
A:	0															
P:	0															
Q:	0															

T-1413a BASIC COUNTER CIRCUIT

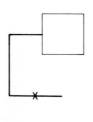

T-1413b INITIAL COUNTER STATE: $A = 0, P = 0, Q = 0$

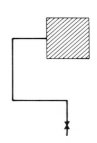

T-1413c $A = 1, P = 1, Q = 0$

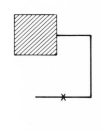

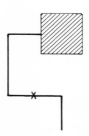

T-1413d $A = 0, P = 1, Q = 1$

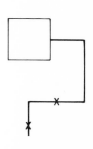

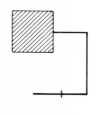

T-1413e $A = 1, P = 0, Q = 1$

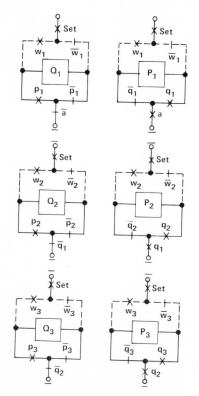

T-1414 THREE-STAGE COUNTER

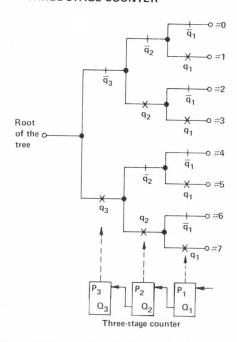

T-1415 A COUNTER-CONTROLLED TREE

	1	2	3	4	5	6	7	....	13	14
a:	0	0	1	1	0	0	1	....	0	0
b:	0	1	1	0	0	1	1	....	0	1

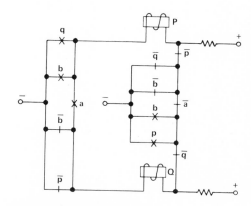

T-1416 DISCUSSION QUESTION 12

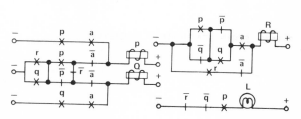

T-1417 PROBLEM 7

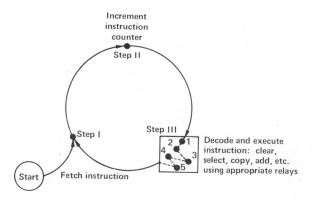

T-1418 INSTRUCTION CYCLE SEQUENCE

Letter	Binary code			Morse code output								
	X	Y	Z	Time interval								
				0	1	2	3	4	5	6	7
A	0	0	0				•		—		
B	0	0	1		—		•		•		•
C	0	1	0		—		•		—		•
D	0	1	1		—		•		•		
E	1	0	0								
F	1	0	1	•			•		—		•
G	1	1	0		—		—		•		•
H	1	1	1	•			•		•		•

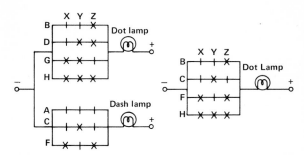

T-1420b MORSE CODER CIRCUITS, TIME 5 AND TIME 7

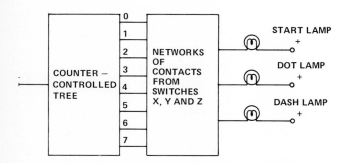

T-1419 MORSE CODE, BIT CODE, AND CONTROL

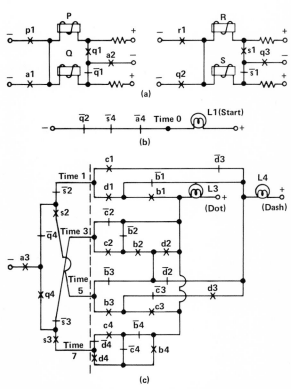

T-1421 COMPLETE MORSE CODE TRANSMITTER CIRCUIT

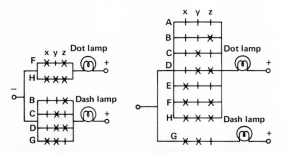

T-1420a MORSE CODER CIRCUITS, TIME 1 AND TIME 3

C | CUES TO QUESTIONS AND PROBLEMS

Questions for Study and Discussion

1. Events can be remembered in association with calendars and other events such as seasons and holidays. Magnetic tape is frequently used. On the electronic level, transistors and certain electromagnetic devices have more or less replaced relays as memory devices.

2. An address is a location where information is stored (location of a memory cell). The opening and closing of switches sets up the correct pathway to a memory cell (relay).

A 3-variable binary code has the potential of up to 8 (2^3) accessible addresses.

A 3-variable decimal code has the potential of up to 1,000 (10^3) accessible addresses.

3. Maximum number of telephone numbers is 10,000,000,000 (10^{10}), which means that the 10-variable decimal code will not have to be changed for a while. (10^8 telephones in North America in 1966.)

4. The shift register enables one to carry out multiplication by adding. The shifting process gives the proper "weight" to the numbers.

5. When the electric circuit is completed in (a), the operation of relay P opens the contacts at $\bar{p}$ and interrupts the circuit; but when this happens the relay is released, the contacts at $\bar{p}$ restore the circuit, and all happens again. This is an electric buzzer circuit, useful as a signaling device.

In (b) the effect is similar although the details differ. When P operates it also operates (closes) p, which short-circuits P and turns it off. Thus the contacts at p open, and the original situation is restored, ready to go round again. This also is a buzzer.

6. a) Relay Q is energized; in other words, a "1" is stored at address 01.

b) Relay R is energized and then deenergized; in other words, a "1" and then a "0" is stored at address 10.

c) Operate switches C and D and then operate and release switch A.

d) Operate C; then operate and release B. (This ensures that if R previously had stored a "1" it would be erased.)

7. A machine memory will remember as long as the operator wishes (and only what the operator wishes, and will forget instantly and completely when this is desired).

8. Human memory is, at least to some degree, selective; moreover, new combinations of remembered ideas are made. (For a notable discussion of this, see *The Road to Xanadu*, by J. L. Lowes.)

9. This should be analyzed by starting with the diagram at the bottom, which shows that L goes on if P is operated and Q is not. But P can be operated only by operating A and B and Q. Therefore, the necessary sequence is: (1) operate B, causing relay Q to operate (contact q closes and holds); (2) operate A, which now can cause P to operate (contact p closes and holds); (3) release B (the lowest contact b in the Q network opens), thus releasing Q, closing contact $\bar{q}$ in the L circuit, and L goes on.

10. a) L goes on if A *and* B are operated; it remains on if either A *or* B but not both is now released. L goes off again when *both A and B* are released.

b) L is initially on if A and B and C are initially unoperated; L will go off if and only if all 3 switches are operated.

11. Operate B (P closes); operate A (P holds); release B (lamp on). To turn lamp off, release A or operate B.

12.

Step	1	2	3	4	5	6	7	8	9	10	11	12	13	14
a	0	0	1	1	0	0	1	1	0	0	1	1	0	0
b	0	1	1	0	0	1	1	0	0	1	1	0	0	1
P	0	0	0	0	0	0	1	1	1	1	1	1	0	0
Q	0	0	0	1	1	1	1	1	1	0	0	0	0	0

Note: This is a difficult problem which is best suited for the eager and intelligent student. Use of the LCB to check the analysis would be a good idea.

Problems

1. a) In Fig. (1) when switch A is operated, relay P energizes and the make contact p closes. It takes about 1 millisecond for the relay to get energized

and close the p contact. In Fig. (2), relay P is shorted by break contact $\bar{p}$ and operating switch A does not affect the relay.

b)In Fig. (1) if relay P is already operated, the operation of switch A will not affect the relay because the p make contact will keep the relay energized. This p make contact used in this manner is called a holding contact. In Fig. (2) if relay P is already operated, it will stay operated until switch A is operated. When switch A is operated (the $\bar{p}$ break contact being already open), the relay will deenergize and $\bar{p}$ break contact will close and short out the relay.

2.a)In Fig. (1) when switch A is operated, the relay becomes energized (a make and $\bar{b}$ break are closed) and p make contact becomes closed. The relay will now remain energized through contact p independent of future states of switch A. If switch B is now operated, its break contact $\bar{b}$ opens and the relay will go to the unoperated state. In Fig. (2) operating switch A and then B will result in the circuit behavior as in Fig. (1). The difference is that there is a b make contact which will short out the relay when switch B is operated.

b)In Fig. (1) if switch B is operated first, the relay will remain deenergized even if switch A is operated because b break will be open. In Fig. (2) operating switch B first will close b make which will short out the relay and future operation of switch A will not affect the relay.

3.a)Circuit (1): Operate A and release it, nothing happens; operate B and P operates, closing p, but when B is released, P goes to the unoperated state.

Circuit (2): Relay P is dependent only on the state of switch B.

Circuit (3): Operate A, which opens the short circuit, and P operates; release A, P remains unchanged; operate B, P releases; release B, original state is restored.

b)Circuit (1): Operate B, relay operates; open B, relay releases; if A is now operated and released, nothing happens.

Circuit (2): When B is operated and then released, P is then operated and then released; when A is operated and then released, P is unoperated and remains so.

Circuit (3): Circuit is initially shorted, therefore operating B has no effect; but when A is operated and then released, relay P is operated and remains so, because the short is removed.

4.Initially unstable, relay is chattering. If, when A is operated, the make contact p is closed, the relay remains operated; but if make contact p is open (and therefore $\bar{p}$ is closed), the relay remains unoperated.

5.Lamp L_a goes on if and only if switch A is operated before switch B. In this case, lamp L_b cannot be lighted. Vice versa for switch B first. Switch C is to reset the circuit to its initial state. It may be of some interest to point out that the same circuit is (or can be) used in fencing competition, where the 2 weapons are fitted with pressure switches and connected to the telltale apparatus by means of long wires running from the backs of the contestants' jackets to take-up reels (rather like windowshade springs) at the 2 ends of the fencing mat or strip.

6.a)Operate switch A; relay Q operates; q make contact closes.

Release switch A; relay Q remains operated; relay P operates; p make contact closes.

Operate switch A; relay Q releases; $\bar{q}$ break contact closes: lamp L turns on.

b)The lamp can only be turned off by turning off the power.

7.

Step	0	1	2	3	4	5	6	7	8
A	0	1	0	1	0	1	0	1	0
P	0	0	0	0	1	1	1	1	0
Q	0	0	1	1	1	1	0	0	0
R	0	1	1	0	0	1	1	0	0

L goes on at step 7 because relay R is released ($\bar{r}$ closes), relay Q is released ($\bar{q}$ closes), and relay P is operated (p closes).

D | DEMONSTRATIONS, LABS, AND PROJECTS

I. Circuits with Memory

The purpose of this experiment is to introduce the concept of machine memory. Before doing the experiment, set up the following demonstrations which illustrate the use of memory devices in every-day life, for controlling supermarket doors and automobile headlights. These examples can be used in conjunction with the discussion of Section 1.

CIRCUIT FOR CONTROLLING SUPER-MARKET DOORS

In many modern stores such as supermarkets, doors open when a person steps onto a mat when entering and remain open until he gets into the store. A memory circuit used to trigger the opening also prevents opening when a person comes from the wrong direction. The following is an LCB circuit which models the operation of a supermarket door:

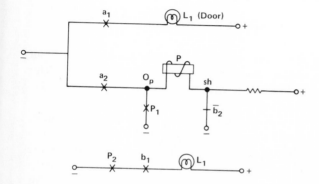

Switch A represents the switch under the mat which is outside the store. Switch B represents the switch under the mat which is inside the store. L_1 represents the door.

The sequence of operations for the above circuit is: Operate switch A (L_1 lights), operate switch B (L_1 remains lit), release switch A, and then release switch B (L_1 goes out). Notice that operating switch B first does not activate the light.

CIRCUIT FOR MODELING THE CONTROL OF AUTOMOBILE HEADLIGHTS

On most cars the change from low to high and back to low beam is done by operating a foot switch. The same switch is used for both low to high and high to low transitions. How does the switch remember the previous condition of the headlight? The following circuit simulates the operation of this type of memory.

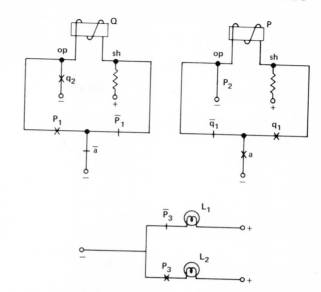

Switch A represents the foot switch. L_1 represents low beam. L_2 represents high beam.

When switch A is operated and released, whichever lamp is on will go out and the other lamp will light. This circuit is basically the counter circuit which is discussed in Section 5. Remember that it is only an electrical model of the mechanical memory mechanism in the headlight system.

This experiment is rather long and can be divided into two parts. The first part, Questions 1-8, deals with the use of relays in memory circuits (stable) and vibrating circuits (unstable). The second part, Questions 9-13, shows how to control and channel information in and out of memory units.

Equipment:

One LCB and one A.C. outlet for each lab group

Answers to Questions:

*1. When switch A is operated, $L1$ is lighted, for switch A is in series with relay P. When switch A is operated, the relay is energized and completes the circuit to $L1$.

*2. When switch B is operated, $L2$ goes off. Switch B is in parallel with the coil of relay Q. When B is operated, the relay coil is shorted, current bypasses the coil, and the relay is deenergized, thus the make contacts of Q are open.

*3.

A	P	L1		B	Q	L2
0	0	0		0	1	1
1	1	1		1	0	0
	(a)				(b)	

*4. When A is operated, $L1$ is lighted and remains lighted regardless of any subsequent changes in the state of switch A. The initial operation of switch A causes relay P to operate and the make contacts (p) then "hold" the circuit in the operated condition.

*5,*6. The circuit of figure 5a buzzes faster than that of figure 5b, for when P is operated the current through the relay coil is reduced to zero and the spring then pulls the armature back, establishing a complete path through the coil once more. When relay Q is operated, a short circuit is completed across the coil. Current can pass through the coil or bypass the coil. Insufficient current passes through the coil to keep it in the operated state. Thus the make contacts of Q open, the short circuit is removed, and the coil is again operated. In figure 5b the current through the coil is never reduced to zero, thus the armature is released more slowly.

*7. Figure 6 represents an unstable arrangement. When power is not available, all relays are in the unoperated state. When power is turned on, relay P is operated, for a complete path from (−) to (+) exists through the break contacts of relay S. As soon as P is operated, Q is operated. Q in turn operates R and R operates S. When S operates, the path through P is broken, P goes to the unoperated state, followed by Q, R, and S. The cycle then repeats, for when S goes to the unoperated state, relay P is operated, etc.

*8. When the circuit of Fig. 6 is changed by replacing the $\bar{s}$ control with an s make contact, the circuit is stable. It is, however, in the off position. All relays are unoperated. If the student momentarily touches the OP of relay S with the end of a wire from Neg, he will hear a series of clicks as the relays P, Q, R, and S snap to and remain in the operated state. Thus the circuit as shown is definitely stable.

*9. Neg, $P1c$; Neg, $A1c$; $A1m$, $B2c$, Pop, $P1m$; $B2b$, $L1$; Neg, $B1c$; $B1m$, Psb.

*10. When switch A is released, $L1$ remains lighted.

*11. "Zeros" dominate "ones" in this circuit, for switch B provides a path with less resistance between negative and positive.

*12. When switch B is operated, $L1$ will glow. This is commonly known as a sneak path.

*13. The address of the cell using relay R is 10; of the cell using S is 11.

Running List for 4 × 1 Memory:

Neg, $B1c$, $A1c$, $P1c$, $Q1c$, $R1c$, $S1c$; $B1m$, $C2c$; $C2b$, $D3c$; $C2m$, $D4c$; $D3b$, Psb; $D3m$, Qsb; $D4b$, Rsb; $D4m$, Ssb; $A1m$, $B2b$, $C1c$; $B2c$, $L1$; $C1b$, $D1c$; $C1m$, $D2c$; $D1b$, $P1m$, Pop; $D1m$, $Q1m$, Qop; $D2b$, $R1m$, Rop; $D2m$, $S1m$, Sop.

II. The Shift Register

This experiment should accompany the study of shifting. Section 4 discusses this topic in detail. This experiment is vital to the study of Section 4, because some pupils may find difficulty in analyzing the circuit diagrams and visualizing the changes caused by input pulses. Here the pupil has an opportunity to observe the changes in the states of the relays. To permit individual students to observe the effects on the 2 stages of the shift register circuit of Fig. 10 (Text page 589), two pupils can work on one LCB. While the first pupil is using relays P and Q, the second pupil can use R and S.

To permit this and to reduce student interaction, the following changes should be made in the circuit of Fig. 10.

Shift Register (Pupil A)

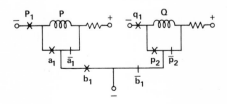

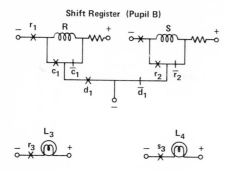

Shift Register (Pupil B)

The state of switches A and C determines whether "1's" or "0's" are stored at P and R respectively. The shifting of stored information takes place with the operation of switches B and D.

Equipment:

One LCB and one A.C. outlet for each student group

Answers to Questions:

*6. Running list for 2-stage shift register: Neg, A3c, P1c, Q1c, Q3c, R1c, S1c, S3c, D2c, D1c; D1m, A1c; D1b, P2c; D2m, Q2c; D2b, R2c; A1m, P1m, Pop; A1b, Psh; P2m, Q1m, Qop; P2b, Qsh; Q2m, R1m, Rop; Q2b, Rsh; R2m, S1m, Sop; R2b, Ssh; A3m, L_1; Q3m, L_2; S3m, L_3.

Switch A is the input and switch D is the shift control. One on-off cycle of D causes information to move one stage to the right from A to Q to S in that order. By changing A when D is off, you can determine whether "0"'s or "1"'s are shifted into the register.

*7. The 4-stage shift register should be assigned to only those students who show interest, and these students should do the work outside of the normal laboratory periods. In other words, this assignment is optional.

III. The Counter Circuit

This experiment should be used with Section 5. The LCB circuit will help to get across the concept of how a machine can be wired to count.

Equipment:

One LCB and one A.C. outlet for each lab group

Answer to Question:

*1.

Switch "A"	0	1	0	1	0	1	0	1	0	1	0	1	0
Relay "P"	0	1	1	0	0	1	1	0	0	1	1	0	0
Relay "Q"	0	0	1	1	0	0	1	1	0	0	1	1	0
Relay "R"	0	0	1	1	1	1	0	0	0	0	1	1	1
Relay "S"	0	0	0	0	1	1	1	0	0	0	0	1
Lamp 4	0	0	1	1	0	0	1	1	0	0	1	1	0
Lamp 3	0	0	0	0	1	1	1	1	0	0	0	0	1

Remember, operating switch A on and off constitutes a count of 1.

IV. An Automatic Morse Code Transmitter

Section 6 explains how a computer decodes instructions. A Morse Code Transmitter is used as an illustration of the control unit of a computer. This experiment illustrates the development of circuits to perform a specific task and enables the pupil to duplicate the circuit and observe its operation.

The effect of the dot and dash readout lamps may be made more dramatic by having the pupils connect a jumper wire from $L3$ to $L4$. A square of masking tape attached to the top of $L2$ and a strip of masking tape with the ends attached to $L3$ and $L4$ heighten the effectiveness of the dot and dash readouts.

Equipment:

One LCB and one A.C. outlet for each lab group

Answers to Questions:

To extend the Morse Code Transmitter to accept 26 letters would require:

*1. 5 input code switches

*2. The counter circuit would remain unchanged. Only 2 stages are required.

*3. The number of readout lamps remains as a starter lamp, a dot lamp, and a dash lamp. However, the circuitry of the dot-dash network becomes more complex, since 5 input switches are needed.

E | EVALUATION

The questions in this section are rated according to the chapter objectives and the performance levels stated in the introduction to the teacher's manual. This group of questions is not intended to be all inclusive, but just as a guide to possible questions. Zeros in the chapter objective column indicate no chapter objective for this question.

Chapter Objective	Performance Level	*Judged to be Relatively Easy:*
		1. In each of the following cases, mark the statement *T* if it is true, but mark it *F* if it is false.
1	I	a) When discussing circuits, we use the word "memory" to mean that past events may affect the future behavior of the circuit.
1	I	b) If memory is incorporated into a circuit, it does not qualify as a logic circuit.
4	I	c) If you push the call button of an automatic elevator but it goes to the ground floor instead of coming to yours, it is not necessary to push the button again.
4	I	d) Some "hall lights" can be turned on or off from more than 2 switches. Memory circuits are always needed to make this possible.
4	I	e) Dialing a telephone number is made possible by the existence of memory circuits.
2	I	f) A relay which has memory controls only its own circuit.
0	I	g) A table of combinations completely describes the state of a network only if the elements of the network are binary in their behavior.
4	I	h) When a memory element which controls another circuit keeps it unchanged, we say the control is done by a "holding contact."
4	I	i) In this diagram of a relay with memory, *"a"* is the input contact and *"b"* is the output contact.

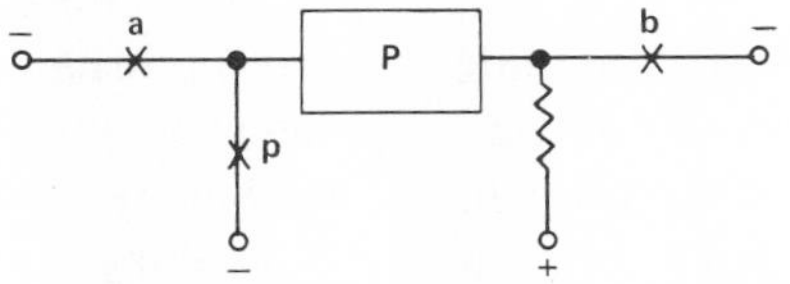

4	I	j) In the diagram for *i*, if switch *A* has been operated once, it can be turned off again without releasing *P*.
4	I	k) In the same diagram, the relay cannot be operated by any action of the switch *B*.
0	I	l) One reason why relays are not used for memories in large computers is that they require too much power.
5	I	m) The number of memory cells that can be addressed in a computer depends on the number of switches used in the address tree.
6	I	n) When a "1" is shifted into one end of a shift register, another "1" is always shifted out at the other end.
6	I	o) One stage of a shift register consists of 2 relays, one with memory, the other without memory.
6	I	p) After a shifting operation has been completed, both relays of any given stage of the shift register will be in the same state.
6	I	q) A counter can be used to control an address tree.
7	I	r) All 26 letters of the alphabet could be represented by a binary code expressed by *X, Y,* and *Z,* each occurring as "1" or "0".
6	I	s) A computer could not follow its program without a counter to make operations take place in order.

Chapter Objective	Performance Level	

Judged to be Relatively Easy:

In all the following questions, check the best answer.

2. All of the following make use of some form of memory device EXCEPT:
   a) a thermostat in a house-heating system.
   b) power brakes on a car.
   c) the record changer of a record player.
   d) a control button for street-crossing lights.
   e) an automatic elevator.

Chapter Objective 3, Performance Level II

3. An adder circuit for two binary numbers having 2 digits each
   a) can be automated if relay circuits with memory are used.
   b) is nearly identical with a shift register for 2 digit numbers.
   c) has a built-in circuit enabling it to be reset to any number.
   d) has no need for memory circuits.
   e) actually does not use relays at all.

Chapter Objective 6, Performance Level I

Judged to be More Difficult:

4.

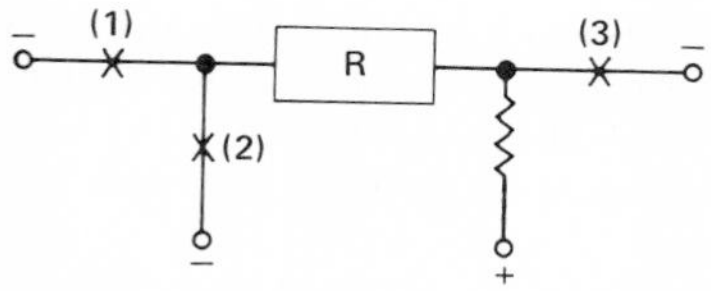

Chapter Objective 4, Performance Level II

The controls in this circuit have been numbered instead of lettered.
   a) To provide R with memory, either (1) or (2) must be controlled by R.
   b) To provide R with memory, (3) must be controlled by R.
   c) To store a "1," operate (1) and (2).
   d) To store a "0," operate (1) but not (2).
   e) This circuit is not suitable for use as a memory.

5.

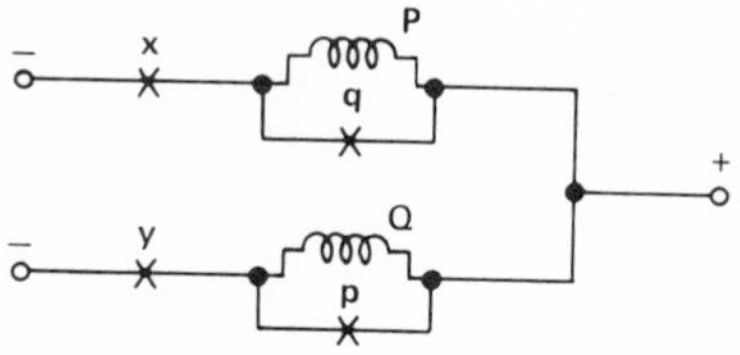

Chapter Objective 4, Performance Level II

These statements refer to the above diagram.
   a) The diagram shows a kind of "double" memory, in which each relay remembers whether the other has been operated.
   b) If switch X is operated, relay P will "latch" in the operated state.
   c) If switch X is operated, it is impossible to operate relay Q by means of switch Y.
   d) If switch Y is operated, relay Q will be shorted and released.
   e) If switch X is operated, relay Q will "latch" in the operated state.

6. These statements refer to the diagram at the top of next page.

   a) To store a "1" in element A, it is necessary to operate switches P and Q and connect point X to +.

   b) To store a "0" in element B, switch P must be operated, Q released, and point Y connected to −.

   c) All cells can be cleared to "0" if point Y is connected to −, switch P is operated, Q is first operated and then released, then P is released.

Chapter Objective 4, Performance Level II

Judged to be More Difficult:

    d) If switches P and Q are operated, point X is in electrical connection with point Y.
    e) If one end of a lamp filament is connected to $-$ and the other end to point X, the lamp will read out all the cells which are storing "1."

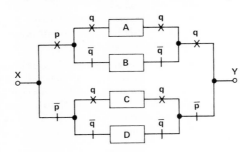

6   II   7. In the system illustrated,
    a) the state of P is determined by whether p or $\bar{p}$ is 1.
    b) P and Q cannot both be in the operated state at the same time.
    c) if Q is released, P can be released by operating A.
    d) if P is released, Q can be released by operating A.
    e) no change in the state of P can occur when A is released.

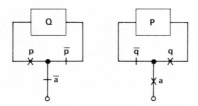

6   II   8.

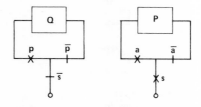

These statements refer to the above diagram.
    a) In order to operate relay P, it is necessary to release A and operate S.
    b) In order to operate relay Q, it is necessary to operate P and release S.
    c) If relay P has operated, Q will release if switch S is released.
    d) The diagram shows 2 stages of a shift register.
    e) The diagram shows 2 stages of a counter.

7   I   9. The "automatic Morse Code Transmitter"
    a) was first used by radio amateurs, then adopted for primitive computers.
    b) could not send all the letters of the alphabet even if modified.
    c) transmits all the letters in turn, once it has been started.
    d) demonstrates how an "op code" can set off a sequence of events.
    e) is entirely unrelated to digital computers.

Answers to Evaluation Questions:

1. a) T   f) F   k) T   p) T
   b) F   g) T   l) T   q) T
   c) T   h) F   m) T   r) F
   d) F   i) F   n) F   s) T
   e) T   j) T   o) F

2. b   6. b

3. d   7. e

4. a   8. b

5. c   9. d

F | FILMS

F-1401 MEMORY DEVICES

Recommendation: Excellent as an introduction to this chapter.

Application: Use the film to illustrate the nature and types of machine memory.

Length and Type: 28 min, color, sound.

Source: #6

Summary: This film explains basic concepts of information storage devices and gives examples of mechanical, electromechanical, magnetic, electrostatic, and photographic memories. It shows how binary information is stored in each of them.

F-1402 "THINKING" MACHINES

Recommendation: Good for limited application.

Application: Enrichment. It can be used to illustrate how a machine "learns" by trial and error.

Length and Type: 20 min, color, sound.

Source: #11

Summary: This film demonstrates approaches and experiments in machine "intelligence." Examples used are a mechanical mouse that learns by trial and error, a chess game against a computer, and a machine that recognizes visual patterns.

F-1403 A COMPUTER GLOSSARY

Recommendation: Good for review of computer terminology.

Application: Film can be used as a summary of computer unit.

Length and Type: 10 min, color, sound.

Source: IBM Film, #2.

Summary: The film defines in basic terms the terminology of computers such as flow chart, Boolean logic, nanosecond, and simulation to give the viewer a better understanding of electronic data processing.

G | GENERAL

I. A Technique for Studying Networks

When discussing in class such networks as that in Fig. 14-4, for example, the following technique will be found very helpful. The networks in question are the kinds in which a sequence of states must be investigated. Copy a sketch of the circuit on the chalkboard with the contacts properly labeled. Relays are conveniently designated by square boxes containing the proper letter. At each spot where contacts are open, the path is broken by a stroke of the eraser, while closed contacts are shown by a continuous chalk line. Changes in the states of the various contacts are swiftly made, and the existence or absence of paths is immediately visible. Of course, it is essential to go over the diagram again with some care every time the state of a switch or relay is changed, to bring the diagram up to date. In some cases it may be a good idea to make a list of contacts by letter and a note of the number of instances of that contact in the diagram. Then you can count, e.g., "4 cases of a and 4 of $\bar{a}$."

II. The Stability of Relays

When we connect the make side of a released relay to minus, action is not instantaneous. In a small fraction of a second the current energizes the coil which magnetizes the core of the relay. Immediately the armature starts to swing toward the operated position. But the mechanical motion requires perhaps a hundredth of a second to complete (the exact rate depending on the strength of the electromagnet, the mass of the armature, and the tension in the spring). Thus there is an appreciable lapse of time between the energizing of the relay and its operation, especially since the mechanical change is much slower than the electrical one. There is a similar transition period between the deenergizing of a relay (when current is interrupted in the coil) and the time when the armature comes to rest and the break contacts are fully closed.

Hence the state of a relay is really not completely represented by the state of its contacts; we need to know as well whether the coil is energized or deenergized. To help keep track of this, we follow the usual convention of using lower-case letters to stand for the make contacts, and 0 or 1 for open or closed. Thus $p = 0$ means make contacts open, relay released; $p = 1$ means make contacts closed, relay operated. We also let capital letters stand for the coils and use 1 or 0 to mean energized or not.

A transition period or time for an armature swing results from the time difference between energizing the coil ($P = 1$) and the operational state of the relay ($p = 1$). That is, a transition follows immediately whenever either (1) $P = 0$ but $p = 1$ (the coil is deenergized but the relay is still operated) or (2) $P = 1$ but $p = 0$ (the coil is energized, but the relay is still released). Whenever the armature is about to move, i.e., a transition is about to occur, the relay is said to be in an *unstable* state.

On the other hand, a stable condition of a relay exists whenever the armature remains at rest. This occurs whenever the state of operation (operated or released) of the relay (p) matches its state of energization (P). That is, a relay is in a stable condition if, and only if,

	(1)	$P = 1$ and $p = 1$,
or	(2)	$P = 0$ and $p = 0$;
i.e.,		$P = p$.

Any relay circuit as a whole is unstable if initially it has a relay in an unstable condition and thereafter it never reaches a stable condition. An example of this is a shunt-controlled buzzer of question 5b. We go through its action as an example of the terminology being used here.

We start with the make contact open. Current starts through the coil, which becomes energized ($P = 1$, $p = 0$, unstable). The unstable condition causes the relay to operate and the make contact to close, thus shunting the relay and deenergizing it ($P = 0$, $p = 1$, unstable). This second unstable condition causes the relay to become released, its make contact to open, and therefore the coil to become energized again ($P = 1$, $p = 0$). But this is the state in which we started. Thus the buzzer, with its repeating cycle, is a typical example of an unstable circuit.

A stable circuit is one which does reach a stable state after passing through, at most, a finite number of unstable conditions. Consider the memory circuit of Fig. 14-1a. If A is operated with B and P initially released ($p = 0$), P becomes energized ($P = 1$, $p = 0$, unstable) so p operates ($P = 1$, $p = 1$, stable). If, on the other hand, A is released, leaving p operated ($p = 1$) and B is then operated, then P is shunted and deenergized ($P = 0$, $p = 1$, unstable), so p releases ($P = 0$, $p = 0$, stable).

In more complicated cases, a properly compiled table of combinations can indicate clearly whether a circuit is stable or unstable. This has been done in the following table for the memory circuit of Fig. 14-1. To construct this table, we first write down the list of the possible states of the contacts. Next we check (in column 4) those cases in which the relay is energized ($a = 1$ OR $p = 1$ or both, AND $b = 0$). The P column is filled out from the preceding, and we then determine the cases in which the relay is in an unstable condition ($p \neq P$). If $p = 1$ but $P = 0$, we know that the relay has been shunted but is not yet released, while if $p = 0$ but $P = 1$, the relay has been energized but is not yet operated. The relay will then change to a state having the same values of a and b (and P), the value of p changing at the same time, to arrive at a state of stability. The arrows beside the diagram indicate the transitions which can occur.

a	b	p	Relay Energized	P	Unstable	Relay State	Transition
0	0	0		0			
0	0	1	v	1			
0	1	0		0			
0	1	1		0	v	Shunted, not yet released	
1	0	0	v	1	v	Energized, not yet operated	
1	0	1	v	1			
1	1	0		0			
1	1	1		0	v	Shunted, not yet released	

We may use the table to learn how a "1" is stored in the memory cell represented by this relay. Let us start with the circuit in the stable state shown in the top row of the table: $a = 0$, $b = 0$, $p = 0$, $P = 0$. The switch A is operated; the circuit temporarily goes into the state $a = 1$, $b = 0$, $p = 0$. Now P becomes 1 because it is energized when A is operated; this state is unstable. The action of the relay itself will cause the next state to be $a = 1$, $b = 0$, $p = 1$; this state is stable. If switch A is released again, the stable state $a = 0$, $b = 0$, and $p = 1$ will result. The momentary operation of switch A has stored a "1" in the relay. To change the state of contacts on the relay it was first necessary to put the circuit into an unstable condition; then the unstable condition caused the relay to change its state of operation.

Looking at a completed table of combinations, we can see immediately whether the corresponding circuit as a whole is stable or unstable. If all unstable conditions lead to other unstable ones, as in the case of the buzzer, the circuit is unstable. If, however, each unstable condition leads eventually to a stable one, as in the table derived in column 1, the circuit is stable.

We can apply these principles as we analyze the action of a counter stage in finer detail than was given in the text. In the table below, the P and Q columns are derived by inspecting Fig. 14-12b. There it can be seen that it is always true that $P = 0$ if $a = 0$ unless $p = 1$ (which means that P was already operated). It is always true that $P = 1$ if $a = 1$ unless $q = 1$ (which shorts the break side of P). Moreover, $Q = 0$ if $a = 0$ unless $p = 1$ (when Q operates) or if $a = 1$ unless $q = 1$ (which means that Q was already operated). It is easier to split the table into 2 segments, one for each relay. The un-

a	p	q	P
0	0	0	0
0	0	1	0
0	1	0	1
0	1	1	1
1	0	0	1*
1	0	1	0
1	1	0	1
1	1	1	0*

a	p	q	Q
0	0	0	0
0	0	1	0*
0	1	0	1*
0	1	1	1
1	0	0	0
1	0	1	1
1	1	0	0
1	1	1	1

stable cases are marked with asterisks, and the transition arrows are marked. We may look at row 1 0 0 (A operated, P and Q released). Since A is operated and Q released, P is energized but not operated (unstable). The resulting transition to row 1 1 0 leaves the circuit in a stable state.

III. Multiplication Using the Shift Register

We write down the product, $M \times N$, of (decimal) 27 × 23 in the following manner. The first product, 3 × 27, is straightforward; but since $23 = 2 \cdot 10^1 + 3 \cdot 10^0$, the second product is really 20 × 27, and so is shifted to the left one space to make room for the final 0.

Weights		10	1	
M		2	7	
N		2	3	
		8	1	$= 3 \cdot 1 \cdot (27)$
	5	4	(0)	$= 2 \cdot 10 \cdot (27)$
	6	2	1	

	512	256	128	64	32	16	8	4	2	1	
Weights	512	256	128	64	32	16	8	4	2	1	
$M = 27$:						1	1	0	1	1	
$N = 23$:						1	0	1	1	1	
Initial partial sum:						0	0	0	0	0	
						+1	1	0	1	1	= 1·1 (M)
First partial sum:						1	1	0	1	1	
					+1	1	0	1	1	(0)	= 1·2 (M)
Second partial sum:				1	0	1	0	0	0	1	
				+1	1	0	1	1	(0	0)	= 1·4 (M)
Third partial sum:			1	0	1	1	1	1	0	1	
			+0	0	0	0	0	(0	0	0)	= 0·8 (M)
Fourth partial sum:			1	0	1	1	1	1	0	1	
		+1	1	0	1	1	(0	0	0	0)	= 1·16 (M)
Final sum:	1	0	0	1	1	0	1	1	0	1	= 621

Of course, if the multiplier had been 234, we should have had 4·1 × (27) + 3·10 × (27) (shift one space) + 2·100 × (27) (shift 2 spaces); and so on for larger multipliers. The last step, finding the sum, needs no comment.

A binary multiplication works on exactly the same multiply, shift, and add basis, but with the multiplication step even easier, because $0 \cdot M = 0$, and $1 \cdot M = M$. However, when the multiplier has more than 2 digits, the addition that terminates the process becomes clumsy. This is especially true in a computer, which is commonly programmed to find the sum of only 2 numbers, so it is usual to employ a slightly different process, called partial sums. The method is illustrated above. In this example of a 5-digit multiplier there are 5 product numbers to be added together, but first 2 are added, then another is added to this sum, and so on, rather than all 5 simultaneously. Thus there are 4 partial sums, each the result of adding to the previous partial sum a shifted version of M multiplied by the appropriate one digit of N. The shifting is accomplished, of course, by means of a shift register.

IV. Preliminary Comment on the Counter Circuit

It has been suggested that with circuits which are based on "flip-flop" action (counters, shifters), there should be an initial discussion of the switch as a pulsing unit. Then the student should have no difficulty in understanding the operation of the relay counter and the like. The following method of development proves useful.

1. Develop the concept that "pulses" are being "counted." The movement of the switch merely permits the production of a series of square electrical pulses: zero voltage when the switch is open and 15 volts when the switch is closed.

2. The single-stage counter consists of two relays which operate alternately so that the equivalent of two pulses are required before either of these relays goes through a cycle of "operate-release." If one of these relays controls a lamp, then each time the lamp glows, 2 pulses have occurred. If the lamp is replaced by another stage of "flip-flop," then 4 initial pulses will be required to produce one complete pulse at the final stage.

3. The following sketch illustrates a simplified version of the counter that many find easier to use in the classroom.

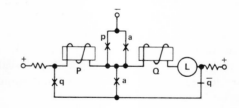

With contacts q and $\bar{q}$ in the unoperated state the closure of manually controlled contact $\bar{a}$ can operate only coil P since coil Q will be short-circuited ($\bar{q}$ and a). Coil P will be latched by operation of contact p.

4. Opening contacts a removes the short circuit across coil Q, so that both P and Q are operated. Coil Q immediately acts on q and $\bar{q}$ to reverse their initial state.

5. The second closure of the contacts a, coupled with the closed state of contact q, will now produce a short circuit across P. The latching contact p is thus released and power to Q flows only through a.

6. When the a contacts are opened for the second time, all power is removed and Q returns to its initial state with the lamp L extinguished.

7. Thus for every 2 square waves at a, only one count is indicated by the blinking lamp.

V. The Combination Lock: A Circuit for Fun

This circuit was designed for the early versions of the LCB, but may be wired up on 2 new boards in parallel, or will fit the new boards individually if the last stage (using relay S) is omitted and the lamp is wired in series with the contact r in the fourth stage down. Contact $\bar{r}$ is obviously to be omitted in this case.

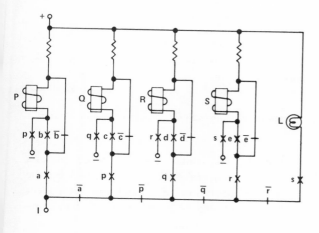

To solve the combination, work from the right. We see (using the diagram as presented) that L will light if switch A and relays P, Q, and R are not operated but S is operated. But S operates only when R and switch E operate. However, this closes its holding contact s, after which r may be opened (and $\bar{r}$ closed) by releasing R. R releases if q and $\bar{d}$ are closed. A pattern now emerges: a relay is operated when the preceding relay and the appropriate switch are operated, then holds until that switch is released. So one can now start at the top:

Operate A, operate B (operating P), release A, operate C (operating Q), release B (releasing P), operate D (operating R), release C (releasing Q), operate E (operating S), release D (releasing R), and the lamp lights to symbolize opening of the lock. When E is released (releasing S), the lock light goes out and the circuit is back where we started.

VI. Sensing Direction of Rotation

For the most part, we want to illustrate examples of feedback logic circuits which are the same as or similar in principle to circuits which are used in actual digital computers. It is natural that important applications of them can be found in the processing of numbers because much of the information about the world around us can be represented in numerical form. However, logic circuits are useful in many problems for which it would be unnatural to think in numerical terms. The example which follows is one of these.

The end view of a rotatable cylindrical shaft is shown below. Half of it is made of an insulating

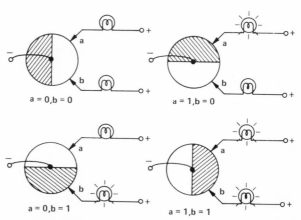

A cylinder with a direction of rotation which is to be determined

material (unshaded) and the other half of a conducting material (shaded) which is connected to the − side of a battery. There are 2 wires which have ends resting upon the surface of the cylinder and the two contacts formed will be called a and b. Each of these contacts is in series with a lamp which lights when (and only when) its contact is closed. As the cylinder rotates, the pair of lamps will be lighted in one of the 4 patterns shown.

By looking at the lamps, it is possible to tell in which direction the cylinder is rotating without actually seeing the cylinder itself. For instance, if the sequence of observations corresponds to···01 (that is, $a = 0$ and $b = 1$), 00, 10, 11, 01, 00··· it is clear from the diagrams that the cylinder is rotating clockwise. The sequence···11, 10, 00, 01, 11, 10··· on the other hand is indicative of counterclockwise rotation. If a human being were to observe the lights and announce correctly the direction of rotation, it would be natural to conclude that he had the capability of reasoning deductively. We shall demonstrate a feedback logic circuit which does the same thing by "looking" at the contacts a and b. We shall leave it to the reader to determine for himself whether it is the circuit which reasons, or whether the human being who designed the circuit did the reasoning.

Our circuit (below) should be considered in two parts; the operation of the first (with the relays P and Q) is independent of that of the second. Whenever the 2 contacts a and b are open, there can be no path for current to the relays P and Q and they must both be unoperated. We shall assume this situation as the starting point for our analysis and consider what happens when the cylinder is rotating clockwise. Initially, the contacts p and q are open and the contacts $\overline{p}$ and $\overline{q}$ are closed.

This initial situation is shown in schematic form below. The heavy lines indicate contacts which are closed and the dashed lines, contacts which are open. Since there are no paths completed to either the P relay or the Q relay, neither will be operated.

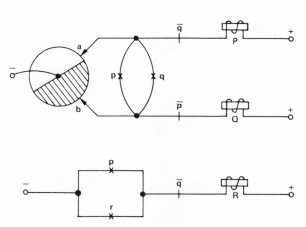

Detailed circuit analysis for clockwise cylinder rotation

Step 1: The contact a closes and completes a path to P. This is followed by the operation of P and the subsequent closing of p and opening of $\overline{p}$. Q remains unoperated.

Step 2: The contact b closes. P remains operated and Q remains unoperated.

Step 3: The contact a opens. P remains operated and Q remains unoperated.

Direction-of-rotation sensing circuit

Step 4: The contact b opens and the path to P is removed. This is followed by the release of P and the subsequent opening of p and closing of $\bar{p}$.

At the end of Step 4, the initial situation again prevails.

During the steps in the diagram, the Q relay never operated and the relay P changed from the unoperated state to the operated state and back again. If the cylinder had been rotating counterclockwise rather than clockwise, the situation would have been reversed; the P relay would never have operated and the relay Q would change from the unoperated state to the operated state and back again. Therefore, if the cylinder is rotating continuously clockwise, the P relay is the only one which ever operates, and if the cylinder is rotating continuously counterclockwise, the Q relay is the only one which ever operates. If each of the relays P and Q has a lamp connected in parallel with its coil, the identity of the lighted lamp will establish the direction of rotation.

Even when the cylinder rotates continuously in one direction, the relay which operates is not operated continuously. Therefore, the appropriate lamp would flash on and off with a frequency which is the same as the frequency of rotation of the cylinder. If it is desirable for a lamp always to be on when the rotation is clockwise and off when the rotation is counterclockwise, then it should be connected in parallel with the coil of the R relay in the diagram in column 1, opposite page. The added relay remembers whether it was the P or Q relay which was operated last and thus also the direction of rotation.

A MINIMICRO COMPUTER

APPROX. TIME: Text: 7 Days   Lab.: 1 Day

A. APPROACH	CLASS PERIODS	B. BLACK & WHITE TRANSPAR-ENCIES	C. CUES (k = key problems) Discussion Questions	Easy	Medium	Hard	D. DEMON-STRATIONS, LABS & PROJECTS	E. EVALU-TION	F. FILMS	G. GENERAL
1. Introduction	1	1501						1	1501	
2. Transferring Binary Information Between Components (Copying)	3	1502 1503a,b 1504 1505	7		2			2		
3. Input, Output, and Memory					3			3,4,5		
4. Arithmetic Unit	1	1506 1507 1508	5				—	6		
5. Instruction Cycle and Control Unit	1		1,2,3,4, 6,8	1k	4,5k			7,8	1502	II, III
6. Final Comment	1									

A Minimicro Computer
15

A | APPROACH

I. Purpose and Organization of the Chapter

In the Teacher's Manual for Chapter 10 it was mentioned that our aim in these last six chapters is to find out what a computer is, how it can be programmed, what switching circuits are typically found in it, and lastly, how these are combined to form a general-purpose computer. Now, to end the course, we have arrived at that ultimate stage.

This chapter has one preliminary duty, namely, to explain how information is transferred or copied from one part of a computer to another. It then repeats part of Chapter 10 but with a new focus: not merely the names and duties of the major components of a computer, but also the manner in which the switching and memory circuits, by now familiar, perform those duties.

II. Objectives for Students

Upon completion of the activities, discussion, and reading in this chapter, students should be able to:

1. Recognize, identify, and interpret the term *general-purpose computer*.

2. Demonstrate (by construction and operation, using an LCB) how to transfer information from one relay to another, and thus justify the statement "bits don't move."

3. Code signed binary numbers on punched cards.

4. Illustrate how a card reader is used to enter data in a computer, and how a computer discloses data with a card punch.

5. Interpret the organization of computer memory, with special reference to storage and retrieval of data.

6. Formulate the method used to add several numbers in an accumulator.

7. Interpret operation codes by reference to the circuits activated by each.

8. Describe the operating cycle of a computer, and the various circuits employed.

9. Infer the effectiveness of computers from knowledge of their structural relationships.

10. Explain, using examples, the slow growth of computers from their origins to their current stage of development.

III. Suggestions for Teaching

In Chapter 10, Sections 4, 5, and 6, especially the last, there was a fairly general description of the structure of a digital computer. It will be wise to review these sections before embarking on Chapter 15, which explains how this structure is built by use of the switching circuits discussed in the last three chapters. Clearly, reviews of these individual circuits are very important at particular stages of this chapter, and reminders are included in the suggestions which follow.

Section 1. Introduction. There are two important ideas here. First is the reminder that the circuits we have been studying are the real thing (granting the differences among hand-operated switches, relays, and their solid-state equivalents). They are so simple and so easy to comprehend that they seem trivial alongside a commercially built computer, but the latter is essentially only clusters of many copies of the simple circuits. Second is that the computer's importance stems not from its numerous circuit copies but from their organization, from the switching arrangements that enable them to be interconnected in an almost endless number of ways, at the programmer's pleasure and at the direction of the programs which he writes. Thus the "minimicro" computer, despite its minuscule size, is a real general-purpose computer.

Section 2. Transferring Binary Information Between Components (Copying). This section needs time and care. In Chapter 10 we read about the early computer called ENIAC and the need to rewire its program board for every new task. The ability to transfer information, to set one relay by electrical means so that its state is identical with that of another, is what made von Neumann's invention of stored programs feasible. Somehow it leaves a strong smell of black magic in the nostrils of the layman, and we cannot overrate the importance of completely eliminating any thought of hocus-pocus from your students' minds. Review Chapter 14, Sections 2 ("The Basic Memory Relay Element") and 4 ("Shifting and Shift Registers"), as well as the corresponding LCB exercises (Labs I and III), and be sure that students recall that a single relay may be used in many circuits at once by means of multiple contacts. If this reminder is not made, the simplified diagrams of a textbook may (even this late in the year) leave them feeling that relay P_1 of a shift register has nothing else to do than set or clear Q_1, which may not be true at all. Even when a relay is not used directly in another circuit, it may control a relay which is. Be sure that they are happy with the idea that a relay in the accumulator, for instance, can be set to the same state as that of a relay in a distant memory cell. Contacts p and $\bar{p}$ of the memory relay can be connected with the 1 and 0 sides of the accumulator relay involved by means of lengthy wires, if necessary, switched into the circuit by Control.

Notice that when method (*b*) of Fig. 15-2 (T-1501) requires that we connect only the *make* side of relay Q to minus, this is because releasing the relay first is equivalent to storing a 0 in it; only if P is at 1 is contact p operated and thus also Q. The card reader (Chapter 13, Lab V) can also be used to illustrate the main idea (copying) of this section.

Section 3. Input, Output, and Memory. (Input) (T-1502). Students who have little experience with electricity may need to have the nature of parallel circuits explained again specifically, so that they understand clearly that the drum with its negative charge can supply electrical energy to all 13 circuits at once if necessary. Here it may be helpful to return briefly to T-1001, depicting a 6-bit code for alphanumeric characters, as well as Chapter 10, GII ("Error Detection and Correction") for check digits, a device that could also be used to supply one of the 13 digits prescribed for our minimicro computer. Another reminder: Section 6 of Chapter 10 describes several other kinds of input and output, often extremely useful though requiring very fancy programming of computers with huge memories. Possibly your school uses IBM cards for recording grades. If so, you can easily pass out copies for comparison with Fig. 10-5, and you can also arrange to have the class see the card punch and card reader in operation. *(Output)* If the card reader is clear, the card punch should cause no trouble. *(Memory)* Before starting the class discussion of this topic, be sure to review Fig. 14-1 or Lab I, Chapter 14 (the basic memory circuit), as well as Fig. 13-10 or Lab IV, Chapter 13 ("Tree Circuits"). T-1503a (same as Fig. 15-5) may help here, and the discussion of different types of memory in Section 6, Chapter 10, should not be forgotten. *(Input and Output Connected to Memory)* In showing how memory can be connected to input and output, you will find an overlay, T-1503b, that changes Fig. 15-5 (as shown in T-1503a) into Fig. 15-7. See also T-1504 (Fig.

15-6). Right here some students will find it sticky going. Even though they grasp each detail, they find it hard to keep all details in mind at once. Specifically, the source of their confusion seems to be that while every digit in a given 13-bit number has the same address, the digits themselves are *not* the same. The address contacts are therefore all set at the same time by the same switches (or relays); the proper base of the address tree (X or Y, T-1503a, for 1 or 0) is set to $-$ for each individual digit, without regard to its neighbors, according to the punched or unpunched condition of the spot on the card that governs the digit. This is all in the textbook, of course, but something is left to the imagination in the diagrams. Therefore we include T-1505 (taken from an earlier form of the text) to emphasize the 13 copies. Notice, by the way, that a $\overline{cp}$ connection is absent for the same reason that in Fig. 15-2(b) there was no need to connect the break side of relay Q to $-$: if a 0 has been stored, no hole is to be punched at that position in the card. But when data are read in, connections have to be provided from the card reader to both the make tree and the break tree. When memory cells are to be connected to the accumulator, the points X and Y are disconnected from card reader and punch (by opening appropriate switch contacts), and other contacts join these points with the accumulator, as described a little later.

Section 4. Arithmetic Unit.

For the adder, review Fig. 13-7 (or Lab II, Chapter 13), and for the reason that the sign bits are needed, Section 4 in the same chapter; also see Section G, Part IV in Chapter 13 for a flow diagram on adding and subtracting. The three registers in the accumulator (Fig. 15-8, T-1506) make possible addition by the method described in the text. The number already in the S register, even if it is zero, is transferred to the A register (clearing S in the process); the number to be added is transferred to the B register by clearing the relays of that register and connecting each one through a "copy" switch with the proper X base of the address tree (the Y base need not be connected because of the preliminary clearing). If necessary, go through the routine a little more explicitly: relay B_1 of the accumulator connects with X of copy 1 in the memory cell, relay B_2 with X of copy 2, etc.

Then A and B are added and the sum turns up in S, where we want it. And so for every number that must be added in. Observe that the preliminary transfer from S to A is not suggested in Fig. 15-8. Those of you who have taught *The Man-Made World* in the past will note that numerous details have been omitted in this edition of the text. These details, mostly having to do with the minutiae of the accumulator's operation, should *not* be resurrected for the classroom.

Section 5. Instruction Cycle and Control Unit.

Review Fig. 14-18; also the resettable counter (Fig. 14-12 through 16, and Lab II of Chapter 14); the circuit to compare two numbers (Fig. 13-9), since op code 3 ("test accumulator contents") requires this scheme to carry out the test, but of course with the switches set by relays; and finally, the Morse coder, especially Figs. 14-22 and 14-25 (Lab IV). The details of the cycle have already been met in Chapter 10, and overhead master T-1011a with its three overlays carry out a cycle which differs from that in this chapter only in the memory cells used and the number to be added to the accumulator (though the way the machine is symbolized in the block diagram is a little different). Therefore it has seemed needless to supply masters for Figs. 15-11 through 15-14. In explaining what the Morse coder is doing, remind the class that the operator of the LCB pulsed the control switch on and off for each step in the mock transmission of the alphabet. In a real computer an oscillator circuit supplies a rapid sequence of timed pulses which serve the same kind of function, operating the various relays in proper order to produce the programmed result. "A computer play" (Section G, Part II) is an interesting way of summarizing the study of computer organization.

Section 6. Final Comment.

There is a wide-open opportunity here for one or more closing sessions of the greatest importance. Students will be quick to notice the similarity between organic evolution and technological evolution; in each case a selection process occurs. In the world of nature there has been a tendency for successful races to evolve in the direction of greater size and complexity, leading to the extinction of some. Among computers, on the other hand, size has been going down as flexibility, speed, and complexity have increased. There is plenty of room for half-baked philosophizing; but is there a real analogy? A more fruitful line for discussion is the often-repeated "It can be done, hence it must be done." Must it? Or must "it" be scrutinized in the light of what is genuinely beneficial? If people decide that some "advance" is in fact a retreat, how do they take steps to block it? How can "people who are informed about both computers and humanity" in fact go about controlling technology and (what is evidently the real problem) the people who misuse it? In these days of political activism do we dare hope that enough people will work hard enough and long enough, at a task that will often seem hopeless, to be successful in saving a world worth living in, and in giving everyone a fair shake at enjoying it?

B I BLACK AND WHITE TRANSPARENCIES

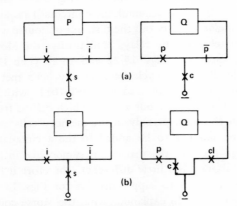

T-1501 SETTING *P*, COPYING ONTO *Q*

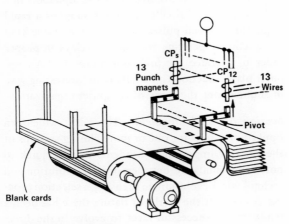

T-1502   CARD PUNCH

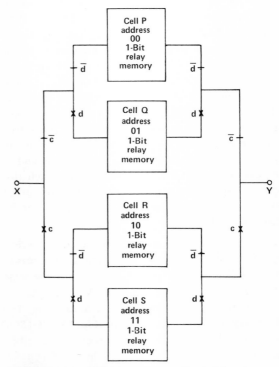

T-1503a 4-CELL ADDRESSABLE MEMORY

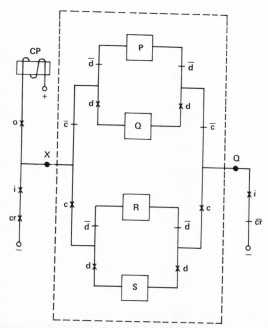

T-1503b CARD PUNCH AND READER CONNECTIONS

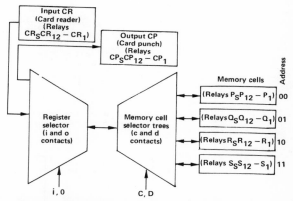

T-1504 INPUT AND OUTPUT CONNECTED TO MEMORY (BLOCK DIAGRAM)

372

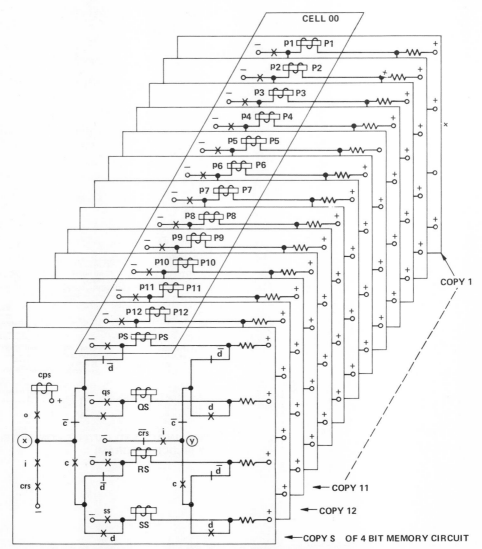

T-1505 CARD READER AND CARD PUNCH CONNECTED TO MEMORY

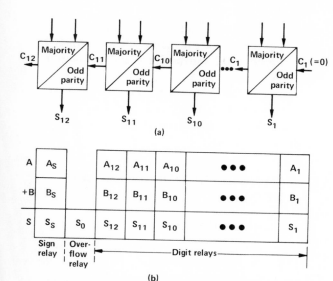

(a)

(b)

T-1506 SYMBOLIC REPRESENTATIONS, BINARY ADDER

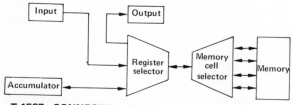

T-1507 CONNECTED INPUT, OUTPUT, ACCUMULATOR, AND MEMORY

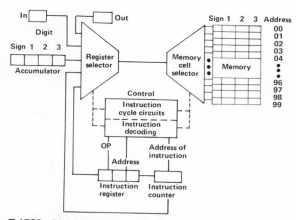

T-1508 BLOCK DIAGRAM OF 3-DECIMAL DIGITS COMPUTER

C | CUES TO QUESTIONS AND PROBLEMS

Questions for Study and Discussion

1. The program counter keeps track of the address of the instruction to be fetched next. The address part of the relevant instruction has a dual purpose (depending on the type of instruction). It may be treated as the address where data for executing an instruction are to be found; or it may be treated as the address to jump to if the instruction is a test (conditional jump) or if the instruction is an unconditional jump.

2. The instruction register is used during the fetch step (Step I) of the instruction cycle. At this time a copy of the *contents* of the current address in the program counter is placed into the instruction register. The current instruction is decoded during Step III of the instruction cycle by Control. Basically, the instruction register merely transfers the information from memory to Control. This transfer is made possible by the IR relays which affect the operation of the decoder circuits.

3. *Step I* Fetch copy of instruction from memory via the register selector to the instruction register (instruction is stored as settings on the IR relays). CARDIAC equivalent—move slides to agree with contents of bug's cell.

Step II Increment the program counter which prepares the machine for Step I of the next cycle. CARDIAC equivalent—move bug ahead one cell.

Step III Decode and execute instruction. The settings of the IR relays control contact networks in the decoder. In essence this decodes the instruction stored in the IR relays. The decoder contact networks in turn control relays in the register selector, which makes execution of instructions possible. CARDIAC equivalent—read instructions in upper window and perform the task as instructed.

4. The execution of an instruction takes place after the instruction decoder section of Control has decoded the instruction from the instruction register. This process of decoding is discussed in the answer to Question 3. The clock pulses, together with the appropriate contact networks (depending on the

instruction) in the decoder, trigger relays in proper order for the execution of the instruction.

5. No, the shift register is used for multiplying. When adding, the majority circuit (adding individual digits) and the odd-parity circuit (carrying digits) are used.

6. No, as far as machine operation is concerned. There may be a possible advantage for the person who programs in machine code.

7. The basic difference between a card reader and a card punch is that one senses data from cards while the other produces data on cards. Since they have different functions, it is not practical to combine them.

8. None of the parts can be eliminated. They are all essential to operation of the computer.

Problems

1. a) The program counter is incremented once.
   b) The instruction register is changed once.
2. Compare Fig. 15-2.

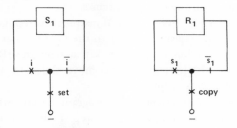

And so on for S_2, R_2, etc.

3.

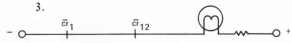

4. Having −003 in address 01 of Fig. 15-13 will change the output but not the program. −602 at address 05 would not change the program if 602 is to be treated as an instruction. The negative only applies when the information at an address is to be treated as data. Therefore we could not predict the effects of the negative sign without knowing in what program these words were to be used.

5. The sequence of operations as described would be no different except for the substitution of an op code "7" in place of "2" wherever the latter occurs, an obvious change in the interpretation of

the op code, and since subtraction replaces addition the contents of the accumulator will become −003.

Step I Fetch instruction at address 04 to instruction register.

Step II Increment instruction counter to 05.

Step III Decode 701 and execute instruction (subtract the word at address 01 from the contents of the accumulator).

D | DEMONSTRATIONS, LABS, AND PROJECTS

I. A Minimicro Computer

This experiment is the culmination of the study of logic circuits. It allows students to see how the combination of simple logic circuits can result in a computer which has all the characteristics of a "real" computer.

Unless you have a class of students who are all very interested in the hardware aspect of digital computers, this activity is best done by a group of students who are interested. These students should be encouraged to build the minimicro computer outside of the regular class periods. When they have completed the wiring, they should demonstrate its operation to the rest of the class. Remember, the important thing is the operation of the device and not its construction.

Equipment:

10 LCB's and 10 A.C. outlets

Comments on the construction of the computer:

1. Make sure that students check the operation of each section of the computer before proceeding to the next section.

2. Remember that the circuits used in the computer use relay contacts instead of manual switch contacts of circuits studied earlier in the course.

3. The following pages contain the running list and wiring procedure for the minimicro computer.

MINIMICRO COMPUTER

In the following circuits, "K" is a convenience "Negative" controlled by relay P_A, which in turn is operated only when relays Q_A, R_A, and S_A are simultaneously operated. Step 11 below may be omitted until Part B if desired. Part A will require boards U, V, and W.

PART A

1. Neg U, Neg V; Neg V, Neg W;
2. b$_{1v}$com, b$_{1w}$com;
3. b$_{1v}$com, b$_{2v}$com; b$_{2v}$com, b$_{3v}$com; b$_{3v}$com, b$_{4v}$com;
4. b$_{1w}$com, b$_{2w}$com; b$_{2w}$com, b$_{3w}$com; b$_{3w}$com, b$_{4w}$com;
5. Neg U, P$_U$op; P$_U$op, Q$_U$op; Q$_U$op, R$_U$op; R$_U$op, S$_U$op:Neg V, P$_V$op;
6. Neg, p$_{1v}$com; p$_{1v}$m, q$_{2v}$com; q$_{2v}$m, P$_U$shunt;
7. Neg, p$_{1u}$com; p$_{1u}$m, Q$_U$shunt;
8. Neg, q$_{1u}$com; q$_{1u}$m, R$_U$shunt;
9. Neg, r$_{1u}$com; r$_{1u}$m, S$_U$shunt;
10. Neg, s$_{1u}$com; s$_{1u}$m, P$_V$shunt.

Another reminder about "K." The "K" referred to in all of the diagrams is located in the B switch section of boards V, W, M, N, X, Y, and Z. If the B switch is unoperated (and it is not used), one is able to use it as a terminal block.

11. b$_{1v}$b, q$_{3a}$c; q$_{3a}$b, r$_{3a}$c; r$_{3a}$m, s$_{3a}$c; s$_{3a}$m, Q$_V$op;
12. b$_{2v}$b, q$_{1v}$c; q$_{1v}$m, Q$_V$op;
13. b$_{3v}$b, q$_{3w}$c; q$_{3w}$m, s$_{4w}$c; s$_{4w}$m, s$_{4v}$c; s$_{4v}$m, Q$_V$shunt;
14. b$_{1v}$b, p$_{2v}$c; p$_{2v}$c, r$_{1v}$m; r$_{1v}$c, R$_V$op; R$_V$op, S$_V$op; r$_{1v}$b, p$_{2v}$m; p$_{2v}$m, s$_{1v}$c; s$_{1v}$b, S$_V$shunt; s$_{1v}$m, R$_V$shunt;
15. b$_{2w}$b, s$_{2w}$c; s$_{2w}$c, p$_{1w}$m; p$_{1w}$c, P$_W$op; P$_W$op, Q$_W$op; p$_{1w}$b, s$_{2w}$m; s$_{2w}$m, q$_{1w}$c; q$_{1w}$b, Q$_W$shunt; q$_{1w}$m, P$_W$shunt;
16. b$_{2v}$b, s$_{2w}$c; b$_{1w}$b, r$_{1w}$m; r$_{1w}$c, R$_W$op; R$_W$op, S$_W$op; r$_{1w}$b, s$_{2v}$m; r$_{1w}$b, s$_{1w}$c; s$_{1w}$b, S$_W$shunt; s$_{1w}$m, R$_W$shunt.

This completes Part A. Testing Part A requires the use of temporary leads which *must* be removed after test. Connect a negative from board V to b$_{4v}$c. Using another single lead, go from b$_{3v}$b on board V to operate terminal of relay Q$_V$. When this final temporary wire is connected, the pulsator circuit should start and the counter circuit should sequence through a complete cycle and halt. Try this two or three times to assure yourself that you have the circuit correct and then remove the temporary leads and start on Part B.

PART B

Part B will require 4 boards, A, I, M, and N, plus the card reader.

1. Neg, p$_{1a}$c; p$_{1a}$c, p$_{2a}$c; p$_{2a}$c, p$_{3a}$c; p$_{3a}$c, p$_{4a}$c;
2. p$_{1a}$b, p$_{2a}$b; p$_{2a}$b, p$_{3a}$b; p$_{3a}$b, p$_{4a}$b; p$_{4a}$b, b$_{1n}$b;
3. b$_{1m}$b, b$_{2m}$b; b$_{2m}$b, b$_{3m}$b; b$_{3m}$b, b$_{4m}$b; b$_{4m}$b, b$_{2w}$b;
4. b$_{1n}$b, b$_{2n}$b; b$_{2n}$b, b$_{3n}$b; b$_{3n}$b, b$_{4n}$b; b$_{4n}$b, b$_{1m}$b;
5. Neg M, Neg N; Neg N, Neg I; Neg I, Neg A; Neg I, Neg CR (Common on "CR" the card reader); Neg I, Neg V;
6. Neg, q$_{4a}$c; q$_{4a}$m, r$_{4a}$c; r$_{4a}$m, s$_{4a}$c; s$_{4a}$m, P$_A$op;
7. CR$_1$, Q$_A$op; CR$_2$, R$_A$op; CR$_3$, S$_A$op; CR$_4$, P$_I$op; CR$_5$, Q$_I$op; CR$_6$, R$_I$op; CR$_7$, S$_I$op;
8. Neg, q$_{1a}$c; q$_{1a}$m, r$_{1a}$c; r$_{1a}$b, s$_{1a}$c; s$_{1a}$m, p$_{1i}$c;
9. P$_{1i}$c, q$_{1i}$c; q$_{1i}$c, r$_{1i}$c; r$_{1i}$c, s$_{1i}$c;
10. p$_{1i}$m, P$_M$op; q$_{1i}$m, Q$_M$op; r$_{1i}$m, R$_M$op; s$_{1i}$m, S$_M$op;
11. b$_{2m}$c, P$_{1m}$c; P$_{1m}$c, q$_{1m}$c; q$_{1m}$c, r$_{1m}$c; r$_{1m}$c, s$_{1m}$c;
12. p$_{1m}$m, P$_M$op; q$_{1m}$m, Q$_M$op; r$_{1m}$m, R$_M$op; s$_{1m}$m, S$_M$op;
13. Neg, q$_{2a}$c; q$_{2a}$m, r$_{2a}$c; r$_{2a}$m, s$_{2a}$c; s$_{2a}$b, p$_{2i}$c; p$_{2i}$c, q$_{2i}$c; q$_{2i}$c, r$_{2i}$c; r$_{2i}$c, s$_{2i}$c;
14. P$_{2i}$m, P$_N$op; q$_{2i}$m, Q$_N$op; r$_{2i}$m, R$_N$op; s$_{2i}$m, S$_N$op;
15. b$_{2n}$c, P$_{1n}$c; P$_{1n}$c, q$_{1n}$c; q$_{1n}$c, r$_{1n}$c; r$_{1n}$c, s$_{1n}$c;
16. p$_{1n}$m, P$_N$op; q$_{1n}$m, Q$_N$op; r$_{1n}$m, R$_N$op; s$_{1n}$m, S$_N$op.

This completes the essential parts of B. To test you may wish to include the readout lamps found on the right-hand side of the schematic for Part D. This will enable you to determine what is stored in memory cells M and N, and also assure you of correct addressing. The lamps are wired as follows:

1. Neg, p$_{4m}$c; p$_{4m}$c, q$_{4m}$c; q$_{4m}$c, r$_{4m}$c; r$_{4m}$c, s$_{4m}$c; p$_{4m}$m, L$_{1m}$; q$_{4m}$m, L$_{2m}$; r$_{4m}$m, L$_{3m}$; s$_{4m}$m, L$_{4m}$;

2.Neg, $p_{4n}c$; $p_{4n}c$, $q_{4n}c$; $q_{4n}c$, $r_{4n}c$; $r_{4n}c$, $s_{4n}c$; $p_{4n}m$, L_{1n}; $q_{4n}m$, L_{2n}; $r_{4n}m$, L_{3n}; $s_{4n}m$, L_{4n}.

You may now test the circuits in the following manner. Holding your special IBM card for the card reader, address memory cell M and enter into it binary "1011." This is accomplished by punching out (from the left) holes number 1, 3, 4, 6, and 7. Placing the card in the reader and pressing the *read* switch, we find the binary value indicated by the lights on board M. Let us then address memory cell N, and enter into it the binary value represented by "1001." This is accomplished by punching out another card in the following manner: from the left, punch out holes number 1, 2, 4, and 7. Once again placing the card in the card reader and pressing the *read* switch, we find the binary value indicated by the lamps on board N. In the above test we are using the first 3 holes as an address and the last 4 as our information. We may further test the computer wired thus far by asking it to halt and reset itself to original state. This is accomplished by punching out holes on another card, numbers 1, 2, and 3. At this time we may also retest Part A of our circuit. Using another IBM card, punch out holes 2 and 3 only. This will actuate the pulsator, run through one cycle and stop. We would then use the card with holes 1, 2, and 3 punched out to remove the temporary negative value "K" and reset the computer to zero.

PART C

Part *C* will require 3 boards labeled *X*, *Y*, and *Z*.

1.$p_{1a}b$, $b_{1x}c$; $b_{1x}c$, $b_{2x}c$; $b_{2x}c$, $b_{3x}c$; $b_{3x}c$, $b_{4x}c$; $b_{4x}c$, $b_{1y}c$;
2.$b_{1y}c$, $b_{2y}c$; $b_{2y}c$, $b_{3y}c$; $b_{3y}c$, $b_{4y}c$; $b_{4y}c$, $b_{1z}c$;
3.$b_{1z}c$, $b_{2z}c$; $b_{2z}c$, $b_{3z}c$; $b_{3z}c$, $b_{4z}c$;
4.Neg X, Neg Y; Neg Y, Neg Z; Neg Z, Neg W.

From this point on we will test each section of the binary adder as we complete it. This will require the use of temporary leads connecting a negative to at least two of the following relays: S_Z, P_Z, Q_Y, R_X, R_Z, S_Y, P_Y, or Q_X. To facilitate the testing process, the following notation will be used: Neg, R_Z,S_Z—which would indicate that a negative should

be connected to R_Z operate and also to S_Z operate. MAKE CERTAIN that all temporary leads are removed immediately following all successful testing.

5.Neg, $r_{1z}c$; $r_{1z}m$, $s_{1z}c$; $s_{1z}m$, $Q_Z$op; $r_{1z}c$, $r_{2z}c$; $r_{2z}m$, $s_{2z}b$; $r_{2z}b$, $s_{2z}m$; $s_{2z}c$, L_{4z}.

TEST: Neg, R_Z, S_Z—Relay Q_Z should then operate. Neg to either R_Z or S_Z but not both and L_{4z} should light.

6.Neg, $s_{1y}c$; $s_{1y}m$, $p_{1z}c$; $p_{1z}c$, $q_{1z}c$; Neg, $p_{2z}c$; $p_{2z}m$, $q_{2z}c$; $p_{1z}m$, $q_{1z}m$; $q_{1z}m$, $q_{2z}m$; $q_{2z}m$, $R_Y$op.

TEST: Neg, S_Y, P_Z—Relay R_Y should operate; also Neg, S_Y,Q_Z—Relay R_Y should operate; also Neg, P_Z, Q_Z—Relay R_Y should operate; finally Neg, S_Y, Q_Z, P_Z—Relay R_Y should operate.

7.Neg, $p_{3z}c$; $p_{3z}m$, $s_{2y}c$; $s_{2y}m$, $q_{3z}m$; $q_{3z}c$, L_{3z}; $p_{3z}b$, $s_{3y}c$; $s_{3y}m$, $q_{3z}b$; $s_{2y}b$, $s_{3y}m$; $s_{3y}b$, $s_{2y}m$.

TEST: Neg, either P_Z or S_Y or Q_Z and L_{3z} should light; also Neg, P_Z, S_Y, Q_Z—L_{3z} should light. Lamp will not operate if 2 relays are actuated at once.

8.Neg, $q_{1y}c$; $q_{1y}c$, $p_{2y}c$; $q_{1y}m$, $p_{1y}c$; $p_{1y}c$, $r_{1y}c$; $p_{2y}m$, $r_{2y}c$; $r_{2y}m$, $r_{1y}m$; $r_{1y}m$, $p_{1y}m$; $p_{1y}m$, S_X op.

TEST: Neg, Q_Y, P_Y—Relay S_X operate. Neg, Q_Y, R_Y—Relay S_X operate. Neg, P_Y, R_Y—Relay S_X operate, and Neg, P_Y, R_Y, Q_Y—S_X operate.

9.Neg, $p_{3y}c$; $p_{3y}m$, $q_{2y}c$; $q_{2y}m$, $r_{3y}m$; $r_{3y}c$, L_{2z}; $p_{3y}b$, $q_{3y}c$; $q_{3y}m$, $r_{3y}b$; $q_{2y}b$, $q_{3y}m$; $q_{3y}b$, $q_{2y}m$.

TEST: Neg, either P_Y, or Q_Y, or R_Y and L_{2z} should light; also Neg, P_Y, Q_Y, R_Y—L_{2z} should light. Lamp will not operate with an even number of relays operated.

10.Neg, $r_{1x}c$; $r_{1x}c$, $q_{2x}c$; $r_{1x}m$, $q_{1x}c$; $q_{1x}c$, $s_{1x}c$; $q_{2x}m$, $s_{2x}c$; $s_{2x}m$, $s_{1x}m$; $s_{1x}m$, $q_{1x}m$; $q_{1x}m$, $P_X$op; Neg, $p_{1x}c$; $p_{1x}m$, L_{4Y}.

TEST: Neg, R_X, Q_X—Relay P_X and L_{4Y} will both operate—this is also true for Neg, R_X, S_X; Neg, Q_X, S_X; and Neg, R_X, Q_X, S_X.

11.Neg, $q_{3x}c$; $q_{3x}m$, $r_{2x}c$; $r_{2x}m$, $s_{3x}m$; $s_{3x}c$, L_{1z}; $q_{3x}b$, $r_{3x}c$; $r_{3x}m$, $s_{3x}b$; $r_{2x}b$, $r_{3x}m$; $r_{3x}b$, $r_{2x}m$.

TEST: Neg, either Q_X, or R_X, or S_X and L_{1Z} should light; also Neg, Q_X, R_X, $S_X - L_{1Z}$ should light. Lamp will not operate if an even number of the above relays are operated.

This completes Part C of the minimicro computer circuit. Because each part has been tested as the wiring proceeded, no further testing is required for Part C.

PART D

Part D will incorporate most of the boards used previously in the computer.

1. $b_{3w}b$, $q_{2w}c$; $q_{2w}b$, $s_{3w}c$; $s_{3w}b$, $s_{3v}c$; $s_{3v}m$, $s_{2m}c$; $s_{2m}c$, $r_{2m}c$; $r_{2m}c$, $q_{2m}c$; $q_{2m}b$, $p_{2m}c$; $p_{2m}c$, L_{1X};

2. $b_{3x}b$, $r_{4x}c$; $b_{4y}b$, $q_{4y}c$; $b_{4z}b$, $p_{4z}c$; $p_{4z}c$, $s_{4z}c$; $s_{2m}m$, $S_Z op$; $s_{4z}m$, $S_Z op$; $r_{2m}m$, $P_Z op$; $p_{4z}m$, $P_Z op$; $q_{2m}m$, $Q_Y op$; $q_{4y}m$, $Q_Y op$; $p_{2m}m$, $R_X op$; $r_{4x}m$, $R_X op$;

3. $b_{3w}b$, $q_{3w}c$; $q_{3w}m$, $s_{4w}c$; $s_{4w}m$, $s_{4v}c$; $s_{4v}b$, $s_{2n}c$; $s_{2n}c$, $r_{2n}c$; $r_{2n}c$, $q_{2n}c$; $q_{2n}c$, $p_{2n}c$; $p_{2n}c$, L_{2X};

4. $b_{2x}b$, $q_{4x}c$; $b_{3y}b$, $p_{4y}c$; $p_{4y}c$, $s_{4y}c$; $b_{3z}b$, $r_{4z}c$; $s_{2n}m$, $R_Z op$; $r_{4z}m$, $R_Z op$; $r_{2n}m$, $S_Y op$; $s_{4y}m$, $S_Y op$; $q_{2n}m$, $P_Y op$; $p_{4y}m$, $P_Y op$; $p_{2n}m$, $Q_X op$; $q_{4x}m$, $Q_X op$.

This completes the basic minimicro computer. In this last section lamps L_{1x} and L_{2x} will indicate when the 2 addends, found in the memory cells M and N, are introduced to the binary adder. These lamps, along with their associated relays, are energized by the action of the binary counter, completed in Part A, on the count of binary "0 0 1" and "1 1 0." The final readout of the computer is the value of the lamps on the boards Z and Y and are representative of the following values:

L_{4Y}	L_{1Z}	L_{2Z}	L_{3Z}	L_{4Z}
2^4	2^3	2^2	2^1	2^0

The lamps located on boards M and N represent the values stored in memory in the same fashion, L_{1M} representing 2^3, L_{2M} representing 2^2, etc. We are now ready to give the computer its final shakedown. We will need 4 IBM-type cards, 2 to store values in the memory cells, 1 to tell the computer

to run and add the 2 values stored in memory, and the final card to instruct the computer to reset the output of the adder to zero and erase the contents of the memory cells. Punch out cards like the following samples (punch out those holes marked with an X) and check your computer.

Card 1.
Memory cell M

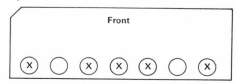

Binary address for M: 1 0 1   Binary value for address: 1 1 0 1

Card 2.
Memory cell N

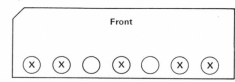

Binary address for N: 1 1 0   Binary value for address: 1 0 1 1

Card 3.
Instruction to RUN

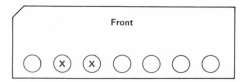

Binary address for this instruction: 0 1 1

Card 4.
Instruction to HALT and RESET

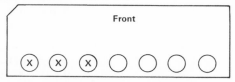

Binary address for this instruction: 1 1 1

As indicated in the schematics and circuits in the computer, only 3 of 8 possible sections of the counter are used—this would then allow you to expand the functions performed by your computer.

Adding other memory cells, with storage power of 2^3, requires another board for each cell. Why not start out with a design to multiply 2 digits?

E | EVALUATION

The questions in this section are rated according to the chapter objectives and the performance levels stated in the introduction to the teacher's manual. This group of questions is not intended to be all inclusive, but just as a guide to possible questions. Zeros in the chapter objective column indicate no chapter objective for this question.

Chapter Objective	Performance Level	
		Judged to be Relatively Easy (there is no "more difficult" test):

In each of the following questions, check the best answer:

Chapter Objective	Performance Level	
1	I	**1.** A general-purpose computer

    a) is unable to perform certain "special" tasks for which other kinds of computer must be provided.

    b) can carry out any task which can be programmed.

    c) will accept as input only punched cards.

    d) cannot produce output on a cathode-ray tube.

    e) is never used for "time-sharing" purposes.

Chapter Objective	Performance Level	
2	I	**2.** When transferring information from one logic circuit of an automatic computer to another,

    a) relays are convenient but not necessary.

    b) only one relay is involved in the process.

    c) it is never necessary to set the "receiving" relay to 0.

    d) a "sending" circuit relay must store either 0 or 1 in a "receiving" circuit relay.

    e) a "receiving" circuit relay sets the "sending" relay to 0 or 1.

Chapter Objective	Performance Level	
3	I	**3.** If an input card for the minimicro computer has a hole punched in only the first column (all the rest left unpunched), the card represents

    a) 1 followed by twelve 0's.

    b) $+ 2^{12}$.

    c) -2^{12}.

    d) $+ 0$.

    e) $- 0$.

Chapter Objective	Performance Level	
4	I	**4.** When a punched card is read by the minimicro computer,

    a) the card punch makes a copy of the input card.

    b) the information is automatically transferred to the next vacant memory cell.

    c) the card-reader relays set the relays of a memory cell to the same states.

    d) the information is regularly transferred directly to the accumulator.

    e) it is necessary to clear the relays of the accumulator first.

Chapter Objective	Performance Level	
5	I	**5.** The CARDIAC computer model contains 100 memory cells for 3-digit decimal numbers.

    a) It would be possible to address as many as 128 cells with the same address trees as needed in CARDIAC.

Judged to be Relatively Easy:

b) The address trees for such a memory would require 10 switches.

c) This means that 100 x 3 or 300 switch contacts would be needed for addressing.

d) If the number of cells in the memory were doubled it would be necessary to double the number of switches in each address tree.

e) If the computer were built to handle 3-digit binary numbers, fewer copies of the basic memory would be needed for each cell.

6
I

6. The reason that an accumulator contains 3 registers (called A, B, and S) is that

a) A and B provide the circuits needed for multiplying and dividing.

b) A and B make a kind of "scratch pad" where all computations are completed before storing the results in S.

c) when information is being transferred, one bit may be placed in A, another in B, until memory is prepared to receive them.

d) it is necessary to provide temporary memory cells (A and B) in the accumulator.

e) we can put the number already in the accumulator into A, a number to be added into B, and the sum into S.

7
I

7. In a certain program the fifth instruction is stored in memory cell 34 and reads 816 ("jump to 16"). When instruction 5 is reached,

a) the jump instruction replaces the usual instruction cycle.

b) cell 99 is reset to 16.

c) control causes the relays in the instruction register to copy those in cell 34.

d) control causes the relays in the instruction register to copy those in cell 16.

e) the instruction counter arranges to have cell 34 copied into cell 16.

7
I

8. Op code 3 ("test the accumulator contents")

a) means that the relays in the accumulator must be copied on the relays controlling one side of a comparator circuit.

b) means that the contents of the S register must be compared with the contents of the memory cell last entered.

c) means that the contents of the A, B, and S registers must be compared with one another.

d) means "compare each digit in the S register with 1. If 1 is always bigger, go on to the next program step."

e) means "set the instruction counter to the address that follows 3."

Answers to Evaluation Questions:

1. b	5. a
2. d	6. e
3. d	7. c
4. c	8. a

F | FILMS

F-1501 DIGITAL COMPUTER TECHNIQUES: COMPUTER UNITS

Recommendation: Good for clarification of computer organization.
Application: Concept development. Best used for review after class discussion of the overall plan for a computer.
Length and Type: 24 min, color, sound.
Source: #14 (Navy Film No. MN 8969O)
Summary: The film describes in a general way the functioning of the major units of a computer: input, output, memory, accumulator, and control. It also shows the purpose of clocking and sequencing.

F-1502 COMPUTERS AND HUMAN BEHAVIOR

Recommendation: Good film to provide a change of pace from the hardware aspect of computers.
Application: Enrichment. Best used near the end of the study of digital computers. Shows a digital computer application in the social sciences.
Length and Type: 30 min, b & w, sound.
Source: #5, #8
Summary: This film explores some of the research being conducted at the Carnegie Institute of Technology with electronic digital computers in an effort to evolve new theories about human mental processes. Dr. Bert Green demonstrates his computer experiments with perception of motion and depth. Dr. Herbert Simon, with the help of a computer, presents his theory of how human beings memorize. Dr. Allan Newell shows how the computer was responsible for creating a new theory of human problem solving.

G | GENERAL

I. Bibliography

"Computers: Their Past, Present, and Future." *The Mathematics Teacher,* January, 1968

Kinzel "Engineering Civilization and Society." *Science,* June 9, 1967

II. A Computer Play

An interesting way of reviewing the concepts discussed in this chapter is to involve students in a skit or play. The following "computer play" has been used with great success to teach the interaction of the various parts of the computer. The idea is to have the students rehearse and act out the various roles played by the different elements of the computer.

Put the block diagram in Fig. 15-10 on the chalkboard, and designate a certain student for each element. Card tags or simple costumes can be used to identify elements (students). The student who is Control is in absolute charge. There should be no extraneous talking whatsoever, and a "messenger" should be used to transfer all information which goes from one element to another.

Control may give terse directions, such as "Memory Cell Selector" (now pointing to the proper student), "select location 14." The student called on may then point to the desired location on the chalkboard diagram. Initially, the program and data should have been loaded in memory, the various registers cleared (0's in them, *not* blanks!), and the first instruction address set in the instruction counter. One feature of this technique is that it focuses attention *at each step* on the particular student (element) involved, and he must know and be able to explain his correct function at that time. This creates tremendous interaction within the class and leads to an excellent teaching-learning situation.

Cast of Components:

Control: Since this is such a large role, 2 students might be asked to share it. One student can be in charge of decoding, while the second student takes care of the instruction cycle.

    Input
    Output
    Register selector
    Memory cell selector
    Memory
    Accumulator
    Instruction register
    Instruction counter

Script: The script (simple program in machine code) can be written on IBM cards and handed to the person playing Memory. As in a real play, the plot (function of the program) is revealed to the audience slowly. To keep the rest of the students (audience) interested, ask them to raise their hands when they think they have figured out the plot. Allow each student in the audience to make only one guess.

Procedure:

1. Students should be told several days in advance of the play date so that they may be prepared to play any role asked of them.
2. A small student committee could be set up to make costumes (e.g., crown for Control) and prepare the script (only if they are not going to be in the play).
3. On the day of the play, actors and roles should be picked by lot.
4. The teacher should act as a prompter.
5. To keep everybody involved, the students who are in the play can be asked to change places with the students in the audience in the middle of the play.

Although this activity models the action of a real play very closely, there are some differences. Every actor must know every role. The actors as well as the audience do not know the plot until the play has been performed. Finally, this play can also be used as an informal way of finding out if students have learned something about the organization of a computer.

III. ECCP-2: A Functional Model Computer Using LCB's

However neatly they work, the separate circuits studied with the LCB—memory counter, adder, and the rest—are indeed separate, and moreover they use mechanical switches although everybody knows that real computers use solid-state circuitry with no moving parts except electric charges. It is likely that questions linger in the minds of some students: Are these LCB circuits perhaps only analogs of the real

thing? Do we have the full story, or have essential connecting links been omitted? ECCP-2, a brainchild of Professor A. van Dam and constructed by him and some of his students at Brown University, is designed to answer these questions. This project is an alternative to the minimicro computer experiment (Lab I).

Employing nothing except 8 LCB's and a couple of hundred feet of extra connecting wire, they have produced an actual working computer. No one should be astonished to learn that it is unpretentious and extremely limited. Its point is that it uses already familiar circuits, and it does work. An observer can monitor what is happening by watching the lights on the boards. The fact that ingenious connections of diodes and transistors, in commercial computers, do no more than switches and relays (except to improve speed and reliability and save space and power) becomes somehow easier to believe.

The operator supplies the timing pulses with a switch, but the computer can be converted to automatic operation: push the Start button, and the program which has been stored is executed without further attention. For this embellishment, either 1 or 2 additional LCB's are needed, depending on the circuit chosen.

Part of the inventor's description follows. ECCP-2 is a binary relay computer designed to demonstrate the concepts of computer operation with a minimum of equipment; it requires 32 four-pole double-throw relays, and associated lights and switches. Its memory capacity is 6 bits, arranged in 2 words of 3 bits each (next page). The instruction format is a single word, with the left 2 bits designating the operation code, and the rightmost bit used for addressing. There are thus 4 instructions in the machine's repertoire. The machine is controlled by a start switch, which enables it to run, a time pulse switch, a stop switch, and memory entry switches. Other switches perform special functions which will be described later, and should be left released. The lights read out as indicated in the diagram on page 383; those shown merely as numbered dots should be removed at first, as they show details of control and tend to confuse while contributing little, if any, to the demonstration.

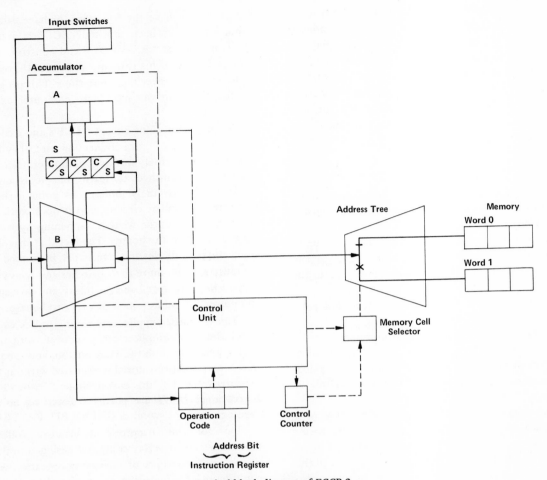

Logical block diagram of ECCP-2

MEMORY

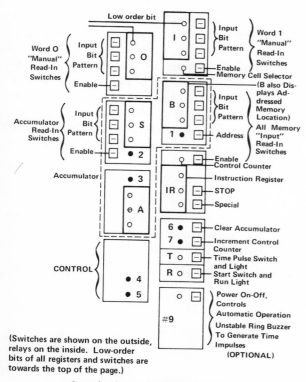

Word O "Manual" Read-In Switches
Input Bit Pattern
Enable

Low order bit

I O

O O

Input Bit Pattern
Enable
Memory Cell Selector

Word 1 "Manual" Read-In Switches

Accumulator Read-In Switches
Input Bit Pattern
Enable

B

1 ●

Input Bit Pattern
Address
Enable

(B also Displays Addressed Memory Location) All Memory "Input" Read-In Switches

Accumulator

● 2

● 3

e A

IR

Control Counter
Instruction Register
STOP
Special

O

6 ●
7 ●
T O
R O

Clear Accumulator
Increment Control Counter
Time Pulse Switch and Light
Start Switch and Run Light

CONTROL

● 4

● 5

#9

O

Power On-Off, Controls Automatic Operation

Unstable Ring Buzzer To Generate Time Impulses

(OPTIONAL)

(Switches are shown on the outside, relays on the inside. Low-order bits of all registers and switches are towards the top of the page.)

Organization of LCB's for ECCP-2

The instruction and execution cycles together require 2 time pulses, the first of which fetches the instruction and increments the control counter, and the second of which performs the indicated function. The instructions are:

00—Halt: At the end of the first time pulse, the machine is removed from the running state, i.e., it will no longer recognize time pulses. (The same result is given by operating the stop switch.) No second time pulse is needed or accepted. On operating the start switch, execution resumes at the next instruction.

01—Store: The contents of the accumulator (S register) are stored at the location in memory given by the address bit.

10—Add (and Skip On Overflow): The contents of the addressed memory location are added to the contents of the accumulator and the result is stored

in the accumulator; if the result is too large, the high-order bit is lost, the 3 low-order bits are saved in the accumulator, and the control counter is incremented again, thus skipping the next instruction. (Since the machine has only 2 words of storage, it will thus repeat the current instruction.)

11—Add: The contents of the accumulator are added to the contents of the addressed word of memory, and the result is stored in the accumulator; if it is too large, only the low-order 3 bits are saved.

A sample program follows: in word 0, "Add from word 0," i.e., 110; and in word 1, "Halt," i.e., 000.

Place the program in memory by operating the word 0 and word 1 ENABLE switches, and set the INPUT BIT PATTERN switches to 110 on the word 0 board, and to 000 on the word 1 board. Then release the ENABLE switches. The control counter must initially be set to 0, which may be accomplished by operating and releasing INCREMENT CONTROL COUNTER switch, until it reads zero after releasing the switch (see preceding diagram for switch and indicator light positions). Operate and release the start switch, thus placing the machine in the running state. Unless otherwise specified, do not leave any control switches (INPUT BIT PATTERN switches excepted) in the operated position, as they may interfere with one another's operation.

While the machine is in the running state, each time the TIME PULSE switch is operated and released, the machine advances one time pulse through the instruction cycle and thus through the stored program.

A description of the execution of the program placed in memory follows:

Initially, the control counter is at 0, the accumulator is cleared, and the machine is in the run state. Operate and release the time pulse switch (FETCH/INCREMENT). The contents of word 0, that is 110, will be copied into the memory communication (B) register and from there into the instruction register. Also, the control counter will be incremented to 1. Operate and release the time pulse switch again (EXECUTE). The contents of the addressed word, word 0, will be copied into the B register, and added to the contents of the accumulator. Operate the time pulse switch (FETCH; do not release yet). Note that the memory cell selector is at 1, thus preparing to fetch from the address indicated by the control counter, which is still at 1; and that the contents of word 1, or 000, have been copied into B, and from B into the instruction register. This is a HALT instruction. Now release the time pulse switch (INCREMENT). The run light will go out, and further operation and release of the time pulse switch has no effect.

A second sample program, word 0 containing a "STORE in word 1" = 011; word 1 containing an "ADD from word 1 and SKIP ON OVERFLOW" = 101 demonstrates the rest of the machine's instruction, but is not described here.

Teachers who are interested in building this model computer will have one immediate question: how long would construction take? The young man who demonstrated it to the writer said, airily: "Oh, a dextrous teacher with two good students should be able to do it in three or four hours." Dr. van Dam, who was listening, translated: as much as a week of afternoons and the weekend. Thus you have a lower bound but not quite an upper bound to the integration.

Detailed directions are available. They include also a computer print-out of the running list, board by board, and a cross-checking list (for *every* terminal used, a record of where the wire should go, thus covering every wire from each end), and even a count of the number of wires required, for each of 5 standard lengths.

Requests should be addressed to:

Professor Andries van Dam
Center for Computer and Information Sciences
182 George Street
Providence, Rhode Island 02912

Please send one dollar to cover postage and handling.

GUN DIGEST®
BOOK OF
CONCEALED CARRY

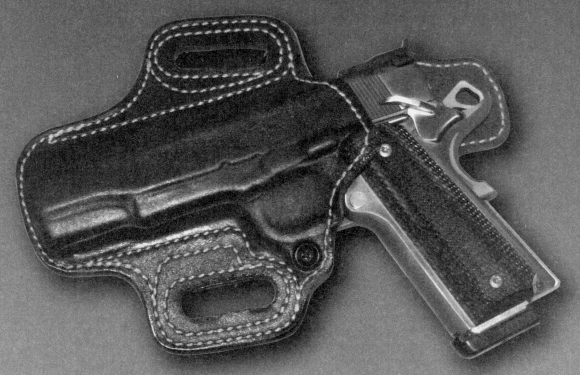

2nd Edition

MASSAD AYOOB

Published by

Gun Digest® Books, an imprint of F+W Media, Inc.
Krause Publications • 700 East State Street • Iola, WI 54990-0001
715-445-2214 • 888-457-2873
www.krausebooks.com

To order books or other products call toll-free 1-800-258-0929
or visit us online at www.gundigeststore.com

Cover photography by Kris Kandler

ISBN-13: 978-1-4402-3267-1
ISBN-10: 1-4402-3267-9

Cover Design by Dave Hauser
Designed by Dave Hauser
Edited Corrina Peterson

Printed in United States of America

Acknowledgments and Dedication

It is a pleasure to acknowledge the contributions of those who made this book possible. Gail Pepin, who took most of the photographs and was indispensable to the editing process on my end. Steve Denney, whose proofreading advice was invaluable, and who was kind enough to write the foreword. Herman Gunter, III who also helped me proofread. Harry Kane, the superb editor at *Combat Handguns* and *Guns & Weapons for Law Enforcement*, who gave me permission to blend into this book some things I had previously written for some of the Harris Publications titles he puts together so tirelessly. Thanks! I never would've made deadline without you!

I may have designed a couple of holsters and come up with a couple of techniques, but this book really comes to you from the countless number of people who have taught me and allowed me to pick their brains over the last nearly fifty years. They are holster designers and gun designers, gunfight survivors and survivors of horrors they were unarmed and helpless to prevent. They range from world handgun champions to novice handgun students, all of whom taught me lessons about how to help people prepare themselves and become ready to quell lethal violence at a moment's notice.

I was merely the conduit of their knowledge, the collecting agent who passed their collective learning experiences on to you, the reader of this book.

It is to all of them that this book is gratefully and respectfully dedicated.

Massad Ayoob, December 2007

CONTENTS

PREFACE

It has been four years since the first edition of the *Gun Digest Book of Concealed Carry*. Things change. More states have gotten on board with shall-issue concealed carry laws. More people in those states and the states that already have such good laws are taking advantage of the opportunity to better protect themselves and their loved ones. Concealed carry is, no pun intended, a booming business.

The industry has responded accordingly. There are new concealment holsters, some of them downright ingenious. There is also a push for laws which better protect the concealed carrier. Florida recently passed one which protected the concealed carrier if their weapon inadvertently became visible. Several states have passed "Stand Your Ground" laws, which rescind any requirement to retreat before using defensive force if attacked in any place where you have a right to be. As we shall see, these have been widely misunderstood, even by some on the gun owners' side of the debate.

The Bottom Line

Self-defense issues are a very mature and well-established body of law, and the carrying of guns is something that has been practically worked out by professionals for a very long time. This is why most of the book you now hold in your hands is as it was when it first came out in 2008: it is, for the most part, every bit as relevant as it was then. That said, both the law and the human condition are dynamic things which change, and that's why 18,000 words have been added to this updated edition.

And, of course, change will continue to take place, and it will always be up to all of us individually to keep up with those changes as they affect us and those we are responsible for protecting.

FOREWORD

Spent casings are inches apart from ex-SWAT cop Steve Denney's new SIG P250 9mm as he tests it with a fast double tap.

I've been carrying concealed firearms since 1968, which was my first year as a sworn law enforcement officer. I was finishing the last year of my Criminology Degree at Florida State University and joined the Tallahassee Police Department as a Reserve Officer. Since then, I've learned a few lessons about concealed carry by trial and error, but my knowledge about firearms has been improved immensely by reading what the experts were saying. In the early 1970s, besides reading articles by people with names like Cooper, Gaylord, Askins, Skelton, etc., I started reading articles from a guy by the name of Massad Ayoob. I began to wonder, who was this Ayoob guy and, more importantly, why did what he wrote actually make sense, based on my own experience? My relationship with Mas' writing was strictly one-sided (he wrote and I read) from then until 1999, when I finally had the chance to take my first LFI course. Since then we have become good friends and I have become an instructor with him for his Lethal Force Institute. That has given me a precious opportunity to see how he acquires and uses the knowledge that he shares with others in his training classes, his writing and his case work as an expert witness. So when he said he was writing a book about concealed carry, I thought: "This has got to be good!"

Well, it is. I have been poring over the manuscript for

> **Concealed carry has been a hot topic in the world of gun ownership for the past two decades or so.**

the past week and I am happy to report that Mas has put together a winner. And a timely winner, at that. Concealed carry has been a hot topic in the world of gun ownership for the past two decades or so. More and more opportunities for decent, law abiding citizens to protect themselves by legally carrying concealed firearms have emerged as State after State has adopted more realistic concealed carry laws. Even so, only about two percent of the people eligible for a concealed carry permit actually apply for one. That is starting to change, however. Of course, September 11, 2001 started folks thinking more seriously about the subject. And most recently, the mass murder of students at Virginia Tech, the shootings in malls in Omaha and Salt Lake City and the armed attacks on religious centers in Arvada and Colorado Springs are causing people to reassess their vulnerability as they go about their daily lives. As more and more people come to the conclusion that they need to take realistic precautions against violent attack, the need for sensible concealed carry advice will continue to expand.

One of the things that has always impressed me about the way Mas works is that he is not just a teacher and not just a writer. He is a true student of firearms, their history and their use. This book reflects his serious research of the subject, as well as his ability to communicate with his audience. The references to many of the legendary names in the firearms world and many of the real-world case studies are not just academic. Mas has known most of the greats. And anyone who knows Mas also knows that he is always asking questions, always analyzing other people's views and always seeking more and more knowledge. It's not just the "names" either. I have been with him when he asked the ordinary man or woman what their impressions were on a particular gun or piece of gear. "How do you like that Beretta," he asked a young highway patrolman we were sharing a gas pump with during a fuel stop on a trip across the Great Plains. "How's that holster workin' for ya," to a Sheriff's Deputy we met at a convenience store. "What do you think they should do to improve that" is a common question we hear when he calls on us to help evaluate some gun or other gear that has been sent to him to "T & E." Beyond the equipment, Mas gathers real-life information about the use of firearms for self defense. Certainly his case work as an expert has given him unique access to incidents from the streets. Some of them are high profile, some rather ordinary. Except to the people involved. Every case has its lessons. And, very often, his students have their stories. Stories that can make the hair on the back of your neck stand up, or bring a tear to your eye. Like the female student who had been the victim of two violent sexual assaults. The first time her attacker succeeded in raping her. The second attacker did not. The difference? The second time she was armed and prepared to defend herself. Or the Roman Catholic priest, who grew up in a foreign country known for its civil strife. He has been shot five times and stabbed once, all in separate incidents. He now lives in the United States, carries every day, and when he quietly relates his story, he simply says: "Never again."

These are the sort of people Mas spends time with as both a teacher and as a student of the human experience. And that experience is what he willingly and skillfully shares with his students and his readers. In this book, he has compiled decades of experience in not just the carrying of firearms, but the shooting of firearms. Mas has been a competitive shooter since the old PPC days. He was a "regular" at the Bianchi Cup and other national matches. He still competes regularly in law enforcement competitions and International Defensive Pistol Association (IDPA) matches. In fact, Mas was one of the first IDPA Four Gun Masters and became *the first* Five Gun Master, when an additional revolver category was established by IDPA a couple of years ago. He is also an avid researcher of the history of carrying firearms and their use by police and ordinary private citizens alike. As such, he was a guest lecturer at a conference of writers and historians in Tombstone, Arizona, assembled to discuss probably the most famous gunfight ever, the shootout at the OK Corral. And, on a more contemporary note, he was requested to represent the "expert witness" point of view on a panel of American Bar Association legal experts who were making a Continuing Legal Education training tape for attorneys. The tape specifically addresses the investigation, prosecution and effective defense of people who have had to use deadly force to protect themselves or others.

> **And, make no mistake, you are your own "First Responder."**

In this book, Mas discusses both WHY we carry and HOW to carry. Mas explains the concepts behind the two styles of holsters he has designed, the LFI Rig and the Ayoob Rear Guard, and why holster selection is such an important part of your carry "system." He also explains the need to practice drawing from concealment, in order to quickly respond to any threat. He explains the rationale behind two drawing methods that he developed: using the StressFire "Cover Crouch" to draw from an ankle rig and the Fingertip Sweep (he calls it "reach out and touch yourself") used to positively clear an open front garment for a smooth same-side draw. Mas began developing his "StressFire" shooting techniques back in the 1970's. By late 1981, at the suggestion of world champion shooter Ray Chapman, he established the Lethal Force Institute and has been instructing "certified card carrying good guys" there ever since. The Chief of Police of the department where Mas serves as a Captain, Russell Lary, has entrusted his son to Mas' tutelage to the extent that he has attended all of the LFI classes, LFI-I, II & III, and he just recently completed the most advanced class, LFI-IV. Yes, Mas really is a Captain in the Grantham, NH Police Department. I know the Chief, and he is delighted to have such a true "human resource" available to the residents of his community.

A lot has changed in the nearly 40 years since I started in this field. A lot happened before that, of course, but I see the next major steps coming in the immediate future. People are tired of being victimized by people who use guns and other weapons illegally. And people are tired of being victimized by anti-gun advocates and the laws and rules for which they are responsible. They have been shown to be worse than ineffective. They have put decent people unnecessarily at risk in "Gun-Free Zones," that are only gun-free to the law abiding. They continue to attempt to thwart efforts to make concealed carry by law abiding people a nation-wide reality. They have made people vulnerable at a time when they should be seriously thinking about, and preparing for, their own self protection. Not to become "vigilantes," but to be able to hold the line against violence, until the professionals can respond. And, make no mistake, you are your own "First Responder." Just as you would have a fire extinguisher in your home or car, or take a course in first aid and CPR, you need to consider how well you are prepared for the other kind of deadly threat that may suddenly present itself: a violent, criminal attack on you or those who depend on you. In this book, Massad Ayoob has brought together all the essential elements that you need to know if you are currently carrying concealed firearms or if you are considering doing so. This is your opportunity to take advantage of all of the research, knowledge and experience that Mas has accumulated over more than four decades. I can't think of a better teacher.

Steve Denney
*Firearms and Defensive Tactics
Instructor, Firearms Training
Contributor to Officer.com,
Former Police Supervisor and
Ordinary Citizen of the USA*

Chapter 1

THE CCW LIFESTYLE

As Gail begins to give him a hug, Steve tucks his elbows into his body and will seem to be hugging back, but his forearm placement will prevent her from feeling the SIG 357 on his right hip or the spare magazine on his left.

enforcement officers) in the middle of those two ends, the seasoned street cops who've seen the reality, have a more realistic view. A great many of them make sure they leave a gun at home for their spouse to use to protect the household while they're gone. They've learned that police are reactive more than proactive, and that the victim has to survive the violent criminal's attack long enough for law enforcement to be summoned and arrive.

I've carried a concealed handgun since I was twelve years old. My grandfather, the first generation of my family to arrive in the USA, was an armed citizen who went for his gun when he was pistol-whipped in his city store by an armed robber. He shot and wounded the man. The suspect fled, only to be killed later that night in a shootout with the city police. The wound my grandfather inflicted slowed him down when he tried to kill the arresting officer, and the cops thanked him for that. My dad had been in his twenties when he had to resort to deadly force in the same city's streets. A would-be murderer put a revolver to his head and pulled the trigger; my dad ducked to the side enough to miss the bullet, but not enough to keep the muzzle blast from destroying his left eardrum. Moments later, my father's return fire had put that man on the ground dying from a 38 slug "center mass," and the thug's accomplice in a fetal position clutching himself and screaming.

It's no wonder that growing up in the 1950s, guns were a part of my life: in the home, and in my father's jewelry store. When I went to work there at age twelve, I carried a loaded gun concealed. There were strategically placed handguns hidden throughout the area behind the counter and in the back room, but Dad was smart enough to know that I wouldn't always be within reach of one when I needed it. The laws in that time and place allowed the practice.

I realized this was some pretty serious stuff, and set to learning all I could about the

If you're reading this book, that tells me that you've either made the decision to CCW (Carry a Concealed Weapon), or are thinking about it. Either one is a good start to enhanced personal safety of oneself and loved ones.

It surprises some people to hear that from a guy who's been carrying a badge for three and a half decades. Surprise: there are more cops who feel the same way than you might think. Fact is, for the most part, the anti-gun cops fall into two narrow categories. One is the chief appointed by an anti-gun mayor or city council, who serves at the pleasure of the appointing authority and can get busted back to Captain – the highest rank normally protected by Civil Service – if he doesn't make himself a mouthpiece for the politician(s) in question. The other is the young rookie who didn't have a gun of his own until he got into the Academy, and associates the weapon with the new identity into which he has invested so much of his time, effort, ego and self-image. It's not something he wants to share with the general public.

Give him time. My experience has been that the great majority of LEOs (law

When you carry a gun, you learn to keep other people from noticing.

If you carry, be competent with your gun. You don't need to be able to shoot this perfect qualification score with a Glock 30 and 45 hardball, but you want to come as close as you can. Confidence and competence intertwine, says Ayoob.

inception. I've also had the privilege of teaching for the International Association of Law Enforcement Firearms Instructors inside and outside the US, and served a couple of years as co-vice chair, with Mark Seiden under Drew Findling, of the forensic evidence committee of the National Association of Criminal Defense Lawyers. I've had the privilege of studying the firearms training of the DEA, NYPD, LAPD, numerous state police agencies, and countless other law enforcement organizations. I've been able to study hands-on with such great shooting champions as Ray Chapman, Frank Garcia, Rob Leatham, and many more. I learned one-on-one from living legends like Charlie Askins, Jim Cirillo, Jeff Cooper, Bill Jordan, Frank McGee and more. Some of the "more" have asked that their names not appear in print, and I will respect that here.

It has been a long and educational road, and with a little luck, it won't be over anytime soon. The bottom line is, I'm not a super-cop as so many of those men literally were. In all these years, though I've had my gun on a lot of people and was starting to pull the trigger a few times, I've never had to shoot a man. With a little luck, that will stay the same, too. I see my role – as an instructor and as the writer of this book – as a funnel of knowledge. You're at the receiving end of the funnel.

Many who carry guns have learned to carry two. Here, twin baby Glocks ride in double shoulder holster by Mitch Rosen.

practice. My dad's customers included lawyers, judges, and his friend the chief of police. I picked all their brains on the issue. What I learned stunned me.

There were books then on gunfighting: how to do it, what to do it with, and how to develop the mindset to do it. Interestingly, there were *none* on *when* to shoot. My dad's lawyer friends told me that even kids like me could use a legal library; we didn't have to be attorneys or law students to get in there, and the librarian would show us how to find what we were looking for. I lived in the state capital, and the State Legal Library had the same rule. As I began that self-education, I found myself thinking, "Somebody ought to write a book about *this* for regular people! When I grow up, if nobody's written that book yet, *I* wanna write it!"

And I did. "In the Gravest Extreme: the Role of the Firearm in Personal Protection" hit print in 1979, and has been a best-seller ever since. And I've been carrying a concealed handgun since the year 1960, in public on a permit since the year 1969. By 1973, I had become a police firearms instructor, and from then to now have taken training as avidly as I've given it. I've been teaching and researching this stuff full time since 1981, when I established Lethal Force Institute (www.ayoob.com). That has included expert witness testimony in weapons, shooting, and assault cases since 1979. From 1987 through 2006, I served as chair of the firearms committee for the American Society of Law Enforcement Trainers, and have been on the advisory board for the International Law Enforcement Educators and Trainers Association since its

When you become accustomed to carrying, you learn to have at least one weak-side holster and ambidextrous gun so you can protect yourself and your loved ones if you sustain an injury to the dominant arm. This is one of author's Springfield Armory 1911s, with ambidextrous safety and left-hand High Noon concealed carry scabbard.

There have been tremendous advances in the last fifty years in holster design, handgun design, and ammunition design. We now have the finest concealed carry firearms, holsters, and defensive rounds that have ever been available. We likewise have techniques that have taken advantage of modern knowledge of the human mind and body that was not available to the famous gunfighters of old. (But the Old Ones have left their lessons to us, and many of those are timeless, too.)

"CCW"

Let's sort out the alphabet soup for those readers new to concealed carry. To those who practice it, CCW can describe the practice of (lawfully) carrying a concealed weapon. It can also be a shorthand noun, e.g., "My CCW is a Colt Commander 45." Unfortunately, to some the letters have a negative connotation. In many jurisdictions, police know them as the abbreviation for the *crime* of *illegally* Carrying a Concealed Weapon.

In some parts of the country, CCW refers to the permit to carry itself, as in: "I carry my CCW next to my driver's license, so I can hand both to the officer if I'm pulled over for speeding." But each state has its own terminology. That little laminated card might be a CPL (Concealed Pistol License), CWP (Concealed Weapons Permit), CHL (Concealed Handgun License), or some other acronym. We're talking about the same

thing. Hell, in the state where I grew up and spent most of my adult life, it was known simply as a "pistol permit." (And, no, we're not going to use these pages to debate whether "license" or "permit" is the proper term. The book is about concealed carry, not what I've come to call Combat Semantics.)

The concealed carry lifestyle changes you. Most of the changes are positive. If you're new to the practice, what this book says will be helpful to you. If you've been doing it for as long as I have or longer, you might find a new trick or two, and at worst will have a book to back up your advice when *you're* sharing this knowledge with *your* students.

Changes

People who don't understand the lifestyle think a gun on your hip will turn you from Dr. Jekyll to Mr. Hyde, or make you "go where angels fear to tread." *Au contraire.* Those who've actually *lived* the CCW lifestyle can tell you that it's just the opposite.

When you carry a gun, you no longer have the option of starting fights, or even keeping the ball rolling when another person starts one with you. When you are armed with a lethal weapon, you carry the burden of what the Courts call a "higher standard of care." Because *you* know a deadly weapon is present, and *you* know that a yelling match or "mere fisticuffs" can now degrade into a killing situation,

Concealed carry means several small changes of habit. If reaching to a high shelf might raise your outer garment and expose holster or gun …

…you learn to reach with the other hand. Similarly, to pick up an object on the ground, you learn to bend at knees instead of waist so the gun at your hip won't "print" through your concealing garment.

law and ethics alike will say that *you of all people* should have known enough to abjure from a violent conflict. This is why a phrase from science-fiction writer Robert Heinlein, popularized by Col. Jeff Cooper, has become a guiding light for CCW practitioners: "An armed society is a polite society." Answering a curse with a curse, or an obscene gesture with a one-finger salute, is no longer your option when you carry a gun.

Another saying among CCW people is, "Concealed means *concealed*." Only the rankest rookie cop or first-time permit-holder will allow the handgun to become visible in anything less than an emergency. In professional circles, people who don't follow this rule are sometimes known as gun-flashers, and are looked down upon with only slightly less opprobrium than the other kind of "flashers."

Responsibility comes with CCW. The responsibility to keep that deadly weapon secured from unauthorized children, incompetent guests in the household, and burglars. The responsibility to use the weapon as judiciously as, in the words of the Courts, "a reasonable and prudent person would do, in the same situation…"

If the gun must be drawn and fired to save your life or the lives of others, there is a responsibility to make certain that your shots fly true. Did you learn to shoot, perhaps even "qualify" with your weapon like a police officer? Or did you just buy it, strap it on, and think it would somehow protect you by itself? Did you become sufficiently skilled with it that, in a state of stress, you could be reasonably and prudently confident of hitting your target and not an innocent bystander? Did you carefully choose ammunition designed to incapacitate a violent attacker, and designed *not* to shoot through and through him and strike a bystander hidden from your view behind him? *Did you become familiar with the laws of your jurisdiction that govern the carrying of firearms and the lawful use of deadly force?*

It's critical that you *learn to draw expeditiously and safely*. A legal gun carrier not instantly recognizable as a Good Guy or Gal, the way a uniformed cop or security guard would be, risks starting a panic if drawing in public. An onlooker perception of "the cop has his gun out, get out of the way" becomes "good Lord, that psycho just pulled a *gun!*" This means that in "iffy circumstances," the plainclothes carrier may have to wait longer to react, putting a premium on drawing speed. In the following pages, we'll emphasize discreet "surreptitious draw" techniques that let you sneak your hand onto the still-hidden gun without frightening the crowds. For the same reason, lack of identifiability, you want to be able to holster that gun smoothly, one-handed, by feel without taking your eyes off the danger in front of you if cops are arriving, because you don't want those tensely responding officers seeing "man with a gun, there now."

Going out and drinking to the point of intoxication in public is not your option if you're carrying a gun. There are places in America where setting foot in a bar stone sober – or, hell, even a liquor store – can cost you your permit and "buy you some time," the latter phrase not in the good sense. There are also places where it's technically legal to get smashed in a gin mill while packing a piece. But there is *no* place in America where that won't get you into very deep trouble if you have to draw the gun in self-defense in that condition.

We who carry guns in public are a minority. We have an unwritten covenant with the rest of society: "You can be assured that we will not endanger you." It's a covenant we must live up to in every way, if we're going to keep the attendant rights and privileges and preserve them for our children and grandchildren.

The practice of CCW comes with a commitment, if you're serious, and that commitment is that you will actually *carry* the damn thing! *Criminal attackers don't make appointments.* The mindset of "I'll only carry it when I think I'll need it" is a false one. I, and anyone my age who's been carrying guns as long as I have, can tell you stories all night of people whose lives were saved because they were carrying guns in places where they didn't think they'd need them. Criminals attack you precisely when you *don't* think you're in a situation where you'll be ready for them. That's what they do for a living. If you are serious, you'll carry your gun like you carry your wallet: daily, constantly, unless it's illegal to do so.

Which brings us to another responsibility: *make sure you're carrying legally!* As you'll see later in these pages, today's situation makes concealed carry legal for more people in more places than at any time in the memory of any living American. If you're in one of those places where legal carry is not possible, I have to advise you, *don't carry there.* Yes, there are people whose lives have been saved by guns they were carrying without benefit of permit. I became, at age 23, one of them. I know more now than I knew at 23, and today, I either wouldn't have been in that place, or would have found a way to legally carry there.

"They won't find out I'm carrying illegally unless I need to use it, and if I need to use it, getting busted for it is the least of my worries." You've heard that, right? Well, *it's a myth!* The likelihood of the gun being found on you after a car crash or medical emergency, the likelihood of it being spotted or felt by someone in contact with you, may be greater than the likelihood of your needing to draw it in self-defense. Remember that in many jurisdictions the first offense of illegally carrying a gun is a felony, often bringing a minimum/mandatory one year imprisonment. And where it's "only a misdemeanor," remember that "only a misdemeanor" means "*only* 364 days in jail." Not to mention a firearms-related crime on your record.

Be smart. Be legal. Carry only where the law allows you to do so.

The Price of the Wardrobes

You don't just go to the pawnshop, buy the cheapest handgun they've got, stuff it in your pocket and go. If you are serious about this, there are wardrobes you'll have to acquire. Three wardrobes, in fact.

The wardrobe of clothing. This will be discussed at length in following chapters, but you will find yourself changing your clothing to "dress around the gun" if you're serious about CCW. I didn't get a big charge out of bringing my gun and holster into the tailor shop to get "court suits" made that would conceal a full-size handgun…but I'm glad I did. I don't especially like the look of Dockers-type sport

When it's so hot you need to take your jacket off and have an ice-cream cone, you do it like this. (Note that paper is held up to read, so head and danger scan aren't "buried.") Unless you need to stand and reach for it, no one will notice…

slacks, at least on my body, but they do a great job of hiding guns, and they've become a staple of the "sport coat and tie" section of my wardrobe. When I see myself in the mirror wearing a vest with a short sleeve shirt, I see Ed Norton from the old TV show "The Honeymooners"… but when you carry a full-size pistol and spare ammo in hot weather, believe me, these garments become your new best friend. You learn to appreciate the extra pockets, too.

You'll discover the "two-inch waist range factor." If your waist size is 38, and you carry a handgun inside the waistband, you'll quickly gravitate toward size 40 for comfort. This will also keep you carrying the gun, since *without* that holster, your pants will feel as if they're going to fall down to your ankles. And the day will come when you gain some weight, and decide that an *outside*-the-belt holster is cheaper than a whole new wardrobe of trousers…

The wardrobe of holsters. This book will explain why different holsters work better in different situations. When I pack a suitcase and go on the road for a few weeks of teaching and/or testifying, there will be more than one holster per gun in the suitcase. The pocket holster for the snub-nosed 38 may bulge obviously in the side pocket of the tailored suit-pants, but that same gun may disappear under the "classic suit straight cuff" of the same trousers in an ankle holster. One inside-the-waistband and one outside-the-waistband hip holster will accompany the primary handgun, and if neither of those is ambidextrous, there will also be a weak-side holster in case I sustain an arm or hand injury

on the road and can't use the dominant hand. (Been there, done that.) A belly-band holster that doubles as a money belt will go in the suitcase too, and I've been known to toss in a shoulder rig to allow for lower back injuries where I won't want weight on the hips, or a case of intestinal flu that might have me dropping my pants constantly in public rest rooms, a situation where hip holsters are tough (though not impossible) to accommodate.

The wardrobe of guns. I've gotten pretty good at gun concealment over the years, but I've learned that I can't hide a full-size 45 automatic in a swim suit. A good friend of mine carries a little Smith & Wesson J-frame Airweight 38 snub-nose revolver in his, though.

A snub-nose 38 is a great little carry gun, and it's a staple of any CCW "gun wardrobe." However, I've been in a lot of places where I was *way* more comfortable with something bigger, easier to shoot accurately and fast, that held more – and more powerful – ammunition.

You'll find yourself buying more firearms as you get into CCW seriously. Some will suit you, and you will keep them for carry. Some will turn out to be great guns but just too big and heavy, and you may keep them as home defense or even recreational weapons. Some will turn out to not be for you, and you'll trade them in for something that works better. That's all OK.

A small gun that will be there in circumstances where you just *can't* carry a bigger one may still save your life. There will be times when a larger gun will give you not only more confidence, but more capability. I've debriefed gunfight survivors who would have died if they'd had only a five-shot 38, but survived because they had something that carried more ammo and let them stay in the fight long enough to win it. So, as time goes on, you'll want at least one small CCW handgun and one larger one. Don't be surprised if, like so many professionals, you find yourself carrying both at once. It's a belt-and-suspenders, "same reason there's a spare tire in my car" kind of thing.

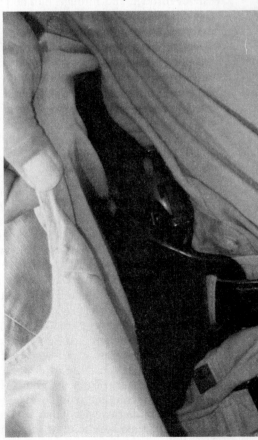

…that you have draped the garment strategically to cover a full-size Beretta police service pistol in a quick-access Dillon holster.

About This Book

This book is not about when you can shoot. That would be *In the Gravest Extreme*. It's not about how to shoot a handgun under stress. That would be *StressFire*. It's not about a total approach to personal safety and crime prevention. That would be *The Truth About Self-Protection*. All three are available from Police Bookshelf, PO Box 122, Concord, NH 03302, (www.ayoob.com). I recommend them, but hell, I *wrote* them, so take the recommendation from whence it comes.

The chapters on guns and holsters are generic. If I don't recommend a particular brand, it doesn't necessarily mean it's a piece of crap; it may just mean that I haven't worked with it long enough to give it a recommendation. Anything I recommend in here by name is something I've tested sufficiently to trust my own life to; I can't do that with every product. I've tested guns that were obviously designed by people who didn't carry them and didn't know how to shoot them, and holsters obviously designed by people who didn't carry concealed handguns. I don't have time to list the junk, nor do I have the time or the financial resources to fight nuisance suits by junk-makers who sue people for telling the truth about their products. If I say it's good, I'm putting my name and reputation on that fact. If I don't mention it, well, I'm just not mentioning it, but remember, there's good stuff out there that I probably just haven't tested yet.

I may be a funnel, but I can't funnel the whole industry.

Some points will be repeated in different chapters. I suppose that reflects a little of the instructor's mantra, "Tell 'em what you're gonna tell 'em; tell 'em; then tell 'em what you told 'em." I think it reflects more the simple reality that in an adult lifetime as an author, I've found that folks read novels straight front to back, but non-fiction books like this a chapter at a time, piece-meal, jumping back and forth. Some points need to be made in context for the sporadic reader.

TV and movie characters are mentioned here a lot. That's because such things have largely defined public perception about concealed carry methods. It needed to be addressed.

In some chapters, you'll see me drawing from under a transparent raincoat. No, I'm not recommending "transparent concealment"! It's a device I hit on to demonstrate concealed draw without hand and weapon being hidden from the learner's view.

In reading this book, it's important to maintain some perspectives.

The *raison d'etre* is important. Carrying a concealed handgun reflects serious understandings about predictable danger in Life, and it brings more serious understandings with it. We'll talk about that.

This book is laid out the way it is for a reason. **Rules of the Road** are important. We'll talk about where you can carry, and where you can't. When you should, and when you shouldn't.

Hardware is important. We'll discuss which handguns have proven themselves best suited for concealed carry for

> ## Use your power wisely. Keep your good people safe.

different purposes in different "dress code" situations. Hardware encompasses not only the guns but the holsters, the ammunition, the reloading devices, and other accessories.

Deployment is important. It's amazing, for instance, how many people have designed and sold belly-band holsters but obviously don't know the most effective ways of either carrying them or drawing from them…not to mention how many people have carried ankle holsters for a career as an armed professional and never learned how to most quickly and efficiently draw from one. Let's see if we can't fix that…

I know it sounds complicated. That's because it *is* complicated. By the time you finish this book, you will have noticed that I've never invoked the currently popular weapons training buzzword that is the "KISS principle." KISS stands for "Keep It Simple, Stupid."

I can't utter that in good conscience, for two reasons.

For one thing, I don't think you're stupid.

For another, I know for *damn* sure it ain't simple.

If anybody wants "simple," the simple fact is, a lot of people died for the lessons that were funneled into this book. Some of them were good guys and gals who died only because they didn't know the things the gunfight survivors and master gunfighters gave me to funnel into the words that follow. And we'll never know how many innocent victims died *because they didn't have a gun, right there and right then that they could have drawn from concealment and used to save their lives and others.*

And I think you know that, too, or you wouldn't be reading this.

Within a few days of my deadline for this book, a mass murderer in Colorado hit two religious institutions, and killed people at both. At the first location, he killed innocent people and sauntered away. There was no one there with the wherewithal to stop him.

At the second death scene, he opened fire in the parking lot, and then entered the building. He didn't get thirty feet before he was interdicted by one Jeanne Assam, a member of the church who was licensed to CCW, had her own gun, and knew how to use it. She shot him down like the mad dog he was, and in his last bullet-riddled moments the only person he could still shoot was himself. He died. No more innocent people did. Jeanne Assam had taught a lesson to us all.

On the pro-gun side, people started posting on the Internet the story of Charl van Wyck, a story I had put into this manuscript months before. I can only hope that the general public will look at both Assam's story *and* Van Wyck's, and the lessons that came before. I am sure – sadly sure – that similar lessons will be written in blood after this book is published.

Thank you for taking the time to read what follows. Thank you for having the courage to be the sheepdog prepared to fight the wolves back away from the lambs. I hope you find the following pages useful.

Use your power wisely. Keep your good people safe.

WHY WE CARRY

Why do we carry? Ask Dr. Suzanna Gratia-Hupp, photographed here while testifying for concealed carry legislation. She watched her parents murdered during the Luby's Cafeteria massacre in Killeen, Texas, helpless to stop the gunman only a few feet away, because law of the period forced her to leave her revolver outside in her car.

The question is constantly asked, "Why do you want to carry a gun?" Here are several proven answers.

Forty-eight of America's fifty states now have at least some provision for law-abiding private citizens to carry loaded, concealed handguns in public. This comes as a shock to many people in American society. Those responsible adults who choose to avail themselves of the concealed carry privilege will constantly be challenged as to this decision by friends, family, co-workers, and others who have not been educated on the issues involved. This is one reason it is always sensible to be extremely discreet about concealed carry, and to not broadcast the fact that one goes legally armed.

At the same time, the old phrase "forewarned is forearmed" applies to the argument as well as the practice itself. Those of us who've had to debate the issue repeatedly, in forums ranging from State Houses where reform concealed carry legislation was on the floor to radio, TV, and print media, have learned that the best response is often a "sound bite." A good sound bite is short, memorable, and so logical that the listener tends to ask himself, "Why didn't I think of that?"

The following effective sound bite answers to the most common challenges against concealed carry have been proven to work time and again. As done here, always be able to back them up with more detail. Keep it logical, and

A much younger Ayoob with one of his kids, today an adult and a parent herself. Here, she's learning about ammunition. In her late teens, she won a national handgun championship title…and not long after, used her legally-carried handgun to defend herself successfully against two large male rape suspects on a city street.

always, *always* apply common sense.

It is generally accepted that the population of this country is approximately three hundred million, and that there are only a bit over 700,000 currently serving police officers. By their nature, wolves attack sheep when the sheepdog isn't there, and criminals are careful to make sure there are no police officers in sight when they attack their victims. This leaves the victim alone to fend for himself or herself.

"Why do you carry a gun?"

Kathy Jackson said it best on her website (www.corneredcat.com): "I carry a gun because I can't carry a policeman."

Carrying a concealed handgun in public is very much like keeping a small fire extinguisher in your car. Neither means that by possessing it, you become an official member of the public safety community. Neither means that you don't need public safety personnel from the fire department or the police department.

But the concealed handgun and the fire extinguisher are each emergency rescue tools designed to allow first responders to crisis to hold the line against death and injury, to control things and save lives, until the designated professionals can get to the scene to do what they're paid to do. That's all the responsibly carried concealed handgun is: emergency rescue equipment for use by a competent

first responder, who in this case, often turns out to be the intended victim of intentional, violent crime.

"But aren't you worried that if more people carry guns, more arguments will escalate into people being shot and killed?"

No. Responsible gun owners are too practical to worry about things that don't happen.

Ever since the 1980s, when Florida started the trend of reform legislation that replaced the elitism and cronyism of the old "discretionary" permit system with the modern, enlightened "shall issue" model, opponents of self-protection and civil liberties have made the argument that "blood would run in the streets." It hasn't happened yet. If anything, statistics show that violent crime against the person seems to go *down* after shall-issue legislation is passed.

In the wake of the recent confirmation of this by Minnesota's experience with their fledgling shall-issue permit system, my old friend Joe Waldron of the Citizens' Committee for the Right to Keep and Bear Arms (CCRKBA) put it as well as it's ever been said. The Committee had noted, "According to the (Minneapolis Star Tribune) newspaper, people with gun permits are far less likely to be involved in a crime, whether it is a physical assault, a drug crime or even drunken driving. Authorities have confirmed that the hysterical predictions about gunfights at traffic stops and danger to children simply have not materialized."

Commented Waldron, executive director of the CCRKBA, "You will not hear an apology or any kind of acknowledgement from the anti-self-defense crowd about the statistics. No doubt they will try to blame the law for crimes committed by people carrying guns illegally. But the newspaper did a good job of sorting out fact from fiction, and it has found that only a miniscule number of licensed citizens have been involved in serious crimes, and a tiny fraction of armed citizens have had their permits revoked.

"We knew all along what Hennepin County Sheriff Rich Stanek told the newspaper: the worst predictions of gun control advocates who bitterly fought to keep this law off the books just haven't come true. We're delighted that the press, which did not support the law, has at least acknowledged the public's right to know how the law is working.

"Minnesota is just one more state where people have been given the opportunity to pass a law and see how it really works. The state's legally-armed citizens have proven not only that they are overwhelmingly responsible with firearms, the data shows that providing the means for citizens to go armed is not a threat to public safety, and never has been."

Concluded Waldron, "The Personal Protection Act (in

Minnesota) has succeeded in destroying the myth that legally-armed citizens are somehow a threat to the general public. We knew they were wrong, and now everybody else knows it, too."

"Why should a person who lives in a low crime area feel they had to carry a gun?"

Famed combat small arms instructor John Farnam said it best. He was teaching an officer survival class to rural police when one officer asked him, "Hey, how often do you think cops get killed around here, anyway?" Farnam's reply was classic: "Same as anywhere. Just once."

In the 19th century, Coffeyville, Kansas and Northfield, Minnesota were quiet, safe towns where no one might have thought ordinary citizens needed guns…until they were robbed by violent, professional robbery gangs from "out of town." One of those gangs was led by Jesse James and Cole Younger, and the other consisted primarily of the infamous Dalton brothers. Both gangs were shot to pieces by armed townsfolk acting in defense of themselves and their communities.

In the early 20th century, the automobile allowed criminals to range even more widely. The John Dillinger/ Baby Face Nelson gangs made a specialty of robbing small town banks and escaping in their high-speed Hudsons and Ford V8s. They, too, felt the sting of armed citizens' gunfire. When robbing a bank in South Bend, Indiana, Baby Face Nelson and Homer Van Meter, both hardened cop-killers, were shot and wounded by a jeweler with a .22 target handgun. Nelson was saved by his bullet proof vest, and Van Meter, while knocked senseless by the bullet that ricocheted off his skull, would have been killed if the shooter's aim had been truer by an inch, or if the armed citizen had launched a more appropriate round. In another bank robbery, John Dillinger and accomplice John Hamilton were each shot in the right shoulder by a retired judge, armed with an antique revolver and firing from a window across the street.

Now, in the 21st century, little has changed. Criminals are highly mobile. They have learned that "the thin blue line" is thinnest in the hinterlands. Police in rural communities can tell you that many of their major crimes are committed by criminals from cities who "commute to the crime scene." And any small town cop can tell you that even "Mayberry, RFD" can grow its own violent criminals without any outside help.

The smaller the town, the more rural your location, the longer it generally takes police to respond to an emergency call. Thus, while in the big picture there may be fewer crimes committed in "low crime communities," that doesn't make them safe by any means…and, more remote from police assistance, the potential victim in such an area has all the more need to be self-sufficient in terms of being able to protect self and loved ones from nomadic criminals.

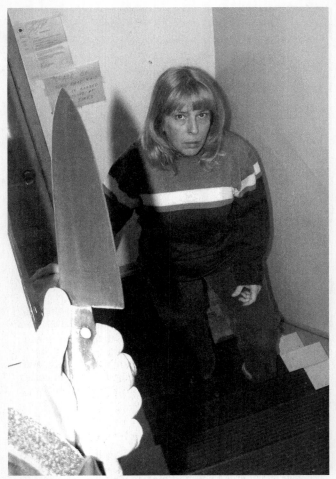
Why carry a gun? Suppose you're a petite female, coming home alone, and are confronted by a knife-armed attacker…

"Why can't you face the fact that a study has proven that a gun in the home is 43 times more likely to kill a member of the household than a burglar?"

Probably because, being logical people, most of us who carry guns detest having to look at such fact-twisting exercises in sophistry.

"Discredited" is a strong word, but the study in question is indeed one of the most thoroughly discredited exercises in twisted statistics of the late 20th century. It compared all deaths by gunfire in two communities of similar size, one in Canada and one in the United States. Under "guns killing householders," it included suicides, many of which typically are the so-called "rational suicide." This is what happens when an individual diagnosed with a terminal disease that brings a long, agonizing death chooses to depart life with dignity. (In some foreign countries, this process is assisted by state-approved euthanasia, not an option in the USA.)

That study's use of human body count as the ultimate

with statistics, how to conveniently manipulate the truth, and how to misinterpret reality. Its proper place would be in a book of "Dirty Debate Tricks That Won't Work in the Long Run," not in any logical discussion of concealed carry that is subjected to critical thinking and honest, fact-based debate.

> *"A review of strategy discussions on Internet gun boards reveals the fact that many people who are licensed to carry guns carry more than one. If this is not an indication of two-gun cowboy mentality, how else can it be explained?"*
>
> **Firearms instructor and author David Kenik was once asked, "Why do you carry three guns?" He calmly replied, "Because four would be ostentatious."**

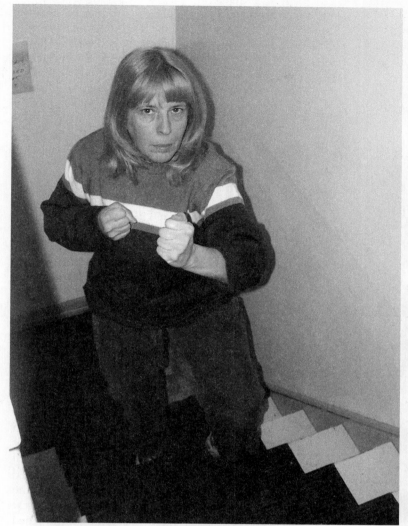

...do you think a martial arts stance will ward him off? Or...

The simple fact is, armed citizens to a large degree make their choice of defensive firearms based on the model of the domestic law enforcement sector. For generations, when the 38 Special revolver was the overwhelming choice of American police, it was also the overwhelming choice of armed citizens. Though freedom of choice allowed the citizenry to carry autoloading pistols before those guns became popular with police, the general replacement of the service revolver with the service pistol in American police work greatly increased the popularity of the semiautomatic pistol in the private sector.

Similarly, the last several decades have seen a vast increase in the number of police officers who carry backup handguns on duty. A number of police departments even issue a second handgun to all sworn personnel for just this purpose. Not surprisingly, the armed citizenry has modeled on this as well, and for the same good reasons.

Any firearm can run out of ammunition, malfunction, be dropped by a wounded "good guy," or be snatched from its legitimate user. In all those cases, recourse to a second handgun is the fastest avenue – and often the *only* avenue – to last-ditch survival.

Just off the top of my head, I can think of at least seven cases where recourse to another immediately-available weapon saved the life of a private citizen caught up in a gunfight. In three of those seven instances, the primary defensive handgun had been snatched away by a homicidal criminal, and the second gun saved the life of the law-abiding citizen, who in each case was able to deploy the backup weapon quickly and effectively. In each of the other four instances, the primary handgun had run dry while shooting

arbiter of a complicated social issue poisoned its results in and of itself. The fact is that most law-abiding citizens who confront criminals and take them at gunpoint, *don't* have to kill them. The latest studies, by Professor John Lott, indicate that in well over 90 percent of such incidents, the felon either flees or submits to citizen's arrest when taken at gunpoint by his intended victim, and none of his blood is shed. The oft-quoted bogus study interprets this benevolent lack of bloodshed 180 degrees away from reality, as if the object of the exercise had been to kill intruders and anything less than a "kill" didn't count for the "good guys." How ironic...a hypocritical attempt to measure safety from murder by body count.

The Federal government's own statistics, at this writing, show that the United States is at an all-time low in gun-related fatal accidents.

Gun ownership quite aside, the cultural mores of each country in the "study" were not taken into consideration. There is simply less violent crime in Canada than in the US, by virtually every measurement, including measurements that factor out possession of firearms.

All told, then, the "43 times more likely" story will be remembered by history as a classic example of how to lie

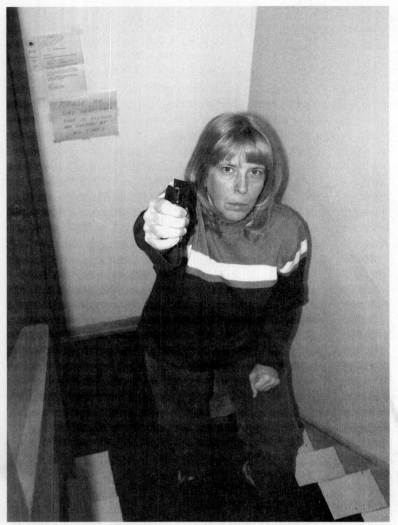

…perhaps this can of pepper spray? Or do you think just maybe …

side hip, and a 38 Special snub-nose revolver in a pocket holster on my non-dominant side. She is perfectly competent with either. Should danger threaten, the common law principle as recognized by state law in this particular jurisdiction would allow me to arm her due to exigent circumstances. Thus, there would be two trained and equipped "threat managers" capable of dealing with the situation, instead of just one.

"You bloodthirsty gun people only carry weapons because you want a chance to hurt or kill someone!"

On the contrary, we carry guns so we will be *less* likely to have to kill or cripple someone. It's called "Peace Through Superior Firepower."

History has shown that the greatest power of the gun is its power to *deter.* Bear in mind that criminals, by definition, target only victims they believe they can overpower. When the intended victim draws a gun, the predator realizes that their erstwhile target has the ability to kill them instantly. This tends to modify their behavior immediately, without a shot being fired.

Remember the Lott study, referenced above, which showed in the 1990s that the overwhelming majority of times a citizen drew a gun to ward off a criminal, the incident ended with no blood being shed on either side of the encounter. The studies of famed criminologist Gary Kleck showed the same thing in the 1980s. A study by the California Attorney General's Office in the 1970s showed it, too.

Another way to see it is to simply take the gun out of the picture, and examine the remaining alternatives. When asked about self-protection, opponents of gun ownership rights will typically suggest pepper spray or an unarmed combat class. Let's look at how well that has worked on the street for police, who have the strongest pepper spray and some of the best unarmed combat training.

While pepper spray certainly has its place at the lower levels of the force continuum, it has never been seriously put forth by police or other protection professionals as adequate for dealing with an armed antagonist. In fact, law enforcement history is rife with criminals so violent that pepper spray had no effect on them, and they did not stop their violent aggression after being sprayed until after officers had been forced to shoot them, or strike them with batons so many times that they had been permanently injured.

Attending any women's rape prevention class or basic self-defense class, one will be taught to attack the assailant's genitals, eyes, or throat, or to pick up some object and strike

it out with armed criminals, and because reloading the empty gun was impractical or even impossible under the circumstances, the ability to instantly transition to a second loaded handgun literally made the difference between life and death.

There is another area in which having a second weapon on one's person can make a huge difference to law-abiding armed citizens when deadly danger threatens. In the "concealed carry community," there are a great many people who only actually carry guns part of the time. The carrying of a back-up handgun allows one competent armed citizen to arm another citizen, who might be equally competent but, at the moment, unarmed in the face of suddenly breaking danger.

For example, at this writing I am spending time with my girlfriend in one of America's largest cities. This particular metropolis has many attractions, but it is also a notoriously high crime area. The lady in question is highly competent with a handgun, in fact is a current regional IDPA (International Defensive Pistol Association) champion, but as it happens, while I am legal to carry in this particular jurisdiction, she is not.

I am carrying a 9mm SIG-Sauer pistol on my dominant

...this 9mm SIG P239 is the likeliest of all to deter him with no bloodshed on either side, or at worst, stop him decisively before he reaches her with his knife?

"You don't have any right to carry guns anyway! The Second Amendment is about the National Guard, not personal protection!"

The Bill of Rights was framed shortly after the American Revolution. A "National Guard" in the time of the revolution would have been Tories loyal to King George and duty-bound to crush the American patriots. Do you really think this was what the framers intended to empower and enable?

him repeatedly in the head. We are talking about crushed testicles, eyes gouged out, suffocation, and fractured skulls resulting in profound brain injuries. All these results fit in the category of life-threatening trauma and/or grave bodily harm: a deadly force level of injury. Deadly force is deadly force, whether delivered with bare hands, clubbed objects, *or* a deadly weapon per se.

The big difference is deterrent effect. It is greatly lacking with "lesser weapons." In one notorious case, a rapist murdered two women because, he said later, he became enraged when one of them sprayed him with a Mace-like substance. A violent aggressor is likely to do little more than laugh if an intended victim he perceives to be smaller or weaker than himself squares off in a martial arts stance.

Contrast this with a victim who draws a gun and is obviously prepared to immediately open fire. The difference in deterrent effect is literally night and day. In terms of body language, a shooting stance with a drawn firearm is the ultimate exclamation point.

Thus, we have an ironic reality. The person who is not armed with a deadly weapon will very likely have to kill or cripple a determined attacker to defeat the threat. By contrast, the person who is armed with a deadly weapon is *hugely* more likely to be able to end the threat with no physical injury on either side, due to the tremendous

deterrent effect offered by their legally carried firearm.

The American Bill of Rights may be the most carefully crafted delineation of individual rights in the history of the human experience. It strains credibility to the breaking point to ask thinking people to believe that somehow, those who wrote it accidentally included a "state's rights" issue near the top of the list. The Bill of Rights was drawn largely from the constitutions of the existing colonies that preceded it, many of which are absolutely explicit about the right to bear arms being an individual right, not a collective one, and many of which expressly include personal and family protection among the reasons for ensuring that right. Anyone who doubts this has not done his homework. Even opponents of individual firearms ownership have admitted, after reviewing the vast body of Constitutional scholarship, that the Second Amendment was indeed originally intended to be an individual right.

The arguments will not be concluded within the lifetimes of anyone reading this. The debate has become too emotional and too polarized. Those persons who have accepted the responsibility for their safety and the safety of those who count on them can only stand prepared to defend, not only innocent lives, but the very practice of carrying weapons to fulfill those responsibilities.

WHERE YOU CAN
(AND CAN'T) CARRY

Many like to believe that the "bear arms" portion of Second Amendment means that the Bill of Rights is all they need for concealed carry. Not in this world. If that sweet little Kahr Elite MK9 is to be carried concealed, you have to be within the law!

When and where to carry a gun is a little like when and where to go nude. In either case, there will be times and places where you'll find it comfortable, and even times and places where others will be happy that you're in that condition. However, there are also times and places where it will be inappropriate, offensive, and even illegal.

Houses of Worship

I remember going to church one Sunday with my older sister when I was a little kid, and being shocked and even outraged when a state trooper who worked that area came in and sat in the pew in front of us, with his big 6 ½" barrel Smith & Wesson Model 27 357 Magnum swinging in plain view in its flapped swivel holster. How dare he bring a deadly weapon into a house of worship!

There has been a lot of water under the bridge since that Sunday, and I have totally changed my view on the topic.

A few years ago, a maniac walked into a religious service being held in a hotel conference room in Wisconsin. He opened fire, and committed mass murder before killing himself. He apparently assumed, correctly, that in a state

In recent years, great advances have been made for concealed carry rights in Midwestern states, but the two worst states for CCW are in that region also. Pistol is the handy, effective 9mm EMP from Springfield Armory.

which had no provision for private citizens to carry concealed handguns in public, no one could stop him from carrying out his monstrous plan. That was exactly how things turned out.

In Texas, not long after then-Governor George W. Bush signed shall-issue concealed carry into law, the law was modified to allow permit-holders to be armed in places of worship. A mass murderer entered a church in Fort Worth, scouted around until he found a prayer meeting peopled exclusively by teenagers, and opened fire there, exacting a terrible toll in human tragedy. He apparently knew that elsewhere in the church, there just might be armed, responsible adults who would shoot back and put him in jeopardy. He carefully selected the one sub-group of victims who, too young to have carry permits under Texas law, would be helpless.

On the West Coast, a rabid anti-Semite looked for Jews to murder. He later admitted that he thought about hitting a synagogue, but feared someone might be armed and shoot back. So, instead, he committed mass murder in a Jewish day care center. This is typical of cowards: they seek unarmed, helpless victims.

All over the world, terrorists have learned that to strike terror literally into the souls of those they intend to intimidate, mass murder at a religious center can get the morbid attention they seek. Militant Islamists have murdered those of other belief systems at houses of worship from the Middle East to Pakistan, and a mad Israeli military reservist killed several innocent Muslims when he opened fire at a mosque. Clergyman Peter Hammond of South Africa lists the following series of terroristic mass murders at churches in his foreword to Charl van Wyk's book, *Shooting Back*. (Christian Liberty Books, Cape Town, South Africa, 2001.)

"When I saw the shocking carnage at St. James Church (in Kenilworth, South Africa), it immediately brought similar bloody scenes flooding back into my mind," wrote Hammond. "Over the last 19 years of missionary work I have personally come across scores of similar atrocities, in Angola, Mozambique, Rwanda and Sudan. In August 1983, Frelimo troops killed 5 pastors and burnt down all 5 churches in Maskito Village, Zambezia Province, Mozambique. In September 1983, Frelimo troops killed over 50 Christians and burned a church in Pasura village. At Chilleso Evangelical Church, in Angola, Cuban troops shot 150 Christians during a church service. At New Adams Farm in Zimbabwe, 16 missionaries and their children were

Where the laws aren't right, work for change! Author leaves Wisconsin State House in Madison after testifying for shall-issue concealed carry. Bill passed Legislature, but when anti-gun governor vetoed it, gun owners' civil rights forces fell one vote short of over-ride.

murdered in November 1987…On 23 June 1978, terrorists who supported Robert Mugabe murdered nine British missionaries and four young children, including a three-week old baby, at the Elim Mission Station."

Added Hammond, "It is worth noting that the only British missionary at the Elim Mission Station who had a firearm – he owned a 38 revolver – was also the only survivor! Being cowards, the terrorists left him alone, preferring defenceless victims. The first the armed man knew about the attack, was when he woke up the next morning to find the base deserted. He later discovered the bodies of his fellow missionaries on the sports field. Gun-free is no guarantee."

The author of the book *Shooting Back: The Right and Duty of Self-Defence*, Charl van Wyk, was in the St. James church that terrible day when the terrorists opened fire. Here is his own account:

He wrote, "Grenades were exploding in flashes of light. Pews shattered under the blasts, sending splinters flying through the air. An automatic assault rifle was being fired and was fast ripping the pews – and whomever, whatever was in its trajectory – to pieces. We were being attacked!

"Instinctively, I knelt down behind the bench in front

of me and pulled out my 38 Special snub-nosed revolver, which I always carried with me. I would have felt undressed without it. Many people could not understand why I would carry a firearm into a church service, but I argued that this was a particularly dangerous time in South Africa…

"…Well my moment of truth had arrived, I thought, as my hands steadied around the revolver. The congregation had thrown themselves down – in order to protect themselves as far as possible from the deluge of flying bullets and shrapnel. By God's grace, the view of the terrorists from my seat, fourth row from the back of the church, was perfect. The building was built like a cinema with the floor sloping towards the stage in front. So without any hesitation, I knelt and aimed, firing two shots at the attackers. This appeared ineffective, as my position was too far from my targets to take precise aim with a snub-nosed revolver. I had to get closer to the terrorists.

"So I started moving to the end of the pew on my haunches and leopard-crawled the rest of the way when I realized that my position was too high up. The only way I could make those heartless thugs stop their vicious attack was to try and move in behind them and then shoot them in the back at close range.

"I sprinted to the back door of the church, pushing a lady out of the way, so that I could kick the door open and not be hindered as I sought to get behind the gunmen to neutralize their attack. As I desperately rounded the corner of the building, outside in the parking area, I saw a man standing next to what was the 'getaway' car. Resting on his hip was his automatic rifle. He had it pointed up to the heavens as if in defiance of the Lordship of Jesus Christ!

"The man was looking in the direction of the door through which they had launched their attack. Was he waiting for people who would make easy targets to come running out, or maybe even for me? I stepped back behind the corner of the wall and prepared to blast the last of my firepower. I strode out in full view of the terrorist and shot my last three rounds. By this time, the others were already in the car. My target jumped into the vehicle and the driver sped away immediately, leaving behind the acrid stench of burning tyres and exhaust fumes…"

Elsewhere in this book, we discuss such factors as the selected carry gun's ammunition capacity, and the carrying of spare ammunition. In this case, van Wyk's five-shot revolver was now empty, but it is telling to examine his first thoughts in the immediate aftermath. Wrote van Wyk, "It's hard to express my feelings as I watched them drive away, but I remember thinking, 'Lord, why haven't I got more ammunition? Why? Why? Why?'"

It turned out that one of van Wyk's shots had wounded one of the terrorists, one Khaya Christopher Makoma, and his first two rounds of return fire had been enough to send the assassins fleeing with their AK47s. At least that was the assessment of the South African Police, never a pro-gun organization, when it issued van Wyk a commendation for his actions. The award read, "Mr. Charl Adriaan van Wyk is hereby commended for outstanding services rendered in that he: on 25 July 1993 endangered his own life in warding off the attack perpetrated on the St. James Congregation in Kenilworth. His action in pursuing the suspects on foot and returning fire prevented further loss of life. One of the suspects wounded in the incident was later arrested."

Charl van Wyk, like many others, cites Biblical confirmation of his choice to be armed. **Proverbs 25:26:** "Like a muddied spring or a polluted well is a righteous man who gives way to the wicked." **Luke 22:36:** "If thou hast not a sword, sell thy cloak and buy one." (This particular quote was a favorite of my old friend Harlon Carter, the dynamic president of the National Rifle Association.) **Nehemiah 4:14:** "Don't be afraid of them. Remember the Lord who is great and awesome, and fight for your brothers, your sons and your daughters, your wives and your homes." **Exodus 22:2:** "If a thief is caught breaking in and is struck so that he dies, the defender is not guilty of bloodshed."

Remember that in the original Hebrew, the Sixth Commandment is not "Thou shalt not kill," but "Thou shalt not commit murder." That is, thou shalt not kill with evil intent.

I have trained many clergymen over the years, most of them the religious leaders of their particular parish or synagogue. One was a Bishop of the Catholic church. Most (not all, but most) of these particular *padres* were scrupulous about making it clear to me that the utmost confidentiality was necessary in regard to their training. It was obvious why that was, but it was a Bishop who said it best. "If it was to get out that I carried a gun every day," said the Bishop, "I would end up as the parish priest in Flat Rock, Iowa."

In some jurisdictions, houses of worship are off-limits for legal concealed carry. In others, it may be OK to carry there in the eyes of the law, but forbidden by that particular church's policy. In some states, you can lose your permit for carrying in a place that is "posted" against the practice. In others, there is no penalty for ignoring a "no-guns" policy, but if your weapon is spotted, you can expect to be asked to leave. If you do not comply, you can then be arrested for "trespass after warning," and in addition to that particular offense, your permit to carry may now be in jeopardy.

Stay within the law, and use common sense. It ain't all about "praise the Lord and pass the ammunition."

Carrying in Schools

The series of mass murders in American schools in the last few years, particularly the atrocity at Columbine High School in Littleton, Colorado in 1999 and the one at Virginia Tech in 2007, have brought up the issue of whether teachers or other school personnel should be armed on campus. The issue has raised some heated discussions on both sides.

Shortly after the Columbine incident, I was called by the *Wall Street Journal* and asked to write a short essay for their op-ed page on the topic, in which I came out strongly for a policy that would allow for volunteer teachers and other staff to be specially trained and authorized to carry concealed handguns while at school. TV's *Today Show* got hold of it, and invited me to appear opposite a spokesman for one of the educators' associations, who totally opposed the idea. No one, he scoffed, had ever heard of such a

In some jurisdictions, a sign like this means the same as "CCW Illegal Here!"

It is generally accepted that it is illegal for a private citizen to wear a gun in a U.S. Post Office, irrespective of concealed carry permits.

suggestion.

I then explained how the Israeli schools have had this system in place since the Maalot massacre of schoolchildren by terrorists in the mid-1970s, and had effectively put an end to such problems. The plainclothes bodyguards were volunteer parents and grandparents as well as teachers, all trained by the Israeli civil guard. When host Matt Lauer sarcastically asked if the plan would include assault weapons, I replied that the discreetly concealed 9mm semiautomatic pistols of the Israelis had worked just fine.

Similar concepts are in place in Peru, the Philippines, and elsewhere. We've also seen proof of the efficacy of an armed citizen response in school shootings in the United States. In Pearl, Mississippi a twisted teen named Luke Woodham stabbed his mother to death to get the key to his estranged father's gun cabinet, and the next morning showed up at school with a 30-30 deer rifle. He opened fire, with fatal results. As Woodham ran to his car, assistant principal Joel Myrick ran to his, and retrieved a compact Colt Officers

There are gun law compendia for many states, but remember that the laws are constantly changing. Review them, but update constantly!

45ACP automatic. He confronted the escaping Woodham, who crawled out of his car and cravenly surrendered. The young murderer had been heading in the direction of a nearby junior high school, still in possession of the death weapon and an ample supply of ammunition.

In Pennsylvania, another crazy punk kid opened fire with a small caliber pistol at an off-grounds school affair. The owner of the venue grabbed a shotgun from his office and took the vicious little punk at gunpoint. The latter, of course, surrendered, and a massacre was very likely averted. In Virginia, a mass shooting at a law school was aborted when two adult students drew their own handguns and took the armed offender at gunpoint, at which time he instantly gave up.

The reality is as obvious as a corpse on display in a funeral home casket. Guns in the hands of good people stop armed bad people from committing mass murder. "Gun-free zones" literally become hunting preserves for the psychopaths who hunt humans.

Federal Buildings

As a general rule, Federal buildings are off-limits for private citizens with firearms, concealed carry permits notwithstanding. If you feel a compelling need to carry a gun in one of those places and don't want to take this advice, phone the office you wish to visit and ask them about their policy. In the unlikely event that they tell you "Sure, it's OK to carry here," get something in writing on Government letterhead with a signature from a responsible individual.

The place most folks with permits especially want to carry is, of course, the Post Office. It's the one office of the Federal government that the private citizen most frequently visits. There has been a great deal of controversy over this issue. Some people interpret the wording of the regulation that generally prohibits firearms from such places as exempting permit-holders. There are others who consider that interpretation to be wishful thinking.

I have occasion to enter Post Office branches all over this country, and there is generally a sign present (sometimes conspicuous, sometimes not) stating flatly that firearms are not permitted on these premises. Stating later in court that what you read on this or that electronic gun forum on the Internet saying you could carry in Post Offices, carried more weight in your mind than a sign posted by that Office flatly prohibiting carry there, is not going to put you in great shape if you are arrested by security there for illegal CCW.

My advice to private citizens is conservative, and simple: "Don't carry a gun inside the United States Post Office, or any other Federal building.

Courthouses

I don't personally know of any courthouses anymore where the private citizen can carry a gun around inside. In a handful of jurisdictions (check *carefully* to see if yours is one) it is legal for the armed citizen to actually check his or her gun into a lockbox at Courthouse Security when they enter, and retrieve it when they leave. These, unfortunately, are few and far between. I have also seen court security personnel literally become hysterical when someone simply asked them about the legality of firearms in the courthouse. ("Oh, my God! A gun! Do you have a gun? *Do you have a gun?!?*")

When in doubt, call Security at the Courthouse in question, and get it sorted out clearly beforehand. Make sure they understand that you are a private citizen with a carry permit, and not a police officer.

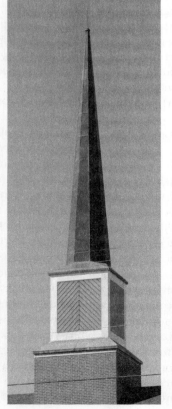

Federal Courthouses in particular take guns very seriously. If you are carrying your gun when you walk through the front door and ask the guards at the metal detectors if you can check your gun, *you're already in violation because you're already inside the courthouse proper.*

For all these reasons, the general rule of thumb is, "Don't bring a gun to the courthouse." If the gun is evidence, talk to the attorney who summoned you there, and he will go through the process of getting the gun brought in, turned over to Security, and brought to the courtroom and back out at the appropriate time.

Alcoholic Beverage Establishments

Gunpowder and alcohol can obviously be a pretty scary mixture. Different jurisdictions handle that in different ways. I used to enjoy visiting the Shortstop, a tavern on LA's Sunset Boulevard. It was the model for the bar Joe Wambaugh called The House of Misery in

"In the place/That has the steeple/They may not welcome/Pistol-packin' people."

his novel, *The Black Marble*. It was a cop bar. Most times I was in there, there were probably only three or four people in the place that weren't carrying guns.

At this writing (2007), it is perfectly legal to carry your gun into a tavern in Massachusetts or New Hampshire, and have a drink or two, if you have a CCW permit. Obviously, if you get drunk and do something stupid with the gun, you can expect to go to prison. It's your responsibility to be, well, *responsible*.

In one case I was called in on recently, a Massachusetts CCW-holder dropped in at his favorite watering spot, and didn't even have time for one drink before a man he well knew to be a viciously brutal bully began harassing a local woman. The armed citizen stepped in, and became the object of the bully's wrath. Bouncers intervened and kept the bully, who was known locally as "Killer," from attacking the permit holder.

In most jurisdictions, concealed carry is illegal in courthouses. Check the laws in any jurisdiction where you carry.

They all left the bar separately, a few minutes apart, the armed citizen leaving last. He was carrying a Beretta 40 in a hip holster under his sweatshirt. As he drove away, he saw a man violently attacking a woman. Pulling over, he saw it was the bully and the woman from the bar, whom the bully had been strangling moments before. He jumped out of his car and ordered the man to let her go. The bully threw her to the ground, screamed "I'll kill you!" and lunged at the CCW holder, who by now had drawn his Beretta. He fired one shot. The assailant went down, mortally wounded, and the rescuer survived a more than three-year legal nightmare that culminated with his acquittal of all the charges (Murder, Manslaughter, and Aggravated Assault) that were lodged against him. If he had not been carrying his gun (legally, under that state's laws) both he and the woman he saved might have been killed or profoundly injured.

Not long ago, a New Hampshire man was having a quiet drink in a city bar, when a weirdo pulled out a gun with murder clearly on his mind. The citizen, licensed to carry his little Kel-Tec "rat gun," drew and shot him. The offender lived, but after being shot gave up his attempts to hurt innocent people and focused solely on surviving his gunshot injuries. To the best of my knowledge, at this writing, the armed citizen who shot him has not been criminally charged. He, too, had a permit and was perfectly legal to carry while drinking moderately and responsibly... *in that jurisdiction.*

In our nation's patchwork quilt of state-by-state laws, things change depending where you are. In North Carolina, you can't even carry your gun into a restaurant that has a liquor license, even if you're not drinking. The same is true in Virginia, with one exception: you can "open carry" a handgun

in a restaurant with a liquor license, and even while consuming alcohol in a bar! Indeed, the VCDL (Virginia Citizens' Defense League) considers the "good restaurant access" factor to be one of the strongest pillars of their advocacy of open handgun carry. One night while teaching a lethal force class in Richmond, some VCDL members took me to the bar at an Outback to make a point. Most were conspicuously carrying handguns in unconcealed holsters. They were not hassled. I couldn't help but notice, though, that the customers at one table nervously summoned a waiter and pointed, with frightened expressions, at the Glock 21 45 automatic on the hip of one VCDL member. The waiter explained that it was legal, and he was sorry, but there was nothing he could do about it.

Then you have the state of Florida, where at this writing, you can suck up all the booze you want in a *restaurant* with a liquor license. However, if the *maitre 'd* says, "Your table will be ready in a few minutes; you can wait in the bar," the second you step over that threshold you're committing a Class IV Felony, and your automatic loss of your concealed carry privilege will be the least of your problems. In that state, even if you are not consuming alcohol, you are forbidden to have your gun in any premises that makes more than 50% of its income from serving alcohol by the drink.

In Texas, not only can't you pack in a bar or a restaurant with a liquor license, you can't even enter a liquor store with your gun on to purchase a bottle of wine to bring home, unopened, for dinner. The same is true in New Mexico. A few years ago in the Albuquerque area, a madman with a knife attacked a woman in a local Wal-Mart and nearly murdered her. He was plunging his knife into her as an armed citizen leaned over the counter with a licensed-to-carry semiautomatic pistol, and shot him dead. All including the victim, who survived, realized he had saved her life. Alas, anti-gun organizations pushed for his prosecution on the grounds that he was illegally carrying the gun, because Wal-Marts typically sell carry-out alcoholic beverages. What saved this heroic gentleman was the fact that he was in the one Wal-Mart in the area that *didn't* have a liquor license.

The lesson is clear. *Know the law regarding the carry of firearms in alcoholic beverage establishments, in the community you happen to be in at the moment.* There is no national standard.

The simplest and most logical course of action is to *stay the hell out of bars when you're carrying a gun.* Even simpler and more logical, *just stay the hell out of bars.*

One of my mentors was the late, great Lt. Frank McGee, the legendary NYPD man who turned that department's Firearms Training Unit into a Firearms *and Tactics* Unit, took

Most jurisdictions forbid carry of concealed weapons at school sporting events.

A majority of jurisdictions forbid private carry of handguns at schools. Author would like to see this change to the proven-safer Israeli paradigm.

Carrying a gun at church is no longer unthinkable, in jurisdictions where it is not expressly forbidden. In a case that happened as this book went to press, an armed citizen gunned down a heavily armed mass murderer at a religious center and saved countless lives.

an overall tactical approach to training that caused the rate of the officers' gunfight survival to skyrocket. During one short period in the 1970s, three police officers were shot and killed in gunfights that occurred while they were off-duty in New York drinking establishments. Under Frank's tutelage, the FTU literally instituted a bloc of "off duty bar-room survival" training.

Frank strongly urged his officers to stay out of bars for one simple reason: bars are full of unknown drunk idiots with guns. I can tell you that he lived what he taught, too. McGee was a man who liked to light up an L&M cigarette and sip a glass of good Scotch…but he liked to do it someplace where it was safe to relax.

One time back in the '80s, Frank and I were guest-teaching at an Instructors' Update class at Smith & Wesson Academy in Springfield, Massachusetts, and both had rooms at a hotel in nearby Chicopee. After class, I invited Frank to join me for a drink in the hotel bar. "The hell with that," growled Frank. "You know why I hate bars. Come on by my room and have some Scotch."

"Ah, c'mon," I teased. "Bars have atmosphere. It'll be fun." I finally cajoled him, against his better judgment, into joining me at the hotel bar. Damned if we weren't just starting our first drinks, when a stereotype butch lesbian started a raging fight with her more "femme" lover in the bar. Frank flashed a triumphant smile at me and said, "See? See?" And then, with the hard-learned people skills of a New York cop, he spoke softly to the couple with a charm that would have evaporated the morning dew from the Blarney Stone, and had the aggressor tearfully apologizing to her lover in minutes.

At which point, we left the bar, me shaking my dumbfounded head. Frank McGee had made the point. All I could mutter was, "How the hell did you *arrange* that?"

I still visit bars occasionally, but less and less as the years go by, and never any more in Florida, New Mexico, or other states with those rules. If I need to meet someone in a bar on business where it's not legal to carry my gun on my person, I secure the gun in the hotel room.

If you use alcohol, use it the way you use guns: responsibly.

And One Other Thing…

You can be driving along, minding your own business, perfectly legal to have your concealed weapon on … and the blue, or red, or blue-and-red lights start flashing in your rear-view mirror. You are about to undergo a routine traffic stop while carrying a loaded gun. How exactly do you handle that?

If this book was larger, I could tell you enough stories for a *loooong* chapter on this topic alone. It isn't, so let's skip the war stories and cut to the bottom line, which is: it's situational. I say that because you'll find yourself in three different kinds of states. 1) Those that require a CCW holder to identify himself or herself immediately upon contact with police who are in the performance of their duties.

Here's a question for the teacher: in jurisdictions where you're legal to have a gun in your glove box but can't carry one any place where alcoholic beverages are sold, where do you stand legally when you visit this drive-through beer store?

In most jurisdictions, your carry permit allows you to be armed in a Wal-Mart... but not in New Mexico if that particular store sells alcoholic beverages.

2) States that don't have that, but do cross reference their CCW files with the state department of motor vehicles, so when a cop runs your license tag he immediately comes up with the fact that the owner is licensed to carry. 3) States where neither of those things are in force.

In the first kind of state, the best way to ID yourself is to carry your CCW card right next to your driver's license, and hand the two to the officer, without saying a word about the CCW. They'll see it, and take it from there. (Many or even most will relax a little, knowing they're dealing with someone who was investigated and deemed a proper person to carry a loaded, concealed handgun in public.) You have not uttered that scary "G-word" that frightens passersby, and young rookie cops who might be riding along tonight.

In the second kind of state, do exactly the same thing. You're not required to by law, but the cop knows when he stops you that you're likely to be carrying, and if he has to ask to find out, he may well see it subconsciously as you practicing "deception by omission of information." Ergo, CCW along with driver's license, as in the previous case.

In the third kind of state, where I'm a sworn officer, neither of the above is the case, and frankly I don't care. If I've pulled you over and I'm worried about you being armed, I'll ask you, at which time I'll expect an honest answer. You blurting at first contact something about having a gun tells me you've got a lot of ego invested in it, and that makes me nervous. But, that's just me. A lot of brother and sister officers in my and similar jurisdictions

tell me that the driver handing over the CCW reassures them. So, go with the short form, which will work wherever you are legal to carry: just fork over the CCW with the DL. The officer performing the stop will take it from there.

If the officer asks you to step out of your vehicle, it means that either you fit the description of someone he's looking for who did A Bad Thing and you'll be patted down, or that you were driving carelessly enough to give him probable cause to believe you might be "under the influence," in which case there is about to be a roadside field sobriety test. While some of my brothers and sisters use the gaze nystagmus test for this, most of us still use the Rohmberg series, which will involve movements such as arms extending out to the sides, which can reveal your holstered weapon. In either case, you don't want finding the gun to come as a surprise. If I was instructed, "Please step out of the car," I would keep my hands in plain sight and motionless and reply, "Certainly, Officer. However, I'm licensed to carry, and I do have it on. Tell me what you want me to do." The statement begins and ends with respectful deference and lawful compliance, and avoids anything that sounds like "I've got a gun," which is generally interpreted as a threatening statement.

I've been on both sides of these stops. Some cops will ask to take custody your gun while the stop is underway. They have the legal right to do that. Don't argue or give them Second Amendment lectures: they'll see it as a dangerous person with a gun who is non-compliant with lawful commands, and your night will quickly go downhill and

Ending up here for a CCW error would be a very bad thing...

...but ending up here because you were helpless is an even worse outcome. Proper planning, mind-set, and knowing the right thing to do can keep you out of both places.

If jurisdiction's prevailing law says "no guns in county or municipal buildings," check to see where that leaves you when you visit the public library.

your carry permit may soon grow wings and leave you. I wouldn't reach for the gun if the officer wanted that. I would say, "Certainly, Officer/Deputy/Trooper. However, I don't want it to look to anyone else as if I'm pulling a gun on an officer. The pistol is in a holster on my right hip. You're welcome to take it. Tell me what you want me to do."

If the officer insists on you handing it over, do it *very* slowly and carefully, with the muzzle in a safe direction and finger clear of the trigger guard. If you can simply unfasten the holster and hand over the holstered weapon, that's even safer.

Would've been easier if you'd just followed the speed limit, huh?

The Bottom Line

The laws of the given jurisdiction in a nation that's a patchwork of gun laws, are the laws you have to follow. It's your responsibility to know the turf in that regard, wherever your travels as a free American take you.

2012 Update: Changes in Where You Can Carry

Since the first edition of this book, the USA has come down to only one state where there is no provision in the law for the private citizen to carry a loaded, concealed handgun in public. That's Illinois, and even there concealed carry has come surprisingly close to passing the state legislature at this writing.

Reciprocity – that is, recognition of out of state concealed carry permits – changes constantly. The best way to stay on top of it is the very up-to-date website www.handgunlaw. us. Shortly prior to this writing, for example, the state of New Mexico see-sawed on the issue, first announcing that it would no longer recognize the permits of several states, then capitulating to popular demand and once again accepting many of the permits it had just publicly rejected.

National reciprocity has lingered for many years on Capitol Hill, but in 2011 House Bill 822 passed the House of Representatives, only to be stalled in the Senate. Even so,

The laws of the given jurisdiction in a nation that's a patchwork of gun laws, are the laws you have to follow.

When this guy pulls you over for a routine stop and you're legally carrying a gun, there are things you need to know beforehand.

that was the farthest the concept has yet gone, and there is hope for it in the future. The anti-gunners practically foam at the mouth over the concept, of course, but, amazingly, some otherwise pro-gun individuals are against it. For some, it is "the principle of the thing," in their minds a violation of state's rights. (Interesting thought. Do they feel their marriage license or driver's license should lose its validity at the border of their home state, too?)

This writer, for one, hopes that national reciprocity will pass. The National Rifle Association and the Second Amendment Foundation have both put a small army of lawyers and law scholars on the matter, and seen no practical downside to national reciprocity. Individual interpretation of principle is fine, but just as economic rhetoric has never fed the hungry, Constitutional rhetoric has never armed the helpless.

Since the first edition of this book went in to the publisher, we've had two great victories in the United States Supreme Court, for which I thank the Second Amendment Foundation in particular. These are the decisions in *Heller v. District of Columbia* (2008) and *McDonald, et. al. v. Chicago,* which finally wrote in stone that the Second Amendment-guaranteed right to keep and bear arms is indeed an individual right. There have been many victories since, at the state and local level, for law abiding gun owners. On the concealed carry side of one of America's most contentious social debates, so-called "gun control," our side is winning.

Author with Otis McDonald, right, the lead named plaintiff in *McDonald v. Chicago,* which resulted in a 2010 US Supreme Court decision confirming individual right to keep and bear arms.

COMPENDIUM OF STATE LAWS GOVERNING FIREARMS

Since state laws are subject to frequent change, this chart is not to be considered legal advice or a restatement of the law. The following chart lists the main provisions of state firearms laws as of the date of publication. In addition to the state provisions, the purchase, sale, and, in certain circumstances, the possession and interstate transportation of firearms are regulated by the Federal Gun Control Act of 1968 as amended by the Firearms Owners' Protection Act of 1986. Also, cities and localities may have their own gun ordinances in addition to federal and state restrictions. Details may be obtained by contacting local law enforcement authorities or by consulting your state's firearms law digest compiled by the NRA Institute for Legislative Action. All fifty states have passed sportsmen's protection laws to halt harrassment.

Compiled by NRA Institute for Legislative Action; 11250 Waples Mill Road; Fairfax, Virginia 22030

State	Gun Ban	Exemptions to NICS2	State Waiting Period-Number of Days		License or Permit to Purchase or Other Prerequisite		Registration	
			Handguns	Longguns	Handguns	Longguns	Handguns	Longguns
Alabama	—	—	—	—	—	—	—	—
Alaska	—	RTC	—	—	—	—	—	—
Arizona	—	RTC	—	—	—	—	—	—
Arkansas	—	RTC[3]	—	—	—	—	—	—
California	X[1]	—	10[5]	10[5,6]	10,11	—	X	X[13]
Colorado	—	—	—	—	—	—	—	—
Connecticut	X[1]	—	14[5,6]	14[5,6]	X[9,11]	—	—	X[13]
Delaware	—	—	—	—	—	—	—	—
Florida	—	—	3[6]	—	—	—	—	—
Georgia	—	RTC	—	—	—	—	—	—
Hawaii	X[1]	L, RTC	—	—	X[9,11]	X[9]	X[12]	X[12]
Idaho	—	RTC	—	—	—	—	—	—
Illinois	7	—	3	2	X[9]	X[9]	X[14]	X[14]
Indiana	—	—	—	—	—	—	—	—
Iowa	—	L, RTC	—	—	X[9]	—	—	—
Kansas	—	—	7	—	7	—	7	—
Kentucky	—	—	—	—	—	—	—	—
Louisiana	—	—	—	—	—	—	—	—
Maine	—	—	—	—	—	—	—	—
Maryland	X[1]	—	7[5]	7[4,5]	X[10,11]	—	—	—
Massachusetts	X[1]	—	—	—	X[9]	X[9]	—	—
Michigan	—	L	—	—	X[9,11]	—	X	—
Minnesota	—	—	7[9]	X[9]	X[9]	X[9]	—	—
Mississippi	—	RTC3	—	—	—	—	—	—
Missouri	—	—	—	—	X[9]	—	—	—
Montana	—	RTC	—	—	—	—	—	—
Nebraska	—	L	—	—	X	—	—	—
Nevada	—	RTC	7	—	—	—	7	—
New Hampshire	—	—	—	—	—	—	—	—
New Jersey	X[1]	—	—	—	X[9]	X[9]	—	X[13]
New Mexico	—	—	—	—	—	—	—	—
New York	X[1]	L, RTC	—	—	X[9,11]	9	X	X[15]
North Carolina	—	L, RTC	—	—	X[9]	—	—	—
North Dakota	—	RTC	—	—	—	—	—	—
Ohio	7	—	7	—	7	—	7	—
Oklahoma	—	—	—	—	—	—	—	—
Oregon	—	—	—	—	—	—	—	—
Pennsylvania	—	—	—	—	—	—	—	—
Rhode Island	—	—	7[5]	7[5]	X[11]	—	—	—
South Carolina	—	RTC	—	—	—	—	—	—
South Dakota	—	—	2	—	—	—	—	—
Tennessee	—	—	—	—	—	—	—	—
Texas	—	RTC	—	—	—	—	—	—
Utah	—	RTC	—	—	—	—	—	—
Vermont	—	—	—	—	—	—	—	—
Virginia	X[1]	—	—	—	X[10]	—	—	—
Washington	—	—	5[8]	—	—	—	—	—
West Virginia	—	—	—	—	—	—	—	—
Wisconsin	—	—	2	—	—	—	—	—
Wyoming	—	RTC	—	—	—	—	—	—
District of Columbia	X[1]	L	—	—	X[9]	X[9]	X[9]	X

COMPENDIUM OF STATE LAWS GOVERNING FIREARMS

**Since state laws are subject to frequent change,
this chart is not to be considered legal advice or a restatement of the law.**

All fifty states have passed sportsmen's protection laws to halt harrassment.

State	Record of Sale Reported to State or Local Govt.	State Provision for Right-to-Carry Concealed	Carrying Openly Prohibited	Owner ID Cards or Licensing	Firearm Rights Constitutional Provision	State Firearms Preemption Laws	Range Protection Law
Alabama	—	M	X[19]	—	X	X	X
Alaska	—	R[17]	—	—	X	X[24]	X
Arizona	—	R	—	—	X	X	X
Arkansas	—	R	X[20]	—	X	X	X
California	X	L	X[21]	—	—	X	X
Colorado	—	R	[22]	—	X	X[22]	X
Connecticut	X	M	X	—	X	X[25]	X
Delaware	—	L	—	—	X	X	X
Florida	—	R	X	—	X	X	X
Georgia	—	R	X	—	X	X	X
Hawaii	X	L	X	X	X	—	—
Idaho	—	R	—	—	X	X	X
Illinois	X	D	X	X	X	—	X
Indiana	—	R	X	—	X	X[26]	X
Iowa	—	M	X	—	—	X	X
Kansas	7	D	7	—	X	—	X
Kentucky	—	R	—	—	X	X	X
Louisiana	—	R	—	—	X	X	X
Maine	—	R	—	—	X	X	X
Maryland	X	L	X	—	—	X	X
Massachusetts	X	L	X	X	X	X[25]	X
Michigan	X	R	X[19]	—	X	X	X
Minnesota	—	R[18]	X	—	—	X	—
Mississippi	—	R	—	—	X	X	X
Missouri	X	R	—	—	X	X	X
Montana	—	R	—	—	X	X	X
Nebraska	—	D	—	—	X	—	—
Nevada	—	R	—	—	X	X	X
New Hampshire	—	R	—	—	X	X	X
New Jersey	X	L	X	X	—	X[25]	X
New Mexico	—	R	—	—	X	X	X
New York	X	L	X	X	—	X[27]	X
North Carolina	X	R	—	—	X	X	X
North Dakota	—	R	X[21]	—	X	X	X
Ohio	7	R	7	7	X	—	X
Oklahoma	—	R	X[21]	—	X	X	X
Oregon	X	R	—	—	X	X	X
Pennsylvania	X	R	X[19]	—	X	X	X
Rhode Island	X	L	X	—	X	X	X
South Carolina	X	R	X	—	X	X	X
South Dakota	X[16]	R	—	—	X	X	X
Tennessee	—	R	X[20]	—	X	X	X
Texas	—	R	X	—	X	X	X
Utah	—	R	X[21]	—	X	X	X
Vermont	—	R[17]	X[20]	—	X	X	X
Virginia	—	R	—	—	X	X	X
Washington	X	R	X[23]	—	X	X	—
West Virginia	—	R	—	—	X	X	X
Wisconsin	—	D	—	—	X	X	X
Wyoming	—	R	—	—	X	X	X
District of Columbia	X	D	X	X	NA	—	—

COMPENDIUM OF STATE LAWS GOVERNING FIREARMS

With over 20,000 "gun control" laws on the books in America, there are two challenges facing every gun owner. First, you owe it to yourself to become familiar with the federal laws on gun ownership. Only by knowing the laws can you avoid innocently breaking one.

Second, while federal legislation receives much more media attention, state legislatures and city councils make many more decisions regarding your right to own and carry firearms. NRA members and all gun owners must take extra care to be aware of anti-gun laws and ordinances at the state and local levels.

Notes:

1. "Assault weapons" are prohibited in **Connecticut, New Jersey** and **New York.** Some local jurisdictions in **Ohio** also ban "assault weapons." **Hawaii** prohibits "assault pistols." **California** bans "assault weapons", .50BMG caliber firearms, some .50 caliber ammunition and "unsafe handguns." **Illinois**: Chicago, Evanston, Oak Park, Morton Grove, Winnetka, Wilmette, and Highland Park prohibit handguns; some cities prohibit other kinds of firearms. **Maryland** prohibits "assault pistols"; the sale or manufacture of any handgun manufactured after Jan. 1, 1985, that does not appear on the Handgun Roster; and the sale of any handgun manufactured after January 1, 2003 that is not equipped with an "integrated mechanical safety device." **Massachusetts**: It is unlawful to sell, transfer or possess "any assault weapon or large capacity feeding device" [more than 10 rounds] that was not legally possessed on September 13, 1994 and the sale of handguns not on the Firearms Roster. The City of Boston has a separate "assault weapons" law. The **District of Columbia** prohibits new acquisition of handguns and any semi-automatic firearm capable of using a detachable ammunition magazine of more than 12 rounds capacity and any handgun not registered after February 5, 1977. **Virginia** prohibits "Street Sweeper" shotguns. (With respect to some of these laws and ordinances, individuals may retain prohibited firearms owned previously, with certain restrictions.) The sunset of the federal assault weapons ban does not affect the validity of state "assault weapons" bans.

2. **National Instant Check System (NICS) exemption codes:**
   RTC-Carry Permit Holders Exempt From NICS
   L-Holders of state licenses to possess or purchase or firearms ID cards exempt from NICS.

3. **NICS exemption notes: Arkansas**: Those issued on and after 4/1/99 qualify. **Mississippi**: Permits issued to security guards do not qualify.

4. **Maryland** subjects purchases of "assault weapons" to a 7-day waiting period.

5. Waiting period for all sales. **California**: 10 days; sales, transfers and loans of handguns can be made through a dealer or through a sheriff's office. **Maryland**: 7 days; purchasers of regulated firearms must undergo background checks performed by the State Police, either through a dealer or directly through the State Police. **Rhode Island**: 7 days; private sales can be made through a dealer or the seller must follow the same guidelines as a sale from a dealer.

6. The waiting period does not apply to a person holding a valid permit or license to carry a firearm. In **Connecticut**, a certificate of eligibility exempts the holder from the waiting period for handgun purchases; a hunting license exempts the holder for long gun purchasers. **California**: transfers of a long gun to a person's parent, child or grandparent are exempt from the waiting period.

7. In certain cities or counties.

8. May be extended by police to 30 days in some circumstances. An individual not holding a driver's license must wait 60 days.

9. **Connecticut**: A certificate of eligibility or a carry permit is required to obtain a handgun and a carry permit is required to transport a handgun outside your home. **District of Columbia**: No handgun may be possessed unless it was registered prior to Sept. 23, 1976 and re-registered by Feb. 5, 1977. A permit to purchase is required for a rifle or shotgun. **Hawaii**: Purchase permits are required for all firearms **Illinois**: A Firearm Owner's Identification Card (FOI) is required to possess or purchase a firearm, must be issued to qualified applicants within 30 days, and is valid for 5 years. **Iowa**: A purchase permit is required for handguns, and is valid for one year. **Massachusetts**: Firearms and feeding devices for firearms are divided into classes. Depending on the class, a firearm identification card (FID) or class A license or class B license is required to possess, purchase, or carry a firearm, ammunition thereof, or firearm feeding device, or "large capacity feeding device." **Michigan**: A handgun purchaser must obtain a license to purchase from local law enforcement, and within 10 days present the license and handgun to obtain a certificate of inspection. **Minnesota**: A handgun transfer or carrying permit, or a 7-day waiting period and handgun transfer report, is required to purchase handguns or "assault weapons" from a dealer. A permit is valid for one year, a transfer report for 30 days. **Missouri**: A purchase permit is required for a handgun, must be issued to qualified applicants within 7 days, and is valid for 30 days. **New Jersey**: Firearm owners must possess a FID, which must be issued to qualified applicants within 30 days. To purchase a handgun, a purchase permit, which must be issued within 30 days to qualified applicants and is valid for 90 days, is required. An FID is required to purchase long guns. **New York**: Purchase, possession and/or carrying of a handgun require a single license, which includes any restrictions made upon the bearer. New York City also requires a license for long guns. **North Carolina**: To purchase a handgun, a license or permit is required, which must be issued to qualified applicants within 30 days.

10. A permit is required to acquire another handgun before 30 days have elapsed following the acquisition of a handgun. In **Virginia**, those with a permit to carry a concealed weapon are exempt from this prohibition.

11. Requires proof of safety training for purchase. **California**: Must have Handgun Safety Certificate receipt, which is valid for five years. **Connecticut**: To receive certificate of eligibility, must complete a handgun safety course approved by the Commissioner of Public Safety. **Hawaii**: Must have completed an approved handgun safety course. **Maryland**: Must complete an approved handgun safety course. **Michigan**: A person must correctly answer 70% of the questions on a basic safety review questionnaire in order to obtain a license to purchase. **New York**: Some counties require a handgun safety training course to receive a license. **Rhode Island**: Must receive a state-issued handgun safety card.

12. Every person arriving in **Hawaii** is required to register any firearm(s) brought into the state within 3 days of arrival of the person or firearm(s), whichever occurs later. Handguns purchased from licensed dealers must be registered within 5 days.

13. "Assault weapon" registration. **California** had two dates by which assault weapons had to be registered or possession after such date would be considered a felony: March 31, 1992 for the named make and model firearms banned in the 1989 legislation and December 31, 2000 for the firearms meeting the definition of the "assault weapons in the 1999 legislation. In **Connecticut**, those firearms banned by specific make and model in the 1993 law had to be registered by October 1, 1994 or possession would be considered a felony. A recent law requires registration of additional guns by October 1, 2003. In **New Jersey**, any "assault weapon" not registered, licensed, or rendered inoperable pursuant to a state police certificate by May 1, 1991, is considered contraband.

14. Chicago only. No handgun not already registered may be possessed.

15. New York City only.

16. Purchasers of handguns who do not possess a permit to carry a pistol must file an application for purchase, which will be retained by the chief of police or sheriff for one year.

17. **Vermont** and **Alaska** law respect your right to carry without a permit. **Alaska** also has a permit to carry system to establish reciprocity with other states.

18. Provisions of this law are stayed pending an ongoing dispute in the courts.

19. Carrying a handgun openly in a motor vehicle requires a license.

20. **Arkansas** prohibits carrying a firearm "with a purpose to employ it as a weapon against a person." **Tennessee** prohibits carrying "with the intent to go armed." **Vermont** prohibits carrying a firearm "with the intent or purpose of injuring another."

21. Loaded.

22. Municipalities may prohibit open carry in government buildings if such prohibition is clearly posted.

23. Local jurisdictions may opt of the prohibition.

24. In the Right to Keep and Bear Arms Amendment of the **Alaska** Constitution.

25. Preemption through judicial ruling. Local regulation may be instituted in **Massachusetts** if ratified by the legislature.

26. Except Gary and East Chicago and local laws enacted before January 1994.

27. Preemption only applies to handguns.

Concealed carry codes:

R: Right-to-Carry "Shall issue" or less restrictive discretionary permit system (**Ala., Conn.**) (See also note #21.)

M: Reasonable May Issue; the state has a permissive may issue law, but the authorities recognize the right to keep and bear arms.

L: Right-to-Carry Limited by local authority's discretion over permit issuance.

D: Right-to-Carry Denied, no permit system exists; concealed carry is prohibited.

PREPARATION AND AFTERMATH

No way out. The Lindsey incident took place in this boxed-in parking lot.

In the entertainment media, gunfights begin with the draw and end with the last shot. In the real world, you need to be prepared beforehand, and ready for the ordeal that is likely to follow.

It's about sunset right now outside my hotel room in Denver, a chilly evening. December 7, 2006. Pearl Harbor is on our minds, of course, this being the anniversary of the sneak attack that changed the history of America and the world. But right now, I'm dealing with a case of a law-abiding gun owner who has suffered a sneak attack from fate.

The case closed today, and it went to the jury about 45 minutes ago. Eleven months earlier, the client, 58, was driving to the Veteran's Administration hospital to pick up some medicine. His name is Larry Lindsey. Already asthmatic, he had just been diagnosed with diabetes, and overall was not in the best of health. He walked with a cane and a pronounced limp, the legacy of an accident on a city

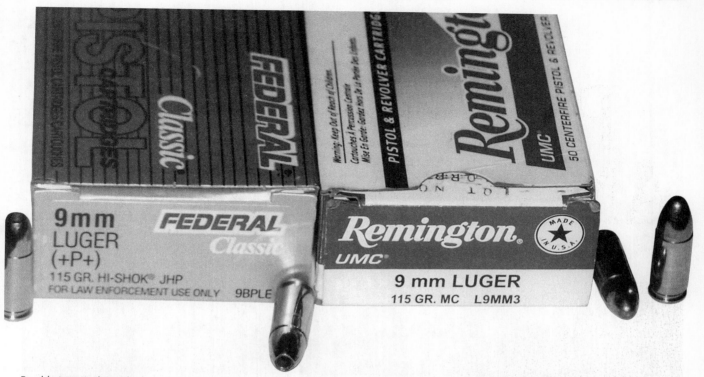

Be able to articulate why you chose the caliber and ammo that were used. Federal +P+ 115-grain JHP *(left)* is an excellent choice in 9mm, but full metal jacket, right, is not.

street a few years earlier when a careless motorist blasted through a red light and ran him down on a crosswalk.

On the Interstate that goes through Denver, a young-looking man in a Ford Taurus, racing zig-zag through the high speed traffic, cut into his lane. The smaller car nearly ran Larry's vehicle off the road. Acutely aware of the dangers posed by such driving – not only reminded constantly by his lingering injury, but by the fact that he had lost loved ones to drunk and reckless drivers in the past – Larry always made a point of calling in such dangerous motorists on his cell phone. But the Taurus had accelerated ahead so quickly, still cutting left and right through traffic, that he hadn't been able to get the license plate number.

He continued on his way. As he reached his exit, he saw a familiar car stopped at the edge of the exit ramp: the tan Taurus, with the same young man at the wheel. Larry instinctively slowed, and suddenly, the vehicle shot out directly in front of him, nearly colliding. Larry swerved and hit the brakes, and barely missed plowing into the concrete wall on the right side of the exit ramp. As he brought his vehicle back on path, Larry saw the Taurus' driver mouth a curse at him and raise his middle finger in contempt ... and then blast through a red light, turning right, in flagrant violation of a big sign that read, "NO RIGHT TURN ON RED."

This, Larry decided, was just too blatant to ignore. When traffic allowed, he too turned right, following the tan Taurus that was now a considerable distance ahead of him. He decided he was going to write down the license number and phone it in. As he drove he dialed 9-1-1 on his

> **Larry always made a point of calling in such dangerous motorists on his cell phone.**

cell phone, and was put on "hold." Ahead of him, he saw the car take a right, then a left. He followed in time to see it pull quickly into the parking lot on his left.

He slowed, turned into the lot – and stopped dead in the narrow mouth of the parking lot. Instead of going to the right where the main parking spaces were, the tan Taurus had pulled into the third slot on the immediate left of the exit, a short row of Handicapped spaces. The vehicle had come to its sudden stop in front of a large HANDICAPPED sign.

Only a few steps away from the vehicle, Larry figured he'd jot down the license number and be out of there. 9-1-1 Dispatch had not yet taken him off "hold."

But other things weren't "holding" at all.

The driver boiled out of the car, coming toward Larry, screaming obscenities. Fifteen or twenty paces ahead of Larry's car, a very tall and strong-looking young man emerged immediately from the apartment house entryway and proceeded toward him at a fast walk. Then another came out behind him.

Five feet eight, pushing sixty, a little overweight, and crippled and sick, Larry wasn't sure he would be a match for one athletic young man, let alone three. The third one seemed to drift away, but the tall one was approaching straight at him and the driver of the Taurus was almost at his left door, screaming "I'll kick your ass! I'll kill you!"

In his younger days, Larry Lindsey had spent eight years in the United States Marine Corps, much of it in Vietnam, where his MOS was Combat Photographer. His issue weapon had been a 1911 45 automatic back then. A gun

Trials can be scary. Law enforcement personnel barricade the streets for a block in each direction around the courthouse because of death threats against the defendant in one case the author worked.

guy all his life, he had grown to like the issue pistol, and had chosen as his personal defense gun a stainless steel Kimber Custom Shop Gold 1911 45. He kept it in his console with pretty much the same load-out to which the USMC had accustomed him: in a holster with loaded magazine and empty chamber, backed up by two more loaded mags in a leather pouch.

Larry flipped open the console and took out the holstered pistol, holding it in plain sight where he hoped they could see it. The man on his left screamed another F-word curse...and his right hand dove under his jacket toward his back, as if going for a pistol.

Larry ripped the holster off the Kimber, jacked a 230-grain Federal Hydra-Shok into the chamber, and brought up the pistol.

Suddenly, the two men were moving back, and Larry wasn't in danger anymore. His cell phone was still in his lap where he had dropped it when he went for his pistol. Glancing behind him, Larry saw an opening in the traffic and he backed out into the street, then drove to the nearest corner and pulled into a parking lot there. He dialed 9-1-1 again, and this time, he got through. He told the dispatcher what happened.

Unfortunately, the tall man who had menaced him had whipped out his own cell phone before Larry was out of the parking lot. His call went in to Dispatch at 3:02 PM, and Larry's did not get in until 3:03. The first responding officer arrived at the scene at 3:10, a respectable eight-minute

In his younger days, Larry Lindsey had spent eight years in the United States Marine Corps, much of it in Vietnam, where his MOS was Combat Photographer.

response time.

That officer would testify that he never received any radio notification that Larry had called in his complaint. He seemed surprised when he was shown the facts on the 9-1-1 call log, in court, by defense attorney Paul Grant.

The same officer would testify that he had decided almost immediately upon his arrival to arrest Larry Lindsey, who was now in the grip of a full-blown asthma attack. After all, two witnesses had identified the crazy man in a state of road rage who had waved a silver-colored pistol at them, and the man had admitted drawing the gun on the pair the officer now considered victims.

Larry Lindsey was arrested at the scene. He was charged with two counts of Felony Menacing, and later released on $50,000 bail.

The trial began on December 6. Jury selection was done by morning, with the prosecution removing almost every gun owner. This is par for the course. Neither side wants someone on the jury who might identify with the people on the other side of the case. Among the twelve jurors and one alternate finally selected there was but a single one who owned firearms. He had two, which he kept empty, fitted with trigger locks, inside a gun safe. A loaded gun, he said during the jury selection process called *voir dire*, was just too dangerous to keep around. This, apparently, was enough to satisfy the prosecutor.

The state took the rest of the day to establish its case. A

story emerged of a nice twenty-something kid, an immigrant from the Middle East with no record, who accidentally cut in front of a motorist who must have been one of those Angry White Males. The driver had boiled up in road rage, followed him for several blocks, pulled in behind him and pulled out a big silver pistol, with which he threatened to "blow his brains out" along with those of his equally innocent twenty-something friend, an immigrant from Eastern Europe, who had done nothing but come out of his apartment building.

The cops took the stand. Yes, said the arresting officer, he had been called to the scene of a crime of threatening to shoot someone without reason… found two complainants willing to testify…found the defendant who admitted having a gun just like the one the complainants had described… and determined immediately that he was guilty and placed him under arrest. Much emphasis was placed on the large caliber of the weapon. The prosecutor elicited from the officer that the hollow-point bullets, 230-grain Federal Hydra-Shok, were designed to expand and tear "larger wounds." And, oh my God, there were *two spare magazines!* Enough bullets to kill two dozen people!

On the morning of December 7, the assistant district attorney would announce that her case was closed. Attorney Paul Grant had chosen to call only two witnesses: the defendant, and me. The ADA strenuously objected to my presence, so an informal hearing was held on the record in chambers.

Reloaded ammo is great for practice, hunting, and competition, says author, but he strongly recommends against it for defense use.

It seems that when Grant had sent the routine list of witnesses he intended to call to the prosecutor who'd had the case previously, the fax had not gone through. He hadn't known that. When he mentioned to the new prosecutor on the case the week before that he would be calling an expert to testify, she went through the roof.

The judge was not happy about the glitch. However, he was diligent in his duties and he recognized that the defendant had certain rights. The prosecutor's questioning of the arresting officer the day before had elicited testimony that made the pistol seem an avatar of malice because of its caliber, its spare magazines, its hollowpoint ammunition; Grant, who had seen that before, argued that he had a right to rebut those arguments. Incredibly, the prosecutor argued that since it came through a material witness instead of an expert, that material could not be rebutted by an expert. Grant responded, successfully, with a logical argument: *whoever* had said it, the poison was in the water, and he had the right to administer an antidote

of his choice. The judge agreed.

Grant wanted me to testify also as to the standards of care for private citizens in such things, the rules of engagement as it were. The prosecutor adamantly objected. I was, she said, going to tell the jury that the defendant's use of the gun was justified, and that issue was something only the jury could determine. The judge asked me what my take was on that.

I explained that I had no intention of going to "the ultimate issue," the guilt or innocence of the defendant, and that I agreed this was a question that only the triers of the facts could answer. However, I added, I believed the defense attorney's job was to show the jury that a reasonable, prudent person, in the same situation and knowing what his client knew, would have done the same thing. The element of "knowing what the defendant knew" required him to show the jury how such decisions are made by lawfully armed citizens, and what the rules of engagement are understood to be. It was to establish those parameters that he had brought me in.

And, of course, the judge agreed.

I went on the stand first thing after court convened. The prosecutor stipulated to my credentials and expertise, a professional move by any advocate against an adverse expert witness because it limits how much of his qualifications and background the jury will hear in the opening moments of testimony.

Defense attorney Grant asked the right questions, and I laid out those "rules of engagement," which will follow shortly in this chapter. We explained the "furtive movement" element: that when someone such as the young Iranian immigrant made a move consistent with going for a gun, and not reasonably consistent with anything else under the circumstances, it would reasonable and prudent of someone such as the defendant to immediately draw his own gun and take him proactively at gunpoint.

One by one, we cut down the shibboleths that had built up around the defendant's choice of gun and ammunition during the prosecution's case. The 45-caliber pistol was quite common in America, very popular in law enforcement, in fact approved for the Denver Police Department and carried by a great many of its officers. The type of gun the defendant had employed was adopted by the United States Military in 1911, had been standard with our armed forces until the mid-1980s, and was still used by our military among pistol teams, the Army's Delta Force, and the Marine Corps' Recon unit, which in fact had recently purchased a quantity of Kimbers functionally identical to the Kimber 45 in evidence.

I explained that generations of American service personnel had returned to civilian life after completing their terms of service, and had decided that if the 1911 45 pistol was good enough to be issued to them by Uncle Sam to protect their country, it was good enough for them to purchase to protect their home and hearth and loved ones. In turn, countless Americans who had never joined the military had been taught by their parents to use those same 45s, and bought one or more when they in turn grew up and made the lawful decision to have a gun to protect themselves and their loved ones. This was why the 1911 was so very popular and common among armed citizens, and also the fact that its design features made it ideal for many forms of pistol matches, which the defendant would testify he had competed in regularly until becoming too physically debilitated to do so.

The two spare magazines that augmented the loaded pistol? I explained that this was a typical "load-out" for those who carried a gun. Since before any of us was born, the standard law enforcement rule was a loaded gun plus enough spare ammunition for two full reloads. I told the jury that they would see uniformed officers in the courthouse during their breaks, and that they would notice each had a double pouch on their duty belts to carry two spare magazines to complement their fully loaded weapon. Since many of them had high-capacity pistols, some would

be carrying as many as 54 duty cartridges on their person, i.e., a fully loaded Glock 17 with 18 9mm rounds in it and two spare 17-round magazines in the pouches. The military load-out, since the 45's adoption in 1911, had been loaded gun in holster plus two magazines in pouches. I pointed out that testimony would show that the defendant had served for some eight years as a USMC combat photographer in Vietnam (where he had been wounded in action) and that every day there he carried what the Government issued him: a 1911 45 auto with an empty chamber and full magazine, and two spare fully loaded magazines, in the holster and double mag pouch he was issued. This was exactly what he'd had in the car with him on the day in question, albeit with eight-round competition magazines instead of seven-round GI mags.

As a competitor for many years, the defendant needed at least two magazines to shoot even prosaic NRA bullseye matches, and three to shoot a stage in IDPA. If he just stopped at the public outdoor range for some shooting – which, records would show, he had done just a couple of days before the incident – there would be a finite amount of actual shooting time in between stand-downs to examine and change targets. During those stand-downs, there would be time to refill the magazines. Then, when it came time to shoot, the guy who came to shoot could spend his shooting time doing more shooting, just as the guy who came to a golf course to play golf would rather play eighteen holes than nine. I could see some of the jurors nodding their heads in affirmation. And of course, should a defensive pistol have to be used for serious purposes, more ammo could be required, or a spare magazine might be necessary to clear a malfunction. They "got it." They realized a person for whom pistol shooting was a sport might want to have multiple loaded magazines for purposes other than mass murder.

The hollowpoints? I explained that virtually every law enforcement agency in the country had adopted such ammunition, including the Denver PD which last I knew had Speer Gold Dot as standard issue for every approved caliber. (Detroit, Michigan is clutched so tightly in the iron fist of political correctness that "hollowpoints" are anathema there, so Detroit coppers are issued Federal Expanding Full Metal Jacket ammunition, in which the operative term is "expanding.") I then went on to point out the reasons for that, which are listed elsewhere in this book but, briefly, include reduced likelihood of ricochet that could endanger bystanders, reduced likelihood of over-penetration that could jeopardize the same innocents, etc. The Federal Hydra-Shok in particular had at one point been the "gold standard" among American police before the coming of higher-tech JHPs from that maker and others, and remains in wide law enforcement use.

Paul Grant closed the direct examination by asking me if I told my students that they might be wise to avoid

> **The trial began on December 6. Jury selection was done by morning, with the prosecution removing almost every gun owner. This is par for the course.**

following dangerous people to report them to police. I told him that was true, and explained why: that folks who came in late and didn't see what you saw could mistake you as the aggressive pursuer chasing a hapless victim, and the result could be a "false positive" that made the good guy look like the bad guy and vice versa. It was a good note on which to end the direct.

Cross-examination was interesting. The seasoned prosecutor was well-spoken and utterly professional. If you drew a gun because you thought the other man was going to draw one, but he turned out to be unarmed, wouldn't that be a mistake? No, I answered, not if the totality of the other man's words and actions were reasonably construable to any prudent person as indicating that he *did* have a gun. Besides, two strong young men threatening to beat up and kill a physically disabled man in his late fifties constituted disparity of force twice over. I had already explained to the jury on direct that disparity of force meant that even ostensibly unarmed men were so likely to kill or cripple you under these violent circumstances that this likelihood constituted the equivalent of one or both of them being armed with a *per se* deadly weapon.

And so it went for almost two and a half hours, until I was done. I headed back to the hotel to wait in case I was called back. Out of hearing of the jury, the prosecutor informed the judge and the defense lawyer that she might call a rebuttal witness, whose purpose would be to refute my testimony. Therefore, I had to stick around for sur-rebuttal, which would involve my taking the stand once again to shoot down the rebuttal testimony.

Which brings us to late afternoon of December 7. I learn after court has adjourned for the day that the prosecutor has given up on rebuttal, the defendant has told his story, and both advocates have given their closing arguments. There's nothing more I can do here. I pick up the phone and make arrangements to fly out early the next morning.

December 8, 2006: I'm in the Atlanta airport waiting to board my connecting flight for the final leg of my journey home when my Treo rings. It's Paul Grant. The jury has come in with the verdict.

Not Guilty on all counts.

Criminal defense lawyers rarely get to defend innocent men. When they do, acquittal is all the sweeter, a perfect validation of such a professional's very existence. A relieved Paul Grant reminds the judge that there is the small matter of some of his client's property, which at this moment has ceased to be evidence in the custody of the Court, which should be returned to his client.

The prosecutor jumps to her feet and says, "Your Honor, the state is preparing a motion for the gun to be destroyed."

The judge looks at her in something close to disbelief and asks, "On what grounds?"

"There's a statute," she blurts.

Patiently, the judge asks, "*What* statute?"

The prosecutor replies that she doesn't know, exactly, but she intends to find it.

Some people just *hate* to lose.

Lessons

A week later, I received an email from the defendant. "This is the first chance since the trial that I have had to actually sit down and compose a letter to properly thank you," he wrote. "The whole ordeal of the trial, coupled with the emotional and financial drain of the previous eleven months had taken such a toll on my wife and myself that we just took a few days off to spend some time with each other. It is amazing just how much better I feel now.

"I can't tell you how much we appreciated your presence in the courtroom, and your testimony. Because of you and Paul, Natasha and I will be spending Christmas together again this year. We both agree that this is our best Christmas ever. We hope that you and your family have a very Merry Christmas, and a Happy New Year!

"The one thing that I never could have anticipated was that the elements of a confrontation with bad guys here in a 'civilized' environment could have so many similarities to an engagement in active combat. There was the same tendency to focus solely on the threat at hand, excluding almost everything else, and the same auditory exclusion and time distortion. The stress of the situation also made it very difficult to remember the chronological order of things.

"It is a very strange sensation to have your mind racing at such speeds as to make the moment seem as if it is taking place in agonizingly slow motion. It's almost impossible to keep tabs on everything at once…assessing the danger, keeping an eye on two or more aggressors (who happen to be in different locations), trying to safely retrieve and handle your handgun, while simultaneously trying to watch the traffic behind you so that you can safely back out of the parking lot. The whole time I was praying that I didn't have to shoot this idiot, but I also realized that pulling the pistol was my only way out of a deadly situation. Thankfully, it did what I intended for it to do. It defused the situation immediately and I was able to extract myself and wait for the police.

"I used my pistol in self defense, knowing full well what the aftermath would most likely be. I knew that Denver almost always prosecutes an individual if he has used a firearm to defend himself, but I also believed that I had no other choice in the matter."

He concluded, "After the trial, a juror asked me if this had changed my mind about carrying a firearm for self defense. Since she claimed to be one of my defenders early on in deliberation, I'm sure that what she meant was that if I had not had my handgun with me that I would not have had to defend myself, yet a second time, in court. Even after the trial and my acquittal of all charges, she still could not see the whole picture, and failed to consider the likely outcome

> **Criminal defense lawyers rarely get to defend innocent men. When they do, acquittal is all the sweeter, a perfect validation of such a professional's very existence.**

She's 5'0", and they're about 6'4". How many elements of "disparity of force" could be present here?

bad guy.

I know what you're thinking: that's not how it should be, and it isn't fair. You're right. It isn't fair, and it isn't how it should be. But, ya know, I don't think you paid the price of this book to find out how I think things should be. I think you paid it to find out how things *are,* and, well, this *is* how they are.

Please don't think that the criminal justice system always goes after the wrong guy. That's actually fairly rare. Most of the time, the system works. But that's partly because, most of the time things "go as usual."

By that I mean, what happens most of the time is that the person who calls in *is* the innocent victim as well as the complainant. Most of the time, the person complained about *is* the perpetrator. After you do criminal justice for a living for a while, it becomes business as usual to accept things as such. Complainant equals victim, complained about equals suspected perpetrator. Soon everyone from the dispatcher who takes the call, to the cop on the beat who responds, to the prosecutor who takes the case to court, accepts this as a matter of course.

That's why, when testifying in this particular case, I used the term "false positive" to the jury. I wasn't there to blame the arresting officer. He worked with what he had to work with. Call says, "Man with gun threatens people." A BadThing. Gets to scene. Complainants confirm, "Yup, threatened us with gun!" Hmmm. Suspect says, "Sure, I pulled the gun – it's right there – and warned that I would shoot, but –"

Well, you and I might also say, "Save it for the judge, buddy, you're under arrest." Probable cause now exists to make the arrest. Sorting out the excuses and alibis? That's largely for the courtroom.

At one point in that trial, I was asked in front of the jury if I was prejudiced against cops. Hardly, I replied; I had *been* a sworn police officer for 33 years, and still was one, albeit on a part time basis. If the assistant district attorney had asked me on cross if I was prejudiced against prosecutors, I would have said much the same: Hardly, because I've spent more than seventeen years as a police prosecutor. (In the state where I serve, selected police officers are sent to a two-week course at the state law enforcement academy after which, if we can pass the stringent final exam, we are declared "police prosecutors." We can prosecute violations and misdemeanors all the way through on our own, and

had I been unarmed. I explained to her that the experience had only reinforced my belief that we live in perilous times, and that I should always carry a firearm to defend myself."

Whew! Where do we begin? Let's start with the obvious.

I can't overemphasize that "false positive effect" that I spoke of in court. This whole thing went the way it did after the gun was put away because the defendant didn't get his story in to the authorities before his antagonists did. The entire criminal justice system is geared on the assumption that whoever calls in first is the complainant, the *victim.* The good guy now, by default, becomes the bad guy: the *suspect.* The *perpetrator.*

In situations like these, you're a contestant in what I've come to call "the race to the telephone." The winner gets to be the good guy, and the loser automatically becomes the can go as far as arraignment with felonies and second seat for the rest of the trial with a "real" prosecutor if he or she wants us to. "Second seat," called "second chair" in some jurisdictions, mean that you're acting as co-pilot to the designated prosecutor who is the pilot. Only a few states have this system, but it works amazingly well.)

Just as I respect cops and prosecutors, I respect physicians and other medical professionals. They rarely make mistakes…but they're human, and they *can* make mistakes. They work daily with reliable systems and protocols that let them diagnose and treat problems. Most of the time, those things perform as intended. But, every now and then, an unforeseen aberration occurs in the way things normally work, and a test registers "positive" when in fact it should register "negative." Professional history, logic, the momentum of routine, and a little thing called "business as usual" now come together, and because the test indicated "positive," the patient is treated as if he had the disease. Hopefully, the wrong treatment is discovered in time to rectify the situation, give the proper treatment, and heal the patient.

The criminal justice system works exactly the same way.

When the guy who started the problem calls in first, and says the good guy is the bad guy, we have the "false positive" result. In the medical example, the symptoms have mimicked those of the given disease, and treatment for that disease is prescribed. In the legal example, actions mimic those of a given crime, so the "patient" is treated as if he had committed the crime. In the medical environment, continued monitoring of the patient's condition will hopefully determine that the wrong treatment was prescribed because of the false positive, and the matter will be rectified. In the legal environment, that usually doesn't happen until you get to court, as was the case for this unfortunate defendant.

So, to make a long story short, the lesson is, *be the complainant! Win that "race to the telephone" in the aftermath of the incident.*

Another lesson, discussed in both direct and cross and worthy of reiteration here, is: *carefully consider the risks before you pursue or even follow a wrongdoer.* As I said on the stand that day in Denver, a private citizen chasing a suspect is a little like a dog chasing a car: he has no idea what he's going to do with his quarry if he catches it, but he will feel an almost irresistible urge to chase it.

Our society sends a very mixed message on this. Somewhere in America almost every day, some brave citizen will chase a thief or follow a bank robber or trail a road-raging driver as Larry did in this case. Often, there is a successful conclusion. Thanks to that concerned citizen's diligence and willingness to "get involved," the person who did the bad act is captured by the police and the public is made safer. Sometimes, it's even the citizen who captures the bad guy, and then the newspapers lionize that good citizen as a hero.

Well, I think that's a good thing, in the moral sense. Back when the English Common Law was formed, it included an element called "hue and cry." A formal police department

would not be established in England until long after, under the great Sir Robert Peel for whom British "bobbies" are nicknamed. In those long ago times, it was understood that citizens had to do their own policing. Thus, it was a public duty to "raise a hue and cry" when one saw a crime committed: to shout "Stop, Thief!" and give chase, hopefully soon joined by a like-minded crowd of good citizens, and lay hands upon the malefactor and hold him until the traveling magistrate could be brought to the village to supervise the imposition of the King's justice. It is from this heritage that we have today's laws creating something called "citizen's arrest" in virtually all of our United States, where the English Common Law remains the model of our system of justice.

However, when the newspaper and TV news stories appear applauding the heroic citizen who led the police to the bad guy or even captured him by his lonesome, please notice that there's almost always a quote from a police spokesman who says, "We appreciate this citizen's heroism, but we have to urge the public not to go after people they see commit crimes. It can be very dangerous."

They ain't just blowing politically correct smoke. The bad guy may just turn on you, just as the car the dog is chasing can suddenly go in reverse and run over the puppy. What are *you* going to do if the bad guy screams at *you*, "I'll blow your f—kin' head off!" as he reaches as if for a pistol?

Well, if you can't get a gun on him as quickly as Larry got a 45 on this guy, you could be on the fast track for your body heat going from 98.6 degrees Fahrenheit to room temperature. And if you *are* as fast as Larry, you can find yourself going through the same terrible ordeal in court that he did.

Maybe you're *faster* than Larry. Let's say you're in the exact same circumstances, and you put a 230-grain Hydra-Shok into the man's center chest, heart into spine, before he can get his gun he reached for first, out of its hiding place. He's what some folks would call DRT: Dead Right There.

The first responding officers will approach the body. IF they find a pistol in his hand, you *may* be home free. But IF they DON'T, you're in deep trouble. You've just shot an unarmed man.

Go back to the way the prosecutor cross-examined me in this case. She was trying to get me to say that if you pull a gun on a man you have reason to believe is going to criminally shoot you with a gun of his own, and he turns out to be unarmed, it's wrong. Well, as I explained, that's plain and simple BS. The law has never demanded that the bad guy actually have a gun, or that the gun be real instead of fake, loaded instead of empty, operable instead of broken and useless. All the law has ever demanded, insofar as the attacker being armed, is that his manifest intent – his obvious intent, as manifested by his words and/or his actions – be such that any prudent person would be reasonable to conclude that he was indeed capable of killing you.

Alas, over the years, a huge number of prosecutors have failed to see that. In law school, deadly force law is a tiny drop in a great sea of tort law, contract law, and general legal

> **Carefully consider the risks before you pursue or even follow a wrongdoer.**

Author, right, observes as lighting experts determine ambient light at a crime scene. This could be a critical element for the jury to weigh.

principles. I've talked to attorneys who spent more time in law school studying maritime law than deadly force or self-defense law. This forces the prosecutor, absent special training, to fall back on legal formulae.

The formula says that the key ingredients of Manslaughter are recklessness or negligence, coupled of course with the death of the alleged victim. Some perceive bad judgment to be the equivalent of recklessness and/or negligence. "Hmmm… you thought he had a gun, but he didn't. Your judgment was obviously wrong. You killed him. Let's see what my law school notes say…bad judgment, plus death, equals…Manslaughter! Yes, that seems to be an appropriate charge." And there you are, in court with your future on the line.

Even if the other guy *did* turn out to have a gun, remember that I only said you *may* be home free. Way back in 1984, I was hired by two famous criminal defense lawyers, Roy Black and Mark Seiden, to speak in the defense of Officer Luis Alvarez. Luis was a Miami street cop who, along with his young rookie partner, was arresting a man for illegal possession of a concealed handgun in a crowded video arcade. The man went for his gun, a stolen RG-14 revolver loaded with hyper-velocity Stinger 22 Long Rifle hollowpoints, and Alvarez shot him dead.

It was a cross-racial shooting, and it triggered a race riot. The city needed a scapegoat, and Alvarez was the chosen sacrifice. He was charged with Manslaughter. Now, at the time the suspect made the drawing movement that led to his death, Alvarez already *knew* this man was armed with a handgun. He had approached him, put a hand on the bulge under the suspect's sweater, and instantly realized that his hand was on a revolver. The cop asked him, "What's that?" The suspect replied – with what would turn out to be his last words on Earth – "It's a gun."

The prosecution, to get a conviction, needed to show that Alvarez had acted recklessly. Their position was that Alvarez should have waited to actually see the man draw the gun. They put forth an expert as a witness who testified, "He shouldn't have fired until he saw the gun." Asked about that when my turn came on the witness stand, my reply was, "If you wait to see the gun, you're going to see what comes out of it." I then did a demonstration and showed the jury how quickly a gun could be drawn from a waistband when carried as it was found on the dying suspect's body. There was a whole lot more to the eight grueling weeks Black and Seiden put in on that trial, from jury selection to verdict, but it ended in an acquittal. Which triggered *another* riot, but that's another story.

Now, let's get back to the Lindsey case, the one in Denver. You will recall the discussion of actions leading up to the final encounter, and how it is important that the jury know and assess how each of the players was acting in the short period of time leading up to the encounter. If you have a case like Lindsey's that's "he said/she said," in this case two complainants versus one defendant and no impartial, objective eyewitnesses, it's going to come down to taking one man's words over those of another, or those of a couple more.

The number of people testifying on one side can be convincing, but is not necessarily the best evidence. (By that standard, if a victim was gang-raped and all the perpetrators solidly denied it, the victim would never get justice.) When it goes to "he said/she said," the relative credibility of each witness's testimony must be weighed separately. This will include other factors in what the court calls "the totality of the circumstances." Therefore, each individual's actions in the short time frame leading up to the encounter can be used by the jury to determine who seemed most likely to have committed a reckless act that disregarded the value of human life.

Let's look at the Larry Lindsey case again with that in mind. Lindsey was a sick man en route to the Veteran's Administration hospital to get much-needed medication, yet he diverted from his own needs to get the license number so he could report the offending vehicle to the authorities before the reckless driver could kill someone. This, I submit, would be seen as a selfless and highly responsible action by a private citizen who had no legal duty to do that, though of course he had the right.

Now, let's look at the chief witness against Larry. How many reckless acts, connotative of irresponsible action and therefore corroborative of Larry's account of the incident, did *this* guy commit? At least five are evident.

(1) He initially cuts Larry off on the Interstate, nearly running him off the road.

(2) He suddenly darts onto the exit ramp and cuts Larry off *again*, nearly forcing his vehicle into a concrete wall this time. (The driver will later admit to this particular offense, but will say that he didn't mean to do it.)

(3) The other driver flipped Larry off. Now, obviously, that's not a "shooting offense," but it shows you that you're dealing with someone who has some hostility going and perhaps an anger management thing. After all, we would all tell our kids that giving the bird to a stranger you've cut off in traffic is provocative at the very least, and therefore, not a responsible thing to do.

(4) Larry saw him blast through a "no right turn on red" light. Another dangerous act that's construable as showing disregard for the safety of oneself and others: more irresponsibility.

(5) In the penultimate moment before the confrontation, the driver who became the complainant *whipped* his car into a handicapped space, with no apparent need for that sort of speed. Again, while obviously not an offense that warrants gunpoint, it's something that shows you an agitated man in a hurry, a man who does not care much about the needs of others…and an irresponsible man.

If you are the juror who has to determine which of these men was most likely to act irresponsibly in the moments that followed, what do their actions in the moments leading up to the confrontation tell us? This is what the courts and the law are looking for when they demand that actions be considered "within the totality of the circumstances."

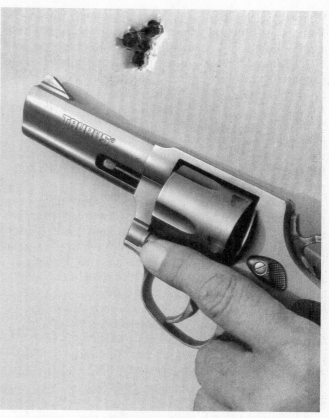

Once you've learned to do it, you can shoot with deadly accuracy at high speed with a good double-action revolver like this Taurus Tracker. There's no good reason to rely on a defense gun with a "hair trigger," opines the author.

Hardware Lessons

Be able to explain your choice of gun and ammunition, and even accessories. There are some who will be your adversaries in court who will make it appear that your having a gun with you at all was paranoid. Be able to articulate why you did choose to arm your home, your shop, or your person. Be able to explain why carrying sufficient ammunition is a practice recommended by responsible firearms professionals for very good reasons, and has nothing to do with any plan to massacre shoppers at the mall.

At this writing, I'm consulting on an *amicus* brief for an appellate case in the Northeast, *Commonwealth v. Pepicelli. Amicus curae* are "friend of the court" briefs, which explain in depth a certain issue in the case at bar. At his original trial, the armed citizen defendant was convicted of criminal homicide after fighting off men who had come after him and endangered others at a family cookout. Aware of a previous pattern of threats, Pepicelli was armed with a Glock pistol and carrying a spare magazine when the incident went down. The prosecution argued that only a man who intended to shoot someone would bring a loaded pistol to a family barbecue…that only a man who intended to shoot many people would carry a spare magazine…and that carrying a high-capacity semiautomatic pistol such as the Glock was somehow nefarious to begin with.

And they got away with that. The reason is, their argument

went unchallenged by a defense lawyer who apparently was not well versed in these particular areas. Pepicelli was convicted and sentenced to prison. His appeal is now underway, under the able direction of Lisa Steele, one of the nation's top appellate lawyers. The original trial lawyer had been wise enough to seek out an expert witness, and he chose Tom Aveni, who is a highly qualified instructor and researcher in the field, and very capable. Unfortunately, the judge refused to allow any testimony in the above areas. It is the exclusion of that testimony that is being challenged in the appeal, and in the various *amicus* briefs that are being submitted.

Ammunition can also be an issue. I have seen many cases where the prosecutors and plaintiff's lawyers have argued that the use of hollow points constitutes malice. Their arguments generally come almost word for word from an article published some thirty years ago in the liberal magazine *The Nation*. This article was titled "The Vietnamization of Main Street." The focus of its attack was the sweeping adoption of hollowpoint ammunition by America's police. The thing reeks of BS and total misconception. It includes phrases such as "bullets shaped like the nacelles of jet engines" and "The bullet doesn't explode, *you* do."

There are several ways to defuse this attack. One that has worked well for me for some years is to advise defense counsel to ask every police officer who testifies during the state's case an important question on cross-examination: "What sort of ammunition do you carry on duty, Officer?" Almost certainly it will prove to be some sort of hollowpoint, though the counselor will want to confirm this well beforehand, prior to asking the question. It's a foolish or too-adventurous attorney who asks a question to which he or she does not already know the answer.

It's still good to have an expert witness for your own side whose training and experience encompasses this area. This guarantees bringing in the testimony that the HPs are less likely to dangerously over-penetrate or ricochet. Such an expert should also bring out the point that since hollowpoints have come into use, most shootings with them end with fewer gunshots inflicted than in the old days, when cops with impotent 158-grain round-nose lead bullets had to empty their revolvers into the bad guys to put them down, and sometimes didn't even stop the fight with *that*.

The more gunshot wounds a man sustains, the more likely he is to die, all other things being equal. The HP round's history of improved "stopping power" means the bad guy has to be shot fewer times to make him cease hostilities. Moreover, because it was designed to stay in the body, the hollowpoint slug will be less likely to punch a second open hole in the body as it exits. This reduces tension pneumothorax, the "sucking chest wound," and some believe it also somewhat reduces hemorrhage. The deeper penetrating "regular bullet" will by definition be capable of piercing more bone structures, blood vessels, organs, etc.

Thus, with all these factors taken into consideration in The Big Picture, a solid argument can be made that the hollow-point bullet is *less lethal* and therefore even safer for the perpetrator who forces you to shoot him!

Some authorities recommend that the armed citizen carry the same round as that used by local law enforcement, on the theory that the prosecutor can't accuse you of using "extra-deadly malicious bullets" if that accusation is likely to tarnish local police who carry the same load. Some folks have attributed this advice to me. This is incorrect. I have mentioned that some experts suggest this, but I wasn't the one who came up with the idea. Is it smart? Well, it is *if* the department in question uses the right ammo! In 1998, if you lived in New York City and wanted to pack the same stuff as the local police department, that would have been 115-grain full metal jacket round nose 9mm "ball," one of the poorest choices for self-defense *or* law enforcement.

One argument against this has been, "Carrying the same load as the local cops might allow opposing counsel to suggest, *Your Honor, the defendant is a wanna-be Rambo! Why, he even loaded his deadly weapon with the same ammunition as our police carry, as if he was impersonating an officer.*

I have to tell you that I don't worry a whole lot about that particular attack. I haven't seen it happen yet. But, of course, someone not seeing it happen yet doesn't mean it hasn't happened yet, or that it won't happen in the future. That being the case, it wouldn't hurt to have an answer to the challenging question, "Is it not true that you loaded with police ammo because you fancy yourself to be a cop, even though you aren't one?"

The best answer is, "No, sir. The police are experts in protection against the kind of criminals who attack citizens. I thought if the ammunition was good enough for the police to use to protect my family, it was good enough for *me* to use to protect my family."

One thing I try to avoid is carrying my department-issue 45 auto or even ammo identical to what my PD issues when I'm not working for the department. The reason is that I don't want the department getting tied into a suit that might evolve from something I had to do to protect myself from death. The lawsuit won't do either entity, me or the department, any good. Each officer on my department is issued a permit to carry a concealed handgun, just like a citizen in our jurisdiction might possess. No, a sworn officer doesn't need a permit to carry a gun off duty, but I like them having the option.

Here's why, and it's kinda complicated, so please follow along. Remember, the lawsuit doesn't seek justice so much as it seeks money. Therefore, the plaintiff will go for the deep pockets. When House Resolution 218 was at long last signed into law by President George W. Bush and became LEOSA, the Law Enforcement Officers' Safety Act, sworn police and honorably retired cops around the country became eligible

> One thing I try to avoid is carrying my department-issue 45 auto or even ammo identical to what my PD issues when I'm not working for the department.

to carry guns nationwide, on their own time, irrespective of arrest powers in a given jurisdiction. I personally think that, in time, this will be the precedent that could get a nationwide concealed carry privilege for armed private citizens who are provably both competent and law-abiding. It establishes a key ingredient called "obvious legislative intent." When LEOSA became law, the obvious intent of the Representatives and Senators who voted for it was to recognize that when bad people attempted to murder good people, it was a good idea to have more armed good guys and gals who might be there to stop the carnage, and it didn't matter if they had the power to arrest the malefactor in that jurisdiction or not. Police chiefs in cities from New York to Chicago have dragged their feet and gotten in the way of other cops carrying there, or their cops carrying elsewhere, but once that is sorted out we'll start seeing "saves" from LEOSA that will prove the obvious legislative intent to be justified. Now, it will be a much shorter step to expanding the privilege to private citizens who can show the same trustworthiness and competency as those cops carrying nationwide.

If I'm outside my jurisdiction and have to shoot someone in self-defense while I'm carrying on LEOSA, my police department is effectively immune from lawsuit. I was not acting under "color of law" on duty; I was merely exercising a privilege granted by the Federal government to me and many others.

If, however, I'm outside my jurisdiction and shoot someone in self-defense *with the company hardware,* the agency can be sued. After all, they *gave me the ammunition and what is now "the death weapon."*

The lawsuit seeks big bucks. I don't have big bucks, and ain't worth suing by my lonesome. But the community any law enforcement agency serves has a tax base that plaintiffs' lawyers do see as representing big bucks. If there's no money there, there is less likely to be a lawsuit at all. Keep the blood out of the water, and you don't attract the sharks.

Avoid the "Hair Trigger Trap." I call it a trap for two reasons. First, cops and civilians and security professionals alike are much more likely to have to take people at gunpoint than to shoot them. If the finger goes to the trigger, as studies show it often does unconsciously, even when the person holding the gun is highly trained, the stage is set for accidental discharge due to several causes first identified by famed physiologist Roger Enoka. These include startle response, postural disturbance, interlimb response, etc. The lighter the trigger pull, the more prone the gun is to such unintentional discharges, often automatically considered "negligent discharges" by firearms professionals.

But there is a much more subtle trap. It has become a cottage industry in shooting-related lawsuits, and to a lesser extent in criminal prosecutions, for opposing counsel to present a false case of accidental discharge when in fact the shooting was intentional. This is because experienced lawyers know that self-defense to a charge of an intentional shooting is what's known in trial tactics parlance as "a perfect defense," but it's much harder for a defendant to prove that he didn't cock the gun and recklessly set the stage for an unintentional hair-trigger discharge.

The best way to avoid that bogus attack is to have a gun whose trigger weight is within factory specifications for police duty as opposed to target shooting. This is an argument against any gun that can be cocked to create a very light pull, unless the single-action pull is at least four pounds or more in weight. This is one reason so many police departments have gone with double-action-only handguns. One reason for the Glock pistol's enormous popularity, particularly among cops, is that BATFE has ruled it to be a double-action-only design. Just don't install the 3.5-pound connector, creating a light pull that the factory says should be used ONLY on competition pistols, and you should be fine.

The handload trap. Use all the reloads you want for practice, or match shooting, or handgun hunting. Heck, I do. But for a home defense gun, concealed carry handgun, or police duty weapon, factory ammo is the way to go. In most cases, the factory round will have better quality control and more reliability than a reloaded cartridge. If you don't believe me, ask anyone with experience as a range officer in any form of handgun competition, "Which is more likely to misfeed or misfire, a factory load or a handload?" Moreover, every factory defense round recommended in this book has a proven track record as a man-stopper in actual gunfights. No home-brewed ammo has that; actual shootings with reloads are very few and far between. (You could assemble a handload that duplicates a given factory load, and save some money, but now you're literally defending your family with a cheap imitation. That's the kind of clone ammo to use for practice, not for street carry.)

Two real problems come up in court with handloads. In *New Jersey v. Daniel Bias,* whether the death of a young woman was suicide or murder at the hands of her husband came down to forensic evidence testing, to wit, the determination of how far the gun muzzle was from her head before the fatal wound was inflicted. However, the death weapon was a Smith & Wesson Model 586 revolver charged with very light reloads in 38 Special +P cases. The police insisted on doing their gunshot residue (GSR) testing with actual +P, which leaves GSR for a considerable distance, and there was none found on her head or hair. Defense experts tested reloads duplicating what the husband said he had made up and put in the gun, and could have shown that these wouldn't have left residue at the distance the gun was when the defense believe it discharged in the victim's own hand.

However, to make a long story short, that evidence never got in. It would have required the court to take the defendant's word for the handload "recipe." Even your reloading records, meticulous as they may be, won't help. You see, *the evidence was manufactured by the defendant,* and that goes for the records as well as the ammo. You can't prove it wasn't some BS you came up with afterward to get away with murder. I have challenged many Internet advocates of defensive handloads to find a case where the defendant's records or testimony as to load was accepted as GSR evidence. None has ever come up with a case.

Some scoff that GSR is unlikely to be an issue. They're wrong. Look at a few random issues of *American Rifleman* magazine's "Armed Citizen" column, and see at what close

Dennis Tueller did a great service for cops and armed citizens alike with his 1983 research that proved the average man could close 7 yards from a standing start and deliver a fatal knife thrust in 1.5 seconds. Here, he explains his research at a deadly force symposium convened by the author at an ASLET seminar, 2006. In the background are noted authorities Brian Stover, Harvey Hedden, and John Holschen.

ranges most of those shootings take place. It's critical for you to be able to prove that the opponent was close enough to kill you with his knife, and he or his advocates in court are likely to tell the jury that he was too far away to present any danger to you. Gunshot residue testing may save you… *if* we can get it in. We regularly introduce GSR testing with factory ammo; I've never seen that *fail* to get in.

How likely is it that GSR will be an issue? Well, let's take a look at my own caseload at the moment. With the Lindsey case finished by a just acquittal, I'm down to ten on the current schedule, a nice round number that's easy to work with. One of those cases involves a citizen who drew a knife to protect himself, and another focuses on a cop who defended himself with blunt force. Neither, obviously, have anything to do with gunshot residue since no guns came into play at all. Of the remaining eight, GSR is an issue in

> **To be justifiable, deadly force must always be a last resort.**

four of them, and in one, it is a compelling issue. That's 40 percent of the cases overall, and *half* of the ten cases in this example. Does that sound as if GSR is "unlikely" to be an issue when *your* shooting comes?

Another thing to worry about with handloads is the argument, "This man was so intent in causing horrible, deadly wounds that regular bullets weren't deadly enough, so he made his own *extra-deadly* bullets!" That was the BS pulled by the prosecution in *State of NH v. Sgt. James Kennedy.* That argument was shot down by Jim Cirillo as expert witness for the defense. However, every courtroom argument is like a gunfight: it's better to avoid it than to have to fight it, and every now and then, the other side can get lucky and win.

By the way, remember those two cases the next time you hear on the Internet, "There has never been a case of anyone getting in trouble for using handloads." The *Kennedy* case ended with an acquittal, and that was justice. However, the *Bias* case went through three trials before the third jury found the kid guilty of Manslaughter and sent him to prison. Both his lawyers told me they felt that if he'd had factory ammo in the gun, they don't think he would have been convicted.

The Rules of Engagement

Every encounter will be different from every other: sometimes hugely, sometimes subtly. The only way to make sure you're right is to follow a formula when you make the decision whether or not to use lethal force. The formulae I'm about to show you are rock-solid, engraved in the stone of the law and what the court calls "common custom and practice" alike.

Deadly force is only permissible in a situation of *immediate, otherwise unavoidable danger of death or great bodily harm to oneself or another innocent person one has the right to protect.* The presence of that situation is determined by the *simultaneous* presence of three criteria: ability, opportunity, and jeopardy.

Ability means the attacker has the power to cause death or great bodily harm: that is, to kill or cause crippling injury. This usually takes the form of a *per se* weapon such as a gun or knife or club, but as noted above, can also manifest itself as *disparity of force.* Force of numbers, a hugely larger and stronger attacker, an able-bodied person attacking the disabled, high skill at unarmed combat *that is known to the shooter,* an adult violently attacking a child, even a male violently attacking a female are examples of disparity of force. Even though they are ostensibly unarmed, their greater size, strength, etc. is so likely to kill or cripple that it becomes the equivalent of a deadly weapon. As noted earlier in this chapter as related to *Colorado v. Larry Lindsey,* a furtive movement that is consistent with going for a weapon (and consistent with nothing else) also suffices to create the ability factor.

Opportunity means the attacker is capable of immediately employing that power. In 1983, Dennis Tueller did the ground-breaking research that proved the average adult male can close a gap of seven yards from a standing start and inflict a fatal stab wound in 1.5 seconds on the average. From 100 yards away, it would take him longer, and shooting a man with a knife from the other end of a football field would probably not be seen as justifiable in most courts today. Within seven or even ten paces, though, the man with the knife has satisfied the opportunity factor.

Jeopardy is the final factor. The opponent must be acting in such a manner that any reasonable, prudent person in your situation would conclude that his intent was to kill or cripple you or the innocent person you deploy your gun to protect. As noted earlier, we're talking about *manifest intent:* an intent expressed in words and/or actions.

There is also an element that must be considered that has become known as *preclusion.* To be justifiable, deadly force must always be a last resort. Preclusion means, was there any way of avoiding this? Not just escape at the scene, but prevention: did *you* do anything to start the fight or "keep the ball rolling"? If you did, it impairs what the courts call "the mantle of innocence."

Some instructors teach preclusion as part of the same formula as ability/opportunity/jeopardy. I disagree, and separate it out in the training I give at Lethal Force Institute and elsewhere. There are two big reasons for this. First, Ability/Opportunity/Jeopardy (AOJ, for short) speaks to the assailant and the threat he presents to you. Preclusion speaks to *you,* and *your* exact situation, and *your* options in a given moment and place. It's "apples and oranges." Both elements need to be considered, but they need to be considered separately.

Second, AOJ is written in stone, but preclusion is fungible. Are you a cop, acting in the line of duty? If so, you have no duty to retreat, and indeed, under certain circumstances your retreat might be construable as cowardice or misfeasance of public office. Were you an armed citizen attacked in public in Florida in the year 2004? If so, the state law said you had a duty to retreat before using lethal force in self-defense. But today, the new (and, I like to think, improved) Florida law allows you to stand your ground without attempting to retreat if you are attacked in any place where you have a right to be. New York and many other states still have "retreat requirements" for public attack.

However, in any jurisdiction, you are allowed to stand your ground without resorting to retreat if you are in your home. It is called the "castle doctrine" because it stems from the ancient English Common Law that held "a man's home is his castle," and attacked there, he need not retreat.

Remember, however, that in any jurisdiction that has a "retreat requirement," retreat is *never* demanded unless it can be accomplished *in complete safety to oneself and other innocent persons.* In other words, you aren't expected to turn your back on a mugger's gun and attempt to outrun a bullet. You aren't expected to run away and leave your children behind, helpless against the attacker, like throwing the babies from the sleigh to placate the pursuing wolves. (Interestingly enough, I've been in cases against ruthless

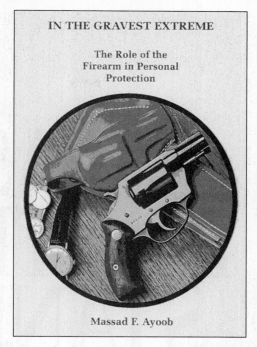

Ayoob wrote *In the Gravest Extreme* to show armed citizens the rules of engagement in deadly force encounters. It is available through Police Bookshelf, PO Box 122, Concord, NH 03302, www.ayoob.com.

lawyers and prostitute expert witnesses who tried to convince juries that you *were* supposed to stoop to such levels. They did not win their cases.)

If this has been a long chapter, it's because it's a very involved corner of concealed carry, and we've barely scratched the surface here. My book *In the Gravest Extreme: the Role of the Firearm in Personal Protection* is devoted to this topic, and has stood the test of time and the courts for more than a quarter of a century. Deadly force law being one of the more mature bodies of law, nothing terribly significant has changed in "the rules of engagement" since it was written. It is available through Police Bookshelf, PO Box 122, Concord, NH 03302, 1-800-624-9049, www.ayoob.com. At the same website you'll find a link for the classes I teach through Lethal Force Institute. The course I'd recommend would be the 40-hour LFI-I, which encompasses the legal/ethical/tactical elements plus several hundred rounds of hands-on combat shooting. If you already feel you're sufficiently competent with the "how" and want more about the "when," consider the weekend (two-day intensive lecture setting) Judicious Use of Deadly Force program.

Power and responsibility are commensurate.

The how and the when can't do it by themselves, though. You need both. Power and responsibility are commensurate. With great power, obviously, comes great responsibility, because power unchecked by responsibility becomes bullying among individuals and terrorism and tyranny in the collective.

At the same time, responsibility without the power to fulfill it may be the ultimate hopelessness.

CASTLE DOCTRINE AND STAND YOUR GROUND LAWS

> **Many states have had (and some still have) laws that require a person attacked in public to retreat before using deadly force in self-defense.**

Between the first edition of this book and the second, some states adopted "castle doctrine" laws that clarified the old English Common Law principle that the citizen's home is his castle, and attacked there, he need not retreat. This had long been the law of the land anyway, when statutory law, case law, and jury instructions were examined *in toto*, but it certainly did not hurt to have it clarified in the statutes.

Many states have had (and some still have) laws that require a person attacked in public to retreat before using deadly force in self-defense. Others have historically allowed a person in that situation to stand their ground and fight without attempting to retreat, so long as they had a right to be in that place, did not start the fight, and were not committing a crime.

It should be noted that even in the so-called "retreat states," *retreat was **only** required when it could be accomplished in complete safety to oneself and other innocent parties.* If it wasn't in the statutes, it was in the case law and/or the states' recommended jury instructions. Some felt it would be good to clarify it in the black and white of the statutes. Sure made

sense to this writer, and I'm glad that those states did so.

Some other states rescinded the retreat requirement with new laws, which allowed the law-abiding citizen to stand their ground anywhere they had a right to be if they were attacked, under the circumstances described above. The proper term for that was simply "rescinding of retreat requirement." If one needed a catchy name to sell it to the legislators and the public, certainly "Stand Your Ground" was appropriate for that. However, since many saw it as extending the Castle Doctrine to public places, and "Castle Doctrine" had a positive ring to it, some on our side decided to call the "Stand Your Ground" laws "Castle Doctrine" laws instead.

That, unfortunately, muddied the waters. Castle Doctrine traditionally speaks to the home; Stand Your Ground historically speaks to any other place where you have a right to be and are not doing anything wrong. As my friend and colleague Clint Smith of Thunder Ranch fame says of some tactical principles, "They're the same, but they're different."

At this writing, I've been swimming with the sharks as an expert witness for the courts, both criminal and civil, for 33 years in cases involving weapons and shootings. I can tell you that the old aphorism from law school is absolutely true: "If the law is on your side, pound on the law…if the facts are on your side, pound on the facts…and if neither the law nor the facts are on your side, pound on the opposing party." Well, you wouldn't have shot someone in self-defense if the

(left) At Cato Institute forum on Stand Your Ground laws, Clayton Cramer gave excellent explanation of these laws' history and societal development…

…Massad Ayoob (below) explained why arguments against such laws did not hold water…

facts and the law weren't on your side, so that leaves the clueless or politically motivated prosecutor wrongfully charging you, or the greed-motivated plaintiff's lawyer suing you, only one avenue by which

…and attorney Steve Jansen explained why he felt Stand Your Ground was a License to Kill.

to attack you. It won't be honest, it won't be clean, and it won't be pretty.

If one issue is, "Why didn't you run when you were attacked in the public park instead of pulling your gun?" and your answer is, "Castle Doctrine allowed me to," you've just opened yourself to the shark attack. The opposing lawyer on cross-examination will hand you a copy of Black's Legal Dictionary and have you read the whole "A man's home is his castle" thing aloud in front of the jury. Then, you can expect him to ask, "Did you consider the public park your castle grounds? Who exactly was it that made you king of us all?" They'll make a monkey out of you and severely damage your credibility. (I don't put words in people's mouths, but if I was the defendant in that situation I would simply answer the question with, "Sir, there was no way I could retreat with complete safety to myself and the others I fired my gun to protect.")

A third, and completely separate legal doctrine is "assumption of reasonableness." This means simply that the person claiming self-defense, if they can prove it to a preponderance of evidence standard in a hearing in front

of an impartial magistrate, cannot be charged with a crime for the act. In 2005, the Florida State Legislature passed a "Stand Your Ground" law – Florida Statute 776.013 – which combined the clarification of the Castle Doctrine principle with the rescinding of the retreat requirement from which it drew its name, *and* the assumption of reasonableness principle.

The fourth and final element associated here is insulation from civil suit, which essentially comes under the umbrella of "tort reform." This is the law that states if the criminal justice system has ruled the shooting to be justifiable, the person who fired should be immune to civil lawsuit.

That is what the "black letter of the law" says. However, *it must be taken in context with other subtleties, such as trial tactics and the mood of the courts.* One has to read the fine print.

Let's look first at Castle Doctrine. There are some situations where it doesn't hold true. If the person you shoot also had a right to be in your home at the time of the shooting, this defense is voided. We see that all the time in domestic violence shootings, when the woman who had to fire was the victim of the abusive husband who attacked her, and with whom she shared the "castle." Ditto roommates, ditto even originally-invited guests who went crazy once they were there.

Stand Your Ground? If the other guy also had a right to be there, it's going to come down to who was the murderous, unlawful aggressor and who was the innocent intended victim who wore what the courts call "the mantle of innocence." For one thing, if the initial attacker tries to break off the assault and flee, and the original innocent victim then shoots him in the back, the "stand your ground" defense for the latter is now off the game board.

Presumption of Reasonableness? Plaintiff's counsel has only to fabricate a theory of a negligent, unintended discharge on your part, and they've gotten past your wall of protection. There is no such thing as a "justifiable accident" in the lexicon of the law.

Immunity from civil lawsuit? To get that, you need to show that your shooting incident has in fact been ruled justifiable. If it has not gone to trial (as it won't, if the prosecutor's office doesn't choose to prosecute, or the grand jury returns "no true bill"), you haven't actually been determined to have fired in self-defense. All that it means is that the prosecutor's office didn't think they could convict you beyond a reasonable doubt. The civil lawsuit standard is much lower, merely preponderance of evidence, which is why so many people who've been held harmless in criminal court have been absolutely hammered in civil court. If the prosecutor's office issues a "memorandum of closure" stating that, in their official opinion, your shooting of your attacker was indeed justifiable, that's pretty strong on your behalf in this stage of the court proceedings. If they simply don't issue such a memorandum, the civil court judge may well decide that it's "an issue for a jury to decide," and you're back in the very financially and emotionally expensive nightmare of being sued by someone trying to take everything you have.

> For one thing, if the initial attacker tries to break off the assault and flee, and the original innocent victim then shoots him in the back, the "stand your ground" defense for the latter is now off the game board.

In the first quarter of 2012, a highly publicized shooting took place in Florida that made these matters an issue of national debate. At the time of this writing, the matter has not been resolved by the courts, and this writer is not in a position to comment on that case until it has been resolved in court. The publicity led to some truly bizarre interpretations of the law, such as saying that "Stand Your Ground" means you can shoot anyone you're remotely afraid of. Totally untrue! Or that it's a "license to kill": again, totally untrue. Or that it lets anyone kill anyone and get away with it by claiming self-defense: yet again, totally untrue. To convict you for a crime in criminal court, the prosecution has to show that you are guilty beyond a reasonable doubt, a standard of certainty generally seen as somewhere between 95% and 99.9%. For you to be cleared under "Presumption of Reasonableness," you will have had to prove to a civil court standard of preponderance of evidence, a greater than 50% certainty, that you did the right thing.

Do the math! If you've already proven that it's more than 50% certain that you did the *right* thing, how on earth could it be proven to a 95%-plus certainty that you did the *wrong* thing?

In April of 2012, Tim Lynch of the Cato Institute brought three of us to their headquarters in Washington, DC, to tell a live audience, which I was told numbered one hundred, and a video audience far greater than that, what we thought of the Stand Your Ground issue. Historian Clayton Cramer opened by explaining how Castle Doctrine, Stand Your Ground, and related concepts had developed over the course of civilization. I was the one who spoke on behalf of Stand Your Ground laws. Steven Jansen of the Association of Prosecuting Attorneys took the side that "Stand Your Ground" was a license to kill. You can see the forum discussion for yourself at http://www.cato.org/event.php?eventid=9141.

"GENTLEMEN (AND LADIES), CHOOSE YOUR WEAPONS"

Three approaches to snag-free carry revolvers

(L) S&W Bodyguard (M/649) with shrouded hammer, DA/SA. *(Center)* factory bobbed hammer on DAO Ruger SP101. *(R)* "hammerless" configuration of DAO S&W Centennial (M/40-1).

One can't carry a concealed weapon without having a concealable weapon. Some are suitable for the concealed carry task, and some are not.

We can't cover every possible choice here. A swing through the Krause catalog will show you whole books on the 1911, the Glock, the SIG-Sauer, the Beretta, the Smith & Wesson series, etc. al. Other good choices from Paladin include *Living with 1911s* and *Living with Glocks* by Robert Boatman, and the outstanding *The Snubby Revolver* by Ed Lovette. I think Lovette's book should be

read by anyone who owns or is thinking of owning a "snub-nose." It puts the whole *genre* in perspective.

As noted earlier, it's more convenient to have a "wardrobe" of concealable handguns, but it's not entirely necessary. Generations of young cops have learned that it's cheaper to buy a concealment holster for their full-size department-issue service handgun than to purchase a whole new gun and leather set for off-duty carry. Similarly, many armed citizens have learned that the full-size handgun they bought for home protection is concealable if they set their mind to it.

The competent shooter loses little going double-action-only with a snubby. This old M/36 Chief Special with Herrett stocks made 5 out of 5 head shots at 20 yards single action *(left)* and double action *(right)*.

Cocked to single action as shown, this S&W 649 can be a problem waiting to happen in a tactical situation. Author prefers double-action-only (DAO) S&Ws.

A bit larger than J-frames, and heavier, Taurus Tracker 45 *(top)* and Ruger SP101 357 *(below)*, are very "shootable" and substantially more powerful than 38s.

Cops have picked up on this, too. In 1967, Ordnance Sgt Louis Seman of the Illinois State Police convinced the ISP to become the first large department in the nation to adopt the Smith & Wesson Model 39 9mm semiautomatic pistol as a duty weapon. The reason was not firepower. At the time, troopers were required to be armed off duty. They carried 4- to 6-inch barrel Colt and Smith & Wesson service revolvers in uniform, and generally wore 2-inch barrel small frame 38 versions of the same guns on their own time. At qualification, the "snubby" scores were dismally inferior to those with the larger revolvers. Seman reasoned, correctly, that the Model

39 auto pistol would be light and flat enough for concealed carry, but would do fine for uniform wear as well. He was proven right: scores skyrocketed, and the troopers became comfortable wearing the slim Smith 9mms on their off-time.

❶

❷

❸

❹

❺

❻

Today's new paradigm: polymer-framed, striker-fired autos. From top: Glock 22 in 40, S&W M&P in 9mm, Springfield XD Tactical in 45 GAP, 45 ACP Kahr P45, 40 cal. Taurus 24/7, and 9mm Ruger SR9.

Many prefer a mix of modern and traditional. These are modern polymer-frame autos with hammer-fired mechanisms. From top right: **(1)** 9mm SIG P250 DAO; **(2)** 45 ACP Heckler & Koch USP45; and **(3)** 45 ACP Ruger P345.

Secrets of experience: moderately long-barrel guns with short grips deliver great shooting performance, and may be easier to carry at the waist than "snubbies." **(4)** Kahr Covert P40 in 40 S&W; **(5)** S&W Model 64 38 Special with 4-inch barrel and Craig Spegel Boot Grips; and **(6)** Colt CCO with 4 1/4-inch barrel of Commander mounted on short Officers frame, in 45 ACP, wearing Barnhart Burner stocks.

More recently, when NYPD went with 16-shot 9mm pistols and gave their officers the choice of the SIG P226 DAO, the heavy S&W Model 5946, or the polymer-frame Glock 19, the overwhelming majority chose the latter. This was partly because the Glock 19 was cheaper (NYPD officers buy their own guns through the department), but also because it was much lighter and the only one of the three options that was truly a "compact." The G19 was easier to carry all the time off duty, or when transferring to a plainclothes assignment.

Just as hunters and sportsmen have historically modeled their rifle choices on the nation's military small arms, America's armed citizens have historically followed the police establishment in choosing defensive handguns. When most of America's cops carried 38 Special revolvers to work, that same type and caliber was the most popular choice of home defense and concealed carry gun. Though private gun enthusiasts embraced auto pistols before American law enforcement in general, they did not switch to autoloaders *en masse* until the police did the same. Today, the snub-nose "detective special" genre remains extremely popular among cops for backup and off-duty wear, and the same style gun is very popular among armed citizens, but both tend toward the autoloader as a rule for full size "heavy duty" handguns.

Let's take just a cursory look at available choices

today. In each weapon type, various sizes and calibers are available. This allows armed citizen and cop alike to have a deep concealment gun, a larger handgun that's concealable under heavier clothing, and perhaps a still larger one for home defense or target practice, *all with the same fire controls and general "feel" for commonality of training and habituation,* so that skills developed with the one will transfer to the other. With some (but not all) combinations, one can also use the larger gun's speedloaders or higher capacity magazines for efficient spare ammo recharging with the smaller gun.

The New Paradigm "Automatics"

The proper term is considered to be "semiautomatic," but for my generation "automatic" was an acceptable descriptor of autoloading pistols which only fired one shot per pull of the trigger, so forgive me if I use it in this book for convenience. We all know what we're talking about.

The most popular *genre* of automatics today are striker-fired pistols with no "hammers" *per se,* and with polymer frames. Pioneered by Heckler and Koch with the VP70Z and HKP9 series pistols of the 1970s and '80s – but *popularized* more than 20 years ago by the market-leading Glock brand

Two approaches to making 1911's butt less protuberant in concealment. Top: shortened Officer's frame on Colt CCO. Center: "Bobtail" configuration developed by Ed Brown, shown on his Executive model pistol. Bottom: standard size 1911 frame for reference, here a Smith SW1911. All 3 are 45 ACP.

S&W lightweight Centennials have been the choice of experts for deep concealment for more than half a century. Top: Original Centennial Airweight, circa 1953. Center, Model 442, early '90s, with Eagle grips. Bottom, Model 340 M&P, with factory-furnished Hogue grips, introduced 2007.

- the polymer frame reduces weight, reduces cost, and is impervious to corrosion. The latter is an important point with guns carried concealed and often exposed to salty, rust-creating human sweat. Most of these pistols will have a trigger pull that's the same from first to last shot, which makes them easier to learn to shoot well. These include the Glock, of course, and also the Springfield Armory XD, the Kahr, Smith & Wesson's successful Military & Police series and cost-effective Sigma line, and the slim, reliable Ruger SR9 among others. The Glock line is far and away the most popular in American police service at this writing, but the S&W M&P is coming on strong in that sector and so, to a lesser degree, is the XD.

Double-action semiautomatics can be had with polymer frames (Beretta Ninety-Two and Px4, the current HK series, SIG P-250 and SIG-Pro, Ruger P95 9mm and P345 45, for example). These require a long, heavy (read "deliberate") pull of the trigger for the first shot, and are considered by some to be less prone to stress-induced accidental discharges for that reason. They can be ordered DAO (double-action-only, with that same heavy pull for every shot, such as the popular Kel-Tec series), or TDA (traditional double action) in which the pistol cocks itself to an easy, light pull for every shot after the first. The latter will be fitted with a decocking lever to safely lower the hammer when the shooting is done. Of course, the same companies – plus Smith & Wesson and many more – offer double-action autos with steel or aluminum frame construction, too.

A classic favorite among American shooters is the single action semiautomatic, typified by the 1911 pistol that has been popular since the eponymous year of its introduction. To be ready for immediate, reactive self-defense, the 1911 type handgun has to be carried cocked and locked (hammer back, thumb safety in the "safe" position) with a live round in the chamber. This alarms some people not in tune with the tradition, and there is no shame for those people to simply go to a double action or striker-fired handgun instead. The 1911 was popular for concealed carry from the beginning because it is extremely *thin* for a gun of its power level, and is therefore very comfortable to wear inside the waistband or even in a shoulder holster. The most popular chambering is the one this gun was designed around, the 45 ACP (**A**utomatic **C**olt **P**istol), but enthusiasts have bought them in 38 Super, 9mm, 10mm, and other chamberings. The 1911 was designed by firearms genius John Moses Browning, who before his death did the initial design work on another famous weapon that bears his name, the Browning Hi-Power. Even slimmer, and capable of holding 14 rounds of 9mm Parabellum, this high quality weapon has something of a cult following in the CCW world.

Revolvers have earned a reputation for good reliability and have been around since the year 1836. A swing-out cylinder double action design is the easiest handgun for new shooters because of its simple "administrative handling," the routine loading and unloading, checking, and cleaning that accompanies all responsible firearms ownership. Its "manual of arms," i.e., its physical operation, is without parallel for simplicity. This is one reason most experts recommend the double-action revolver as a "starter gun" for new shooters.

Model 642 Airweight 38 Spl. may be today's "best buy" in a carry snub, opines author.

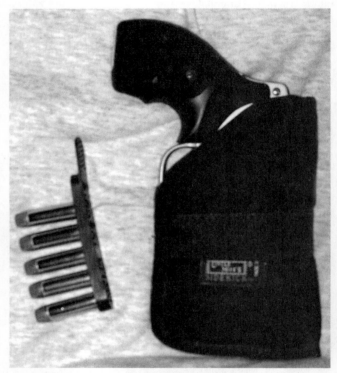

642 with Uncle Mike's grips and pocket holster, backed by Speed Strip, and loaded with 135-grain Gold Dot 38 Spl. +P is an excellent everyday carry snubby set-up.

Revolver or Auto

As you assess your particular balance of needs, you'll find some stark differences between the attributes of the double action revolver and the semiautomatic pistol. Let's go for a quick overview.

All autoloading pistols have long bearing surfaces between slide and frame, making them sensitive to proper lubrication. They are also depended on clean, pristine magazines with unfatigued springs. Thus, auto pistols are more maintenance intensive than revolvers, which can be left unlubricated and at rest literally for decades with no degradation in function. Military spec auto pistols such as the Glock, Beretta, SIG, etc. have large tolerances between

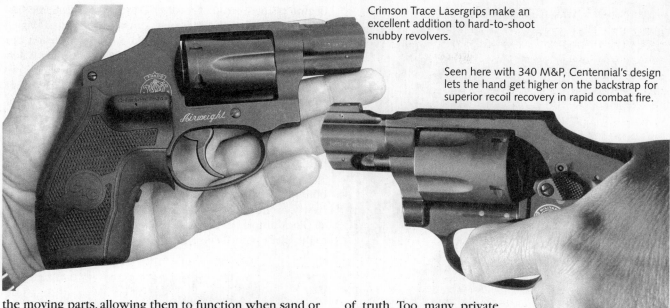

Crimson Trace Lasergrips make an excellent addition to hard-to-shoot snubby revolvers.

Seen here with 340 M&P, Centennial's design lets the hand get higher on the backstrap for superior recoil recovery in rapid combat fire.

the moving parts, allowing them to function when sand or dirt get in the mechanism; the more finely fitted revolvers may choke if dropped in a sand pile or immersed in mud. Thus, while the revolver is more forgiving of lack of routine maintenance, the automatic is more forgiving of field abuse.

In the serious defense calibers (38 Special and up) revolvers have only five shots in the small frame models, six in the standard frame, and occasionally seven or eight in the larger, progressively harder to conceal sizes. The smallest 9mm autos start at seven rounds on board, quickly progress to ten or eleven, and if you can carry a light polymer-frame, full size 9mm auto, you're up to 18 rounds or so, twenty if you don't mind a small magazine extension protruding from the butt. With quick-interchanging magazines, the autos are also much faster to reload. By any measure, if firepower's what you want, a semiautomatic is what you need.

Most semiautomatics can jam if pressed against an assailant's body before firing, as can happen in a belly-to-belly fight to the death or rape attempt. The pressure will push most autos' slides out of battery, or firing alignment of the parts, preventing even one shot from being fired. If the first shot discharges, viscous blood, fat, and brain matter may be back-blasted from a shot against bare flesh into the barrel bushing area of the autoloader as it cycles, preventing the slide from closing into battery for a subsequent shot. With a revolver, however, this is not a consideration. If your likeliest threat profile is a contact-distance mugging, rape, or murder attempt, the revolver will give you an advantage. Muzzle contact shots are particularly devastating since the violently expanding gases of the muzzle blast are directed into the opponent's body, causing massive additional damage.

Revolver shooters have tended historically to practice with light loads, using mild wadcutters or feeble 130-grain generic 38 Special range loads for training, and then loading monster Elmer Keith Memorial Magnum loads of 357 persuasion for the street. Cops got away from that long ago, because they realized that light loads didn't prepare the officer to hit with a hard-kicking gun at the moment

of truth. Too many private citizens still delude themselves this way. An advantage of the auto pistol is that it won't *run* with light loads, forcing the shooter into relevant practice.

Shorter, more efficient auto pistol loads tend to produce less muzzle flash at night than revolver ammo of equivalent power levels, i.e., 38 Special versus 9mm, 357 Magnum versus 357 SIG, or 45 Colt versus 45 ACP or 45 GAP (**G**lock **A**uto **P**istol). The less muzzle flash, the less the shooter is blinded by his or her own weapon, another advantage to the auto.

Autos tend to have squared-off "handles" that press tightly against the body, particularly in pocket, ankle, belly-band, or other deep concealment carry modes. This means the fingers of the drawing hand may have to fight a little to get between the flesh and the gun to gain a drawing grasp. The rounded profile of the small frame revolver allows a much faster grasp, hence a much faster draw. Score a point for the revolver here, particularly in pocket, ankle, or belly-band carry.

Revolvers tend, overall, to be somewhat more reliable than auto pistols, which can jam from being held with a limp wrist, from using too short or too long a cartridge, or from lack of lubrication or magazine damage. Particularly for non-experienced shooters and those who don't routinely lubricate their guns, this gives the "wheelgun" a reliability edge. (Auto shooters, remember to lubricate your carry gun monthly, even if you don't shoot it. Lubricant is liquid; it drains and evaporates.) If you carry in an ankle holster, grit builds up on the gun quickly. Only a few "military-spec" small autos seem to survive this buildup without jamming: the Kel-Tec P11 and P3AT, the baby Glocks, and the Kahrs, for example. Revolvers tolerate this grit buildup in ankle holsters much better.

One thing we've seen more and more since autoloaders became predominant in police work is that if they are carried with a manual safety locked in the "safe" position, they offer an element of proprietary nature to the user if a criminal gains control of the weapon. This feature is generally the province of auto pistols instead of revolvers. However, the K-frame (38-size frame) or larger S&W revolver can be converted to Magna-Trigger configuration by Rick Devoid. Such a conversion can only be fired by someone wearing a magnetic ring. When my little ones were not yet at an age of responsibility, my "house gun" (and often my carry gun) was a 4-inch barrel Smith & Wesson 357, MagnaTriggered. It will come out of retirement now that I've got grandkids. I gave a 2 1/2-inch barrel MagnaTrigger Combat Magnum to my youngest when she became a mom – Devoid tuned the action, too – while her older sister was comfortable with her pet S&W Model 3913 9mm automatic in this regard, since it is equipped with both manual safety and magazine disconnector safety. Devoid (www.tarnhelm.com) can also fit a Cominolli thumb safety for all Glock pistols but the Model 36, offering proprietary nature to the user to Glock fans.

Ayoob says "Friends don't let friends carry mouse guns." Compared to S&W 40-1 38 *(top)*, the NAA 22 Magnum *(center)* and 22 Short *(bottom)* mini-revolvers should be seen as enjoyable recreational guns, not fighting weapons, he feels.

P3AT by Kel-Tec is reliable in current production, says author, and certainly light and flat.

There is such a thing as "too big" in defensive revolvers, such as the 460 Smith & Wesson. Author whimsically holds 8 3/8-inch version, left, and short barrel "emergency" model, right.

Kel-Tec P3AT (below J-frame S&W shown for comparison) is extremely flat and easy to carry, but author does not trust its 380 cartridge as much as he does 38 Spl. +P.

Concealed Carry Gun Features

Whatever your choice, there are some features that are particularly suitable for concealed carry. You want a carry gun that is **snag-free.** No sharp edges. Nothing to hook on clothing and reveal the pistol, or wear holes in the garments, or catch on fabric and fatally stall a defensive draw. If you just have to have a sharp-edged, non-ramped front sight, make sure your holster has a "sight channel" that will prevent "catching." Some shooters really do have a need for adjustable rear sights – they're carrying a hunting handgun or match handgun that needs to be precisely zeroed, and may need the sights adjusted to take advantage of different ammunition power levels – the edges of those sights should be rounded, even if a custom gunsmith has to do it.

Make sure the grip and grip-frame area give the hand enough traction if wet with sweat or blood or rain. The defensive handgun, remember, is an emergency tool. Smooth metal frames coupled with pearl or even ivory "handles," if the latter don't have finger grooves, might as well be coated with wet soap. Some secure grip surfaces can be *too* tacky for concealed carry. Depending on the garments, "rubber" grips have been known to catch inner clothing surfaces and hike up the garment to reveal the handgun. Skateboard-like grips that lock the gun solidly into the hand can abrade coat linings. I find I can wear them next to bare skin, but a lot of my colleagues find them agonizing. On the other hand, some of those folks can wear cocobolo grips next to their skin, but in my

The old revolver paradigm, seen with S&W 38 Specials. From top: 6-inch K38 for pistol team use, 4-inch Combat Masterpiece for uniform wear, and 2-inch Chiefs Special for concealment needs.

The carry gun of your choice will probably be available in a variety of size formats. Here are the four currently produced 9mm Glocks. From top: target size G34; service size G17; compact G19; subcompact G26.

There are other factors to consider, but these are the key points. They help to explain why serious shooters today seem to prefer autoloaders, but most experts recommend revolvers for beginners and for that class of gun owners that expert Mark Moritz defined as NDPs, or non-dedicated personnel. It also explains why the revolver is so popular as a hideout/backup gun among even highly trained gun people.

When in doubt, do what I do. With a service-grade automatic on my hip and a light, snub-nosed revolver in my pocket, I figure I'm covered whether St. Peter turns out to be a Bill Jordan/revolver fan or a Jeff Cooper auto fan when I meet him on Judgment Day…

Commonality of training and ammo, duality of purpose. Top, Glock 31 with Scott Warren night sights and InSight M3X white light unit, for police patrol and home defense. Below, Glock 33 with Trijicon night sights for backup and concealed carry. Both fire the powerful 357 SIG cartridge, and smaller gun will work with larger gun's magazines.

Your model of choice may be available in various lengths. These are single-action-only SIG P220 45s. From top: 5-inch barrel target model, 4 1/4-inch service model, and 3.9-inch "Carry" model.

case they cause an angry red rash. There are a lot of individualistic little tastes that you develop over years of concealed carry, and they tend to be highly subjective.

Night sights are a good idea. Most armed encounters occur in dim light, and Tritium sights can help. When you wake up in pitch darkness in a strange motel room, those glowing sight dots guide your hand to the bedside defense sidearm like airstrip landing lights. Laser sights, particularly the convenient designs such as LaserMax (replacing the recoil spring under the barrel in popular autos), and the Crimson Trace LaserGrip (bolt-on, for popular revolvers and autos) can enhance your hit potential in the dark. They're a Godsend for those with vision problems that allow them to identify a threat, but don't let them focus on gunsights that are at arm's length. The deterrent effect of the red laser dot on a suspect at gunpoint may have been over-rated by manufacturers and advertisers, but if there's a chance of that working, it's a chance you want on your side. Laser sights are

also a tremendous training aid in dry fire and even live fire, allowing the shooter to better become accustomed to holding the gun as steady as possible as the index finger smoo-oothly rolls the trigger back until the shot.

White light attachments make great sense for home defense, and it is logical to purchase as an all-around defense pistol an autoloader that has integral frame rails that allow slide-on/slide-off units by SureFire, InSight, Streamlight, Blackhawk, and so on. Police are going to larger holsters made to carry light-mounted guns, and a few manufacturers (Blade-Tech, for one) produce concealable holsters that carry light-mounted automatics. As the light units become smaller, this practice will become more practical for concealed carry.

Thickness is an important dimension in CCW selection. Top to bottom, left: Springfield XD, Glock 22, Kimber 1911, SIG P226. From top at right: Kahr P40, S&W K-frame, S&W J-frame, and Browning Hi-Power. Note slimness of 1911 and Hi-Power formats, a reason for their popularity among CCW professionals.

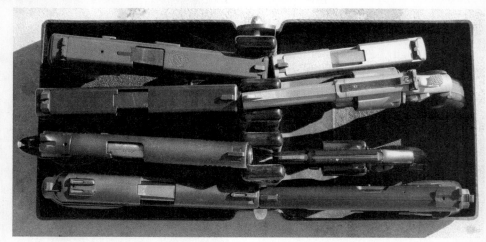

Size and Shape Factors

Bulges under the clothing are the key enemy of effective concealment, and the "handle" area of the gun tends to be the biggest offender here. The long grip-frame of a full-size duty pistol is best concealed by carrying it on the strong-side hip, tilted sharply forward until the backstrap of the grip is pointed almost at the armpit. This may require a slight crouch to effect the draw, but that's something most people do in a high-stress danger situation anyway.

Carry gun of author's oldest daughter is this Sokol-tuned S&W Model 39. It holds nine rounds of 9mm and is a perfect carry size. SIG's analogous pistol, the P239, was advertised as "Personal Size," for good reason.

Nonetheless, smaller gun butts are a plus for concealment. One of the lesser recognized concealment secrets is that a medium-length barrel coupled with a minimized grip frame can give the carrier the best of both worlds. Three good examples would be the K-frame Smith & Wesson revolver with a 4-inch barrel and stocks cut level with the metal butt; my favorite concealed carry Colt 45 auto among the extensive line the company has offered since 1911, the CCO with 4 1/4-inch Commander barrel and commensurate length slide mounted on the short-butt Lightweight Officers frame; and the popular Kahr Covert series, in which the barrel/slide of their standard-length guns (compact by most other makers' standards) is mated with the stubby frame of their Micro models. With autos, this generally reduces cartridge capacity by a round or two due to the necessarily shorter magazine, but that's a reasonable price to pay for a gun that conceals like a snubby but shoots like a service pistol. My old friend Marty Hayes, the master shooter and instructor who directs Firearms Academy of Seattle, once created a Glock 40 perfect for concealed carry that I called the Glock 22-1/2. He took the standard service-size sixteen-shot Glock 22 and shortened its butt to

This hammer-shrouded Colt Detective Special picked up this much lint and dirt carried in an ankle holster between cop-owner's range qualifications. It still worked, one reason author likes revolvers for pocket and ankle wear.

take the 13-round Glock 23 magazine. This gave maximum concealment, still offered an excellent grasp, and a total of fourteen versus sixteen rounds was not deemed to be an unfair price to pay for the improved concealment.

Rounded butts work well. Ed Brown came up with a "bobtail" lower rear end for his own line of factory custom 1911 automatics, which he has licensed to the Dan Wesson company for their brand and which is available for custom gunsmithing as well. With any handgun (revolvers are particularly suitable) rounding the edges of the grips at the bottom will improve concealability.

Additional Safety Factors

The trigger pull should be *smooth* on a defensive handgun, but *not particularly light*. One factor that occurs to human beings under stress is vasoconstriction. Blood flow is redirected away from the extremities and into the internal organs and major muscle groups, as if to "fuel the furnace" for the superhuman effort about to come. This is why frightened Caucasians become deathly pale, and it is why people in life-threatening stress situations become grossly clumsy. A light trigger pull can now much more easily discharge prematurely and unintentionally.

There are two problems with this. One is the potential for unintentional discharge itself. (Yeah, I know, it's trendy to call it "negligent discharge" unless there was a mechanical defect. I've worked in the criminal justice system since 1972, and I still believe in the "innocent until proven

Author has carried this Browning Hi-Power, tuned by Cylinder & Slide Shop, coast to coast in the U.S.A. and from Europe to Africa. Great feel and "shootability" combine with thinness to make it more concealable than it looks in profile. Worldwide availability of Browning parts and 9mm Luger ammo doesn't hurt, either.

Gun expert Dean Speir pronounced the Glock 30 the ideal concealed carry pistol. Match-accurate and totally reliable with duty loads, it carries 11 rounds of 45 ACP.

Laser sights are useful, especially in poor light. Here author centers a target after dusk with Ruger SP101 revolver equipped with Crimson Trace LaserGrips.

Subcompact 1911s are popular among professionals. Famed instructor Gila Hayes carries hers, an Ultra Compact 9mm Springfield Armory, as shown with modified safety, sights, and LaserGrips added.

guilty" part. The automatic assumption of negligence if the discharge was not caused by mechanical failure seems to have arisen from firearms academies sponsored by liability conscious firearms manufacturers. I'm still comfortable with the term "accidental discharge" (AD) until negligence has been clearly and convincingly proven.)

Accidental discharges, sometimes with tragic and fatal results, *have* been clearly and convincingly related to very light trigger pulls over the years by countless police departments. Decades ago, the police departments of Los Angeles and New York City went to double-action-only revolvers, because so many bad things had happened with revolvers cocked to single action. NYPD now mandates a nearly twelve-pound (NY2, or "New York Plus") trigger module in all Glock pistols carried by members of their service. The New York State Police, for the exact same

Crimson Trace LaserGrip activates when middle finger depresses button on front of grip in normal firing grasp. It's shown here on a Smith & Wesson Titanium Model 342 38 Special.

Precision shots are needed in self-defense more often than folks think. Late model S&W M/40-1 *(right)*, has better sights than such J-frame S&Ws used to have, but even better are those on Model 340 PD *(left)*. Big AO Express night sight in front is easy to pick up in close, fast shooting, and the eye settles it into generous U-notch rear sight if precision shot is needed.

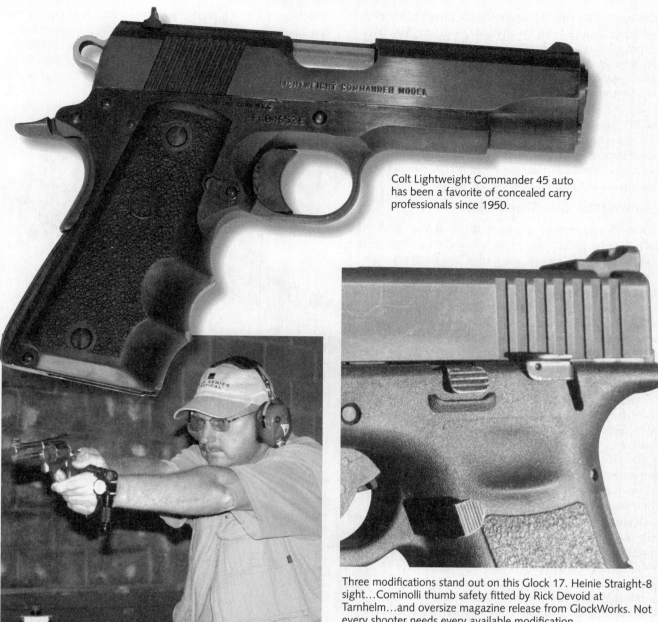

Colt Lightweight Commander 45 auto has been a favorite of concealed carry professionals since 1950.

Three modifications stand out on this Glock 17. Heinie Straight-8 sight…Cominolli thumb safety fitted by Rick Devoid at Tarnhelm…and oversize magazine release from GlockWorks. Not every shooter needs every available modification.

Good lights are essential to self-defense in poor light. FL/GA Regional Champion with Enhanced Service Revolver, Jon Strayer, demonstrates the very useful Liberator flashlight by First Light, Inc. at 2007 national championships. Affixing quickly to the back of the hand, it leaves both hands free. Revolver is Mulkerin Custom S&W 45.

reason, pioneered the original "New York trigger" (NY1) for the Glock 17 9mms they adopted in the 1980s, and for the Glock 37 45 GAPs they carry today. This brings pull weight up to 7.75-8.0 pounds. It works well under stress for accurate hits; it's actually less likely to break than the standard trigger spring it replaces; and I for one have it in each of the several Glocks I regularly carry concealed. In a 1911 pistol, no street-wise police instructor or gunsmith will recommend a single-action pull weight of less than four pounds, and most suggest something closer to five.

The second problem with the light trigger pull is the false allegation of an accidental discharge. Here's the situation I've seen play out over and over again in both civil and criminal cases over the years. Good guy shoots bad guy. Publicity-hungry prosecutor or money-hungry plaintiff's lawyer needs a scapegoat to grab political or financial profit. This attorney fabricates a case of accidental discharge due to recklessly cocking hammer and creating hair trigger (or carrying pistol that would always fire with "hair trigger"). This BS allegation is dignified in court as the accuser's "theory of the case." Without this frail hook on which to hang the bogus case, it probably would have gone away. Instead, the shooter who fired in self-defense goes through a nightmarish (and nightmarishly expensive) ordeal. See the "Aftermath" chapter.

One is wisest to avoid it entirely. The revolvers I carry for personal defense will fire double action only. Some came that way from the factory and some were modified. My carry autos are either double action (with heavier-than-target-grade trigger pulls even on single action), my XDs have 6 to 7 pound trigger pulls, none of my carry 1911s are lighter than 4 pounds, and as noted my carry Glocks have New York triggers in the 7-8 pound pull range. Anyone who tells you it's impossible to shoot well with these guns, doesn't know how to shoot. I've won IDPA matches with Glock and XD pistols in the above pull weights, and for three years running won the NH Police Association annual state shoot with a Glock 22 that had a New York trigger, shooting against some who had put 3.5 pound pulls in their guns before the match.

Selecting the Gun Wardrobe

In a clothing store, it's hard to go wrong with "the basics": "basic black," gray pinstripe, and all of that. In the world of CCW, the first of "the basics" is a small revolver.

S&W's J-frame series is the odds-on choice of professionals. High quality, smart engineering, and a wide range to choose from: 22, 32 H&R Magnum (off and on), 38 Special, and 357 Magnum. My advice would be to go with the 38 Special, though the little 22 Kit Guns make great "understudies" for cheap practice. An all-steel 2-inch (actually 1 7/8-inch barrel in most cases) will run about 20 ounces. The aluminum frame Airweights go about 15 ounces, a profound difference when the gun is carried in a pocket or on the ankle, but much less noticeable in a belt holster. The AirLites are available in various mixes of Titanium and Scandium, and are proportionally expensive due to the rare materials used in their construction, but they can get down to the eleven and twelve ounce weight range. There's no excuse *not* to carry when adequately powerful handguns come this light.

Of course, the lighter the gun, the harder it kicks with the same ammunition. The all-steel small frames aren't too bad, even with 38 Special +P ammo. The Airweights are downright unpleasant, and after I've finished a 50-shot qualification I'm glad it's over. The AirLites, however, are downright painful, and with Magnum loads they're torture devices. I find them more painful to shoot than the mighty Smith & Wesson 500 Magnum hunting revolver, by far. If you get them in 357, load them with 38s and do yourself a favor.

It's a myth, by the way, that it's OK to practice with mild loads but carry monster Magnums because somehow, fight or flight reflex will make up for the kick in an actual defensive shooting. True, the dump of nor-epinephrine and endorphins that accompanies high level body alarm reaction may block the pain of the recoil, but that won't keep a too-powerful gun from twisting in your hand and preventing you from getting fast, accurate follow-up shots. You don't need me to tell you that a hit with a 38 Special beats a miss with a 357 Magnum.

The J-frame – a 32-size frame with a cylinder bored out for five 38 rounds instead of six 32s – can be had in three styles, all dating back to the period between 1949 and 1955. The original Chiefs Special series is the "conventional style" double-action revolver, with exposed hammer that

Modern paradigm handguns are widely considered inferior to the classic 1911 45, but that's not necessarily so. In the single-action 45 division, CDP, the top three places at the 2007 IDPA National Championships went in order to David Olhasso with Springfield Armory XD45 *(top)*, David Sevigny with Glock 21SF *(center)*, and Ernest Langdon with S&W M&P *(below)*, all in 45 ACP.

allows thumb-cocking to single action. The Bodyguard style is that gun with a built-in "hammer shroud" patterned after the bolt-on Colt shroud introduced shortly before, which keeps the hammer spur from snagging on clothing or pocket linings during a fast draw. A small button-size portion of the hammer is exposed to allow thumb-cocking for light-pull single-action shots. The third variation is the Centennial series, known colloquially as a "hammerless" but actually having a hammer that is totally enclosed inside its streamlined frame.

It is generally accepted that for fast defensive shooting, double action is the way to go. With this in mind, the Centennial is clearly the best bet, followed by the Bodyguard, followed by the Chiefs. The reason is found by analyzing shooter ergonomics in live fire, not theory born in dry fire.

When a revolver recoils, it wants to torque its muzzle up

This late model S&W has current style cylinder latch, designed not to ding the thumb upon recoil, and above it the Internal Locking System, which purists despise and new shooters seem to like.

Introduced in 2007, this Model 40-1 Classic was the first S&W in years to appear without the internal lock. It has the old "lemon-squeezer" grip safety, and traditional square latch that purists associate with the S&W breed.

and to the side. With the conventional-hammer Chiefs series, the butt can roll up into the web of the hand, getting after one to three shots to a position where that web of the hand blocks the hammer and prevents subsequent shots from being fired until the gun is re-gripped. That won't happen with the Bodyguard, whose hammer is shielded within its slot, and whose shroud is shaped in a way that catches at the web of the hand and prevents "roll-up." The Centennial is even better, because not only can't the gun roll up, but in addition the shape of the rear frame allows the shooter's hand to grasp the gun higher. This lowers the bore axis *vis-à-vis* the gun hand and arm, keeping the muzzle down, and maximally enhancing the shooter's recoil recovery rate for the most accurate possible rapid fire.

Because the Centennial can *only* be fired double action, it also prevents cocked gun accidents and possible false accusations of same. All these reasons have combined to make the Centennial series not only the most popular of the J-frames overall, but in most years of late the best seller among J-frames overall.

Factoring in cost, shootability, and portability, the S&W Model 642 Airweight is my personal choice among all those available, most of which I own or have owned and all of which I've shot. It's the one I'd personally recommend. Taurus has a line of similar revolvers in all three hammer styles which are acceptable alternatives, trading less fancy finish for a lower price tag.

Going up a notch, there are slightly larger revolvers that are more powerful. The two I could most strongly recommend are the snub-nosed Ruger SP101 357 Magnum and the 2-inch barrel Taurus Tracker in 45 ACP. The latter takes the rimless auto pistol cartridges in a fast-loading "moon clip," and mine shoots to point of aim at 25 yards with groups like a service revolver's. The SP also has target-grade accuracy. Each has extra-cushiony trips to bring their recoil down to manageable levels. In the 25-ounce weight range, these are too heavy for my taste for pocket or ankle carry, but for the person who wants a small, powerful snubby in a belt holster, they're great.

Next on the "concealed handgun wardrobe necessities list" is a compact semiautomatic pistol, if you're comfortable with that type of handgun. Glocks in compact (G19 9mm, G23 .40,

Carry gun choice involves a balance of "heavier gun easier to shoot, lighter gun easier to carry." Author weighs choice between 14 oz. Kahr PM9 (left, all black) and 22 ounce Kahr MK9 (stainless, right). Each is a 7-shot 9mm of identical overall dimensions.

G32 .357 SIG, G30 .45 ACP, and G38 .45 GAP) are all good choices. So are the many other compact (i.e., medium size) modern autos you'll find in the *Gun Digest*, where there's more space to pore over the various models and size/weight specifications than here. In the 1911, Commander and Officers size work well. For many, something more *sub-compact* fits the body better. These would include the "baby Glocks" in the same calibers, the Micro-series Kahrs, and the smallest of the 1911s by their many makers.

Finally, a full-size gun makes particular sense under cold-weather wardrobes, which can amply conceal them. In cold weather, with gloved or cold-numbed hands, a pistol with a longer grip-frame may be easier to handle. I like something with a large trigger guard, and whose trigger won't rebound

Subcompact carry guns can be "too small for your hand," necessitating technique changes. Trigger reach is so short on this Kahr that author's trigger finger is blocked by thumb in traditional grasp; thumb will need to come up. Little finger is tucked under short butt since there's no room for it on the frame…

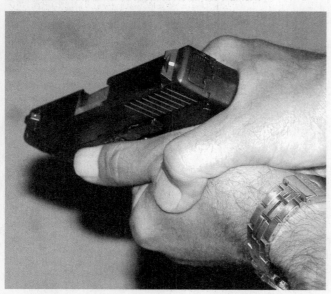

…author's two-hand grasp on the Kahr puts firing thumb on support hand out of the way of trigger finger, and support hand thumb well forward to avoid the sharp edge on the Kahr's slide release lever.

so far forward that it can snag on or be blocked by thick glove material, which could make it fail to re-set. A TDA auto pistol will generally fill that bill, as will the Glock or XD. I get leery of single-action pistols when cold or gloves have further reduced a vasoconstricted hand's ability to feel the trigger, and the glove-blocking factor leaves most revolvers out entirely.

The bottom line of "concealed handgun wardrobe selection" is this: the gun's size and shape must fit hand, body, and clothing selection alike. You probably don't dress the same every day. When you "dress to kill" (forgive me, I couldn't resist) you also need to vary that particular "wardrobe" to better suit your daily needs.

Final advice: In the immortal words of author and big game hunter Robert Ruark, "Use Enough Gun." Small-caliber weapons simply don't have the "oomph" to stop a violent human being. I coined the phrase "Friends don't let friends carry mouse-guns," and I'll stick by that. The cessation of homicidal human threat is the *raison d'etre* of CCW. If the Weapon you're Carrying Concealed isn't powerful enough to do that job, you've undercut the whole purpose of the mission. I personally draw the line above the marginal 380 ACP and consider the minimums to be 38 Special +P in a revolver and 9mm Luger in a semiautomatic pistol. On the top end, only master shooters can handle the violent recoil of 41 and 44 Magnums. For most people, the best bet is in a caliber range that encompasses 38 Special, 357 Magnum, 9mm Luger, 40 Smith & Wesson, 10mm Auto, 45 ACP, and 45 GAP. There are other rarely-carried rounds within that range, but any of those – with proper high-tech hollow-point defensive ammunition – can be reasonably counted on to get you through the night.

For more on gun and ammo selection, I'd refer you to my *Gun Digest Book of Combat Handgunnery, Sixth Edition,* available from Krause. The bottom line is, it's not about "what gun did you have" so much as it's about "did you have a gun?" Modern ultra-compact, ultra-light 38 Special and 9mm Luger handguns give you adequate power in extremely small and light packages. You just don't have to settle for anything less, when innocent lives – including your life and the lives of those you most love – will likely be at stake if and when the shooting starts.

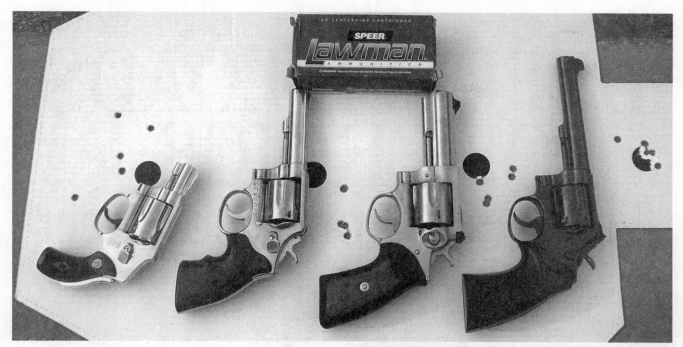

Longer barrel equals easier to shoot accurately, harder to carry. Left to right: 2" barrel S&W J-frame Centennial has produced a roughly 4" group. S&W Model 64 and Ruger GP100 with 4" barrels have shot much tighter. Best group of all came with 6" barrel S&W K-38, far right. All fired at 25 yards with Speer Lawman 158-grain +P .38 Special ammo.

S&W M&P 11-shot 45 ACP has optional thumb safety, comes with rails to hold this Streamlight white light attachment. Somewhere out there is a handgun with exactly the features you want.

Even gun color is a debatable issue. Some like matte black, as in the Kahr PM9 above, because it doesn't call attention to the gun. Others *want* the bad guy to realize he's at gunpoint, and like the conspicuous silver color of stainless MK9, below, by the same maker.

DEFENSE LOADS OF CHOICE:
The Word From The Street

Sterile lab testing in ballistic gelatin is great, but the ultimate laboratory is the street, the author maintains. Here are the loads that seem to be doing best there, input written in blood from gunfights police departments have experienced with this ammunition.

Premium lines from four big makers, covering four popular calibers. This, for the most part, is the type of round the author recommends.

Defensive ammunition choice is about picking what works best to neutralize armed and dangerous human beings before they can maim or murder. Scientific testing of ammo in ballistic gelatin can help predict bullet performance in the field, but at the end of the day, it is the performance and not the prediction that will matter.

Thirty-four years of carrying a sworn police officer's badge, 20 years as chair of the firearms committee of the American Society of Law Enforcement trainers, and several years now on the advisory board of the International Law Enforcement Educators and Trainers Association have combined with several trips to major seminars of groups like the International Law Enforcement Firearms Instructors Association and the International Homicide Investigators Seminars to give me a solid base of cops who've investigated a lot of shootings for their departments. These aren't "war stories," they are full investigations of shootings including evidence recovery, complete autopsy and forensic ballistic testing protocols, and intensive debriefings of the shooters and the witnesses. From that collective pool of knowledge emerges a profile of which duty cartridges perform the best.

OBVIOUSLY, POLICE ISSUE AMMUNITION IS USED IN A SIGNIFICANT MAJORITY OF THESE SHOOTINGS. That's why police duty calibers and loads have the strongest "data bases" to learn from.

Fortunately for armed citizens, they and the police tend to choose the same calibers. Picking a load that has proven itself on duty with the police gives the armed citizen added confidence in what their chosen gun/cartridge combination can deliver. As many have noted, using ammunition that is widely issued to police is a strong defense against unmeritorious courtroom allegations such as, "He used evil hollow point bullets that rend and tear, and that shows he had malice in his heart!"

Let's look at what the "street feedback" is indicating is working best in the "ultimate laboratory" these days.

38 Special

Concealed carry permit instructors tell me that the 38 Special revolver, usually in compact short-barrel form, is one of the most common guns brought to their classes by students, and often the single gun that their graduates most commonly carry on the street. For most of the 20th Century, this caliber revolver was also by far the most popular in law enforcement, with plainclothes and off duty officers generally carrying "snubbies," and uniformed personnel generally carrying larger framed, longer barrel models.

At this writing, there are still thousands of senior cops carrying "grandfathered" 38 revolvers on duty in New York City and Chicago, and many more who carry them as backup or off-duty guns. In fact, the snub-nose 38 seems to be the most popular police backup handgun to this day, and is still widely used for off duty carry.

Only two cartridges really stand out as head and shoulders above the large pack of available 38 Special rounds. These are the "FBI load" and the "New York load."

The FBI load gets its sobriquet from the fact that this round was adopted by the Federal Bureau of Investigation circa 1972, right after Winchester introduced it. It was also adopted by the Chicago PD, and remains the 38 Special load of issue there to this day. Metro-Dade (now Miami-

Dade) police likewise found it to perform superbly, as did cops throughout the U.S.A., and it continues to be known by some locally as the "Chicago load" or "Metro load." This cartridge comprises an all-lead, semi-wadcutter shaped hollowpoint bullet at +P velocity.

It works particularly well out of a 4-inch barrel, but cops quickly discovered that the projectile generally upset and expanded at least to some degree – even out of short barrels that reduced velocity. The reason was that with no tough copper jacket to peel back, the soft lead expanded more easily in flesh.

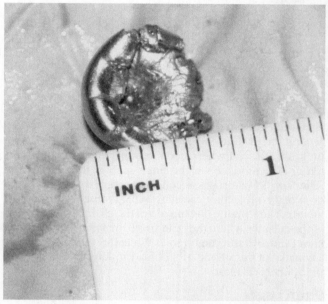

This 230-grain standard velocity Gold Dot 45 ACP bullet expanded to some 60-caliber after striking bone, kept on going to deliver massive wound track. Expansion was not textbook, but neither are living things. Gold Dot has done very well in officer-involved shootings.

HST is Federal's current top defense load. These two bullets expanded differently because they met different resistance. The one on left went through a hog's heavy skull before utterly destroying the brain; the one on the right entered the shoulder and tore a large wound through the chest. Both animals were stopped instantly. +P 230-grain 45 round was doing better than 950 fps from 5-inch barrel.

Base-on view of expanded 45 ACP Federal HST 230-grain +P bullet that instantly dropped a man-size hog with a chest shot. Bullet destroyed both lungs and top of heart, expanded to approximately 90-caliber.

Seen from bottom, this Winchester Ranger 127-grain +P+ 9mm round expanded to slightly over 60-caliber, and at 1250 foot seconds impact velocity did massive and instantly fatal damage to a man-size hog.

Base-on view of still-bloody HST 230/45 +P recovered from hog shot in skull and killed instantly. Expanded diameter is a hair under an inch at widest point. Irregular expansion was due to striking heavy bone on slight angle, which did not deviate bullet from its trajectory. Penetration depth was optimal.

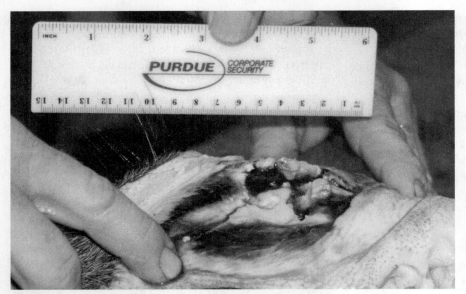

Federal 9BPLE, a 115-grain +P+ jacketed hollowpoint, shattered skull of hog at entry point for a more than 2-inch area, went on to virtually liquefy brain and lodge in base of skull. Truly massive damage, optimum penetration.

Remington Golden Saber 124-grain +P from 4-inch barrel Glock 19 killed man-size hog cleanly and instantly with one shot, penetrated deeply, and expanded to roughly 50-caliber.

Winchester and Remington both produce this 158-grain LSWCHP +P round. The Remington seems to have the softer lead of the two, and therefore, opens a bit more dramatically. This is a good thing.

A few years ago, NYPD realized it still had some three thousand officers carrying 38 Special service revolvers as primary handguns, and that the overwhelming majority of their plus/minus 35,000 sworn personnel carried snub-38s as backup and off-duty guns. They approached Speer to create a load that would optimize 38 Special terminal ballistics when fired from a revolver with a barrel measuring 1-7/8 inches. Ernest Durham at Speer led the project, and the result has now become known colloquially as the NYPD load. It comprises a wide-mouthed 135-grain Gold

Dot bonded, jacketed hollowpoint at +P velocity.

In numerous shootings with both snubs and 4-inch service revolvers, NYPD officials tell me that they are more than satisfied. Because of the lighter bullet, it kicks less than the FBI load, and because of the modern Gold Dot technology, it expands widely and reliably. They have found it to be a good man-stopper.

Either will work well. In a snubby, I prefer the Gold Dot for two reasons. First, the lighter recoil is helpful in fast, accurate shooting. Second, the all-lead FBI load is more lightly crimped than the Gold Dot, and when fired in a super-light snubby in the ten or eleven ounce weight range, such as the Titanium or Scandium S&W AirLites, recoil is so severe that after a shot or two, the projectiles can start pulling loose from the case mouths. They "prairie dog" up out of the chamber at the front of the cylinder, where they can strike the forcing cone of the barrel and lock the gun up solid. While this can happen with any make of the all-lead +P FBI load, it does not occur with the Speer NYPD load.

9mm Luger

The 9mm Luger (aka 9X19, 9mm Parabellum, 9mm NATO) is one of the most popular among armed citizens, and also still widely used by the nation's police. As a result, we have a huge amount of street experience to tap into as to what works well and what doesn't in this caliber.

In the late 1980s through most of the 1990s, 147-grain hollowpoints of conventional copper jacketed construction were the trendy issue rounds. They worked spottily – sometimes they expanded, and sometimes they just punched narrow little through and through wounds like ball ammo – and as a result, most departments that used this stuff either switched to more powerful calibers, or went to 9mm ammo that was going faster, with lighter bullets.

For many years, the "Illinois State Police load" – a 115-grain standard JHP launched at some 1300 fps – proved itself to be the most decisive man-stopper available. It still works great. Federal's version of this load, the 9BPLE, is standard issue for the DeKalb County lawmen, on the tough turf that surrounds and encompasses Atlanta, Georgia. These guys get into so many firefights that they've drawn political heat for "shooting too many people." They have proven that when they shoot people with a 115-grain JHP doing 1300 foot seconds out of their issue Beretta service pistols, the bad guys go down and stop trying to kill them. This is A Good Thing.

Other loadings have emerged that have the same decisive stopping power in 9mm. They include Winchester's

127-grain Ranger series +P+ at 1250 foot-seconds, and Speer's Gold Dot 124-grain +P at the same velocity. Chicago PD switched to the 124-grain +P after multiple dismal stopping failures with 147-grain subsonic, and NYPD has used this round with great effect for some fifteen years. Both are delighted with it. Orlando cops are issued P226 SIGs and 127-grain +P+ Winchester, and many shootings since, they've found it to be as effective as any handgun caliber could be.

Personally, I carry the 9BPLE in one particular Beretta that shoots it better than any other carry load, and Winchester Ranger 127 grain +P+ in virtually all my other 9mm pistols, long or short barrel.

Some folks have bought into the theory that the 147-grain subsonic has been so widely recommended by authority figures, it *must* be good. The fact is, there's a new generation of 147-grain subsonic that *is* pretty darn good. It utilizes new-generation high-tech expanding bullet technology expressly engineered to make the bullets open up at velocity below the speed of sound. These include the CCI Speer Gold Dot, the Federal HST, and the Winchester Ranger.

Amarillo, Texas Police report excellent results with their issue load for those officers who choose 9mm pistols, the 147-grain Gold Dot. A major department in the Pacific Northwest is now issuing Federal HST 147-grain subsonic, and reports excellent results in numerous shootings. LAPD and LA County Sheriff's Department find that fewer officers and deputies are opting for larger caliber guns bought out of their own pockets, because they are reassured by how well Winchester Ranger 147-grain 9mm has worked for their brothers and sisters in numerous line of duty shootings.

Still, the faster bullets seem to be the way to go. There is much more corollary tissue damage around the wound channels with the faster 9mms, with medical examiners documenting "macerated" flesh, that is, tissue chopped up like burrito filling. You don't see that with subsonic rounds, even though a high-tech modern 147 grain may actually expand very slightly more than a lighter 9mm bullet, simply because it has "more lead to spread."

Winchester Ranger SXT is an example of *modern* 147-grain 9mm subsonic hollowpoints that have proven themselves suitable to police and citizen self-defense use. Earlier versions of this cartridge expanded erratically and often over-penetrated.

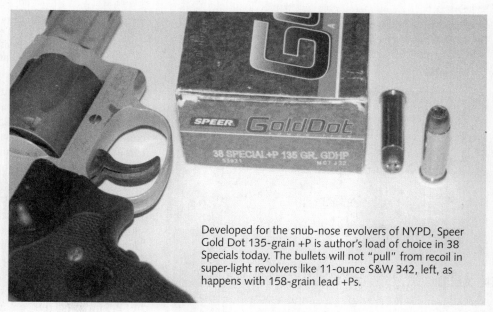

Developed for the snub-nose revolvers of NYPD, Speer Gold Dot 135-grain +P is author's load of choice in 38 Specials today. The bullets will not "pull" from recoil in super-light revolvers like 11-ounce S&W 342, left, as happens with 158-grain lead +Ps.

357 Magnum

One cartridge stands above all others in this caliber in the history of American law enforcement: the 125-grain semi-jacketed hollowpoint loaded to a velocity in the 1400 foot-second range (from a 4-inch barrel). Some experts argue whether the wide-mouthed Federal version of this load, or the scallop-jacket Remington version that originally popularized the 125-grain 357 among cops, is the single best of the breed. It seems to be an argument akin to how many angels can dance on the head of a pin. The Winchester 125-grain Magnum load does not have either of those features, but worked every bit as well for such departments as the Maine State Police when they carried 357 revolvers.

This round tends to create a wound channel that is nine to eleven inches deep, but very wide, with tremendous damage around the radius of the wound track. It also has a

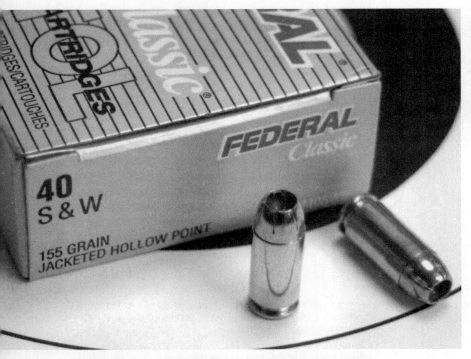

Affordably priced Classic line Federal 155-grain JHP has performed superbly in 40 S&W shootings by police in the field. Sometimes you don't need premium-price ammo to "carry with confidence."

Check your carry ammunition carefully before loading. Even the best manufacturers can make mistakes. This visibly defective 9mm ball cartridge came out of a factory box.

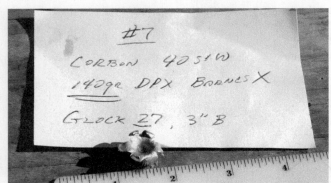

This 140-grain 40 S&W Cor-Bon DPX, using all-copper Barnes X bullet, did a satisfactory job of quickly killing a large hog.

This Speer Gold Dot 124 grain +P 9mm round from 4-inch Glock 19 instantly killed a large hog, did massive internal damage, and had expanded impressively by the time it stopped at optimum penetration depth. This load has worked famously well for NYPD for several years in many shootings.

nasty muzzle blast and pretty sharp recoil. The great combat shooting trainer and combat pistol champion Ray Chapman used to say that the 125-grain Magnum load's almost magical stopping power was the only reason to load 357 instead of 38 Special +P ammunition into a fighting revolver chambered for the Magnum round. I tend to agree.

When departments such as City of Indianapolis Police Department, and the state troopers of Kentucky and Indiana issued that load, there were literally tons of bad guys shot with 125-grain Magnums, and they tended to go down "right now." Texas Department of Public Safety personnel were known to refer to this round's "lightning bolt effect," and I knew Kentucky troopers who called it "the magic bullet." Even though velocity dropped considerably from the 2.5-inch barrels of Indiana State Police detectives' Combat Magnums, or from the 3-inch Military & Police 357s of Indianapolis plainclothesmen, the bad guys seem to go down just as fast. The 125 grain 357 Magnum semi-jacketed hollow point earned its title, bestowed by expert Ed Sanow, as "King of the Street," and this remains the Magnum load of choice today. I have no personal preference between the Federal, Remington, and Winchester brands.

357 SIG

In the early '90s, spurred by Texas troopers and rangers who loved the SIG 45 pistol but missed that "lightning bolt" stopping power effect of their old 357 Magnum revolvers, SIG worked with Federal Cartridge to create the 357 SIG round. It resembles a 40 S&W necked down to 9mm, though the actual construction is somewhat more complicated than that. Different companies load to different velocities, and depending on pistol and barrel, factory 125-grain JHPs

Relative bullet expansion. Left, Winchester 127-grain SXT 9mm; center and right, Federal HST +P 45 bullets, each 230-grains. Larger bullets have "more lead to spread," but lighter bullets can be run to higher velocities. Each creates massive wounds.

gun, and the 45 auto's larger caliber. It succeeded hugely at that in police work, being chosen by more law enforcement agencies today than any other. It has become popular among armed citizens for that exact same compromise factor.

First generation ammo, a 180-grain subsonic with a conventional JHP bullet, did better than expected, but still wasn't spectacular. It pretty much duplicates the ballistics of the old 38/40 blackpowder handgun load of the 19th century frontier. I've run across a lot of shoot-throughs with 180-grain standard JHP, more than would be desirable for home defense. Those who like the 180-grain subsonic's ballistics want to go with high tech hollowpoints that open more aggressively, penetrate a little less, and seem to produce a more decisive stopping effect. The 180-grain Gold Dot has earned a good reputation in cities such as Boston and Milwaukee. The 180-grain Federal HST has produced some truly impressive one-shot stops in the Pacific Northwest. The 180-grain Winchester Ranger, particularly in its latest iteration, also works distinctly better than a conventional copper-jacketed bullet of this weight and velocity.

It appears that the medium-weight bullets at higher velocities are providing the best combination of penetration

are delivering 1325 to over 1400 fps.

High-tech bullets that open rapidly but stay together seem to work best in this caliber. The most widely proven is the Gold Dot. From Texas to Virginia, it has been kicking butt with no horror stories of stopping failures. New Mexico State Troopers fell in love with the 357 SIG a few years ago, and stayed with that cartridge when they ordered their new S&W M&P auto pistols. North Carolina Highway Patrol gave up its beloved Beretta pistols after more than twenty years to adopt the SIG-Sauer, because they could get it chambered for 357 SIG.

Gunfights indicate that this cartridge is particularly good for shooting through auto sheet metal and window glass, yet does not deliver on the street the dangerous over-penetration that some gelatin tests had indicated might happen. The spent, expanded bullets are normally recovered from the far side of the criminal's body, or from his clothing, or from the ground within a few feet behind where he was located when shot.

Winchester Ranger in 125-grain 357 SIG has worked well in actual shootings. Remington Bonded Golden Saber in 125-grain 357 SIG is deliciously accurate, and performs superbly in FBI protocol gelatin testing, though I haven't run across any actual shootings with it yet. The overwhelming majority of 357 SIG shootings by police have occurred with the 125-grain Speer Gold Dot, and it has worked so well it is unquestionably the most "street proven" load in this caliber.

40 Smith & Wesson

Introduced in 1990 by S&W and Winchester, this 9mm Luger-length 10mm cartridge was designed to split the difference between the 9mm's higher round count in the

Why carry spare ammo? Something could muck up the magazine in your gun. If this muddy 1911 9mm mag was not properly cleaned, it would be a jam waiting to happen the next time it was put in a defensive firearm.

With one 17-round magazine in place, two more in the belt, and one more round topped off in the chamber, this Glock 17 puts 52 shots at the wearer's immediate disposal.

depth, expansion, and overall decisiveness of ending encounters. Not the 165-grain subsonic .40 – the so-called "minus-P" – but 165-grain JHPs traveling at 1140 or so feet per second, and 155-grainers at about 1200 fps. The latter has worked very well for the U.S. Border Patrol, which seems to have used mostly the Remington brand. Other non-high-tech .40 caliber JHPs in this weight range that have delivered impressive performance are the Federal Classic and the Winchester Silvertip, both 155-grainers. These are also less expensive than the top-line premium lines.

High-tech bullets still do well in this weight range, though. The 165-grain Winchester Ranger and Speer Gold Dot seem to lead the pack by a narrow margin.

45 ACP

A standard pressure 230-grain 45 ACP with conventional JHP bullet pretty much duplicates the recoil and trajectory of GI hardball in the same weight, allowing cost-effective training once the user is certain the given pistol will feed the hollowpoint of choice. The 45's big bullet and well-earned reputation for stopping power make it more forgiving of less-than-optimum ammo choices, though you still want to stay away from full metal jacket because of its tendency to grossly over-penetrate, and to ricochet.

In a low-priced round, generic Winchester 230-grain JHP "white box" is a street-proven choice. It used to be sold in boxes marked "For Law Enforcement Only," if that tells you anything. For maximum effect, though, a premium bullet is the way to go. Federal's Hydra-Shok is a well-proven man-stopper, long the "gold standard," and still a good choice today, but expansion characteristics (especially through intervening substances) are enhanced in the new HST line from the same maker. CCI Gold Dot has worked well for numerous departments in both 200- and 230-grain

weights; Remington 230-grain Golden Saber has worked quite well in the hands of certain units during the War on Terror; and one state police agency I'm aware of has experienced a string of one-shot stops with the Winchester SXT/Ranger 230 grain. These are all standard pressure loads.

Short barrel 45 ACPs are extremely popular among armed citizens today. CCI offers a Gold Dot Short Barrel 45 load, especially designed to open to full effect at lower velocities. I haven't run across any actual shootings with it yet, but gel testing indicates that it has met its design parameters.

The +P 45 ACP has worked well in 185-, 200-, and 230-grain loadings. The 185-grain +P has earned a good "stopping power" rep in its conventional JHP loading from Remington and is also available in Hydra-Shok and HST formats from Federal, and in Remington's own high-tech Golden Saber line. As a rule of thumb, the 185-grain +P round will shoot pretty much to point of aim/point of impact out to roughly 100 yards in a pistol sighted in for 230-grain standard pressure 45 ACP at 25 yards. That makes it of special purpose interest to those in rural areas who can anticipate unusually long shots with their pistols.

The 45 GAP, or Glock Auto Pistol, is a shortened and strengthened 45 ACP round at standard pressure. Guns for it have been produced by Glock, ParaOrdnance, and Springfield Armory. The state troopers of Georgia, New York, and Pennsylvania have adopted the Glock in 45 GAP as standard, and shootings with it using 200-grain Speer Gold Dot and 230-grain Winchester Ranger have thus far proven it to be the absolute equal of the 45 ACP with the same bullets. Look for this round to gain in popularity in years to come.

That concludes the feedback from the street, with the calibers most used by cops and, therefore, most thoroughly evaluated in the wake of intensive

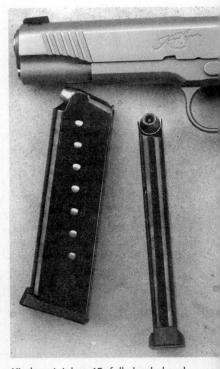

Kimber stainless 45, fully loaded and backed with two more eight-round ACT magazines of Federal 230-grain Hydra-Shok, gives the wearer a 22-round load-out. Elsewhere in the book, read the story of the man who got in trouble for carrying just such an outfit, but was acquitted once rationale for spare ammo was explained to jury.

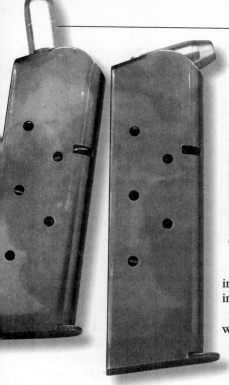

Another reason to carry spare ammo. Topmost round position on each of these 1911 magazines has been compromised by clearing extraction failure/double feed malfunction. A fresh magazine ready to grab and reload can be a lifesaver in such circumstances.

investigation of officer-involved shootings.

At the time of this writing, it's the best this writer has to offer.

THE DANGERS OF OVERPENETRATING BULLETS

One critical rule of firearms safety is that the bullet must stay in its intended backstop. No responsible shooter would go to one of the older indoor shooting ranges that have a warning poster saying "LEAD BULLETS ONLY, JACKETED BULLETS CAN PIERCE BACKSTOP" and then proceed to pump hard-jacketed bullets into that frail backing.

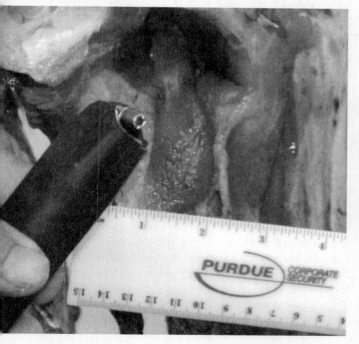

Winchester Ranger SXT 127-grain +P+ ammo in Glock magazine, compared to hole through muscle tissue made by such a bullet on hog. Remember this the next time someone tells you the bullet can only destroy what it physically touches.

Full metal jacket 9mm ammo like this has been known to be an impotent man-stopper for a century, and it horrendously over-penetrates in living tissue. After many innocent over-penetration casualties with it, NYPD dropped this ammo for hollowpoint, and solved the problem.

On the street, the only safe backstop for the defensive handgun's bullets is the body of the offender. Therefore, it is not exactly responsible to be firing bullets that are likely to shoot through and through the assailant. This is one of the main reasons law enforcement in its virtual entirety has gone to expanding bullet handgun ammunition in this country. It was a lesson written in blood.

Seven Cases Highlight the Reality

In 1999, New York City became almost the last major police department to adopt hollow point ammunition. They did so in the face of huge, long-term opposition based on political correctness and the erroneous perception of hollowpoints as wicked "dum-dum bullets." One reason they were able to pass it was that the city fathers had been made to realize how much danger the supposedly "humane, Geneva Convention-approved" ammunition previously used presented to innocent bystanders and police officers when the duty weapons were fired in self-defense or defense of others by the officers.

From the early '90s adoption of 16-shot 9mm pistols (Glock 19, SIG-SAUER P226 DAO, and Smith & Wesson Model 5946) through 1999, NYPD issued a full metal jacket "hardball" round, comprising a round-nose 115 grain bullet in the mid-1100 fps velocity range. *The New York Times* exposed the following facts in its startling report on the matter:

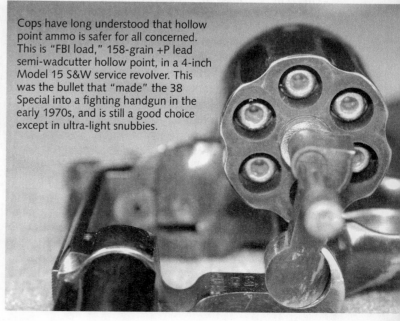

Cops have long understood that hollow point ammo is safer for all concerned. This is "FBI load," 158-grain +P lead semi-wadcutter hollow point, in a 4-inch Model 15 S&W service revolver. This was the bullet that "made" the 38 Special into a fighting handgun in the early 1970s, and is still a good choice except in ultra-light snubbies.

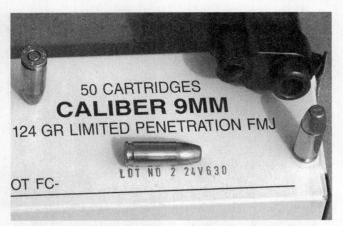

Even the U.S. military is looking at switching from ball ammo to expanding bullets. This is Federal's "Limited Penetration FMJ" …

…and causing bullet to expand to 50-caliber or better.

"According to statistics released by the department, 15 innocent bystanders were struck by police officers using full metal jacket bullets during 1995 and 1996, the police said. Eight were hit directly, five were hit by bullets that had passed through other people and two were hit by bullets that had passed through objects," stated the *Times*.

In other words, in rough numbers, 53 percent of these tragic occurrences were apparently missed shots, while 33 percent were "shoot-throughs" of violent felony suspects. Counting bullets that went through objects to hit presumably unseen innocent victims (13 percent), that tells us that roughly 46 percent of these innocent bystanders were shot by over-penetrating bullets that "pierced their backstops." Let's call those victims **Cases One Through Seven.**

17 Officers Shot Due to Over-Penetration

The *Times* continued, "In that same period, 44 police officers were struck by gunfire using the old ammunition: 21 were hit directly, 2 were struck by bullets that ricocheted and 17 were struck by bullets that passed through other people." In round numbers, 52 percent of those "friendly fire" casualties were hit by bullets that apparently missed their intended targets. 42 percent passed through the bodies of the intended targets after the bullets struck the people they were aimed at. Let's tally *those* victims of over-

penetration as **Cases Eight through Twenty-Four.**

Why would officers hit more of their own brethren than "civilian" bystanders in this fashion? For the simple reason that while victims and potential innocent bystanders tend to flee danger scenes, the cops are conditioned to "ride to the sound of the guns." In a close-quarters situation where a violent criminal is attempting to harm or even murder another officer, cops try to grab him or stop him or even maneuver into a position from which to shoot him. All these actions can put them in the line of fire of brother officers.

Tunnel vision occurs in a majority of life-threatening encounters. This is the perceptual phenomenon of being able to see only the threat and being unable to cognitively recognize other people or objects that might be in the line of fire. Moreover, *the body of the offender may simply block the shooter's view of the brother officer who is trying to apprehend or restrain the attacker from behind.* In these situations, a "shoot-through" is highly likely to kill or cripple one of the Good Guys and Gals.

What does this have to do with private citizens' use of CCW handguns? Only this: *Where the cops jump in to protect their brother and sister officers, brave citizens may step in to protect their **actual** brothers and sisters, husbands and wives, sons and daughters, or fathers and mothers. Now it is your loved ones who are behind the offender – unseen by you – when you discharge your CCW weapon.*

Those 115-grain jacketed ball 9mm rounds will pierce more than two feet of muscle tissue simulating ballistic gelatin. So will 230-grain full metal jacket 45 hardball. By contrast, the depth of the average adult male thorax is probably no more than ten inches, from front of chest to back. Nor is it solid muscle: the spongy tissue and large air volume of the human lung offer little resistance to a bullet. It's not just about New York City and 9mms. In Arizona some years ago, a peace officer fired his 45 service automatic at a large male offender rushing him with a knife. He couldn't see that a brother officer was running up behind the offender to grab and restrain him. His gunfire dropped the offender…and passed through his body with enough force to deeply pierce the abdomen of the second cop, who had been trying to rescue the one who fired. That wounded officer almost died from those injuries, inflicted unintentionally by shoot-through with 230-grain full metal jacket 45 ACP. Call that incident **Case Twenty-Five.**

Many years ago in Los Angeles, an Aryan Brotherhood thug took several people hostage in an office. He demanded an escape vehicle and threatened to start shooting hostages if he didn't get one. A vehicle was provided, and he got into the car with the victims. At this point, the LAPD SWAT team launched smoke, and two members of the team whom I happened to know moved forward through the gray cloud, their issue Colt 45 automatics up and ready. When the perpetrator reached for his pistol, the cops opened fire, using department-issue 230-grain hardball. They fired four shots between them, and killed the offender before he could launch a single bullet of his own. Autopsy showed any of the four hits would have been quickly fatal. However, only one of those bullets stayed in the offender's body. One of the three exiting slugs struck one of the hostages. Fortunately,

Federal 158-grain lead hollowpoint +P, fired from 2-inch S&W into chest of hog. The bullet killed quickly, expanded to approximately 50-caliber.

the wound was not in a life-threatening location. LAPD quickly switched to hollowpoints, which is what they use today. Lesson learned. Call it **Case Twenty-Six.**

Ball Stops Poorly

Particularly in the small calibers, ball ammunition is infamous for its poor stopping power. When the Illinois State Police issued ball for their 9mm S&W pistols from 1967 through the early 1970s, their Ordnance Section told me, they never had a single one-shot stop on an armed felon unless he was hit in the brain or spinal cord. This led the ISP on an odyssey in search of more effective ammo, which culminated in the famously effective "Illinois State Police load," a 115-grain jacketed 9mm hollowpoint at +P+ pressure and 1300 fps velocity. Today, Illinois troopers carry 180-grain high-tech hollowpoint in 40 S&W caliber service pistols.

In **Case Twenty-Seven,** NYPD's last high-profile shooting incident with 9mm ball ammo, four plainclothes officers engaged a young man named Amadou Diallo when he turned on them pulling an object that appeared, in the poor light, to be a small automatic pistol. All four opened fire, and some five seconds later they had fired some 41 shots. Nineteen of those bullets struck Diallo before he went down and dropped the object he was holding, which turned out to be a black nylon wallet. Sixteen of the nineteen bullets had over-penetrated. Diallo died of his wounds. After a long and arduous trial, all four officers were acquitted. Had these officers been issued the department's new 124-grain Speer Gold Dot +P hollowpoints in time, there is an excellent chance that he would have gone down much sooner, perhaps with as little as one gunshot wound, giving Diallo a far better chance of survival. No such horror stories have happened on NYPD since the hollowpoint ammo has been general issue.

Micro Kahr 9mm comes with spare magazine with finger extension that holds seven rounds, not counting eighth in chamber. With this kind of cartridge capacity, carrying spare ammo is all the more important.

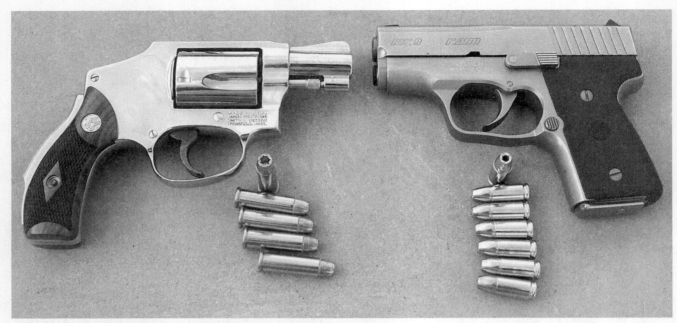

Another reason for carrying spare ammo is the fact that today's small carry guns don't carry that many rounds "on board." S&W J-frame, left, holds 5 38 Special cartridges, and Kahr MK9 at right holds 7 9mms.

Forensic Concerns

When a bullet goes through and through a human body, it is not always possible to correctly determine entry from exit, particularly if the gunshot victim lives long enough for the healing process to begin. Consider **Case Twenty-Eight,** in which the O.J. Simpson lawyers defending him against charges of murdering his wife and her young male acquaintance laid plans to impeach one of the state's medical examiners by bringing up a previous case in which he had mistakenly diagnosed a through and through gunshot wound, confusing back-to-front and front-to-back.

In late 2007, this writer was involved in a murder case in Massachusetts where it was alleged that the defendant had shot his opponent in the back of the neck, with the bullet exiting his face, implying that he was in no danger and therefore could not have acted in self-defense. The death weapon was a Beretta Model 96F pistol, and the death bullet was a 180-grain round of full metal jacket UMC 40-caliber practice ammunition. In fact, the bullet had entered the face of the attacking man, and coursed rearward and downward before exiting the neck. However, the assailant lived for a week before he succumbed. During that time, he was lying supine in a hospital bed with his body weight pressing the exit hole down against dressings and bed clothes as his body worked to heal the injury. This gave the wound a puckered appearance consistent with an entry wound. At the same time, doctors and nurses were treating the open wound in the face, debriding it to prevent necrosis, so by the time he finally died, *that* wound had been cratered outward and mimicked an exit instead of an entry. The medical examiner had, apparently for these reasons, determined after death that entry was in the back and exit was in the front. Not until trial, after a three-year ordeal, did treating physicians familiar with gunshot wounds testify that when the "victim" came in, they diagnosed the wound as front entry/rear exit. Defense experts concurred, and the jury acquitted, as they

should have. But **Case Twenty-Nine** probably wouldn't have gone to trial at all if the defendant had loaded his gun with proper hollow points, which almost certainly would have left the mushroomed bullet embedded inside the back of the neck and shown beyond a shadow of a doubt that the attacker was in fact shot from the front.

Years before, in the Tampa area, I had been involved in a similar case that showed even the wrong hollowpoint can over-penetrate and cause the same confusion. In **Case Thirty,** a young undercover narc became involved in a struggle with an armed dope dealer who tried to kill him. The cop was able to turn the suspect's own gun on him, a snub-nosed Colt Lawman 357 Magnum revolver loaded with 158-grain semi-jacketed Magnum hollow points, which have a history of frequently over-penetrating. At very close range, the high velocity bullet caused a large, "explosive wound of entry" in the soft tissues of the throat, and being largely spent when it exited the back of the neck, left a smaller wound at that point. Once again, the suspect lived for many days, lying supine and undergoing treatment. After he died, the state's pathologist concluded that the small wound in the back of the neck must have been the entry, and the larger one in front must have been the exit, leading to the theory that he had been "shot in the back of the neck in a police execution." Fortunately, the pathologist had the presence of mind to section out the wound track and preserve the flesh in Formalin, and it was sent to the Southwest Institute of Pathology for deeper examination. There, gunshot residue embedded in the throat area of the wound track conclusively proved the bullet had come in from the front, exonerating the wrongfully accused young officer. But if the distance had been another couple of feet apart at the time the shot was fired, that critical exculpatory evidence would not have been there. This is another reason why it's best to use a bullet designed to stay inside the human body.

Irresponsible Attitudes

Some people either just don't get it, or have a totally irresponsible attitude. A popular Internet gun forum recently had a thread in its Caliber Corner section titled, "Why is over-penetration bad?" Most of those who posted had a pretty good grasp on the issue. One or two responsible, gun-wise participants even posted a link to the *New York Times* story and statistics above.

Yet, even after that was posted, one participant wrote (the caps are his): "I have NEVER read ANY article or report addressing IDENTIFIED and actually occurring secondary victims." Now, you can put that down to simple ignorance, or haste in posting an opinion in a discussion he had not read and brought himself up to speed with. But how would you explain the following?

One fellow posted in the same discussion thread, "…and should over-penetration occur, oh well. The chances of it hitting someone else is practically non-existent."

Well, let's do the math. 46 percent of wounded innocent bystanders being hit by bullets that went through offenders' bodies or through objects that hopefully should have acted as backstops, is not "practically non-existent" by any stretch of the imagination. 42 percent of cops shot by friendly fire taking bullets that passed through the felony suspect first are not "practically non-existent." On the contrary, they are hugely significant.

In that same thread, one poster callously said, "It's too bad about the bystanders. I call it gene pool cleansing."

I don't think any comment is necessary on that one.

Never forget that we live in a time when police detectives are smart enough to get a warrant to seize the computers of those they investigate. Technology originally developed to track pornographers, child molesters, and white collar criminals will be applied to determine what Internet boards you may have posted to. When statements like "It's too bad about the bystanders. I call it gene pool cleansing," are discovered and tracked to the suspect, his conviction for something from attempted murder upward is almost a slam-dunk.

Ignorance won't save you. You've heard and read people say that over-penetration is irrelevant because missed shots are a more likely danger. First, a defense that says in essence, "You must forgive me *this* mistake because I figured I'd probably make a much *worse* mistake" is a frail reed that will not withstand the gale-force winds of cross-examination. Second, 53 percent misses versus 46 percent shoot-throughs in the unintentional bystander shootings in New York hardly makes the latter "irrelevant." 52% misses versus 42 percent shoot-throughs in the friendly fire shootings of cops in the same study obviously shows that the over-penetrating bullet is not an "irrelevant" danger.

The next time some Internet ninja advises you to load ball ammo for home or public defense, think of the above thirty cases. They are documented reality. And they are not the only such cases.

Collective reality has given us a message, and it is this: Save the over-penetrating "hardball" for range practice. Load your concealed carry or home defense handgun with ammunition designed, and proven to be likely, to stay inside the body of the offender who forces you to shoot him. It's the responsible thing to do.

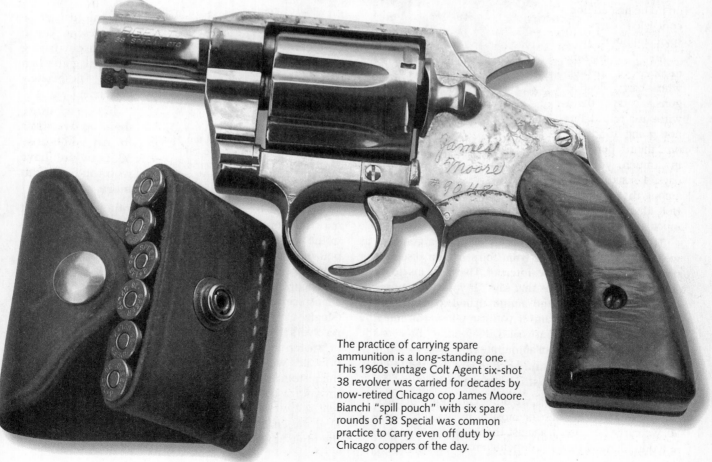

The practice of carrying spare ammunition is a long-standing one. This 1960s vintage Colt Agent six-shot 38 revolver was carried for decades by now-retired Chicago cop James Moore. Bianchi "spill pouch" with six spare rounds of 38 Special was common practice to carry even off duty by Chicago coppers of the day.

CONCEALED CARRY AND SPARE AMMO

The extra space in this second edition of *Gun Digest Book of Concealed Carry* allows me to get into something I barely had room to touch on in the first edition: concealed carry of spare ammunition.

An amazing number of people who carry loaded guns carry them without a reload. I'm not going to dump on them here—in my (much) younger days, I used to be among their number. Hell, I had a gun, didn't I? And I was a good shot, right? How much ammo was I likely to need, anyway?

The years taught me the fallacy of those arguments, as well as others that I hear from folks in gun discussions, particularly those on the Internet. There seems to be a strange "Interwebz" ethos that says, "If you carry more (or more powerful) guns and ammo than I, you must be a paranoid mall ninja … and if you carry less, you must be a sheeple." I dunno about that. Let's look at some of the excuses not to carry extra ammunition.

Odds are I'm not gonna have to fire this thing at all, let alone run it dry and still be in a gunfight.

True enough. Trouble is, we don't carry guns because of the odds of needing one, or most of us wouldn't carry at all. We carry because if, against the odds, we *do* need one and don't have it, the cost of being unable to save our own

You need more than just a gun to deal with the entire self-defense spectrum. Here's the Kubotan-like DeJammer keychain the author developed decades ago, and pepper spray. They are two useful options for different intermediate defense needs.

life and the lives of those who count on us to protect them is so catastrophic as to be simply unacceptable. If you are in the uncommon situation where you run the gun dry and the danger is still present, you're back to not having a loaded gun when you desperately need one.

If I need more than the five shots in my snub-nose 38, I couldn't have won the fight with more.

No. If you haven't won the fight with five shots, all it means is, you need more than five shots to win the fight. In the 1970s, the Illinois State Police gave me free rein to poll their troopers and study their gunfights, back when they were the only troopers in the country carrying auto-loading pistols. I was able to identify 13 troopers who almost certainly survived because they had auto-loaders (single-stack 9mm S&W Model 39s) instead of the six-shot revolvers they carried before. Nine of those were survivors of "snatch the cop's gun and kill him with it" assaults, and prevailed when they felt themselves losing the struggle for the pistol either because the bad guy couldn't get the gun off safe, or because the trooper had pressed the magazine release button and activated the disconnector safety that kept the chambered round from firing. More germane to the topic at hand, however, four of these officers survived

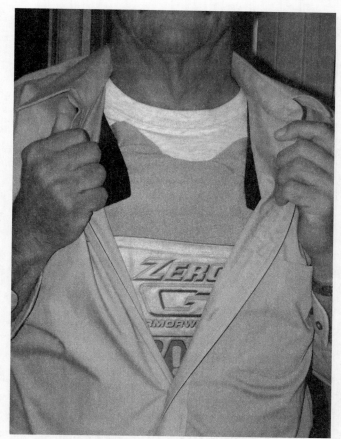

Soft body armor costs the price of a good gun, is concealable, and defeats the other guy's gun at his most likely point of aim.

because they had more firepower remaining when they went past five or six shots. Trooper Ken Kaas, with the seventh shot from his 9mm, dropped a shotgun-wielding attacker who was rushing him. (The gunman survived and reportedly told his attorney that he had been counting and was sure the cop had fired "all six" and emptied his service revolver when the perp broke cover and charged the trooper; he didn't know Illinois troopers carried semi-automatic pistols.) Sargent Glessner Davis shot and killed a shotgun-armed murderer with either the seventh or the eighth shot in his department issue Model 39. Troopers Bob Kolowski and Lloyd Burchette shot it out with a homicidal outlaw biker and both emptied their 9mms, with Kolowski reloading and sustaining fire before the gunman fell dying. They had fired 20-some rounds between them and hit him 13 times before he was unable to continue the fight. Illinois troopers in uniform today carry Glock 22 pistols loaded with sixteen 40-caliber hollowpoints and backed up with two more 15-round magazines on their duty belts.

But those guys are all cops! I'm not a cop!

Doesn't matter. You're facing the same scumbags they face. I've run across the occasional case where the private citizen has run dry, reloaded, and prevailed. I've also run into cases where they emptied their gun and the danger was still there. A good friend of mine, Richard Davis, shot it out with three armed robbery suspects in a Detroit alley many years ago. When the last round in his six-shot revolver went off, he had severely wounded one opponent, seriously

wounded a second, and slightly wounded a third. With no spare ammo he had nothing to do but run, at which time one of the perps shot him twice. He survived—and learned to carry powerful semi-automatic pistols with spare ammunition.

Consider two famous armed citizen cases on opposite sides of the nation. Lance Thomas, a watch repairman in Los Angeles, was involved in four gunfights against a total of 11 perpetrators. He won them all, shooting six men and killing five of them. He evolved the practice of having multiple guns always within reach and simply grabbing another if the one he was holding ran empty. In one shootout, he emptied three 38 and 357 revolvers. In Richmond, Virginia, two brothers who ran a jewelry store filled the shop with 38s behind the counter, so one would be in reach of almost any employee should there be a robbery. The day came when they were hit by two old pros who belonged to the Dixie Mafia, one wielding a 1911 45 auto and the other a sawed-off shotgun. In the blazing gun battle that followed, one brother had need to fire both a 357 Magnum revolver and a Remington 870 12-gauge pump shotgun, while the other went through several Rossi 38 Special revolvers, before the two gunmen were dead on the floor. (One of the store employees got a lick in with a Ruger 44 Magnum, too.) Suffice it to say, if these good armed citizens had gone with an attitude of "If I can't do it with five or six shots, I can't do it at all," they—and innocent customers an d/or employees—would almost certainly be dead now.

But those guys had guns all over the place they could reach. I'm an armed citizen, out and about—I can't do what they did.

No. And if they'd had just had one gun with no spare ammunition they couldn't have, either. Which is why I've come to recommend that if you carry a gun, it's an *awfully* good idea to carry spare ammunition for it. Why do you suppose every uniformed street cop you see has that ammo pouch on the duty belt? Remember, you're preparing yourself to face, alone, the exact same violent criminals for which society has armed those police officers in anticipation of facing. That equipage comes from a long institutional history of gunfights with criminals, a history well understood by modern police. The lawfully armed citizen can learn from it.

I carry an 18-shot auto pistol, so I don't have to worry about running out of ammunition.

While that's debatable, you do have to worry about your auto pistol malfunctioning. It happens to the best of them, and any gunsmith or armorer will tell you that assuming you're using good quality ammunition, the single most common cause of an autoloader's stoppage is something going wrong with the magazine. Clearing the stoppage and getting back to fighting may require replacing the defective or compromised magazine with a fresh one. It would be nice to have that instantly accessible on your person, instead of home in your gun safe or a block away in your vehicle's glove box.

Another predictable occurrence is the struggle for the gun. As noted in my study of Illinois Troopers with Smith

& Wesson Model 39 pistols, that one department alone had several "saves," when the trooper deliberately "killed the gun" by pressing the mag release during the struggle. Suppose you've done that successfully *and* retained control of the gun—and the bad guy now pulls a knife. With your magazine lost on the ground in the dark, you have, at best, a single-shot pistol with which to defend yourself, and not even that if your gun has the disconnector safety feature. Because their departments have had saves in this circumstance, I can point out police agencies from California to New Hampshire that insist on this feature in their service pistols. Departments so equipped and trained usually also mandate that their personnel carry at least one spare magazine on plainclothes duty and two when on uniformed patrol, in part so that, in such a situation, they can slap a fresh magazine into the duty pistol and "bring it back to life."

The other side of this is that in the struggle for the gun, the offending hands on the pistol may accidentally release the magazine. When the good guy regains control of the pistol, it would be awfully good if he could get a fresh mag into the gun and "make it whole" again.

Well, if my five shots or six shots or whatever shots aren't enough and I'm out of ammo, I'll just run away.

An amusing suggestion, but if you could have run away, why didn't you do so before? The very fact that you're in a situation that has required you to empty a gun at one or more human beings probably indicates that if you turn and run, you'll just get a few bullets in the back. Pretty tough to outrun those.

Concealing Spare Ammunition

Let's look separately at the two primary types of defensive handgun. One is the ubiquitous semi-automatic pistol. The other is the double-action revolver, which, for very good reasons, refuses to die. Their "ammo feeders" are differently shaped and differently inserted, hence the need to carry them differently.

Autoloaders

The spare magazine is relatively flat and, in my experience, is best carried in a belt pouch on the side of the body opposite the holster. Vertical carry is best for concealment and fastest for access, and reloading will be more positive if each magazine is carried with the bullet noses forward. For concealed carry, I don't see any need at all for a flapped mag pouch. It slows down access, and the extra flap of leather or nylon adds unnecessary bulk and bulge. Just make sure you have a good, friction-tight fit and you'll have all the security you need, with maximum speed and access.

Most of us carry the mag pouch just behind the left hip if we're right-handed, vice versa if we're southpaws. With an open-front concealment garment, such as a vest or a sport coat or an unbuttoned sport shirt, this minimizes the

The SnagMag, developed by a career plainclothes lawman, yields a spare Glock magazine from a trouser pocket.

Here's the SnagMag with a full-length Glock magazine, seen from the outside.

The SnagMag again, and from the side that faces the wearer's leg when it's worn in the side trouser pocket.

likelihood of the magazine becoming visible. Too, weight on the corresponding point at the opposite side of the body seems to "balance" the weight of the holstered pistol and increase overall body comfort once you are used to the presence of the object.

This principle is one thing that made Richard Gallagher's concept of the Original Jackass Shoulder System, the forerunner of his Galco brand, so famously popular and so widely imitated. The weight of the gun hung suspended in one armpit, with the weight of the two magazines (and perhaps also handcuffs), under the other. Another advantage, of course, was that the user's critical gear was all on one harness that he could be quickly throw on if a danger call took him from the Condition White of total relaxation to the brighter colors of "sudden call to arms."

A number of the people have gone with the currently popular AIWB (appendix/inside-the-waistband) carry, which places the holstered pistol on the dominant-hand side of their navel. Those who carry the pistol like this will often place the spare magazine pouch at a corresponding point on the other side of the navel. Again, it's a matter of "balance," and also keys in a little bit with the hands reaching to corresponding parts of the body during crisis, assuming that practice and training have drilled in the game plan well.

Some people carry their spare magazines in their pockets. I did so when I was very young and discovered that

a generic eyeglass case with pocket clip that cost 29 cents at Woolworth's would hold a 1911 magazine in a trouser pocket without revealing its shape (though I needed a folded-up matchbook cover or two in the bottom of it to get the magazine up high enough in the pouch that I could retrieve it). By the time I hit my twenties, though, decent, concealable magazine pouches were available and I could afford to buy them.

There are a few pocket magazine carriers available, but none are as fast to access as simply reaching under the same garment that concealed the pistol and snatching one out of a belt-mounted pouch. In ordinary clothing, a magazine will make a coat pocket or cardigan sweater pocket sag a bit. Many dedicated gun concealment vests have elastic pockets to hold magazines upright. They conceal the shape well, but they tend to sag a bit. If the elastic is tight, the garment tends to rise with the magazine you're pulling on, and this also prevents it from coming cleanly away from the pocket in some iterations.

This writer wears BDU pants as default casual wear, and when carrying a mag in a pocket prefers the dedicated "magazine pocket," also known as "cell phone pocket," on the non-dominant hand side. With just the magazine in there, it tends to shift around a little bit. However, I discovered that if I put a compact, high-intensity flashlight with a pocket clip in the front of that pocket/pouch and

(top left) At rest, the SnagMag looks like a pocketknife…

(left) …and the magazine is withdrawn thus.

(above) Here's another view of the SnagMag magazine carrier, in casual pants.

the pistol magazine behind it, it conceals like a charm and the flashlight in front holds the magazine in a vertical position that does not shift appreciably. The BDU-type pants normally have a Velcro-closing pocket flap. I close down the rear portion, which hides the magazine perfectly. One end of the flashlight protrudes visibly upward, and that's fine; it's only a flashlight and doesn't need to be concealed. I find that the flashlight goes unnoticed from supermarkets to banks to airports.

When concealment is the highest priority and the wearer is dressed lightly, as with an un-tucked polo shirt or t-shirt (one size larger than normal, remember, with straight drape instead of waist taper!), an inside-the-waistband magazine carrier will be just as much more concealable as an inside-the-waistband gun holster. Of course, you still have to remember that if the pants were bought to fit just you, now the waistband has to encompass just you and a holstered gun, and a spare magazine and its carrier. This means that you'll need a larger waistband size than what you would normally wear.

An inside-the-waistband magazine pouch brings some of the same concerns as an inside-the-waistband holster and some of its own. Certain pistol magazines—early Smith & Wessons, early H&K designs, and damn near all the serious-caliber SIGs when they had sheet-metal floorplates—have sharp edges that will dig mercilessly into skin, all the more so if you're a bit fleshy about the waist. Way back in the '80s, when I collaborated with Ted Blocker on the LFI Concealment Rig, the original inside-the-waistband mag pouch left the whole floorplate and lower part of the magazine exposed to the reaching hand. It was very fast to reload from. However, some folks with some magazines—myself included, I admit—found sharp-edged protruding floorplates digging into us so uncomfortably we couldn't wear the darn things. Ted revised the design to incorporate a shield between the entire magazine and the body. This greatly increased comfort, but also somewhat slowed down the speed of getting the magazine out of the pouch. That's always going to be the tradeoff here.

The "Baby Glock" is seen as a hideout or backup gun, but here's Mike Ross showing the form that has won multiple Glock matches for him with his little G26 9mm.

Mike Ross has won multiple matches against full size Glocks with his "baby" Glock 26, shown here. Note that it is loaded with full-length 17-round Glock 17 magazine.

Autoloaders are fast to reload. This MAG student's ejected magazine is falling, as he is about to thrust fresh magazine into butt of pistol.

Glock 30 magazine rides comfortably and discreetly next to SureFire E2D light in cell phone pocket of these cargo pants.

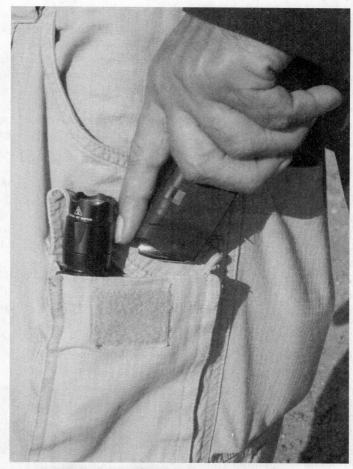

Outside the waistband, the pouch tends to be more comfortable. You still want it to ride tight to the body for concealment, though. These days, my favorites of that type are the Kydex units produced by Blade-Tech in double pouches, and by Ky-Tac in single-mag pouches. For Glocks (bargain alert here!) I've honestly found nothing better than Glock's own simple, super-cheap magazine pouch, which is also ambidextrous. It comes with little ladder-steps in the belt loops that can be easily cut by the owner to fit narrow or wide belts without flopping or wobbling, and to also ride high or low. I've won IDPA matches reloading from these pouches. They are fast, they are tight-to-the-body concealable, they are comfortable, and they are secure. Helluva deal.

How many spare mags to carry? It depends. I've met cops who carry four double-stack magazines when on duty. My department issues a single-stack .45 auto, and when I'm in uniform I carry three to four spare eight-round magazines on the duty belt. On my own time, I carry two spare magazines for a single-stack pistol and at least one for a double-stack. I also normally carry a backup handgun, and on patrol I have a .223 semi-automatic rifle with multiple magazines and a shotgun with an ample supply of shells on board in the vehicle. Our military personnel in combat zones, of course, carry more—and those who don't really believe they'll ever need to fire their defensive firearm, carry less.

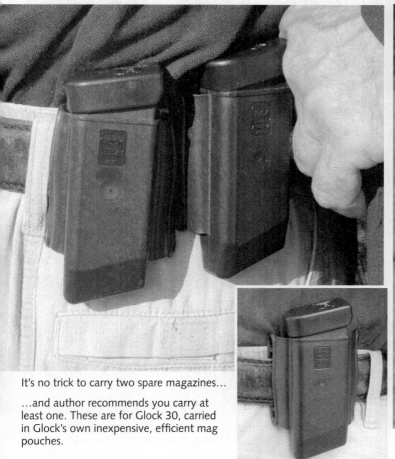

It's no trick to carry two spare magazines…

…and author recommends you carry at least one. These are for Glock 30, carried in Glock's own inexpensive, efficient mag pouches.

Proper grasp of auto pistol magazine for reload.

Revolvers

While we do have seven- and eight-shot revolvers in combat calibers today, your typical double-action revolver is still a six-shooter, and the single most popular concealed carry format for wheel-guns is the small-frame five-shooter. The latter may also still be the single most commonly carried backup gun for police, armed security, and law-abiding private citizens.

When you're traveling and living out of hotels and rental cars, the fewer guns you need to be responsible for, the better.

I know that early in this chapter I made it clear that the more rounds you have in your gun, the better off you are once the shooting starts. At the same time, in all candor, I'll tell you that in the 52 weeks of the year preceding my writing of this chapter, I carried one or another Smith & Wesson 357 Magnum revolver as my primary weapon for 12 of them. Each practitioner has his or her reasons for carrying the gun they choose on a given day or week or month. In my case, I'm both a competitive handgun shooter and a firearms instructor. On the match shooting side of it, most of my teammates are younger than me and consider revolvers to be quaint museum artifacts. However, if our team wants to sweep all the five categories of an IDPA match and, say, two of those categories are for revolvers, we geezers who are practiced in the ancient, arcane art of double-action revolver shooting and reloading are, therefore, asked to shoot in one of those divisions at such matches. When you're traveling and living out of hotels and rental cars, the fewer guns you need to be responsible for, the better. On one five-week trip and another seven-week tour last year, there was a state championship among other matches for the one, and a title defense in Stock Service Revolver class at a regional championship, along with local IDPA and Steel matches on the other. From the instructor side of it, most of my staff instructors, like most of my shooting teammates, are younger than me and into autos, and so somebody had to have the hardware to teach the students who came with revolvers. The resident geezer (me) gets elected again.

On the first trip, I took a trio of S&W 357 Mags, including a little five-shot Military & Police 340 pocket gun that never

needed to be fired, and two six-shot Combat Magnums, a 3-inch and a 4-inch. I reasoned that it would be a good idea to have a backup match gun anyway, and I brought left- and right-hand Bianchi holsters. For most of the trip I wore just one Combat Mag behind the left hip and one behind the right. Sure enough, a Model 19 developed problems and got sidelined until I could send it for repair, but the 3-inch Model 66 backup earned me division winner in one match and First Master/second overall Stock Service Revolver at the state shoot.

On the other trip, I brought a Bob Lloyd-tuned 4-inch S&W 686 as primary, with the 340 M&P and a 9mm Glock 26 as backup. Nothing went wrong with the guns, and the 686 won all three matches I shot with it, including the Stock Service Revolver class and the title defense at the 2011 South Mountain Showdown in Phoenix.

Spare ammo during those 12 weeks? Quite apart from the additional guns, I always had at least one speedloader at hand plus a Bianchi Speed Strip and a 2x2x2 pouch of revolver ammo on my person. It's simply not that heavy and not that hard to carry. The Speed Strip was in the right cargo pocket on the thigh of my BDU pants, the speedloader(s) in the right side pocket of my concealment vest, and the

HKS speedloader and Bianchi Speed Strip are long-proven spare ammo carriers for J-frame S&W snub-nose revolvers like this one, here equipped with Crimson Trace LaserGrips. Ammo is Speer's excellent 135-grain Gold Dot +P 38 Special.

Speedloaders greatly improve revolver firepower. Here, *en route* to taking First Master and second place behind soon to be World Champ Craig Buckland at the 2010 East Coast U.S. IDPA championship, the author is closing the cylinder of his Reichard-tuned S&W Model 15 as the speedloader falls away at knee level. Note that eyes are downrange on the "threat."

cartridge pouch on the left of my belt in front of the hip (I'm right-handed).

I strongly suggest that, while we carry our spare auto pistol magazines placed for the non-dominant hand, most people are better off to put their spare *revolver* ammo on the gun hand side, where the dominant hand can reach it. The reasoning for this is simple. Inserting a large object (pistol magazine) into a large receptacle (auto pistol butt) is a simple gross motor skill and can be accomplished easily with the less dexterous hand. Reloading an auto that way saves time and motion, and it is as close to a universally taught technique as exists in the world of pistolcraft. However, inserting multiple small objects (cartridges) simultaneously into multiple small receptacles (the chambers in a revolver's cylinder) is unquestionably a fine motor skill, and nature decrees that most of us will perform this task more efficiently by using the more dexterous hand to do it.

There are a handful of ace shooters who can keep the revolver in the dominant hand and quickly reload the cylinder with the non-dominant hand, but this requires either tremendous natural dexterity with the loading hand or constant (read daily) practice. Most of us will get faster,

more positive results, and sooner, using the dominant hand to insert the cartridges into a revolver. This is particularly true when loading one or two cartridges at a time by hand out of an ammo pouch, belt loops, or a Speed Strip or Tuff Strip.

Speedloaders, which hold a gun-load of cartridges for a particular revolver, are the fastest way to reload this type of handgun. The full moon clip is the fastest of speedloaders, since the whole thing goes into the gun. This saves an extra movement, to wit, discarding the empty loader after it has dropped its payload into the cylinder. The moon clip also

J-frame HKS speedloaders carry comfortably, discreetly, and accessibly in the business card pocket-within-pocket of this blazer.

expedites the first step you take to reload a revolver after opening its cylinder, that of ejecting the spent cartridges from the chambers. With all six or however many clipped together, no one of them can hang up under the ejector star and jam the gun.

However, moon clips are delicate and can be bent in ordinary pocket carry or riding in a soft pouch. A bent loader may not allow the cylinder to close or, perhaps more treacherously, may allow the cylinder to close but now fit so tightly that the cylinder can't rotate, which of course prevents the gun from firing.

Most revolver users who rely on speedloaders do it with conventional loaders, the most popular of which are the push-release Safariland and the HKS, which releases the cartridges via a knob that turns clockwise. I've found personally over the years that the Safariland is faster, while the HKS is sturdier and stands up to longer use. For that reason, if I'll be keeping the loader in a pocket or automobile glove box, I'll go with the HKS, and if I'm shooting for speed in a match, I'll use the Safariland, specifically their large but very fast Comp III.

For concealed carry, the problem is that the loader is about the same diameter as the cylinder of the revolver itself, which many find the most difficult part of that type of gun to conceal, since it's generally the widest part. Speedloaders tend to bulge and sag in jacket pockets and front trouser pockets. One exception is the "business card pocket" generally found inside the right front pocket of many men's suit-coats and blazers. It's just the right size for a five-shot J-frame speedloader, and some manufacturers cut them a bit larger, which will fit a K-frame loader. (Of course, any such coat can have one custom-tailored in.) Being suspended by a "pocket within a pocket," I've found that this sags and bulges much less than just dropping one into a jacket pocket.

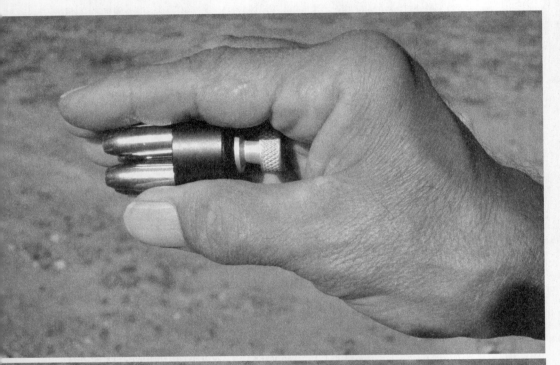

(top) Author's recommended grasp of speedloader. Fingertips ahead of bullet noses shape hand to find cylinder by feel in the dark. Loader is 5-shot HKS.

(above) Author's recommended grasp of Bianchi Speed Strip. Index finger holds strip like a scalpel for accurate placement, middle finger securely holds empty space below 5th round.

Another "pocket exception" is found with the cell phone pockets on the sides of some BDU/cargo pants. Just as a spare pistol magazine fits nicely into the off-side pocket, I've found that the long Safariland Comp III speedloader (a more rugged unit, in my experience, than the smaller Safarilands more commonly encountered in concealed carry), will fit perfectly in the cell phone pocket on the gun hand side. It's reasonably fast, and though a dedicated eye could discern that there's something in that pocket, the small bulge doesn't resemble a weapon and tends to go completely unnoticed. I like the long Comp III for this, because it stays oriented in position and is the fastest to bring out of the pocket and into action.

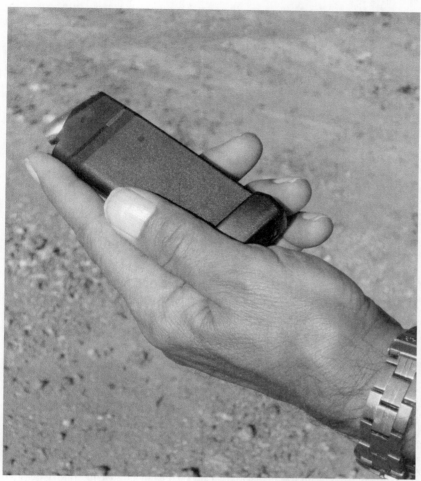

Author's recommended grasp of speedloader. Fingertips ahead of bullet noses shape hand to find cylinder by feel in the dark. Loader is 5-shot HKS.

vary on this), and being at the outer edge of the pocket toward the hip, I don't end up sitting on it.

For the belt, there are a couple of very fast speedloader pouches suitable for concealment. I generally wear them right in front of the holster. One is the loader clip from Ted Blocker Holsters and designed by the legendary Ted Blocker himself. Made of wire coated with soft plastic, it holds an HKS loader with spring tension between the body of the loader and the release knob. Half the cartridges ride inside the waistband, half outside, dramatically reducing the profile of the loader and therefore minimizing bulge.

Before the Ted Blocker clip, there was another carrier which, if memory serves, was originally designed by another holster-making legend, Gene DeSantis. Open on the sides, it also holds the loader with three rounds inside the belt and three out, but its retaining mechanism is a leather flap that goes over the top of the loader and snaps to the flip-down front of the pouch.

With loose fitting trousers (cargo pants, or the Dockers-type popular at this writing), the hip pockets are often capacious enough to carry a speedloader. The smaller ones in my experience will roll around, bringing them to uncomfortable and bulging positions and causing them to become more visible to onlookers, not to mention they're harder to get hold of when you need them. Once again, counterintuitive though it seems, the big Safariland Comp III comes to the rescue. Being right-handed, I put mine in the right outer corner of the right hip pocket, with a folded handkerchief occupying the rest of that pocket's space. The handkerchief is enough to keep the loader vertical and therefore always in the same place, always quickly accessible. Its rounded edge goes into the hollow on the outer side of the gluteus, which reduces bulge (some folks' mileage may

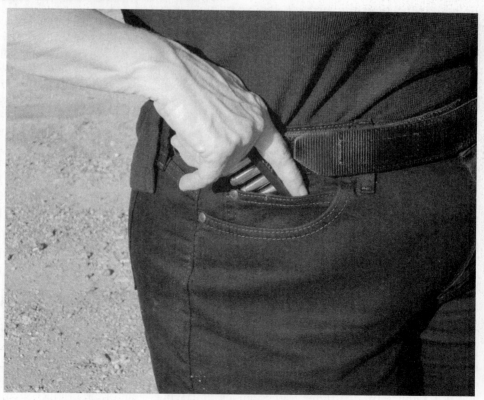

This lady carries Speed Strip in watch pocket of jeans to back up her S&W Airweight .38 Special.

To access the loader in this pouch, the shooter brings the hand down to the belt and, reaching through the open sides, grasps the body of the loader between the thumb on one side and the middle finger on the other. This positions the index finger to flip open the retaining flap, allowing the loader to come free and get on its way to the gun. It has become one of the most widely copied pieces of gunleather on the market, and many makers now offer this type of pouch. With this style, I definitely prefer to use the HKS. The reason is that the Safariland releases when its center-pin hits the axis of the revolver's cylinder, and that same center-pin is in contact with the top edge of the belt when riding in this type of pouch. It is possible—not everyday likely, but possible—to bend over sharply enough during strenuous activity to force the Safariland loader down hard enough onto the belt to release the cartridges into the pouch.

With spill pouch, author uses left palm as "loading tray." Ejector rod of J-frame S&W is slid between first two fingers, dominant hand loads cartridges one or (as shown) two at a time.

Still, many combinations of body shape and dress code will make it simply impossible for the revolver user to carry a speedloader comfortably, accessibly, and discreetly concealed. That user is going to need another spare ammo carry system. Some of the old ways still work, and some work better than others. The oldest system for carrying revolver cartridges goes back to the 19th century, those being the individual cartridge loops. They mount on a leather "slide," and for concealment you don't want cowboy gear, you want a six-loop slide. The key is to have the loops at the top edge of the unit. This allows your fingers to come in under the bullet noses and push them up, where the thumb and the two first fingers can grab them firmly by the rims and guide them into the revolver chambers. (Hint: "Slant" them in on a slight angle, which guides hollowpoint bullets more surely into those tight-fitting resting places.) It's not hard to learn to do it two rounds at a time, though it obviously takes some practice. I've seen a very few people who can do three cartridges at a time, and the operative term there is "very few." My good friend of 30-some years, the late Jim Cirillo, came up with a belt-loop system that set the loops out away from the leather slide. This was certainly faster, and was adopted by Don Hume leather, among others, but was not really ideal for concealment for the very reason that it pushed the ammo forward, increasing bulge under

concealing garments. Jim designed those loops for both competition and duty wear, neither of which involved concealment. I had the privilege of seeing Cirillo wear them on duty, in New York, and winning matches with them in other places, in the early 1970s.

Because the cartridges are exposed, it's important to keep the cartridge loop slide back from the front of an open front garment to maintain concealment. They work well under closed-front garments. Under the open-front type, you want them back toward the hip—but not *behind* the hip, because they're much more difficult to reach from there.

Another old concept is the dump pouch, sometimes called a spill pouch. Flip open the flap, and the payload of cartridges falls into your hand. This leaves you holding five or six or however many cartridges and trying to get them into the gun. If you dump them into the dominant hand, you have to literally juggle them, trying to get one or two at a time into the gun, while hoping to keep the rest from falling to the ground. Over the years, during "the revolver days," I, for one, found it much easier to dump them into the palm of my (left) support hand after ejecting the empties out of the cylinder, then slide the ejector rod between the index and middle fingers of my left hand, whose palm held the cartridges like a loading tray. The right hand would then pick the cartridges from the palm and insert them into the gun. Whichever way you did it, we all found, the dump pouch was far from the fastest way to reload a revolver.

In the latter half of the 20th century and before speedloaders became popular, John Bianchi developed the Bianchi Speed Strip. It could ride in one of those dump pouches and was and is way faster than loose rounds in the self-same pouch. More important for the concealed carrier, the Speed Strip and the later Tuff Strip are amenable to hiding in other places. One such spot is the traditional watch pocket, that little hidey-hole which rides inside the right-side front pocket of most jeans. Another is the low-riding cargo pocket on cargo pants and shorts. The round speedloader and the rigid auto pistol magazine tends to bounce uncomfortably against the leg when carried in that pocket, but the little cartridge strip seems to go unnoticed there.

Being both flat and slightly flexible, speed strips ride more comfortably and more concealably in the front pockets of most trousers and in coat pockets. Remember that business card "pocket within a pocket" in blazers and suit-coats? I discovered early on that Bianchi's strip fit there perfectly, with great comfort and a concealability factor that approached invisibility.

Nothing is perfect. I discovered over the years that lead hollowpoint bullets would become deformed from constant pocket carry in strips. This can have a deleterious effect on both accuracy and bullet expansion, if they have to be used for their intended purposes. Jacketed hollowpoints survive

pocket carry much better. They can still pick up pocket lint in their hollow cavities, though, and foreign matter in that cavity will never help the bullet. A separate location dedicated to the cartridge strip—ammo pouch, watch pocket, whatever—seems to be the best place to put this particular spare ammo device.

Of course, one can always just dump loose ammo in the pockets. The trouble with that is that it's even more awkward to get to when you need it than the worst of the ancient dump pouches. With tight clothing, the outlines of the cartridges will be obviously visible, and it will take an agonizingly long time to dig each round out of its repository. It will also take prehensile fingers to claw loose cartridges out of the front pocket in a tight pair of jeans if you are crouching or kneeling behind cover while under fire.

The Bottom Line

As the late, great master firearms instructor Jeff Cooper pointed out, the function of the gun is to launch bullets. Back as far as the 1970s, another great master, John Farnam, quantifiably proved that the average person can fire five shots in a second from a semi-automatic pistol with a short trigger reset, and four shots per second with a double-action revolver. A Good Person fighting for their or their family's lives will very likely fire as fast as is humanly possible. Some will fire faster than average. Consider those facts and do the math. Remember that it's not about the odds, it's about being prepared for the worst case scenario. A gun without ammunition is a very poor weapon—and a gun without spare ammunition is a very temporary gun.

Full moon clip, seen here with Performance Center S&W Model 625 in .45 ACP, is the fastest way to reload a revolver.

Chapter 9

LIGHTS
FOR CONCEALED CARRY

We have a wide variety of gun-mounted lights available today. These are some of the ones the author uses regularly.

Most of us who've been in the gun-carrying business for a long time carry artificial illumination as regularly and religiously as we carry firearms. Let me tell you why.

First, unlike the gun, it's something you'll find yourself actually *using* every day. As a bonus, when those around you know you always have it with you, they react with appreciation instead of the fear that sometimes comes when they learn you're armed. The day rarely goes by when I don't utilize one of my pocket flashlights for some mundane chore, which often begins when someone says, "Hey, Mas, can I borrow your flashlight?"

At the next level up, a flashlight can be an injury prevention tool in any number of ways. Ever walk through an icy parking lot or a patch of woods in near-total darkness? The light can prevent everything from a harmless but annoying and messy fall in the mud, to a twisted ankle, to a step into nowhere that could have dropped you ten feet and left you with a broken spine or fractured skull.

Third, there are more emergencies that require light than require gunfire. Even if you consider yourself a night owl (in which case you need to carry illumination all the more), *homo sapiens* is a diurnal species, not a nocturnal one. We simply don't see well in the dark. It has been said that on a moonless night, a human being with 20/20 vision and no artificial illumination can see no better than a person declared "legally blind" can see in broad daylight. From

searching for signs of life under the smoke pall at a fire scene, to checking pupil response in the eyes of a possible head injury victim to – well, use your imagination – there are countless emergencies in which a good light source can literally be a life-saver.

One of my graduates was in the Twin Towers when the unspeakable disaster occurred. He was one of the survivors. He will never forget the mass terror of people trying to get down the interminable stairwells in pitch darkness. He has made a point of never being without at least one powerful, pocket size "tactical flashlight" ever since, whether or not he happens to be armed.

Fourth, there are countless self-protection situations that don't rise to the level of the gun, but can be better controlled if you have a powerful light immediately at hand. Is that a wild animal behind the tree, as you walk your dog down the country lane in the dark? The flashlight will tell you in time to avoid you or your pet being bitten by what might be a rabid beast. Countless police officers, and probably a few civilians, have forestalled violence with a quick sweep of a powerful light beam across the eyes that swept the suspect's night vision away with it, leading to non-violent resolution when things might have turned out otherwise.

Fifth, if you know how to use it, some pocketsize lights can serve as an impact tool, an intermediate force weapon, in a hand-to-hand fight that does not yet rise to the level of

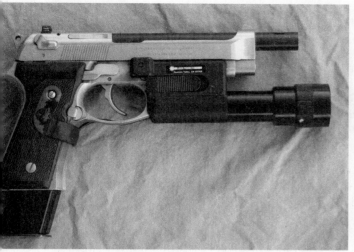

We've come a long way, baby. 20 years ago this big SureFire Weaponlight on Jarvis Custom Beretta 92 was state of the art… still functional today for outside wear or home defense, but too big for concealed carry.

deadly force. We'll discuss that more shortly, but suffice to say that training is essential to make this application work effectively and end well.

Finally, illumination that is *always, instantly available* is an essential complement to a defensive firearm that is *always, instantly available.*

When The Gun Needs Light

There are several reasons why the person who carries a gun is best served by also carrying a light.

The flashlight lets you find your way to the encounter and back. A huge percentage of gunfights occur in less than High Noon lighting conditions. Total darkness is fairly rare in gunfights, but it can certainly happen. Under some circumstances, the light can show you a lurking felon in time to keep your distance and avoid a confrontation at all. If you're on unfamiliar ground, in the moments before the encounter when you're at a Condition Orange level of knowing something is wrong but not exactly what it is, the light may have shown you where cover is: cover you can take to save your life, and cover your opponent might already be lurking behind, waiting in ambush. If it turns out that you do get into a gunfight, and win, the flashlight can show you where your dropped cell phone is to call 9-1-1…show you where your downed opponent's accomplice is waiting to avenge his henchman as soon as you drop your guard…and allow you to wave responding police and paramedics to the scene as they begin to arrive.

And more…once again, use your own imagination.

The flashlight allows you to identify a threat. When you've had to take that shortcut through a city alley to get to your car in the pouring rain, the small but powerful personal carry flashlight allows you to see whether that person suddenly emerging from the shadows in front of you is a restaurant employee coming out the back door to dump the garbage, or a rapist or mugger who has been lying in wait. When you arrive after nightfall at the family cabin for a vacation you and your spouse are sharing with

your brother and his wife, and the power is out, and a human figure moves suddenly in front of you in the dark, that flashlight lets you see whether it's a potentially violent burglar you surprised in the act…or your own brother, who unexpectedly arrived ahead of you.

The flashlight allows you to harmlessly, temporarily blind a person who threatens you, or to distract a person who is attacking someone else, and buy you time to save your life or that of the other innocent potential victim. No, that little pocket thingy hanging from your keychain won't do it. But since the time of the classic old SureFire 6P we've had personal-size lights that can generate that effect in deep darkness. The longer the criminal has been waiting in the dark for his chance to pounce, the more his pupils will have dilated and the more blinding effect your light will create.

We'll look shortly at the techniques that have evolved over the decades for police and other Good Guys and Gals to illuminate a human target while firing a gun to save innocent life. All of these techniques assume that the person who has become the target is doing something so horrible that he must be stopped **instantly** from pulling the trigger of the gun he's aiming at a victim, or stopped from plunging his knife into the throat of an innocent person.

If that were the situation, wouldn't it be kind of nice if something happened that caused that criminal to suddenly turn his head away? Any physiologist or martial artist can tell you, "Where the head goes, the body follows." Something that pulls the Bad Guy's body – and with it, the Bad Guy's knife or gun – off the intended target, buys the Good Guy time to make the shot that will hopefully end the deadly danger more decisively.

Developing A Repertoire of CCW Lights

There is no one gun that fulfills every concealed carry need with every conceivable wardrobe, and the same is true of what some like to call "tactical illumination tools." There's hardware you can carry in the car with a view toward unlimbering in an emergency. There's hardware you can have in the master bedroom for self-defense that would be impossible to walk around carrying in public. But there's also stuff you can carry with pretty much any dress code this side of a nudist camp, and that's equally true of both lighting tools and defensive firearms.

It's easier to have a whole lot of flashlights than a whole lot of guns. No one is likely to kill someone with a stolen flashlight, so you don't need to buy a safe to keep it in. They're way cheaper than guns. You can give them to anyone you want without doing paperwork, a "pass it forward" kind of recycling when you find something better for yourself, but realize that your older unit is still better than what the giftee has. In my circle of friends and loved ones and associates, I've lost track of how many guns I've given as presents over the years…but I can tell you, I've given out a whole lot more flashlights.

Some people have a lifestyle at home where they can have a loaded gun instantly accessible in every room. Some don't. EVERYONE this side of prison has a lifestyle where there can be a flashlight in every room, and that's a pretty

Each light performs a sometimes dramatically different, sometimes slightly different function.

and you have some background in self-defense with short stick techniques (or dedicated flashlight self-defense), you're holding a tool with which you can block, parry, strike, and more. No, you're not going to have much luck walking around carrying it concealed.

Next down in the photo is SureFire's lowest priced flashlight at this writing, the hugely popular Nitrolon. It's essentially a 6P model with lighter, less expensive construction, but the same reliability as the old standby that preceded it. Very handy for all-around use, and concealable if need be.

Below that is the flashlight I carried daily for about a decade and a half, the classic SureFire 6P. It can be carried in any of several ways. My feeling was, "It's a flashlight, so why the hell do I have to conceal it in the first place?" I came up with what I believe to have been the first horizontal carrier, which put the light at the front of the belt. Being right-handed, I carried it with the lens to the left, so my left hand could quickly draw it and flow into a Harries pistol/ flashlight technique. I even wore it with suits. Ninety-nine percent of the world never noticed, and the other one percent only said something

handy thing when the power and the lights go out and you don't know when they're coming back on. Indulge yourself. If you run across a flashlight you like, buy it. If you don't end up carrying it next year, it will still do you or someone else some good by being on a shelf, in a desk drawer, or in an automobile glove box somewhere.

Let's look at one small array, in which each light performs a sometimes dramatically different, sometimes slightly different function.

Topmost in the photo is a two-cell Mag-Lite from my significant other's car. She has owned it since before we met. Yep, it's old tech: D-cell batteries. But she can replenish the batteries at any gas station or convenience store. If you have to get out of the car on the proverbial dark and stormy night to assist a stranger in an unknown situation,

like, "Cool way to carry a flashlight. Why didn't I think of that?" Blade-Tech and others now make this type of carrier as a regular catalog item. It comes quickly off the belt and slides into a briefcase if one feels they need to button the front of the suit coat to look more formal.

Fourth down in the image is the next game-changer from SureFire, the E2D Executive Defender. It's equipped with a pocket clip and narrow enough for a trouser pocket. I personally find it ideal for the cell phone pocket in the BDU pants that replaced jeans in my personal wardrobe for casual wear. No one notices its lamp protruding from the front of the flapped pocket on upper thigh – remember, *it's only a flashlight!* – and it gives a light output comparable to the big police flashlights of yesteryear.

Below that, slightly larger, is one of the Brite-Strikes, still small enough to be carried in the same fashion as the E2D. I'll often carry this one when I'm out in plainclothes with brother officers, because it has a strobe option that, as we'll see shortly, is particularly useful when employed between cooperating partners.

Sixth down in the photo is another Brite-Strike product, the slender EPLI (Executive Protection Lighting Instrument). The size of a fat fountain pen, this conceals well when wardrobe requires a tailored suit or super-light beachwear. It's my current default light on the rare days in my life today when "concealment" is an absolute priority.

Seventh in the picture is a Streamlight 100C. Very bright for its size, it fits into small pockets.

At the bottom we close as we began, with old-school MagLite technology, the classic and ubiquitous Mini-MagLite. A game-changer when it first came out (back when most cops still carried service revolvers), it doesn't have enough light output to blind. It does, however, let you see stuff you couldn't see without a flashlight. It's cheap and expendable, but remarkably reliable. Its AA batteries are cheap and easy to replace. It's what you hand to the person in the office who says, "Can I borrow your flashlight to find my pen that rolled under the file cabinet?" The Mini-Mag saves wasting more expensive battery life with your primary tactical concealed carry flashlight.

No, it's not the only light I carry concealed (though it was, "back in the day," when it was "the only game in town" for that). The Mini-Mag was designed by Don Kellner, the original Kel-Lite police flashlight designer, when he was approached by Tak Kubota's associate John Peters. Kubota had developed the brilliant Kubotan™ self-defense device, a wand-shaped keychain that could be used for strikes, key-slashes, and wristlocks and pressure point takedowns for self-defense. Kubota and Peters were interested in a flashlight that could be used with their techniques and also be utilitarian. The result was what may be the most popular "personal carry flashlight" of modern times.

The Mini-MagLite is my daily carry "backup flashlight." Tailored suit, BDUs or whatever, it sits vertical to the outside of the wallet in my hip pocket, always in position to reach, and comfortable 24-7.

Let's look at some hardware that has become controversial and try to make some sense of the controversy.

Strobe Flashlights

Beginning with the Blackhawk Gladius a few years ago, compact flashlights with an optional strobe feature have become popular in some quarters, and tend to be either loved or hated. Personally, I don't use one for EDC (everyday carry), but if working in tandem with a partner, I like to have one of us equipped with the strobe option. Here's why.

The SureFire Academy, when I went there before the Gladius came out, was already teaching a rapid manipulation of the conventional high-intensity flashlight to create a strobe effect, aimed at the suspect's face to disorient him. It works. He won't fall to the ground in convulsions or throw up or anything, but it does indeed interfere with his visual processing, particularly on the outer parts of his scanning field. That is, if partner A is strobing him in the face, it will take him a lot longer to see partner B approaching on his flank, and he might even fail to see that partner in time to mount effective resistance to arrest.

That's the good news with the strobe option. The other good news is that you can turn it to solid beam instead.

The bad news is, just as the bright, rapidly flashing light disorients the man you're beaming it at, it can disorient *you*, albeit to a lesser extent. Notice I said it *can*, not that it necessarily *will*. Vision itself, and how our brain processes what we see, seems to be a very individual thing. Back in the time of discotheques, I couldn't bear to be in those places with the stroboscopic lighting, but some folks practically lived in that environment in the 1970s. It was during that same decade that I developed my long-lasting love/hate relationship with strobes as police car roof lights. I appreciated the fact that on a snowy, curvy road in the dark of night, the strobes would literally light up the sky and keep an innocent driver from coming around a corner too fast and rear-ending my patrol car during a traffic stop. But I hated the fact that, though they affected the unknown driver I had stopped in front of my police vehicle, they had some degree of that effect on me.

The effect in question is this: your eye sees what's happening when the light is on what you're looking at. Then, for an instant when the light is off, you can't see what the person is actually doing. However, the image burned in your brain is telling you what it saw an instant ago. That slows your ability to recognize a threat and react to it.

Then why do I think it might be a handy option to have if you are working with a partner? Because one can put the strobe in the face of the opponent while the other holds a conventional, solid light beam on that suspect's hands. This allows them to be seen constantly, even though the view will dim slightly between each strobe of the other light.

They say, "You pays your money and you takes your choice." I say you try the equipment under as close as you can get to the conditions in which you'll actually be doing the emergency work, and then you'll have the knowledge to take the *right* choice when you pay your money. To each their own...wisely.

The Gun-Mounted Light

Crude flashlights attached to guns have been around since the early 1900s. They didn't become really viable until the 1980s, with SureFire leading the way. In the law enforcement sector, it was to the best of my knowledge the pioneering, trend-setting LAPD SWAT Team that first used them, found them good, and spread their doctrine to other such teams.

The rationale was obvious: you can see to identify your target, you can get a sight picture so perfectly silhouetted it looks like something out of a marksmanship manual, *and* you can apply both hands to control your weapon with speed and accuracy since you don't need a separate hand to hold the illumination device.

But there was and is one huge downside. With the two hands on the gun, the only light you have is the one on the gun...and this means that *everything you illuminate, you are pointing a loaded gun at!*

(top) For smaller handguns like this XD(m) Compact, we have still-powerful, properly sized white light units like the InSight X2.

(above) All white light units are not created equal. This one, on a Ruger SR9 Compact, proved next to useless in author's opinion.

For this reason and for a very long time, I told students that I wasn't comfortable with a light mounted on a gun unless in the legal and ethical principle called "The Doctrine of Competing Harms," there was some compelling danger that outweighed this one. For instance, the SWAT cop, who could be expected to have both hands on the weapon when going in where there was great reason to believe a known armed and dangerous felon lay in wait, or a

K9 officer who had to keep one hand on his dog's lead and only had one hand left to control both gun and illumination device simultaneously.

Over the years, I came to modify my position on that. Experience both in the field and in teaching taught me the advantage of having the light on the gun in certain situations. In the early 1990s, I was serving as chair of the firearms committee of the American Society of Law Enforcement Trainers (ASLET) when we held our annual international conference in West Palm Beach, Florida, hosted by the Palm Beach County Sheriff's Office, an agency which has long been a role-model leader in law enforcement use of force training. Bill Testa, commander of a SWAT team there, invited me along on a raid after class. I quickly accepted; I had known Bill from previous shared training experiences, and knew him and his team to be top-notch professionals.

As the SWAT team rolled from the van and moved rapidly toward the house, a man appeared behind a front window of the target premises, pulling the curtain open. As my hand went to my own Colt .45 auto, I saw Bill Testa snap his Benelli Super 90 12 gauge semiautomatic shotgun to his shoulder and put the beam of the SureFire light on its fore-end right in the suspect's eyes. The man raised his hands to his eyes and spun away. Entry was swiftly accomplished and arrests were made with no bloodshed.

Some people, under some other circumstances, might have shot him. The powerful light had not only showed Bill the man had no gun, but had caused the man to turn away and cease to present himself as a threat.

Before long I had a SureFire light-equipped fore-end on my own department issue HK MP5 submachinegun, and another for one of my 870 shotguns. Along about then I also put one of the then-big and bulky dedicated SureFire lights on a custom home defense pistol, a Beretta 92 with extended Magna-Ported barrel, extended 20-round magazine, night sights, and a Bill Jarvis action.

So, where does all this fit in a concealed carry book? I feel it fits as follows.

For concealed carry *per se*, over the years gun-mounted lights by SureFire, Streamlight, InSight, and other manufacturers became small enough to fit in holsters. First, there were the big lights on the big holsters that K9 officers had worn, and by the early 2000s, had made great popularity inroads with rank and file police patrol officers. In an emergency, where the officer had to draw the service pistol in an "iffy" situation, they allowed a last-minute verification before the officer pulled the trigger that this was indeed a deadly threat, and it was indeed a knife instead of a car key in the opponent's hand, and therefore, it was indeed a situation where the officer needed to shoot.

That exact same dynamic can be a lifesaver on either side of the gun when the private citizen has to draw his or her concealed handgun in an emergency situation.

The first non-uniform holsters for flashlight-mounted handguns were bulky things…*concealable* holsters, but not *concealment* holsters. By that I mean, yes, you could conceal them under a London Fog overcoat or an oversize shooter's vest, but you weren't going to hide that rig under a well-fitting suit or an untucked, one-size large polo shirt.

Seen from the front, Concealment Solutions Mamba holster conceals IWB a full size Glock 17 with Advantage Sights and mounted SureFire white light unit…

…seen from side, the full size gun is concealable on average size adult male…

…the full size Glock with SureFire X200 light draws quickly and cleanly from IWB Concealment Solutions Mamba holster.

Time went on. Holster makers figured how to conceal these bulkier objects. By last winter, when I was on home turf, I found myself carrying daily a full-size Glock 31 in .357 SIG with a SureFire light attached. It rode in an inside the waistband holster from Concealment Solutions. There was a slight bump from the flashlight part that might have been visible just over my right hip pocket, but no one seemed to notice. If they did, they probably just thought I had a fat butt. On unseasonably warm days, when I could go without a coat, it all concealed just fine under an untucked polo shirt one size larger than I normally wear.

Why was "winter" mentioned? Simply because when the earth tilts away from the sun on its axis far enough to change the climate, it also changes how many hours of sunlight we get. There is simply more "night time" in winter, and when you're out and about, there's that much more likelihood that your emergency will occur in poor light. Moreover, no one needs to buy a book such as this one to figure out that in colder weather you're wearing more clothing and bulkier clothing, which means that you can hide bigger hardware discreetly. Hell, the Bad Guys have already figured it out. Back in the 1970s, Richard Davis quantified it. Richard was the armed citizen who "bullet-proofed America's police" when he got into a shootout with three armed robbers, shot 'em all, and took a couple of bullets himself in the process. Sitting in the hospital being treated for two gunshot wounds, this brilliant man not only figured out that there had to be

something better to stop bullets with than your own body, he introduced the soft body armor that has since saved thousands of lives. As the entrepreneur/inventor running Second Chance Body Armor Company, he did studies in which he noticed that not only did more bad guys carry guns with which to shoot arresting officers during winter than in summer, but also that more of them carried bigger guns during the cooler seasons. If the Bad Guys can take that advantage, so can we Good Guys and Gals.

A flashlight mounted below the frame of the pistol generally extends beyond the front of the muzzle. There is good news and bad news here, and in this writer's opinion the good news outweighs the bad. The bad news is muzzle blast and heat are going to hammer the flashlight. You will want to clean gunpowder residue off the lens after every practice shooting session. Fortunately, most such "white light" units have been engineered to stand up to this.

The good news is the protruding lamp of the light unit creates "stand-off capability." This is critical because when the muzzles of most semiautomatic pistols are pressed against a firm surface – such as a human body – the pressure forces the barrel/slide assembly to the rear and pushes it "out of battery." That is, it moves the working parts out of the alignment required for the gun to fire…and it will no longer discharge when the trigger is pulled.

It is not at all uncommon for a criminal's lethal assault to happen so "up close and personal" that the only option

Different flashlight/gun holsters perform different functions. For open carry on his rural property, author likes this very fast Blade-Tech…

…which, seen here from the front, protrudes from the body more than some other designs…

…and whose outer edge can lean a full two inches away from the body. Draw is very fast, however.

except to die is to shoot the attacker at muzzle contact distance, sometimes using a degree of forward push that is known as "press-contact." This concern is one reason some streetwise people still carry revolvers in the time of semiautomatic pistol dominance in the world of the handgun.

The flashlight protruding from below the muzzle and in front of it creates the "stand-off effect": it is the light that's in contact, not the gun. The parts remain "in battery" and the gun will still fire.

It can literally be the difference between life and death. In a case in Florida, a law enforcement officer was murderously attacked by two criminals and had to fire in self-defense. He shot the first one at muzzle contact with his non-flashlight-equipped double action 9mm. The bullet killed that one assailant, but "blowback effect" sent enough flesh and blood into the muzzle area of his pistol that it did not return to battery after the first shot. He swung the gun to the second man and pulled the trigger, but nothing happened; his gun was out of battery. Before he could clear the malfunction he was shot and killed by the second assailant.

In Minnesota, an officer losing a fight and knowing he was about to die shoved his striker-fired duty pistol against his attacker's body and pulled the trigger. Nothing happened. The pistol, not equipped with a flashlight, was now out of battery. A near-miracle that was not mechanically gun-related was all that saved this officer's life.

In Jacksonville, Florida, a suspect shot a courageous young cop named Jared Reston in the face with a .45

automatic. Reston fell backward into a dry retention pond, and the would-be cop-killer stood above him and shot him several more times, with multiple potentially fatal bullets fortunately stopping on the officer's ballistic vest. He drew his Glock 22 and returned fire, hitting the opponent several times. The attacker fell forward and landed on top of him, still capable of killing him, and Jared pressed his .40 caliber pistol against the man's head and pulled the trigger three times, ending the fight. He survived to return to full duty, on both patrol and SWAT assignments.

Jared Reston survived, in my opinion, in part because his Glock was fitted with a TLR-1 white light unit. When he put it forcefully against the homicidal attacker's head and pulled the trigger for the first of those three shots, the bullet shattered the maxillo-facial structure but didn't reach the brain, and wouldn't have stopped the man from shooting him again. However, while a non-light-equipped gun might very well have failed to function after the first shot or even *for* the first, the stand-off effect of the TLR light allowed Jared to keep shooting when his opponent didn't stop fighting, and allow him to "brain" the gunman and bring the death battle his opponent had initiated to a righteous conclusion.

As a rule, those who lawfully carry a concealed firearm in public also keep firearms readily available in the home for family protection. The light on the home defense gun serves a limited purpose: when the bad guys are kicking down the door and all the family members have been marshaled into the safe room, and you've counted noses and determined that whatever is kicking down the door is something that is going to severely harm your family, *that* is *definitely* time to apply both hands to the gun for accurate, fast shooting. And yes, it's all the better if you have those hands on a suitably loaded home defense carbine or shotgun. THEN, the light can give you the final verification that it is truly someone who needs to be shot, before you start pressing the trigger.

But, please, hear me on this: *Any time you need to search with a light to find out what is going on, for heaven's sake PLEASE use a separate light to search, so you don't point the gun at everything illuminated by your white light beam!* If the pistol's muzzle is down and the person you illuminate in your separately hand-held light turns out to be someone you don't need to shoot – which happens more often than you might think, in real life – at least you haven't been pointing a gun at them.

Pointing a lethal weapon at someone you have no right to take at gunpoint fits the description of the very serious felony of Aggravated Assault. Even if the person you erroneously pointed the gun at during your "house search" is a member of your family or extended family and not likely to press charges, you will have still inflicted a psychological wound that will never entirely heal.

The best way I can explain it is, treat the light mounted on your gun the way a responsible hunter treats the telescopic sight on his hunting gun. You don't use your riflescope to scan for the quarry, because there is a very high likelihood that you'll end up looking through that scope at another hunter or a hiker in the woods. Pointing the gun at that person still constitutes Aggravated Assault, and if you are

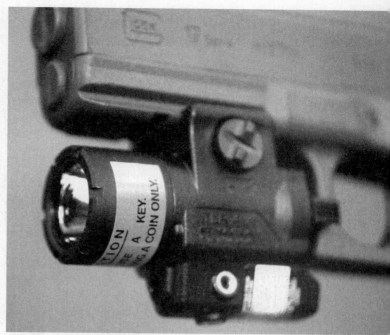

The latest TLR-4 flashlight from Streamlight encompasses both white light and laser dot, in tandem or separate.

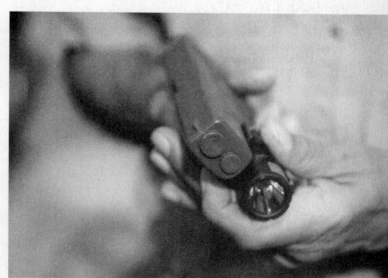

TLR light system from Streamlight rolls onto the frame sideways, keeping hand behind the muzzle of a loaded pistol.

reported for doing so you can expect that charge in criminal court at worst, and the loss of your hunting license at best, even if no shot is fired.

This is why the responsible hunter uses binoculars to *scan* for game, and the scoped rifle to aim at the recognized quarry. At that moment, the magnified and improved vision afforded by the telescopic sight allows the hunter to *verify* that he is indeed aiming at a deer instead of a human being or a domestic sheep, that he is indeed aiming at a legal buck instead of an illegal doe.

I respectfully submit that it is very much the same thing with the lighting device and the gun. You use a separate hand-held light to *search and identify*, the same way the responsible hunter uses binoculars to scan and determine

Laser sights are popular on small frame revolvers like these S&Ws. Top, Crimson Trace LaserGrip; below, LaserMax unit.

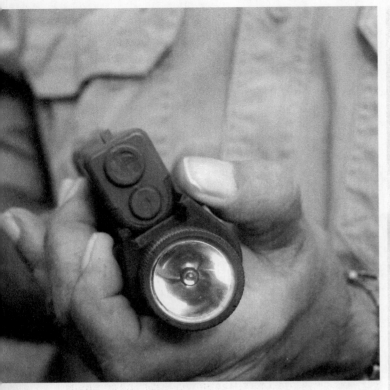

(above) Lights that slide onto the front go on and off faster, but put the hand in front of the muzzle, which gives police chiefs and firearms instructors nightmares.

(below) Author emphatically suggests that gun-mounted light be backed up with separate hand-held light for search functions.

(right) "Grommets" on these lights facilitate the Rogers technique of mating hand-held flashlight with handgun.

a target, and you use the light mounted on the gun to *verify* that this is indeed a "shoot" target before you pull the trigger.

Properly used, this hardware gives all involved one more safety net to prevent tragedy. Improperly used, it can lead directly to such tragedy.

The hunter with his finger on the trigger as he searches for a deer through his riflescope may be so startled by seeing a buck that the "startle response" pulls the trigger for him before he is certain of his target. The exact same thing can happen when the light on the gun is used for searching. Yeah, yeah, I know: we're supposed to keep our finger off the trigger until we've decided to shoot. However, that requires a perfect human being at the controls, one who is incapable of making a mistake. Neither you nor I are perfect human beings incapable of making a mistake. There hasn't been such a human being for at least a couple of thousand years. However, the other element of the comparison also holds true: in the last instant before a tragic bullet is mistakenly launched, the gun-mounted light can provide a life-saving verification of target identity.

My take: use the gun-mounted light, but use it wisely and carefully, and in tandem with a separate, dedicated flashlight to perform search functions.

Laser Sighting

Some of the white light units discussed above, which attach to firearms, also come with laser attachments. Laser sights have been around since the 1980s, though it wasn't until later that they became small enough to adapt to concealable firearms. Usable laser sights were actually on the market before gun-mounted lights got small enough for CCW work.

The lasers have their place, so long as one doesn't allow oneself to be oversold on the concept. They need to be checked regularly to verify that the beam is on target, and of course, they are battery dependent.

Most of us find the projected laser dot slower to get on target than regular sights, assuming that we can *see* those conventional sights. It's a matter of geometry. Getting the red line that projects from the gun to the aiming point on a target a distance away, is a little like wielding a weightless wand of a length that equals that distance and touching the spot we want to hit.

Some proponents of the concept assure us that the Bad Guy will be terrified into peaceful surrender when he perceives the red dot on his chest. While this has doubtless happened, it would be a stretch of the imagination to expect that it would happen every time the laser dot centered on a suspect's body. I was present at one incident where it had the opposite effect, and provoked a homicidal response. You don't spend your days looking down at your chest for laser dots; why would the Bad Guys be looking there?

Don't focus on questionable attributes of the laser-equipped handgun when it has multiple *real* advantages. There are many people, particularly those with older eyes, who can see well enough at a distance to identify a threat target, but are unable to focus sharply on their gun sights. The projected red (or green) dot may work very well for someone in such a situation.

The laser has proven to be a tremendous training tool for shooters. When they refuse to accept that they're jerking the trigger, watching the laser dot on target during dry fire tells the tale decisively. Conversely, one of the few shortcuts to learning trigger control is to watch the dot on the point of aim, and hold it there without it moving as the trigger is slowly brought back until the dry-fire "click" of the unloaded gun. The non-shootable dedicated laser pistol known as the SIRT is quite useful in this respect, and has proven itself in the training environment in the last couple of years before this Second Edition of the *Gun Digest Book of Concealed Carry* was written. Resembling a Glock pistol (other types are believed to be in the pipeline), it projects one dot on the target like a regular laser sight, and then another from the bore axis as the "shot" is fired, to show where it would have hit. The trigger resets itself.

Laser sights are particularly useful on small pocketsize handguns with tiny, hard-to-see conventional sights. Think in terms of the J-frame S&W, Ruger, and Taurus small frame revolvers, and the super-small .380 pistols such as the Kel-Tec P3AT, Ruger LCP, and Kahr P380. Crimson Trace makes LaserGrips for small to large revolvers and for full-size service autos, and their LaserGuard for the smaller autoloaders. LaserMax, which came out with a popular laser unit that replaces the recoil spring guide rod in semi-autos, also has a laser unit that attaches to the side of a J-frame revolver. Laser-Lyte makes one that affixes to the side of the rear sight on some compact to service-size autos. Finally, in 2010, Smith & Wesson made proprietary InSight laser units integral with their newly introduced Bodyguard series, a polymer-framed .38 Special five-shot and a double action only .380 pocket pistol.

Crimson Trace sent a great many LaserGrips for the Beretta M9 to America's armed service personnel in Iraq and Afghanistan. In the dimness of house-to-house combat in the one place and in searching the dark caves of the other, the laser sights made many friends among our troops. Standard issue US military service pistols are not usually fitted with night sights.

How effective are the laser sights in poor light? That's where they come into their own – so long as the user can see the target well enough to identify it. Working with a group of very experienced colleagues in Live Oak, Florida, we tested the various systems intensively during night shoots on eight-inch steel plates. Shooting with conventional sights and no illumination on a dark night resulted in slow and relatively dismal performance. Shooting with the gun in the firing hand and the flashlight in the support hand proved distinctly better. Gun-mounted white light gave even better results. However, so long as there was enough light to see the target, the laser sight proved faster and more accurate than any of the previous systems. Best of all, by a slight margin, was the combination light and laser sight.

When shooting with a laser-equipped handgun, bear in mind that the bore is not in perfect alignment with the laser sight, and you may need some "Kentucky windage" accordingly. With a laser sight only below the bore, and attached to the gun's light rail – not my own idea of the best laser sighting system, because for that amount of bulk,

With last two fingers FIRMLY holding globe of the lamp, thumb and index finger turn on a Mini-MagLite one-handed. Technique requires relatively strong fingers...and practice.

I'd want some white light – we found the best bet was determining how far above the underslung laser's dot the bullet would hit, and using a six o'clock hold proportional to the distance. The same is true with the white/light laser combinations, and you can expect a difference of as much as two inches or more with some units, because with the laser generally located below the light's lamp, it is that far below the barrel axis. With the popular Crimson Trace LaserGrips, the laser module is located on the right grip panel. I adjust it to project the beam parallel to the bore, and accept the fact that the bullet will go about a half an inch left of the

dot and, at most reasonable distances, about an inch high.

Trying to adjust a laser sight so the bullet strikes exactly "on the dot" is an exercise in frustration. Once again, geometry is at work. The bullet will only "hit the dot" at the exact distance for which it was sighted in. With LaserGrips, at shorter distances the dot will be low right of the line of the bullet, and at longer yardages than the distance for which it was sighted, the dot will be progressively more high and left of the trajectory. By adjusting the beam to run parallel to the bore, you'll have a consistent, easily remembered point of impact that's one inch high and half an inch left of the

The versatile Harries flashlight/pistol technique requires back of hand to back of hand lock-in...

...and puts the shooter in a bent-elbows classic Weaver stance...

bullet's trajectory line.

Are laser sights worth it? So long as you play to their strengths and avoid their weaknesses, I think they are. Use them as auxiliary sights for special purposes instead of your main default, unless you simply can't see your sights even under normal conditions, and I think you'll find them worth the money. My regular backup gun is a J-frame Smith & Wesson equipped with LaserGrips, and I for one have been very happy with it.

Coordinating the Handgun With a Separate Flashlight

Most concealed carry guns at the writing of this second edition won't have lights attached, though that may change as technology progresses and the light units become smaller and relatively more powerful. For now, it still makes a lot of sense to be able to coordinate a conventional flashlight in the support hand with the firearm in the gun hand. Several techniques developed for this have proven themselves in the field over the decades.

The first was the **FBI technique,** going back to the first half of the 20th century, and developed by the eponymous agency. The shooter fires one-handed, as the flashlight is held out to the side of the shooter at arm's length, and sometimes held high as well. The theory was that the opponent would see the light and shoot at it, not realizing that he was aiming away from the torso and head of the Good Guy holding the light. While that might have been true of weak, early flashlights of the Eveready variety, the ploy is somewhat compromised by the powerful lights of today. Particularly indoors, all that light reflects off walls and particularly from

ceilings, which are generally white. The result can be that the Good Guy, who thinks he's actually invisible to the side of the light beam, is actually illuminated by the reflected light, and from an opponent's eye view is in fact as visible as if a low-watt light bulb had been turned on over the Good Guy's head. The FBI technique comes into its own, however, if the user can duck behind a tree, with the light projecting from one side, and aiming eye and gun hand emerging from the other side.

Going back to the early days of Jeff Cooper's group and the dawn of what the Colonel called The Modern Technique of the Pistol is the **Harries technique.** Cooper's colleague Michael Harries developed what is perhaps the most versatile such technique in terms of use with different types of flashlight. The handgun is held in the conventional manner. The support hand, holding the flashlight with the lens protruding from the bottom of the fist, goes "back of hand to back of hand" with the firing hand. It's primarily a search technique; that is, you assume the position before you start moving, not as a reaction to the threat as you draw the gun. The thumb operates a butt-cap light switch, and the middle finger operates the switch if it's mounted on the side of the flashlight.

The Harries technique can be fatiguing over the long term. As originally taught, the backs of the hands press against each other, an unnatural action that we don't do any other time in life, resulting in fatigue. Some instructors teach to use this technique by pressing the gun butt down against the wrist of the firing hand. It works well around the right side of a barricade for a right-handed shooter, but is awkward and carries the upper body out too far on the left

...which looks like this from "the business end."

side of the wall. The opposite will be true for left-handed shooters.

The Harries technique pretty much forces the shooter into a classic Weaver stance, with both elbows bent.

Another Cooper associate, Ray Chapman, developed the **Chapman technique** shortly after the Harries. Ray, the first world champion of the combat pistol and the man Cooper himself nicknamed "The Maestro," preferred to hold the pistol in the conventional manner and grasp the light in a conventional hold with the support hand, the lens of the flashlight on the thumb side. Designed for the flashlights of the day, which were operated by sliding switches or buttons on the side of the light, the Chapman method starts with the support hand configured like an "OK" sign. Thumb and forefinger encircle the light, with the thumb on the switch. The lower three fingers of the support hand wrap around

Author's technique, designed for sudden, reactive shooting. Support hand holds only light, firing hand holds only gun…

The Chapman flashlight/pistol technique. Flashlight hand forms "OK" sign, with thumb running side-mounted light switch, and three bottom fingers supporting firing hand.

the firing hand, reinforcing the shooter's hold on the pistol.

With a heavy flashlight, Ray's technique can be fatiguing at arm's length, but fatigue is relieved with a long light by simply resting the buttcap against the upper abdomen with the gun in a tactical high ready position. It looks a little like the way the flag bearer carries the flagpole in a parade. Like the Harries, this is a search technique, and is designed to be assumed before the shooter starts moving, not suddenly as

…and from this perspective, we can see that light is angled upward to go into opponent's eyes, while gun is level on opponent's center chest.

Author likes this technique for short butt-switch flashlight, but behind cover, the barricade can block the flashlight beam.

a reaction. It can be used with a Weaver stance, an Isosceles, or Ray's own modified Weaver stance. It works well on either side of the barricade. It does not, however, translate well to the short, butt-button lights of today.

I developed the **Ayoob technique** in the '70s, back when our primary flashlights were the big Kel-Lites with side buttons. I intended it as a reaction technique, for when the flashlight was being held for ordinary illumination tasks with the globe protruding from the thumb-side of the hand, and the gun was still in the holster. With this method, one simply draws the gun and extends it full length toward the threat, with the firing hand dedicated to the pistol, and thrusts the flashlight arm forward to full extension, too. Both elbows lock in an Isosceles stance, with "base of thumb against base of thumb" for hand-to-hand contact. With natural wrist angle, this slants the line of the light beam somewhat upward. From near-contact to about seven yards, this puts the light directly in the opponent's eyes (I wanted maximum blinding potential) and the muzzle in line with the center of the opponent's chest.

Downsides? Developed for the older style lights, it does not adapt well to butt-cap switches. Beyond seven yards, geometry being what it is, either the light will go high or the shots will go low.

The **Rogers "cigar" technique** came next, if I recall correctly, developed by the brilliant holster designer, shooting champion, and FBI alumnus Bill Rogers. He built it around the SureFire 6P with butt-mounted pressure switch. The light is held between index and middle fingers like a cigar. The middle finger and two lower digits wrap around

the gun hand for two-hand firing support, and the top fingers pull the butt of the light back into the drumstick of the thumb, which activates the button. This is an accurate, effective, fatigue-free technique. The flashlight industry saw so much potential in it that SureFire brought out their Z-model with a rubber grommet placed to facilitate it, a feature widely copied by other makers. If the light is carried butt-up in pocket or belt, it can actually be drawn simultaneous with the gun, a technique that requires practice but is worth developing.

This is how the support hand manages the "cigar" or "syringe" technique, developed by Bill Rogers.

The Rogers technique, as seen from the front…   …and from the side.

The **neck technique** is associated with SureFire Academy. The short light is held with the thumb on the end-cap button and the lamp projecting from the bottom of the support-side fist. It is then brought up to the side of the neck or the jaw line. This puts the beam in a relatively natural position to look where the head is looking. Firing is done one-handed. Some like it because it can light up the gun and the sights. I personally dislike it for the same reason: I find light glaring on the gun and particularly the

Neck placement of flashlight works well for some, but not for everyone.

sights in the dark distracts me too much from identifying the target and aiming at it. With the beam on target only, you get the silhouette of the sight picture, which I for one find easier to index. Vision being a highly individual thing, so obviously is the preference for flashlight techniques.

Finally, when the big Mag-Lites gave way to the pocketsize SureFire and its many copies, I found it useful to simply quick-draw the light with the left hand, the globe protruding from the bottom of the fist, and bring it to center chest. This pointed the light where the head and upper body were pointing. It centered the beam very well and didn't glare on my gun and sights. A downside: when you're behind cover, that cover can block the light unless you're more exposed than you want to be.

Try the different techniques. Find at least one that works well for you when you set up beforehand to search, and one that can allow you to quickly draw the gun and bring it up to coordinate with the light in sudden reactive situations. They day may come when you'll be glad you did.

Flashlight as Weapon

Whether as a less-lethal option to the gun or the only thing in your possession that can serve as a weapon, a flashlight can be an effective defense tool if you know what to

The old FBI technique does not work as well with butt-activated lights projecting from the bottom of the fist, as it does from older style side-switch lights, which project from the thumb side of the hand.

do with it. The long police-style flashlight shouldn't be used like a Cro-Magnon's club; the overhand swing can smash a skull and accidentally kill or maim someone you're merely trying to subdue, and in any case is easy for a streetwise opponent to block or evade a downward swing. Spend some time learning flashlight defensive techniques from a qualified instructor, or short stick fighting techniques from someone who teaches a martial art that incorporates that sort of weaponry. In the conventional illumination grasp, a four- or five-cell light along the lower edge of the forearm becomes a formidable blocking (and striking) tool. A few hours of training will show you a variety of blocks, less-lethal strikes, and even grappling techniques. Pick the length depending on the length of your forearm: when held normally, you want its length to truncate before it reaches to your own elbow. A C-cell light is slimmer to grasp, and lighter and faster to swing for most people, than the heavy D-size lights. Look for the book *Defensive Tactics With Flashlights* by John Peters.

Even the humble Mini-MagLite can become an effective defense tool. Look for *The Kubotan Manual* by Takayuki Kubota. Both books were available from Police Bookshelf, PO Box 122, Concord, NH 03302 at this writing. Kubota developed his namesake Kubotan, a small keychain-size plastic wand, to deliver a variety of pressure point attacks and counters, strikes, and wristlocks and takedowns. Every single Kubotan technique will work with the Mini-Mag, which is legal to carry anywhere, even in courtrooms, schools, and commercial aircraft.

The bottom line? For the person who carries a gun, a small but powerful flashlight is an essential complement to the equipment.

He who controls the light need not fear the darkness.

First Light flashlight straps onto hand, leaving palms and fingers free for two hand shooting, grasping and fighting, or whatever. A useful tool!

HIP HOLSTERS

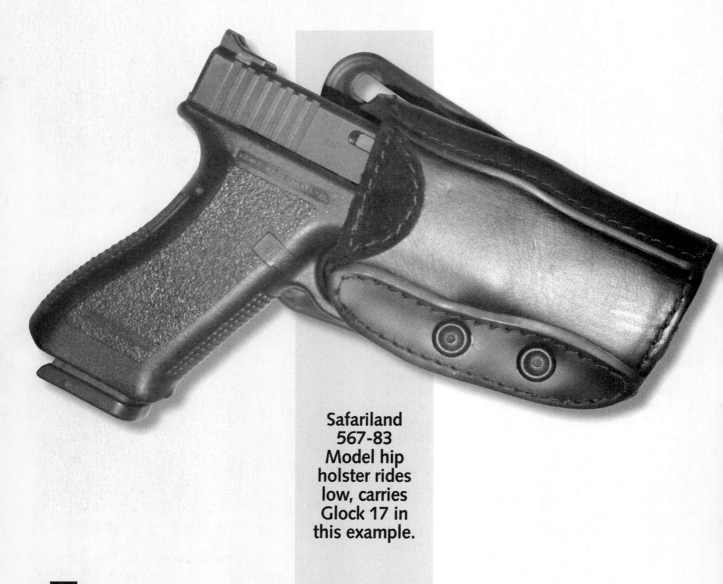

Safariland 567-83 Model hip holster rides low, carries Glock 17 in this example.

The strong-side hip – i.e., the gun hand-side hip – is the odds-on choice for weapon placement for most of those who carry concealed handguns today. It is also the standard location for law enforcement officers in uniform. This is probably not coincidental.

Many ranges, police academies, and shooting schools will allow *only* strong-side holsters. The theory behind this is that cross draw (including shoulder and fanny pack carries) will cause the gun muzzles to cross other shooters and range officers when weapons are drawn or holstered. Some also worry about the safety of pocket draw and ankle draw. There are action shooting sports – PPC and IDPA, to name two – where anything but a strong-side belt holster is expressly forbidden. Once again, safety is the cited reason.

It is worthwhile to look at other such

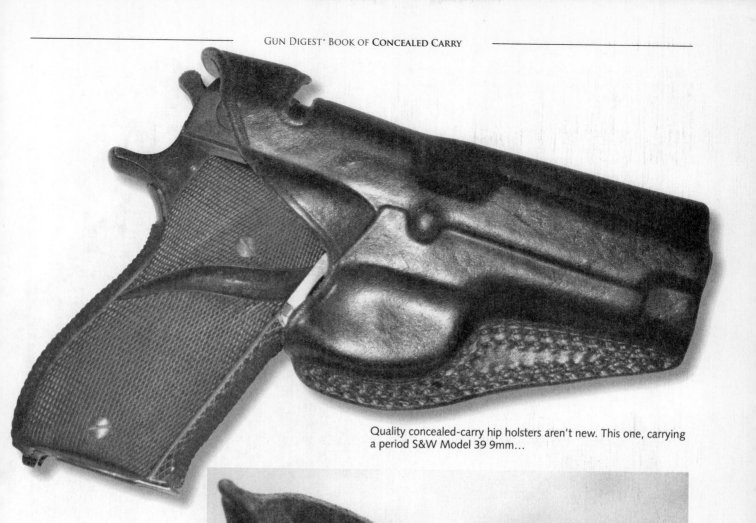

Quality concealed-carry hip holsters aren't new. This one, carrying a period S&W Model 39 9mm…

…was made circa 1974 by Seventrees, the innovative company led by the late Paris Theodore.

sports where cross draw holsters *are* allowed…but are seldom seen. In the early days of IPSC, cross draws actually dominated the winner's circle for a while. Ray Chapman wore one when he captured the first world championship of the sport. Today, however, even though it's still allowed, the cross draw has all but disappeared from that sport. A little history is in order. In the mid-1970s, a common IPSC start position was standing with hands clasped at centerline of the torso. With a front cross draw, this allowed the gun hand to be positioned barely above the pistol grip at the moment the start signal went off. IPSC started to go more toward hands-shoulder-high start positions (to give everyone a more level playing field, and to better allow range officers to see if a hand went prematurely to the gun), and the last such match I shot used mostly start positions with hands relaxed at the sides. These positions favored a gun on the same side as the dominant hand. In any case, a strong-side holster brings the gun on target faster because, standing properly, the weapon is already in line with the mark and does not have to be swept across the target.

We saw the same in NRA Action Shooting. Mickey Fowler for many years had a monopoly on the Bianchi Cup, using a front cross draw, specifically an ISI Competition Rig he and his colleague Mike Dalton had designed with Ted Blocker. However, in later years, the Cup has always been won with a straight-draw hip holster.

Because they begin at the academy with handguns on their dominant hand side, cops tend to stay with the same location for plainclothes wear. Habituation is a powerful thing. Master holster maker and historian John Bianchi invokes Bianchi's Law: the same gun, in the same place, all the time. It makes the reactive draw second nature.

We saw this in action in the IPSC world in the late

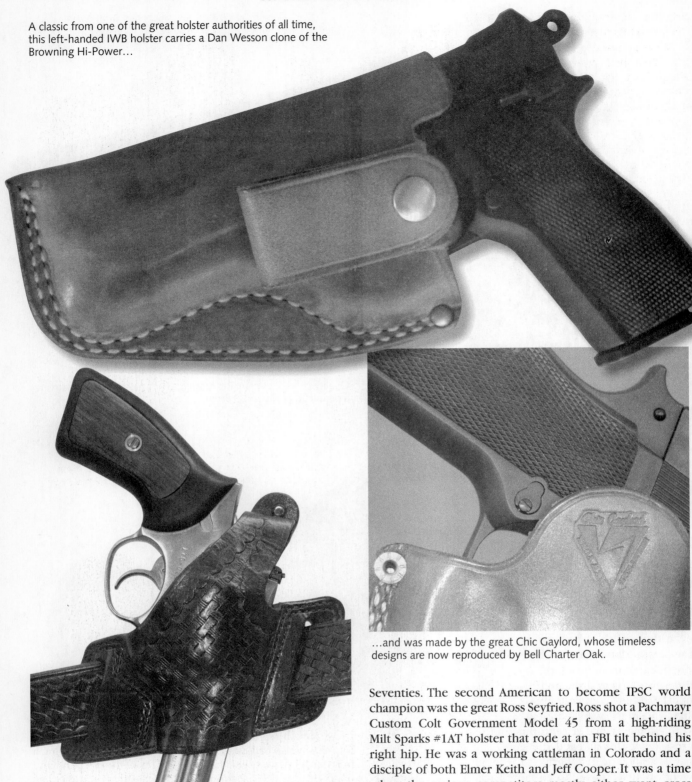

A classic from one of the great holster authorities of all time, this left-handed IWB holster carries a Dan Wesson clone of the Browning Hi-Power...

...and was made by the great Chic Gaylord, whose timeless designs are now reproduced by Bell Charter Oak.

Bianchi Black Widow has either-side belt loops for tight carry of this Ruger GP100 357 against body, and fast thumb-break safety strap. It rides on a mated Bianchi dress gun belt. Holster and belt are more than 20 years old and in excellent condition, a tribute to Bianchi quality.

Seventies. The second American to become IPSC world champion was the great Ross Seyfried. Ross shot a Pachmayr Custom Colt Government Model 45 from a high-riding Milt Sparks #1AT holster that rode at an FBI tilt behind his right hip. He was a working cattleman in Colorado and a disciple of both Elmer Keith and Jeff Cooper. It was a time when the serious competitors mostly either went cross draw, or wore elaborate speed rigs low on the hip. One who chose the latter was a multimillionaire for whom IPSC was purely sport. Frustrated that Ross had beaten him at the national championships in Denver, this fellow hired a sports physiologist to explain to him how Seyfried had managed to beat him. "I don't understand it," the frustrated professional told the wealthy sportsman in essence after viewing tapes of Seyfried. "Your way is faster than his. The way this Seyfried fellow carries his gun is mechanically slower."

What physiologist and rich guy alike had missed was one simple fact: the multi-millionaire only strapped on his fancy quick-draw holster on match day and at practice sessions. Ross Seyfried wore a #1AT Milt Sparks holster behind his hip every day of his life, though in the saddle on the ranch he carried a 4-inch Smith & Wesson Model 29 44 Magnum. Ross and that holster had developed a symbiotic relationship. Reaching to that spot had become second nature, and made him faster from there than a part-time pistol packer with a more sophisticated, more expensive "speed rig."

Strong-Side Hip Advantages

If the navel is 12 o'clock, a properly worn concealment hip holster puts a right-handed man's gun at 3:30. In this position, just behind the ileac crest of the pelvis, clothing comes down in a natural drape from the latissimus dorsi to cover the gun without bulge. On a guy of average build, the holstered gun finds itself nestled in a natural hollow below the kidney area. With the jacket opened in the front, the gun is usually invisible from the front. Being just behind the hip, a holstered gun in this location does not seem to get in the way of bucket seats nor most furniture, and doesn't press into the body when the wearer leans back against a chair surface.

Because of its proximity to the gun hand, and because the gun can come directly up on target from the holster, the strong-side draw is naturally fast. For males, simply bringing the elbow straight back brings the hand almost automatically to the gun.

Disadvantages

The hip draw does not lend itself to a surreptitious draw – that is, starting with the hand already on the gun, unnoticed – unless the practitioner can get the gun-side third of his body behind some concealing object or structure.

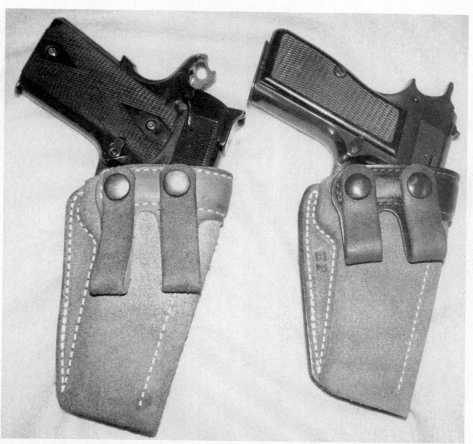

Designed by the late Bruce Nelson, these rough-out Summer Special IWB holsters were produced by Milt Sparks. Left, standard version for Morris Custom Colt 45 automatic. Right, narrow belt loop model to go with corresponding thick but narrow dress belt for suits, also by Sparks, here with Browning Hi-Power.

Author says at least one ambidextrous model is imperative to the holster wardrobe. This is Glock's own, in very economical polymer, with a Glock 30 45 auto.

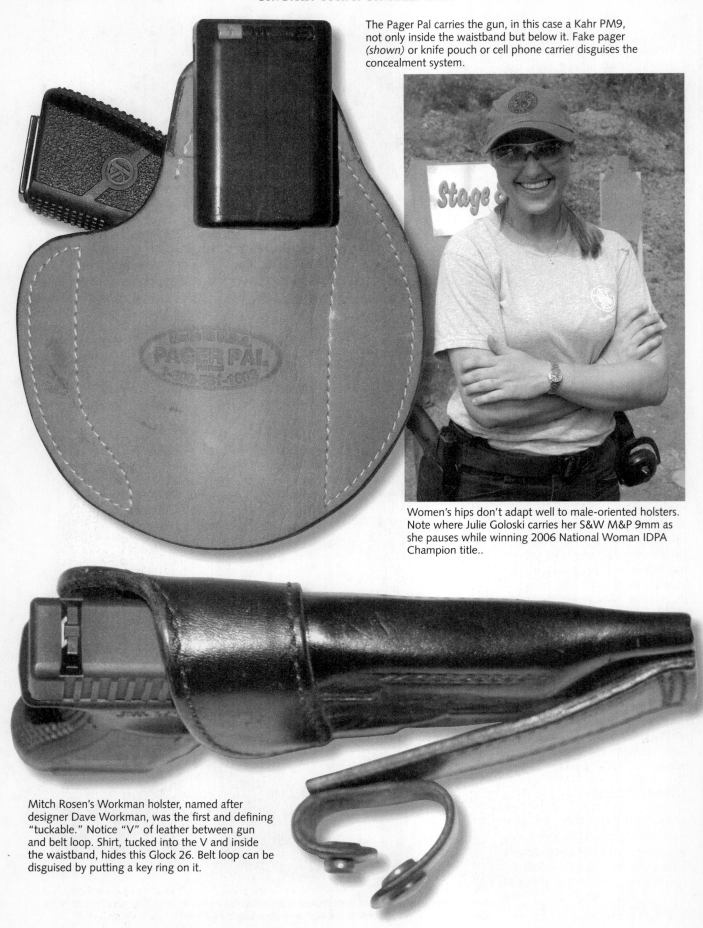

The Pager Pal carries the gun, in this case a Kahr PM9, not only inside the waistband but below it. Fake pager *(shown)* or knife pouch or cell phone carrier disguises the concealment system.

Women's hips don't adapt well to male-oriented holsters. Note where Julie Goloski carries her S&W M&P 9mm as she pauses while winning 2006 National Woman IDPA Champion title..

Mitch Rosen's Workman holster, named after designer Dave Workman, was the first and defining "tuckable." Notice "V" of leather between gun and belt loop. Shirt, tucked into the V and inside the waistband, hides this Glock 26. Belt loop can be disguised by putting a key ring on it.

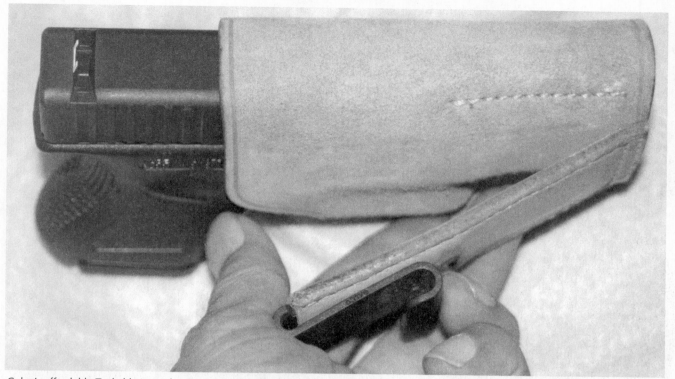

Galco's affordable Tuckable is suede-out (a.k.a. "rough-out") and secures to belt with low profile polymer J-clip. Pistol is Glock 26 9mm.

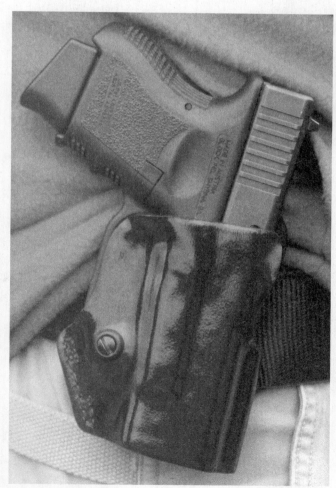

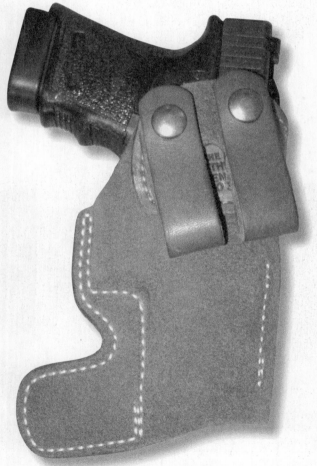

This Safariland synthetic OWB holds Glock 39 subcompact 45 GAP tight to the body of a state police instructor.

"Deep Concealment Special" IWB holster designed by Elmer McEvoy at Leather Arsenal has rearward flange to help keep holster from digging into body, or shifting. Pistol is Glock 30 in 45 ACP.

Exotic leathers have become a status symbol among CCW people. This ParaOrdnance SSP 45 automatic lives in this sharkskin OWB holster/belt combo by Aker.

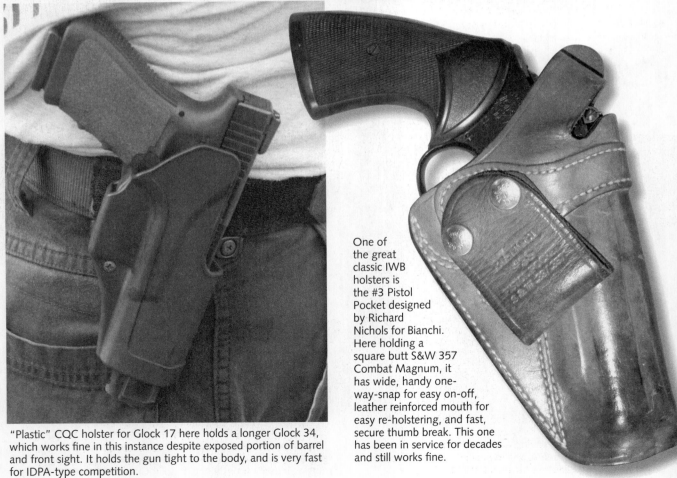

"Plastic" CQC holster for Glock 17 here holds a longer Glock 34, which works fine in this instance despite exposed portion of barrel and front sight. It holds the gun tight to the body, and is very fast for IDPA-type competition.

One of the great classic IWB holsters is the #3 Pistol Pocket designed by Richard Nichols for Bianchi. Here holding a square butt S&W 357 Combat Magnum, it has wide, handy one-way-snap for easy on-off, leather reinforced mouth for easy re-holstering, and fast, secure thumb break. This one has been in service for decades and still works fine.

STREET TIP: If weight of gun is pulling pants down, don't pull it back up like this. It looks as if you're going for a gun. INSTEAD…

…pull whole belt up, with both hands, like this. Now, you're just another guy "doing a guy thing" and "hitching up his pants," and don't broadcast the fact that you're "carrying."

Author designed the popular Ayoob Rear Guard (ARG) holster for Mitch Rosen. It rides inside the waistband, weight of gun levered forward by rear-placed belt loop to prevent "printing." This example is in sharkskin and carries S&W 1911 45 auto.

Replaceable belt-clip modules of Kydex IWB holster by Mach 2, the Honorman, "flex" and help conceal this Glock 27 without shifting. Note also "body shield" to keep sweat away from gun, and sharp gun edges away from underlying skin and clothing.

Author demonstrates his "fingertip draw," which he calls "Reach Out and Touch Yourself." As draw from under open-front garment begins, all four fingertips touch abdomen's centerline…

… and, *fingertips maintaining torso contact,* hand sweeps back to gun. Note that knife edge of hand has begun to sweep the Woolrich Elite vest to the rear…

…and will instantly and positively sweep it *all the way* to the rear, and *hold it out of the way* until hand has taken its drawing grasp, shown. Carry combo is Beretta 92G 9mm in Milt Sparks Executive Companion IWB holster.

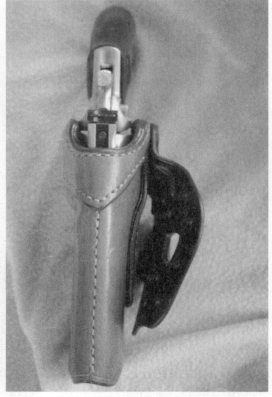

Author explains why he doesn't like paddle holsters, but why they can work for some people in some situations. This is one of the best of the breed, by Aker, carrying Ruger GP100 357 Magnum.

STREET TIP: When you feel the gun butt moving to the rear and "printing," DON'T adjust it like this. It will be obvious to anyone in line of sight that you're "carrying." INSTEAD…

…use your forearm behind your back to push the gun forward, stretch back a little, and you look to the world like someone with a sore back, not someone carrying a gun.

Blackhawk SERPA is a snatch-resistant, concealable rig that effectively hides this S&W M&P 9mm under a coat. It has been adjusted to desirable forward tilt angle. Finger paddle is easily released by owner's safely extended trigger finger when draw begins.

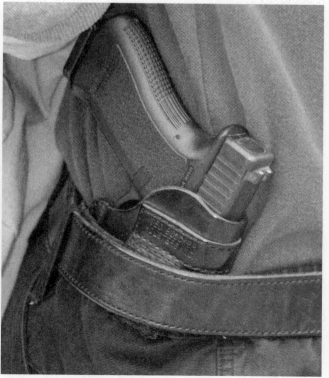

Concealment Rig by Ted Blocker makes this full-size Glock 17 concealable for its average-size male owner.

Because of the higher, more flaring pelvis and shorter torso, women don't find this carry nearly as comfortable or as fast as men. As noted elsewhere in this book, cross draw and shoulder carry seem more effective for many women.

Christine Cunningham, an instructor and competitor in the Pacific Northwest, is also a holster-maker. She specializes in "by women, for women" concealed carry gear. Her stuff is tops in quality and function, and very well thought out. You'll find much good advice, as well as many useful products, at her website, www.womenshooters. com.

The gun behind the hip is positioned so as to be sensitive to exposure and bulge when the wearer bends down or leans forward. This simply means the

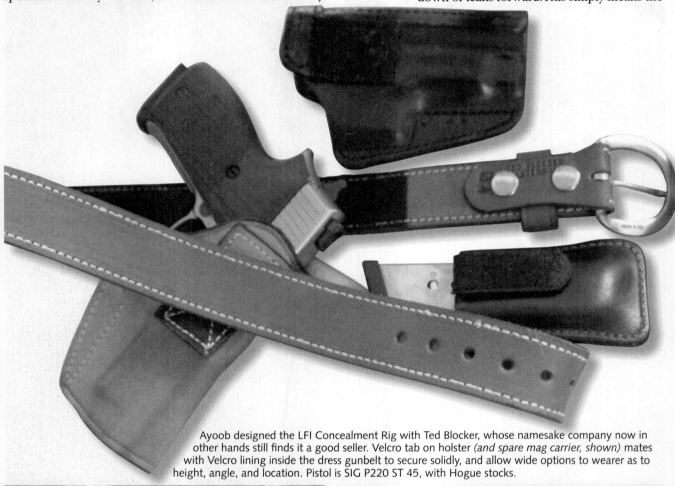

Ayoob designed the LFI Concealment Rig with Ted Blocker, whose namesake company now in other hands still finds it a good seller. Velcro tab on holster *(and spare mag carrier, shown)* mates with Velcro lining inside the dress gunbelt to secure solidly, and allow wide options to wearer as to height, angle, and location. Pistol is SIG P220 ST 45, with Hogue stocks.

Author demonstrates proper hip draw continuum while winning Wisconsin State Service Revolver Championship, IDPA 2007. GP100 is blurring as it comes up to pectoralis position, in line to already hit a fast-coming, close range threat…

…and then extends for precise aim with mandatory one-hand head-shots from behind simulated cover.

STREET TIP: When driving, you don't want your hip holstered gun trapped by seat belt and concealing garment. Here, safety belt is fastened…

...but then driver should reach under seat belt and grab the concealing garment...

...and *pull it free of the seat belt!* It's not the seat belt that usually traps a hip holstered gun, it's the coat that is trapped by the seat belt. Now...

practitioner has to learn different ways to perform these motions in public. See photos.

Belt Holster Options

Continuing with the "clock" concept, let's look at different spots on the belt for holster placement. 12 o'clock, centerline of the abdomen, will be comfortable only with a small, short-barrel gun. It's a quick and natural position, particularly for women thanks to their relatively higher belt-lines. My older daughter, tall and slender, prefers to carry her S&W Model 3913 9mm here, in an Alessi Talon inside the waistband holster, or a belly-band. It disappears under an untucked blouse, shirt, or sweater, but provides very fast access.

1 o'clock to 2 o'clock becomes the so-called "appendix position." An open front garment must be kept fastened to keep it hidden, but a short-barrel gun works great here for access during fighting and grappling. A top trainer who is still active in undercover police work and teaches under the nickname "Southnarc" favors this location, with his retired cop father's hammer-shrouded Colt Cobra 38 snub-nose inside the waistband at the appendix. It is very fast. Some top IPSC speed demons, such as Jerry "the Burner" Barnhart carry their competition guns in speed rigs at the same location. A small gun conceals well here under untucked closed-front garments. However, the appendix carry causes all but the shortest guns to dig into the juncture of thigh and groin when seated, and the muzzle is pointing at genitals and femoral artery. There are those of us who find

...you're "ready to ride," and your hand can quickly get to your sidearm.

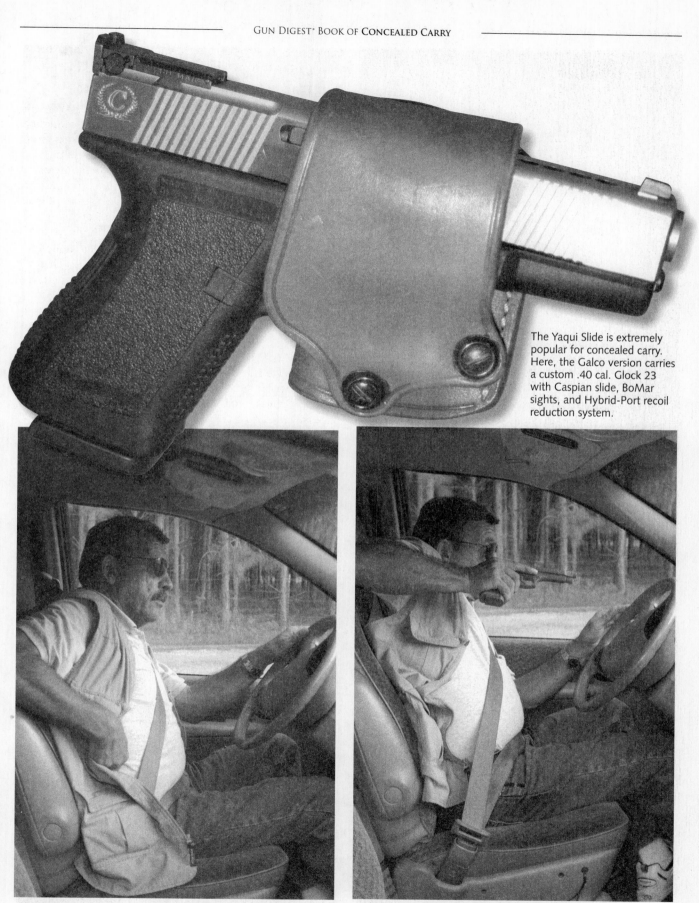

The Yaqui Slide is extremely popular for concealed carry. Here, the Galco version carries a custom .40 cal. Glock 23 with Caspian slide, BoMar sights, and Hybrid-Port recoil reduction system.

STREET TIP: Here's how to draw from hip holster while seat belted behind a steering wheel. Gun hand does "fingertip draw," which clears cover garment even in static position…

…and author rocks upper body sharply to left to create more range of movement for right arm, which draws Blackhawk dummy of Beretta 92 used for demo, *lifting it up and over steering wheel to prevent snagging there…*

...and driver is quickly in a ready-to-shoot posture.

this incongruous with our purposes for concealed carry, one of which is to *prevent* weapons being pointed at such vulnerable parts of our bodies.

Moving more to the side, the true 3 o'clock position is not ideal for all day concealed wear. Riding on the protuberance

Holster-makers are keeping up with tactical trends. This southpaw cop carries his department-issue Glock 22 with white light unit already mounted, in concealable Blade-Tech holster off duty.

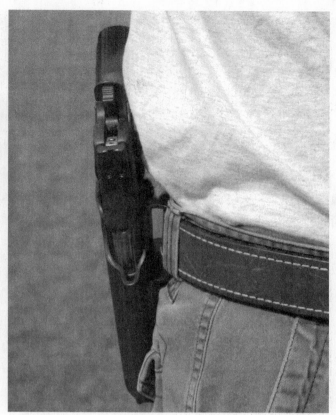

Comparisons in concealability. Dave Lauck Custom full-size 1911 45 leans out a little from the body in Lauck outside-the-waistband (OWB) Kydex holster...

...but same gun is tighter to the body in Elmer McEvoy Quad Concealment holster worn "in the belt" (ITB), between belt and trousers. However...

...inside-the-waistband holster by Secret Squirrel carries same gun even closer, and concealing garment can come all the way up to belt without revealing holstered gun.

With tunnel loop at back and rear-mounted belt loop, this Derry Gallagher scabbard carries an N-frame (.44 size) S&W Model 27-2 357 Magnum with 4-inch barrel with surprisingly good concealment.

of the hip, the gun protrudes accordingly, calling attention to itself even under big, heavy coats. The holstered gun at 3 o'clock will grate mercilessly on the hip-bone. Cops get away with it in uniform because their holsters have orthopedically curved shanks, and the weight is distributed on their wide Sam Browne belts. Neither mitigating factor will be at work in a concealment holster.

3:30, just behind the hip, seems to be optimum for comfort, concealment, and speed. It's where most professionals end up parking their holsters.

By the time you hit 4 o'clock, there is more likelihood of the butt protruding. When you hit 6 o'clock, the true MOB (middle of back) or SOB (small of back) position, you're getting into dangerous territory. The SOB is an SOB in more ways than one. While accessible to either hand, it can be mercilessly uncomfortable when you are seated. The rear center hem is the first part of an outer garment that lifts when you bend forward or sit down. The gun butt can catch the hem and completely expose the holstered gun. You can't see it and usually can't feel it, meaning you're the only one in the shopping mall who *won't* know that your weapon is exposed.

Another extreme danger of this carry is that any fall that lands you flat on your back will be the equivalent of landing on a rock with your lumbar spine. Very serious injury can result.

Yet another problem with SOB carry is that you can't

exert any significant downward pressure to hold the gun in place when trying to counter a gun snatch attempt. Moreover, biomechanically, you are pretty much putting yourself in an armlock when drawing. As a rule of thumb, any technique that requires you to put yourself in an armlock when defending yourself is a technique you should probably re-evaluate.

Inside or Outside the Belt

An inside-the-waistband (IWB) holster will conceal the gun better. Simple as that. The drape of the pants from the waist down blends the shape of the holstered gun with that of the

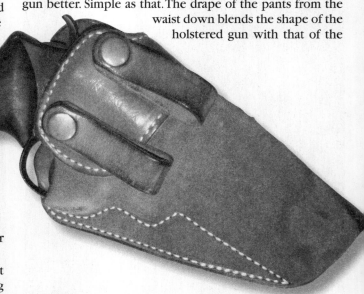

Milt Sparks Summer Special holster, worn from decades of service, still works fine. This classic IWB carries an equally well-worn Smith & Wesson Model 58 41 Magnum service revolver.

Author demonstrates "Hackathorn Rip," his preferred technique for drawing from hip holster under closed-front garment. Support hand grabs hem of shirt at appendix position…

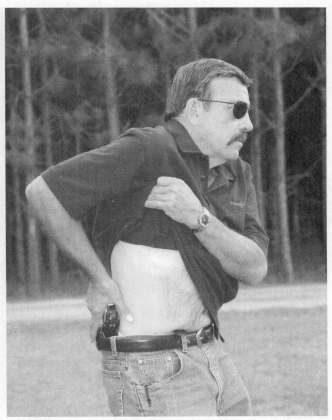

…and jerks it upward toward shoulder, as gun hand goes for sidearm, in this case full-size custom Beretta 92 in Milt Sparks IWB holster…

…as pistol "rocks and locks" upward into draw, support hand releases garment, and…

…shooter is on target in strong firing stance with maximum speed.

STREET TIP: Rocking hip to side away from holster (i.e., to left with right-handed draw) speeds draw from under closed front garment because it helps pull holster out from under pistol.

body. The hem of the concealing garment has to rise above the belt to reveal the hidden weapon. This carry allows average size guys like me to carry full-size service handguns concealed under nothing more than an opaque, untucked tee or polo shirt, one size large. Held tight to the body by belt pressure, this design minimizes bulge.

Some have tried IWB and found it uncomfortable. This is because their pants were sized for *them,* and now contain them – plus a holstered gun. For preliminary comfort testing, unbutton the pants at the waist and let out the belt a notch, and try it again. If it's comfortable now, nature is telling you to let out the pants if possible, or start buying trousers two inches larger in the waist. As noted elsewhere here, this practice "keeps you honest" (i.e., keeps you carrying) because now the pants won't fit right *without* the gun in its IWB holster.

Belt clips don't secure as well as leather loops, for the most part. There are exceptions, such as the appropriately named Alessi Talon, the clips used by Blocker on their DA-2, and the modular Kydex clips on the Mach-2 Honorman holster. Cheaper IWB holsters are notorious for their poor clips.

The IWB holster stays in place largely through belt pressure, so you want a rigid holster mouth to keep the opening from collapsing and interfering with re-holstering. The classic Bianchi #3 Pistol Pocket, a Richard Nichols design, used stiff leather reinforcement for this. Most others followed the lead of the late Bruce Nelson in his famous Summer Special design, and used leather-covered steel inserts to keep the holster mouth open. On rigid Kydex, of

One-hand-only draw from under closed front garment is critical to know, says author, demonstrating his own technique. Support hand rises in close-range block position as thumb of gun hand catches shirt hem…

…and pulls it straight upward. Hand now drops into drawing grasp…

…and gun comes up on target in "rock and lock" motion for one-handed firing if necessary, from close-range "protected gun position."

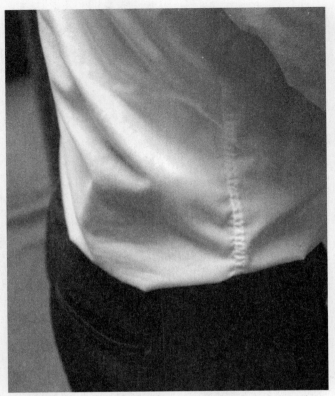

This executive's white dress shirt is just slightly bloused above his pinstripe suit pants…

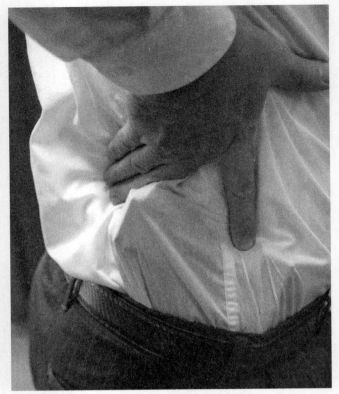

…but pressing hand reveals the presence of a full-size Glock service pistol, completely hidden beneath in a belly band holster in strong-side hip draw position.

course, the material does this by itself.

Inside the waistband, slimness becomes more important, one reason the flat Browning Hi-Power and 1911 pistols are so popular with those who prefer this carry format. The fatter the gun, the more the belt is pushed out from the body. This allows the pants to start sliding down in the holster area, causing frequent need for readjustment.

Because the gun is tight to the body, sometimes against bare skin or sweat-soaked shirts, many makers have built "shielding" into the design to protect the gun from sweat, and bare skin from sharp edges. This works pretty well, but can slow the thumb's access to a perfect pre-draw grasp, depending on gun design and hand size.

I've only designed two holsters in my life. Both were IWB. The first, designed with Ted Blocker, is the LFI Concealment Rig. It's comprised of a dress gun belt lined with Velcro, and your choice of open top or thumb-break safety strap holster with coordinated Velcro tab. This lets the concealing garment ride all the way to the *top* edge of your belt without revealing anything, and perhaps more important, lets you adjust the holster almost infinitely for your particular needs: high, low, *exact* degree of rake (orientation of muzzle) and tilt (orientation of butt) that you want. High versus low is important if, like me, you have to switch between suit pants and uniform pants that tend to ride at the waist, and jeans/cords/BDUs that tend to ride slightly lower at the hips. Now the gun is in exactly the same where-you-want-it spot no matter what you're wearing. The combination of Velcro shear factor and belt tension holds it in place. It's very secure, and I've taught weapon retention classes with one without it coming loose. Matching magazine pouches

are available, and the LFI Concealment Rig also works as a cross draw.

The other was designed for Mitch Rosen, at his request. He wanted an open-top rig that would carry a heavy, full-size fighting handgun without the weight of the loaded magazine in its butt tilting it backward to "print," or expose itself through clothing. I designed an FBI-tilt IWB scabbard with a single strong belt loop at the *rear,* behind the gun, where the loop's bulk wouldn't add to the holster's. In this position, the holster "levered" the gun forward and prevented it from tilting backwards. I called it the Rear Guard, because the loop at the rear guarded against rearward holster shifting. Mitch was kind enough to call it the Ayoob Rear Guard. It was shortened to ARG, which I've always pronounced as Ay-Arr-Gee. Unfortunately, folks started pronouncing the acronym in one syllable, which sounded like "Arrgghh." I suppose I should just be glad I didn't name it Super Holster Inside Trousers. After 9/11/01, Mitch changed the name to American Rear Guard. Still the same excellent holster, though.

The belly-band is a variation of inside-the-waistband carry, approximately four inches of elastic strapping with a gun pouch. It is worn best at belt level, "over the underwear and under the over-wear." The first of these I ever saw was a John Bianchi prototype in *Gun World* magazine, circa 1960. Bianchi didn't bring it out back then, but in a few years, a firm in Brooklyn named MMGR did. I wore an MMGR belly-band to my grad school tests one hot summer day when I was 21, and noticed the day I got home that the beautiful blue finish of my S&W Model 36 Chief Special had turned brown on the side next to my body. Some later belly-band

This Don Hume IWB holster, here in lefty version holding Glock 19, is an excellent value.

designs, such as the Gould & Goodrich, used a separate plastic shield on the gun pouch to protect the weapon from this, but expect some degree of sweat exposure with this type of carry. The Tenifer finish of the Glock pistols seems to stand up to this best, followed by the similar Mellonite finish used on S&W M&P autos, followed by industrial hard chrome finishes and stainless. The Glocks will discolor after long carry in this fashion, but won't actually rust.

While I prefer the belly-band in the front cross draw position for a 2-inch 38, larger guns work best behind the hip. They're a great alternative under a tucked-in shirt for those who work in business suit environments and must take the suit coat off in the office, but can't afford for the gun to become visible. A "Hackathorn rip" movement is the best drawing option here. I also know medical professionals in gun-free zones in high crime areas, who wear small handguns this way under their scrubs.

There are many good belly-bands. My personal favorite has always been the unfortunately discontinued Bianchi Ranger, with built-in money belt. It has been my companion all over the world. I've carried S&W 4-inch 44 Magnums in it, perfectly concealed on the streets in cities from South Africa to Europe.

Since they offer little protection against sharp edges, belly-bands work best with edge-free guns. That said, properly adjusted they can be incredibly comfortable. One downside to them, though, is that you practically need a shoe-horn to get the gun back in. The near-impossibility of

quickly reholstering means that regular range practice is out of the question, and you have to have an action plan that includes putting the gun away in pocket or waistband after making a belly-band draw on the street.

The "tuckable" is a different breed, the latest development in this area and one of the most widely copied. It goes back to Dave Workman, a holster-maker who is also a leading Second Amendment advocate and gun author. For those with office dress codes, Dave came up with an inside the waistband holster that had a separate paddle that secured on the belt, creating a deep "V" between the holster and that securing portion, into which a dress shirt could be tucked. Worn at 3:30, or in the appendix position, or at 11 o'clock in a front cross draw, it hid the gun perfectly. The snap-on belt loop could be disguised as a key holder simply by putting a small key ring in the loop. When he looked for a larger manufacturer to handle the design, I steered Dave to Mitch Rosen, who introduced it to the world as The Workman. It instantly became the most copied new rig in the holster field. This style also functions perfectly well as an ordinary inside the waistband holster.

Another IWB variation that goes *deep* inside the waistband is the Pager Pal. A flat semi-disk of leather contains a small revolver or auto that rides inside the pants and *below* the belt, hooked onto the belt by a camouflaged pager, cell phone carrier, knife pouch, etc. When carried cross draw, the support hand grabs the pager or whatever and pulls upward, exposing the holster for the gun hand's

Author only trusts a few metal belt clip-type IWB holsters to stay in place. One is this Don Hume, here holding a 4-inch custom Kimber.

draw. I found that if you don't have a large butt, you can carry it on your strong side behind the hip and knife the hand down inside the pants to get at the gun. Not my first choice, but an interesting option that some have found useful.

Outside the Belt

Outside-the-waistband (OWB) is more comfortable, but requires more effort for concealment. The most concealable designs copy to some degree the Pancake holsters of Roy Baker. Rounded, thus their eponymous shape, Baker's holsters and some of today's copies have three belt slots, one in the rear and two in the front. This allows the shooter to set up for forward "FBI" tilt, straight up hip-draw, or straight up cross draw. With the belt tensioning the holster fore and aft of the actual scabbard body, the gun is pulled in tighter to the hip for better concealment.

The Yaqui Slide holster, a "skeleton" design popularized by Milt Sparks, is handy in that it fits a number of different barrel length guns with the same frame. Points to note with it, though: 1) If sitting in an armchair and the arm of the chair bumps the gun muzzle, the whole gun can be pushed up and out of the holster. 2) Carbon and dirt on the gun after firing can, while it's holstered, transfer to the underlying trousers. 3) Sharp-edged sights, or deep Picatinny-style rails on the dust cover (lower front of frame) of some modern military style auto pistols, can snag on the bottom edge of the Yaqui

Slide, dangerously stalling the draw. 4) Back in the '70s, a selling point of this design was that it could stay on the belt with the gun removed, and would often go unrecognized as a holster. This is probably not the case today. The Don Hume version is certainly a best buy for quality vis-à-vis price today, and a key objectionable point to this particular style is removed with models that have thumb-break safety snaps, as offered by Bianchi, Ted Blocker, and others.

With any strong-side hip holster, a 4-inch barrel revolver or 5-inch barrel auto pistol are about the max in overall length that will carry comfortably before the muzzle hits the chair or seat when you sit down, causing some awkwardness and discomfort factor. Larger men, with larger butts and higher beltlines, can perhaps get away with longer handguns.

An outside-the-belt holster is particularly vulnerable to the gun leaning outward because of the butt portion's weight. Each generation of pistol packers seems to discover that a 3-inch or particularly 4-inch revolver, or a similar size auto, may actually conceal better because the longer barrel bears lightly against hip or leg, pushing the butt in toward the torso to better maintain concealment.

The In-Between Option

For some, at least in some circumstances, the most viable option is a gun carried ITB, or in the belt, that is, between the belt and the trousers. This allows the user to wear trousers that fit him normally, but the belt pressure pulls the gun in tight as on IWB. However, the IWB advantages of allowing

Skeletonized holsters and aggressive M1913 rails don't mix. This first-generation Glock 21SF so equipped appears to fit perfectly in a regular Galco Yaqui Slide for standard G21 but, in drawing, the deeply-cut accessory notches can catch the edge of the holster and dangerously snag the draw.

the bottom of the garment to rise higher without revealing the gun, and of breaking up the outline of the holstered gun, are lost. Mitch Rosen's appropriately titled "Middleman" is one holster designed expressly for this purpose. Another that is perfectly adaptable to this is the Quad Concealment from Elmer MacEvoy's company Leather Arsenal. Its name comes from the fact that this ingenious and extremely useful rig can be worn outside the belt or between belt and trousers, and can be worn either way ambidextrously.

Paddle Holsters

Some belt holsters are made with a paddle that goes inside the waistband, securing on the belt and holding the holstered gun outside the pants. The one strong point of this design is convenience: easy on, relatively easy off. I don't care for them for the following reasons. 1) I've seen too many fail to secure, resulting in the holster coming out with the gun. It's funny at a match or a class, but on the street, it would get you killed. The only thing that would save you would be if your opponent was laughing at you too hard to shoot straight. 2) Since the belt is securing on the paddle rather than the holster itself, guns carried in this fashion tend to lean out away from the body, compromising concealment. 3) The juncture of paddle and holster body is, by nature, weak. I've seen even the best brands break here, yielding the holstered gun to the "attacker," in weapon retention drills. 4) The convenient on/off nature of this holster fosters an "I'll wear it when I need it" mentality, causing the gun to be left behind and to not be present when, unpredictably, it *is* needed.

There are many companies that make high quality paddle holsters, but none can get past these inherent weaknesses in the paddle concept. Go to the same maker, turn the page of their catalog, and order one of their holsters that *properly* secures to a good dress gun belt.

Construction

Leather or synthetic? Leather is the classic, and so long as it gets an occasional application of neatsfoot oil or other leather treatment, won't "squeak." Cowhide is by far the most common. Horsehide has its fans: it is thinner and proportionally more rigid, but seems to scratch more easily. Sharkskin is expensive, but extremely handsome and very long-lasting and scuff-resistant. It may last you longer than it did the shark. (I often wear sharkskin belts in court. Doesn't ward the lawyers off or anything, but seems appropriate, especially during some cross-examinations.) Elephant hide? Hellaciously expensive, but certainly tough, and predictably thicker than you probably need. Alligator and snakeskin holsters seem better suited to "show" than "go." For the most part, cowhide and horsehide are where it's at.

Rough-out or grain-out? The latter rules with outside-the-waistband carry. The only guy who ever seemed to like rough-side-out belt scabbards was John Wayne, who wore a personally-owned rig of that kind in many of his cowboy movies. It tends to hold sand and dust. The guy who popularized rough-out holster design in concealed carry was the late, great Bruce Nelson, whose Summer Special design was hugely popularized by another departed giant of the industry, Milt Sparks. They found that inside-the-waistband, the rough outer surface had enough friction with clothing to help keep the holster from shifting position; early versions had only one belt attachment loop, and were less stable than the later, improved two-loop Summer Special variations. As a bonus, the smooth grain of the leather was now toward the gun, less likely to trap sand and dust and cause wear on the finish. Some theorized that this also made the draw smoother. However, sweat tended to rapidly migrate through these holsters to the gun, much more so than grain-out IWB holsters that seem to repel perspiration better.

Plastics, particularly Kydex, do not loosen with age like leather, nor do they tend to start out too tight and need a break-in, again a common thing with good leather. Kydex certainly provides more sweat protection to the gun. However, I'm not persuaded that they're longer lasting. The reason is that their belt attachments are more likely to break. In retention training, with constant struggles for the neutralized guns between two men moving full power, I've seen a lot more Kydex and generic plastic holsters break than leather ones. The most secure of the Kydex holsters are the inside-the-belt variations. A genuine tactical problem with Kydex is that it makes a distinctive noise when the gun is drawn or holstered. Sometimes, the concealed handgun carrier wants a *surreptitious draw,* in which the weapon is slipped out of the holster unnoticed. This is much more difficult with Kydex and requires aching slowness. Score a point for traditional leather in that situation.

However, one advantage of Kydex holsters is that the better ones come with spacers in their belt loops to allow the wearer to adjust the holster to properly fit belts of different widths. For the person switching between casual pants and dress pants, the latter generally mandating narrow belts due to fashion pressure or belt loop size, this can be an advantage. The better Kydex holsters today, such as the Blade-Tech, can ride sufficiently tight to the body for good concealment. They also lend themselves better than leather to carrying a pistol already mounted with flashlight, with reasonable concealment.

There are very few fabric holsters, i.e., ballistic nylon, which will stand up. Most make it difficult to re-holster. For the most part, the "cloth" holsters are at their best as cheap "belt-mounted gun bags" that hold the gun for plinking sessions at the range, and not for daily carry in what might become a dangerous tactical environment.

Security Devices

"Snatch-resistant" concealment holsters are discussed in the Open Carry chapter. However, they should not be neglected in concealed carry. People who haven't learned to properly activate retention devices call them "suicide straps," and prefer open top. They will tell you, "It's concealed, so you don't have to worry about someone grabbing it." *Rubbish!* Your attacker may know from previous contact with you that you carry a pistol, and even where you carry it. He may have spotted it when scoping you out. Or you might get into a fight and the other guy wraps his arms around your waist for a bear hug or throw and feels the gun, at which time the fight for the pistol is on.

It is good to have at least one "level of security," that is, one additional thing the suspect has to do to shoot you with your gun in addition to the obvious movement of pulling it out of the holster. An on-safe pistol should count as one level of security. So should a thumb-break safety device. A hidden or "secret" release device may count as two levels. A holster requiring a push in an unusual direction to draw is another level. It's not a bad idea for the holster to have at least one "level of security."

A safety strap can also keep the gun in the holster when something other than a hand pulls at it. The gun butt can catch in brush when sliding down a hillside, or on a counter you're pushed against in a physical fight, or simply come out if you take a tumble butt-over-teakettle. There have been cases of guns falling out of holsters on amusement park rides that put the rushing riders upside-down.

Some, like me, justify the occasional wear of open-top holsters with their extensive experience in handgun retention training. However, even we are likely to have at least a safety strap when out in the brush or performing

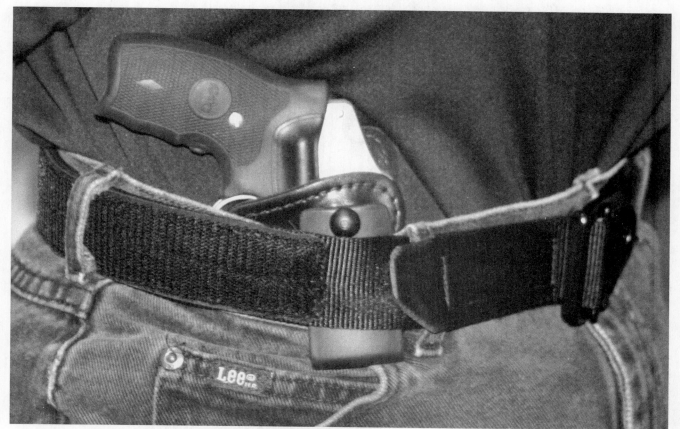

Appendix carry. As shown, it works particularly well for females. Combo is S&W 342 with LaserGrips in Safariland J-hook IWB designed by Bill Rogers.

other strenuous physical activity, or when "open carrying" as police investigators at the station or other environments that increase the likelihood of a gun-snatch attempt.

With practice and proper technique, the difference between open-top and thumb-break in drawing speed is a very thin fraction of a second, a fair price to pay for the added security.

Belt Factors

Holsters and belts are as symbiotic as automobiles and tires. We firearms trainers can tell you *ad nauseum* of students who come in with expensive guns in holsters that should have a Fruit of the Loom label, or may be proof incarnate that you can skin a chicken and tan its hide and make a holster out of it. However, we can also tell you about the students who come in with fine guns in top quality holsters that are hanging off crappy, floppy, narrow little belts whose institutional memory is probably the words, "Attention K-Mart shoppers!"

Even the best holster will, on a poor belt, hang outward from the body. It will shift its position constantly, violating the twin needs of discretion and comfort. There may be so much slop between the belt and the holster's belt loops, and so much undesirable flexibility in the belt itself, that you can exert the drawing movement for an inch or more and the gun has not begun to leave the holster.

The belt should be fairly stiff, and should be fitted tightly to the holster loops. Often, the easiest way to achieve this is to use a "mated" gun and dress gun belt from the same maker.

This also gives a certain pride of ownership. Looks great at an open carry barbecue. Of course, we carry them *concealed* for the most part, so it's not really a fashion statement, just a matter of personal satisfaction. I personally don't care who made the belt and the holster, I care that they go together.

You wouldn't save up to buy a Volvo or a Mercedes to keep your family safe, and then put on two-ply retread tires. Counterproductive. Ditto a good gun in a crappy holster, or a good gun in a good holster on a crappy belt. I would rather have a $300 police trade-in handgun in a good holster on a good belt, than a $3000 custom pistol in an inappropriate holster on an inappropriate belt. The man with the latter combination will inevitably lose a quick-draw contest to the equally skilled man armed with the former.

For those who don't care for leather, top-quality nylon dress gun belts such as the defining Wilderness Instructor's Belt will work fine with casual clothing, and companies like Blackhawk make narrow *faux* leather belts with matching-loop holsters that will work well in concealment. "Armed and green," as it were.

A larger gun in a well-selected holster will carry more comfortably and in more discreet concealment than a smaller gun in a poorly-selected holster on an inappropriate belt. Gun, holster, and belt are all part of a system, and if any of those links fail, the whole chain will fail. We're talking about life-saving emergency rescue equipment here. Failure is unacceptable.

CROSS DRAW

The cross draw holster – carrying the handgun butt forward, on the hip opposite the dominant hand – seems to be one of those "love it or hate it" issues among experienced *pistoleros*. There are several handgun sports that actually ban them as safety hazards. But there are also some folks out there who find them perfect for their needs.

Let's look at the upsides and downsides, and at how to streamline the cross draw

Polymer-framed 9mm Kahr PM9 rides inside and below the waistband, and was designed for cross draw wear.

concept in ways that may help get past the concerns of the detractors. First, let's define some terms.

Assorted Cross Draw Concepts

There are cross draws, and there are cross draws.

Conventional cross draw generally puts the gun all the way over on the opposite hip.

Transparent raincoat is used to demonstrate cross draw. If garment is closed, front position shown can work well, but zippered garment like this should be fastened no higher than abdomen, and buttoned garment should have unbuttoned open space near the gun…

…assuming target/threat is in camera's position, first movement is to step back with dominant side hip. Support hand begins to rise, partly to block attack and partly to clear it from path of practitioner's own muzzle. Gun hands fingers begin to form "spear hand" configuration…

Front cross draw brings the gun to a point between hip and belt buckle, what would be the appendix position for a southpaw. This was the position once favored by IPSC shooters, and by the Illinois State Police back in the Seventies and earlier. It's also a favorite location for belly-band carry.

This is also a top choice for placing the second single-action revolver required in Cowboy Action shooting.

Fanny packs are often worn in a position that, effectively, puts them in a cross draw location.

Shoulder holsters require a variation of cross draw to bring the handgun into action.

Backup gun rigs attached to body armor are normally worn like vertical shoulder holsters, and therefore call for cross draw techniques and tactics.

The Kramer Confidante, a tee-shirt with built-in gun pockets under the armpits, is designed for wear under a dress shirt or casual shirt. The draw is the same as that from a conventional shoulder holster: a variation of cross draw.

Cross Draw Advantages

Many of those who choose the cross draw do it because of **range of movement issues.** Proportionally more female than male cops and CCW civilians carry cross draw than their male counterparts. This is because with a female and a male of the same height, you can expect the woman to have a shorter torso, a higher pelvis, and relatively longer and more limber arms (vis-à-vis the torso) than men. A woman can reach farther under her off-side arm for a shoulder holster, and farther toward her opposite side hip, for these reasons. A cross draw belt holster or shoulder rig that might be literally out of reach of a brawny, broad-shouldered man might be perfectly accessible when worn by his sister.

For women, the cross draw is also an alternative to the problems that come with strong-side hip holsters that have been designed "by men, for men." The higher hips and more pronounced buttocks of the average woman push the muzzle area of a strong-side holster outward, which concomitantly pushes the butt in toward the body. Because of the higher belt line, a gun "handle" that sits comfortably

…as support hand continues to rise, spear hand "knifes" through coat opening for smooth access to gun …

…access is achieved on Com-Tac dummy Glock 19 (used here for safety purposes), trigger finger straight and clear. Now…

in the hollow beneath a man's ribcage can press with excruciating discomfort into a woman's ribs. When the most popular solution doesn't work, you need to explore less popular alternatives, and cross draw/shoulder carry is one.

It's not just a woman's issue. One of my fellow gun writers has some serious arthritic issues that limit the range of movement of his shoulder. He finds the conventional hip holsters of his youth to be awkward and uncomfortable, and excruciatingly slow. So, he wears his sidearm, usually a 1911 45 auto, cross draw on the opposite hip. *Voila:* problem solved.

Many bodyguard chauffeurs and others who must constantly be seated, especially at the wheel of an automobile, have come to appreciate across-the-body carry. Many types of car seats inhibit the elbow's flexion and therefore the reach of the gun hand when going for a strong-side hip scabbard while sitting in a vehicle. A quick reach down across the front of the body is generally faster. In the 1990s, a new breed of holster called the "counter-car-jack" rig made a brief appearance, though it did not seem to catch on. It held the pistol butt down, with the barrel almost horizontal, just to the off-side of midline of the abdomen.

Men behind the wheel found it deadly fast. It did, however, have some downsides when one got out of the vehicle.

Hunting advantages. In the game fields, I learned to appreciate a sidearm in a cross draw holster. If it was backup to a long gun, the main gun's stock was no longer banging into the handgun's butt all the time. If travel involved ATVs and such, the cross draw seemed more accessible. Shoulder holsters have always been hunting favorites because the outer coat totally protects even big handguns from inclement weather.

I'm not a horseman – the closest I've come to hunting with a horse has been driving to the deer woods in a Ford Bronco – but friends who have hunted a lot on horseback tell me the cross draw is much more accessible to a person in the saddle. This is one reason cross draw was so popular among genuine cowboys in the Old West. At the OK Corral shootout, witnesses said Billy Clanton drew his 44-40 Colt Frontier Six-Shooter from a cross draw rig. And he was pretty quick with it. Wyatt Earp had gone into the fight with his own Colt 45 in the capacious, custom-made pocket of his overcoat, with his hand on the gun to start. Yet, when Clanton went to draw, he was so fast from his cross draw scabbard that both Wyatt and Virgil Earp testified later that

…pistol is drawn across chest, rocking up toward threat …

…and body is ideally positioned for classic Weaver stance.

Billy and Wyatt had fired simultaneously at the opening moment of the gunfight.

Weak hand accessibility. If you need to get to your sidearm with your non-dominant hand, nothing is faster than a gun already holstered on that hand's side. With a regular cross draw rig on the belt, you simply use the "cavalry draw." Turn your weak hand so the thumb is pointing to the rear and the metacarpal bones are toward your torso. Grab the pistol and lift. As it starts to clear the holster, point the muzzle down in front of you. The gun will now be upside-down. Rotate your hand to conventional gun orientation as you bring it up on target, and you'll avoid the common "cavalry draw" mistake of crossing your own body with the gun muzzle.

Is this fast? Well, on the Old West frontier, there were those who carried their guns butt forward and *always* did a cavalry draw from them! These included the men of the U.S. Cavalry itself, who carried their sabers on their left hips positioned for draw with the presumed-to-be-dominant right hand, and their service revolvers on their right hips in butt-forward flap holsters. The rationale was that if the cavalry trooper needed a weapon in either hand, a revolver was easier to manipulate with the "weak hand" than a saber,

and a conventional cross draw would be executed with the weak hand. If the dominant hand reached for the gun, it would do so with the "cavalry draw" described above.

James Butler "Wild Bill" Hickok carried a matched pair of Colt Navy 36-caliber revolvers at his waist, butts forward at the points of his hips. He used the cavalry draw exclusively…and he shot his way into history as, some said, the deadliest gunfighter of his time.

Compatibility with heavy winter coats. A knee-length overcoat is not the easiest thing to sweep out of the way when you need to suddenly, reactively draw a handgun from a strong-side hip holster. On the other hand, a shoulder or cross draw belt rig is very fast for a right-handed man or a left-handed woman to reach, through the *front* of the winter coat. All that is required is a coat design that allows one button to be left undone to allow access. (I say right-handed men and left-handed women, because men's coats button to the left and women's, to the right.)

One bitterly cold, dark night in the winter of 1970 I was wearing a heavy winter overcoat over a suit as I stepped out of a hotel and made my way through the biting wind to the far, dim corner of the parking lot where I'd had to leave my car. To make a long story short, I "saw the muggers

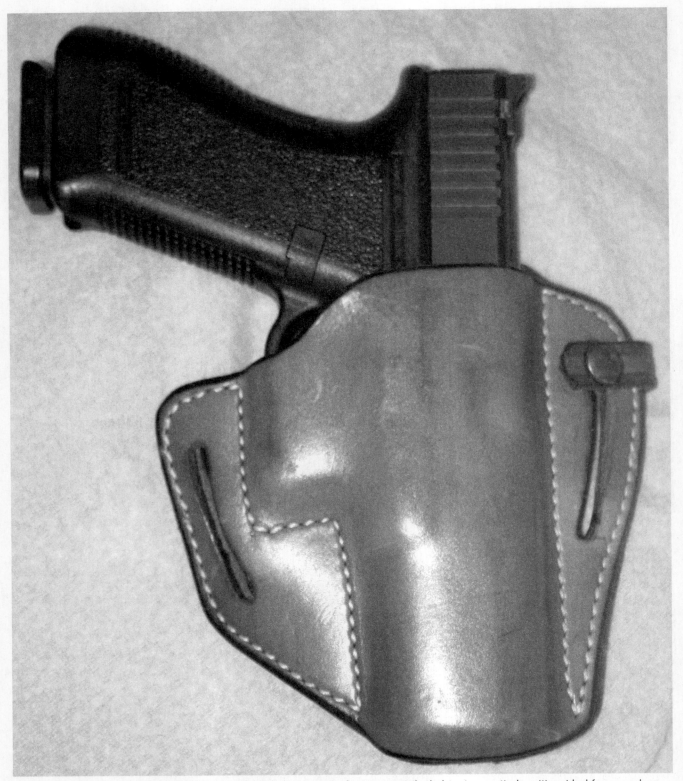

Slider loop in right *(forward)* slot of Blocker DA-2 hip holster is moved up to orient the holster in a vertical position, ideal for cross-draw carry. Pistol is Glock 17 full-size 9mm with Heinie night sights.

coming," and unbuttoned both coats so I could get at the Smith & Wesson 38 I was carrying in a Bucheimer scabbard behind my right hip. When they made their move, I made mine, and once my gun came out it was all over. On the way home, I kept thinking about how it might have ended if they'd been more stealthy, and my gun had been buttoned under two coats when I needed to get it quickly. From then on, for a long time after, I carried my gun in a cross draw or shoulder holster in deep winter.

Compatibility with likely "hand start" position. Back in the Seventies, when IPSC (the International Practical Shooting Confederation) first got up and running, the front

The cavalry draw. Assume this old fat guy's right arm has been hit by first opposing fire, and his only gun is in a cross draw Aker holster, butt forward on his left hip…

…left thumb sweeps back coat as palm turns outward and slides between gun and torso…

cross draw was hugely popular. Concealment has never been an issue in IPSC, so a big 45 auto just to port of the belt buckle posed no problems in that regard. Ray Chapman, and many other champions of the day, shot from cross draw. Ray designed the popular Chapman Hi-Ride holster for Bianchi, and the (Ken) Hackathorn Special was a bestseller for Milt Sparks Leather, often worn butt forward.

Why the popularity? Only a few of us seem to remember that back then, one of the most popular start positions at the beginning of a course of fire was with the hands clasped at midline of the body. This put the gun hand just an inch or two above the grip-frame, and gave the user of a front cross draw holster a "running start." Many of the hip holsters "back in the day" were low slung, even using thigh tie-downs and riding on buscadero-like belts. The also popular "hands up" start position put a high-riding cross draw closer within the shooter's reach than many of the strong-side rigs. As time went on, it was discovered that moving your Chapman Hi-Ride or your Hack Special to the gun-hand side of the belt buckle made things just as quick, and soon the cross draw was a relic of the past among IPSC's top contenders.

The Bianchi Cup has always used a hands-up start position.

I was there when Ron Lerch won the first, drawing his Colt 45 from a front cross draw, and for the years following when Mickey Fowler *ruled* the Cup, drawing his custom Government Model from the ISI front cross draw rig he had co-designed with manufacturer Ted Blocker, and named after International Shootists, Inc., the school he founded with training partner Mike Dalton, another ace gunner.

What does any of this have to do with serious pistol packing? Only this: there were times and places where men who knew where their hands would be when they began their draw, and had a lot riding on the outcome, chose the front cross draw position because it was faster to reach.

If you carry a gun for defense, when the day comes, you'll have a lot bigger stakes on the table than even so prestigious a trophy as the Bianchi Cup. If you can figure out a way to have your hands closer to the gun before trouble starts, in situations where you can't just haul it out when you smell danger, the cross draw tends to lend itself to early readiness.

Fold your arms at your chest, and let your gun hand slip inside your jacket. Ta-da! Your gun hand is already on your shoulder-holstered pistol, and ready to draw. The two key

...with "hand backward," conventional grasp is taken. Thumb would pop safety strap if there was one, and then take grasping position as shown...

...gun is pulled straight up along given holster's natural drawing path, and when barrel or slide area have cleared, gun is rotated butt outward...

portions of a draw are *access* and *presentation*. Access – getting to the gun and taking a drawing grasp – is the toughest part. Our tests show that starting with the hand on the gun cuts your draw-and-fire time roughly in half. With the cross draw shoulder rig, arms folded across the chest puts you discreetly in position.

Cross draw holster on the belt? The same technique works, simply lowering the folded arms midriff high. Belly-band holster in a front cross draw position? Slide the gun hand in through the opening above the belt that you'll have if you leave the second button above that belt undone. Take your drawing grasp. Let your free hand fold over that gun hand. Slouch forward a little. You look like a scared guy wringing his hands in a body language "surrender" position...but the belly gun is already in your hand, and you're ready to draw with the fast, efficient technique that made Chapman, Fowler, and Dalton the famous champions they are.

This, I submit, is a good thing to have on your side of a fight.

Disadvantages of Cross Draw

Cross draw is nowhere near as popular as it used to be. Remember the old TV series *Dragnet*, where Jack Webb as Joe Friday always had his snub-nose 38 butt forward on the opposite hip? Remember how many other cop shows of the Fifties and even the Sixties had detectives carrying their guns the same way?

That's almost gone now. I very rarely see cross draw holsters on plainclothes cops anymore, and when I do, they're usually on the hips of female officers for reasons discussed earlier. Shoulder holsters are somewhat more common, but less so than they once were, even though today's shoulder rigs are the best and most comfortable that have ever existed.

As far as uniform wear, the cross draw duty holster has been relegated to the police museum. When I was young, cross draw was standard uniform equipment for Metro-Dade officers in Miami, and for the state troopers of Florida, Illinois, Iowa, Michigan and Washington. The last stubborn holdout, the Iowa State Patrol, switched to Safariland security

...and that way, muzzle never crosses own body as Odin Press dummy of S&W 38 is thrust forward and simultaneously rotated upright ...

... and shooter is in a strong firing stance, here using "McMillan/ Chapman tilt."

holsters on the strong-side hip just a few years ago for their S&W 4046 Smith & Wesson 40s. They recently replaced those guns with S&W's new Military & Police autos in the same caliber, but stayed with the strong-side Safarilands. Today, there is not a single major police department in the United States that issues or, to my knowledge, even authorizes cross draw holsters for personnel in uniform.

One of the biggest complaints about the cross draw was that the forward butt made the gun altogether too accessible to an opponent you were facing. Indeed, with the gun all the way over on the opposite hip, it was literally more accessible to a facing man than to the wearer, if they were positioned to each other squarely. Bill Jordan warned against cross draws for just this reason.

The late, great gun expert Dean Grennell was a good friend of mine, and one day he told me that early in his short police career, he equipped himself with a 3 1/2-inch barrel S&W heavy frame 357 Magnum in a cross draw holster that looked just spiffy, and seemed handy to reach when he was at the wheel of the cruiser in the Great Lakes area community he served. Then, one day after lunch, he was washing his hands at the rest room sink and, looking in the

mirror, realized just how inviting that forward-projecting gun butt would look to a man standing in front of the uniformed officer. On his next shift of duty, he told me, his Smith & Wesson Magnum was in a strong-side hip holster.

Another big problem, particularly when the gun was worn as a true cross draw all the way over on the opposite hip, was that the draw could sweep the range officer behind the shooter on the range, and would definitely sweep the shooter on the holster side. This is why cross draw has been banned from police combat/PPC competition since its inception in the late 1950s. This is why it has been banned in IDPA (International Defensive Pistol Association) competition since that organization was founded in 1996. I recall visiting the Iowa State Law Enforcement Academy about thirty years ago, back when Iowa state troopers carried S&W Model 13 357 Magnum revolvers in cross draw flap holsters. I learned that when Iowa State Patrol recruits came through the Academy, they were forbidden to use their issue duty holsters, and instead were furnished by the Academy with FBI-style straight-draw scabbards for the strong side hip.

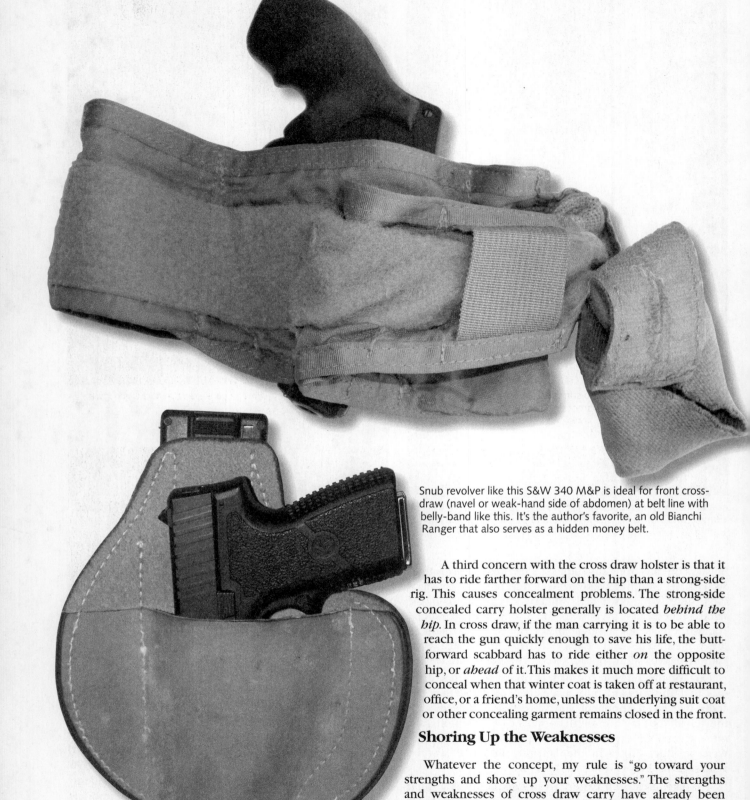

Snub revolver like this S&W 340 M&P is ideal for front cross-draw (navel or weak-hand side of abdomen) at belt line with belly-band like this. It's the author's favorite, an old Bianchi Ranger that also serves as a hidden money belt.

Polymer-framed 9mm Kahr PM9 rides inside and *below* the waistband, and was designed for cross draw wear. This is the side that faces the wearer.

A third concern with the cross draw holster is that it has to ride farther forward on the hip than a strong-side rig. This causes concealment problems. The strong-side concealed carry holster generally is located *behind the hip.* In cross draw, if the man carrying it is to be able to reach the gun quickly enough to save his life, the butt-forward scabbard has to ride either *on* the opposite hip, or *ahead* of it. This makes it much more difficult to conceal when that winter coat is taken off at restaurant, office, or a friend's home, unless the underlying suit coat or other concealing garment remains closed in the front.

Shoring Up the Weaknesses

Whatever the concept, my rule is "go toward your strengths and shore up your weaknesses." The strengths and weaknesses of cross draw carry have already been identified. Let's look at how to shore up the identified weaknesses if you've decided to, at least sometimes, carry the gun opposite your gun hand.

Handgun retention. Take a tip from the Illinois State Police. For the last several years of cross draw carry with their Smith & Wesson Model 39 9mm autos before switching

Cross draw lends itself well to surreptitious draw. Regular jacket would hide what this transparent one reveals: standing with arms crossed, author already has drawing grasp of dummy Glock in cross-draw LFI Concealment Rig.

Another option for cross draw. If concealing garment is open as shown…

…support hand can grab garment as shown and peel it back, giving drawing hand faster and clearer access to the LFI Concealment Rig worn here cross draw …

…but this technique takes somewhat more effort to keep support hand out of gun muzzle's drawing path, and that hand may be busy warding off an attacker.

to strong-side holsters in the late 1970s, they wore their flap duty rigs in a *front* cross draw position, with the gun tilted about 30 degrees toward the dominant hand. Like the Iowa State Patrol and the Michigan State Police, they taught troopers to lift the flap with their nearby weak hand, and draw with the strong hand.

The draw would start from the interview position, with the weak side (which, with cross draw, is the holster side) of their body toward the threat. When this stance is combined with the 30-degree angle of holster rake, the butt is no longer "offered" to the man in front of you. Indeed, it's your muzzle that's pointing toward him. This is a *much* more defensible posture from which to start a struggle for the holstered weapon!

With a cross draw holster on the belt, the Lindell System (Kansas City system) proven for three decades now and created by Jim Lindell, will work. You simply treat the right-handed cross draw holster on your left side as if you were a left-handed person carrying your weapon on your dominant side. The entire repertoire of techniques will work fine.

The Lindell System has never really addressed shoulder holsters. I teach my students a set of shoulder rig retention techniques that were developed by Terry Campbell, late of the Marion County (Ohio) Sheriff's Department, one of the toughest and best defensive tactics instructors I've ever had the privilege of training with. No handgun retention technique (at least, none of the ones that actually work on the street) can be taught in a magazine article or a chapter of a book. But, make no mistake, retention techniques that will protect cross draw and shoulder holsters do in fact exist.

"Sweeping" and Safety Problems. Yes, the cross draw is banned in IDPA, PPC, and most police academies. That said, it's still allowed to my knowledge in NRA Action Pistol Shooting (including the Bianchi Cup), IPSC, and of course, cowboy action matches. The requirement that makes it safe in those venues is the one you want to use religiously for your own practice "for the street."

Always remember: "If it's not safe to practice on the range, you'll never build enough repetitions to make it work reflexively and safely in the real world."

To make the across-the-body draw safe and efficient, drill in the following steps. They'll work with conventional cross draw, front cross draw, belly-band, fanny pack, shoulder holster, *et. al.*

Step one: Take a step back with the leg on your gun hand side, turning the holster side toward the threat.

Step two: Drop the gun hand straight down to the grip-frame. As you do so, raise your non-dominant hand as shown in photos, into a blocking position. This will keep your gun arm clear of your muzzle's path.

Step three: As you draw, bring the pistol back across your body toward your strong hand side until the muzzle comes up and into the target. There should be no "sweep" laterally: the muzzle should come right up out of the holster and toward the threat.

Reaching through a conveniently unbuttoned opening to belly-band positioned for front cross-draw is one of the fastest ways to bring a little J-frame snub into action.

Cross draw as shown is best access to AirLite S&W, worn in hidden pocket behind breast pocket of this Woolrich Elite shirt designed by Ferdinand Coelho. Thumb is on top of hammer area to reduce the combined width profile of the drawing hand and the gun, smoothing and accelerating the draw.

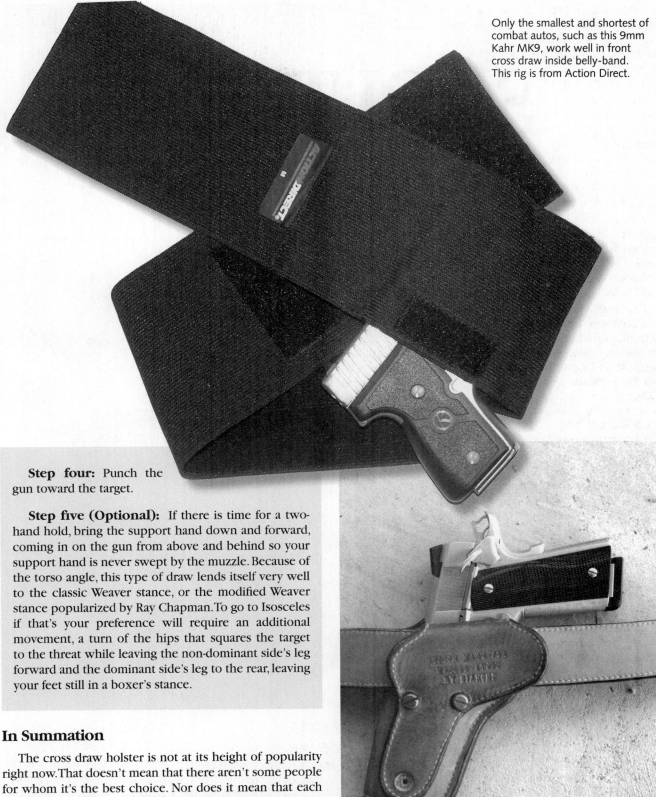

Only the smallest and shortest of combat autos, such as this 9mm Kahr MK9, work well in front cross draw inside belly-band. This rig is from Action Direct.

Step four: Punch the gun toward the target.

Step five (Optional): If there is time for a two-hand hold, bring the support hand down and forward, coming in on the gun from above and behind so your support hand is never swept by the muzzle. Because of the torso angle, this type of draw lends itself very well to the classic Weaver stance, or the modified Weaver stance popularized by Ray Chapman. To go to Isosceles if that's your preference will require an additional movement, a turn of the hips that squares the target to the threat while leaving the non-dominant side's leg forward and the dominant side's leg to the rear, leaving your feet still in a boxer's stance.

In Summation

The cross draw holster is not at its height of popularity right now. That doesn't mean that there aren't some people for whom it's the best choice. Nor does it mean that each and every one of us might not find some special purpose that is best fulfilled by some sort of across-the-body carry.

It's like so many other things. It's safe if you do it correctly, and may even be more efficient. But when any of us go to a new technique – or resurrect an old one, like this – we have the responsibility of making sure we're doing it correctly, and making the right choice for the right reason.

The Chapman Hi-Ride was Bianchi's competition holster commonly used as front cross draw. This one was custom made by the factory for long-slide competition pistol. Les Baer 45 is shown here.

SHOULDER HOLSTERS

Bianchi X15 shoulder rig that must be a quarter century old, but still works perfectly.

The driving rain sweeps the night streets and sidewalks of the city, making them look like glistening pools of ink, streetlights and automobile headlamps sending swords of light across their oily surfaces. You pull up the collar of your trench coat, and tug the brim of your dripping fedora a little lower down over your eyes. You reach inside the coat to feel the reassuring solidity of the gun in your shoulder holster…

Ah, yes, the shoulder holster is a part of whole *noir* scene, in movies and novels alike. Frank Sinatra carried a Colt pocket model in a Heiser-type shoulder holster in *Suddenly,* and one biographer says he wore the identical combination, loaded, under his custom tux and suit coats, in a time when most carry permits were discretionary and most movie stars could get them. Robert Stack as Eliot Ness carried a Colt Official Police 4-inch in a

Recommended draw from vertical shoulder holster. Transparent raincoat used here for illustration purposes reveals a vertical shoulder holster, with Odin Press dummy 1911 pistol used for safety reasons.

Movement begins with gun hand side quartering back from threat, support hand rising to block attack, and to get it out of shooter's own gun-path. Gun hand fingers form "spear hand" that knifes into opening of coat, which is fastened up to solar plexus…

butt-up spring clip shoulder rig of the Heiser style, as did all his men on the TV show. Playing the same role in the movie *The Untouchables*, Kevin Costner wore a Colt 1911 auto in a shoulder rig. As a matter of fact, the real Eliot Ness *did* wear a shoulder holster, and a Colt. However, Ness' Colt seems to have been an early 38 Detective Special with a 2-inch barrel.

On the printed page, the mid-20th century saw Mickey Spillane's classic "hard-boiled private eye," Mike Hammer, carrying a 45 automatic in a shoulder rig. In one book – I want to say "Vengeance Is Mine," but I'm working from memory here – Hammer replaces a lost 45 with a military surplus Colt 1911 bought from a New York City gun dealer. In the last of the novels, *The Black Alley,* Hammer's shoulder holster carries an updated, commercial Colt 45 auto, the Combat Commander. A popular paperback private

eye of the 1960s, Shell Scott, was armed by author Richard S. Prather with a snub-nose Colt Detective Special 38 in a "clamshell shoulder holster," which I always pictured as a Berns-Martin Lightning.

The glamorous image of the shoulder holster went beyond private investigators. One of today's best-selling novelists is Laurell K. Hamilton, who's most popular character is "Anita Blake, Vampire Hunter." Set in an alternate reality in which vampires and assorted were-beasts are out of the closet, politically active, and legally protected, they can only be slain if a judge signs a warrant and dispatches a Licensed Vampire Hunter like the heroine. A petite female, Anita Blake was armed by her creator with a Browning Hi-Power and a Star StarFire, both loaded with all-silver 9mm hollowpoints, and one carried in a shoulder holster with the other backing it up in an inside-the-waistband holster.

…and takes firm drawing grasp. Now…

…gun hand draws, NOT down and out, but STRAIGHT ACROSS CHEST, which will clear support arm now and also …

What character in modern adventure fiction could be more famous than James Bond, Agent 007? The late Ian Fleming equipped him with a Beretta 25 in a chamois shoulder holster in the early novels. (This ignored the fact that chamois would probably hold moisture and rust the gun it contained, which is probably why you never see anyone in the holster industry actually making the things out of chamois.) In *Doctor No,* Fleming summoned the assistance of leading British handgun authority Geoffrey Boothroyd, who more or less played a cameo as himself in the novel, but apparently Fleming didn't keep good notes of Boothroyd's advice. 007 wound up with a 32-caliber Walther PPK in a Berns-Martin Triple Draw holster, which could be worn as either a belt or shoulder rig. Problem was, this design secured on the cylinder and was available for revolvers only, not autoloaders such as the Walther.

When the Zodiac Killer stalked San Francisco, the crack SFPD investigator who hunted him was the famed Dave Toschi. Photos of the period show Toschi wearing a short-barrel revolver in a shoulder rig. Toschi is said to be the real-life model for the character Steve McQueen played in *Bullitt,* and in that move McQueen wore a 2 1/2-inch barrel Colt Diamondback 38 Special in an upside-down Safariland shoulder holster.

Real Life

Why so much "reel life" before getting to "real life" use of

shoulder holsters? The reason is, no holster choice has been so much influenced by the entertainment media – print, film, and television – as the shoulder rig. In their classic *non*-fiction text on holsters, *Blue Steel and Gunleather,* John Bianchi and Richard Nichols said, "Perhaps no other category of holsters has more nostalgic appeal. Although such holsters were first used many decades earlier, the cops-and-robbers movies of the Thirties, followed by subsequent prohibition movies of the Forties and Fifties brought shoulder holsters to the attention of the public. The old gangster-versus-police films featuring James Cagney, Edward G. Robinson, and Humphrey Bogart (who were alternately cast as good and bad guys), were liberally sprinkled with a wide variety of shoulder holsters. Wardrobe and property departments made liberal use of the dramatic impact of these harness rigs."

The fact is, though, that art was imitating life, as it should have been. Nichols and Bianchi were correct to note that the shoulder holster had long preceded cinema. Dr. John "Doc" Holliday was known to frequently wear one, and as noted, so did the real Eliot Ness. Shoulder rigs were seen on the other side of the law in the Roaring Twenties and the Depression years, as well. Baby Face Nelson was partial to shoulder rigs. So was John Dillinger, who had been observed wearing a twin shoulder rig with a pair of Colt 45 automatics by the nervous folks who dropped a dime on him at the Little Bohemia Lodge and set the stage for what was then

...more quickly get the muzzle on the threat ...

...and smoothly flow into a classic Weaver stance.

the FBI's most humiliating debacle. (Dillinger didn't wear shoulder holsters or 45s when they weren't suitable for his lifestyle, though. On the hot summer night when he was killed outside the Biograph Theater in Chicago, he was coatless, and carrying a Colt 380 automatic in his pants pocket, and a spare magazine of UMC 380 ball ammo in another pocket.)

Real Life, Not Reel Life

Shoulder rigs were more popular in the time of Eliot Ness than now. Part of that came from most folks not yet having figured out that good gun belts were necessary for hip holsters, and part of it was that hip holsters hadn't yet come anywhere close to today's state of the art.

Nowadays, cops and armed citizens alike vastly prefer belt carry to shoulder carry, but that does not by any means make the shoulder holster obsolete for gun concealment. There are several situations where they come in handy.

Female Practitioners

Female users seem proportionally much happier with shoulder rigs, particularly detectives who wear guns constantly and daily. Many of the factors on the male body that make the strong-side hip holster a guy's favorite, are not present on his sister, even if she's the same height. The female torso is proportionally shorter than the male's, and her pelvis proportionally much higher and usually a lot

more flared. The gun butt that rests just perfectly below the ribcage behind the brother's hip digs painfully into his sister's floating ribs, due to the higher pelvis and shorter torso. Moreover, the flare of her hip pushes the bottom of the holster outward at the barrel end, which concomitantly forces the butt end uncomfortably into her side. As if this is not enough, the weapon sits so high that she practically has to disarticulate her shoulder joint to perform a proper hip draw.

If the hip holster is a "by males, for males" design that is ideal for most men and difficult for many or even most women, the shoulder holster turns out to be the exact opposite. A great many men, particularly big guys, have tried shoulder rigs and found them mercilessly uncomfortable, while women do not have the same problems with them as their brothers.

Once again, it's a case of *vive la différence*. A woman's torso tends to be narrower through the chest and rib cage area than that of a man the same height, and her arms will be proportionally longer and usually, more limber. This makes certain angles of shoulder holster carry – notably the 45-degree muzzle up/butt down position, and especially the muzzle straight up position – difficult for the male to reach in terms of proper grasp and draw. This becomes increasingly worse as the male gets more broad-shouldered (forcing his arm to reach farther) and more broad-chested (also impeding his reach in that direction.)

Old and new. New Ed Brown Executive Carry .45 auto rests in a Bianchi X15 shoulder rig that must be a quarter century old, but still works perfectly.

Try this simple test. Put together a man and a woman of roughly the same height, and ask each to raise their left arm and reach their right arm across the left armpit area where the shoulder holster would hang. See how far they can reach. Most males will run out of range of movement with the tip of their longest finger somewhere in the armpit area. Typically, though, the *female* will be able to reach around so far that she can pat herself on the shoulder blade, and I've seen a very few women so slender and flexible, their middle finger could touch their spine.

In other words, *she* can reach much farther in the direction a shoulder holster draw requires, than *he* can.

There are other reasons so many women prefer shoulder rigs. Only the most casual female wardrobe will allow the sort of quality dress gunbelt that men can wear even with business suits. The self-suspensory nature of the shoulder holster solves that problem nicely. Hanging a spare magazine or two under the off-side arm from a flat, soft, well-designed piece of leather or synthetic seems to be more comfortable and less protuberant than hanging it on the belt. And, if she has a narrow waist, space there is at a premium, but there's a vacant place to hang gear right there under the armpit.

Constantly Seated Practitioners

Some occupational requirements force the person wearing the gun to be constantly seated. A teller's cage. An office or cubicle. Behind a steering wheel. A wheelchair. Many practitioners have found a comfortable shoulder rig to work well in these applications. However, the optimum word is "comfortable."

You can achieve the same goals with a cross draw belt holster, but the shoulder rig has some advantages. Depending which side of the seat you're on, the armed driver or bodyguard/chauffeur may find seat belts getting in

Baby Glock 27 that backs up this officer's Glock 22 is carried in holster clipped to body armor, reached with support-side hand shoulder holster style.

Shoulder holsters lend themselves to weak-hand draw. Here, with vertical rig, left hand comes in palm out to take drawing grasp…

…and is rocked out muzzle forward, upside down, to keep gun from crossing its own user …

the way of the cross draw holster. A "shoulder system" with spare ammo suspended beneath the armpit opposite the holster may also give faster access to spare magazines than would a belt pouch for a seated person.

These "reach" factors may significantly favor the person who is constantly planted in other types of seats. An armchair's arms, and those of a wheelchair, can catch a hip holster on either side of the body. The shoulder rig will literally be "above all that."

There can be a downside, however, and again it goes to comfort factor. "Concealed means *c led*," and in an automobile, that means a covering garment must constantly be worn. The long-haul driver with a handgun holstered on either side of his belt can generally take his coat off, and it will probably go unnoticed by anyone not in the vehicle with him, or not leaning into the vehicle and peering in. Not so the shoulder rig. Failure to realize this led to the fortunate arrest of American terrorist Timothy McVeigh, who was stopped by a lawman who spotted McVeigh driving while wearing a Glock 45 auto in an uncovered shoulder holster. The policeman drew his own Glock and arrested McVeigh at gunpoint. Apparently more comfortable blowing up

children with explosives from a safe distance than he was facing armed good guys, McVeigh meekly surrendered.

The shoulder holster works well for "drivers" of conveyances other than automobiles. Most of the police pilots I've flown with – and virtually all of the police *helicopter* pilots – wore shoulder holsters.

That goes for farm vehicles such as tractors, as well. Don't forget, part of a day's labor on a working farm is getting under the tractor or the machinery to fix it. If a snake slithers along at that point, it might be difficult to get at your hip. No one has a better perspective on this than my old friend Frank James. A well-recognized authority on firearms and the gun industry, Frank also owns a successful working farm. In fact, his good-natured nickname among friends is "Farmer Frank." One of those friends is noted weapons expert Rich Grassi. In the 2008 edition of Harris Publications' *Concealed Carry* annual, Rich asked half a dozen of us what we carried on our own time and why, and called the article "Carry Guns of the Professionals." Frank James had the following to say:

"Unlike many in the gun-writing field, I am an advocate of the shoulder holster because in my experience, waist or hip-mounted holsters are poor choices during operation

...and is rotated upright as it is thrust forward into the threat. Dummy .45 is from Odin Press, used here for photographer's safety.

This horizontal shoulder rig, the Stylemaster by Mitch Rosen, conceals even on an average size torso with the "baby Glock."

and/or the repair of farm machinery.

"Throughout the harvest, I usually rely on an S&W M657 41 Magnum with a custom 4-inch barrel and a Walt Rauch-designed gold bead front sight. This revolver is routinely carried in an A.E. Nelson Model 58 shoulder holster with the old-style Al Goerg shoulder harness. On certain occasions I will substitute a custom-built Heinie Springfield Armory 10mm 1911 pistol for the S&W M657. This is my second Heinie 10mm 1911 pistol, since I wore the first one (built on a Colt Delta Elite) out, but I've also worn out three different S&W 41 Magnum revolvers. The holster used with the 1911 is the Galco Miami Classic, but I adjust the holster to a highly angled rake with the muzzle up and the butt down because that makes the whole thing less prone to snagging on hoses, levers, and other stuff," Frank concludes.

Shoulder System Users

The man who invented both the concept and the term "shoulder system" is generally conceded to be Richard Gallagher, with his early Jackass Shoulder System line that became the cornerstone of his later Galco gunleather empire. Here we had a comfortable figure-eight harness that did not put direct pressure on the neck. Under the armpit opposite the dominant hand swung the holster, which could be adjusted from horizontal draw if the gun was short enough to conceal that way, to 45 degrees or more angle of muzzle up/butt down. And, on the opposite side, there were pouches for ammunition – loose revolver cartridges, auto pistol magazines, even speedloaders later – and handcuffs.

This absolutely captivated the type of plainclothes officer who is uncomfortable carrying a gun all day. By pulling open the desk drawer when an emergency call came in, this practitioner could don the shoulder rig as easily as

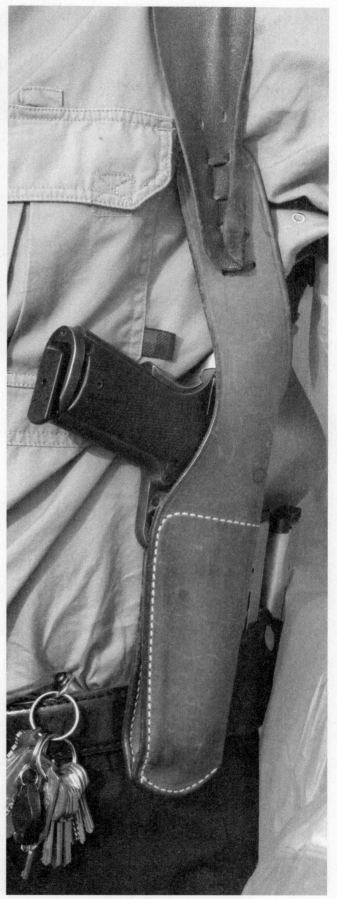

Bianchi's classic X15, shown here with Kimber 45 auto.

Horizontal shoulder holster needs subtly different draw from vertical style. Here dummy Glock is visible in Rosen holster under arm, thanks to transparent jacket…

…as draw begins, gun-hand-side leg steps back, pivoting body as shown, while support hand rises to blocking position and fingertips of drawing hand knife through opening in coat, which as shown should be fastened no higher than solar plexus…

throwing on a coat, and *voila!* Gun, ammo, and cuffs were suddenly onboard and ready to go in one smooth swoop.

There are those of us who don't care for this approach, since we know that one might be away from that desk drawer, or wherever the shoulder rig is stored, when the call to arms comes. We prefer to put our gear on in the morning and take it off when we are certain we will no longer need it. However, we have to realize that not everyone who carries a gun on the side of the Good Guys n' Gals shares this attitude. A quickly donned set of gun-and-gear beats hell out of *no* gun and gear, and that's why, even if this had been Richard Gallagher's only design, it would have earned him a place in the history of great holster designers.

Another useful purpose for the shoulder system is the bedside "roll-out kit." Only the most paranoid (or those at genuinely red alert level of risk) sleep with their guns on. When the burglar alarm goes off or the glass breaks, a shoulder rig right by the bed allows the awakened home defender to do exactly what that lax-about-carrying cop does with *his* shoulder system. In a trice, with little more than a shrug of the shoulders, the necessary gear is strapped to him even if he doesn't have time to fully get dressed. A small, powerful flashlight clipped to the shoulder strap, perhaps even a pouch attached for a cell phone, and the defender is equipped to "roll out" and handle necessary defensive task.

The "Orthopedic" Shoulder Rig

One reason I keep shoulder holsters in my personal wardrobe is that over the years, I've occasionally "thrown my back out." It always seemed to be something in the lumbar region. There are also hip injuries that can make anything heavy worn on a belt (or even a belt itself) intolerable. In situations like that, a shoulder holster can be a Godsend.

Indulge me in a little personal remembrance. In the early 1990s, I managed to throw my lower back out big time. The doc told me in no uncertain terms that I was not to have *any* weight on my belt. If I was going to do police work, he said, it would have to be administrative or investigative, so I wouldn't need to be in uniform, because he had treated a lot of police back patients and knew how heavy the Sam Browne duty belt was.

"No problem," I told him. "I'm sure my chief will let me do plainclothes for a while. I'll just wear a shoulder holster."

He looked at me, dead-level serious, and answered, "Make sure you wear one on each side."

There was a long moment of silence. I ventured uncertainly, "Uh, you're kidding me, right?"

"Not at all," snapped the doc. "Think about it. Your lower back is trying to heal. Your lower back supports your upper body. If weight is off-center on one side of your upper body, your lower back isn't going to heal, is it?"

I went home to the holster room and cobbled together a double rig for a pair of Smith & Wesson revolvers. The harness and the left-hand holster were from an early Bill Rogers design, and the right-hand holster was from an old Jackass Shoulder System. It was exactly balanced. The short-barrel K-frames were adjusted to horizontal carry, held securely in place by thumb-snaps, and were very quick to get at. And, sure enough, my lower back sighed in relief.

And I felt like Sonny Crockett's older, stranger brother.

...gun hand takes firm grasping hold with all but trigger finger, as thumb releases safety strap. Meanwhile, support arm has risen higher than usual to Najiola-style block ...

...and now pistol is drawn straight rearward across chest, quickly coming to bear on opponent and without crossing shooter's own left arm ...

Sonny Crockett was the character played by actor Don Johnson on the then-popular TV series, *Miami Vice*. Show creator Michael Mann was big into both cutting edge guns and authenticity. He had the Crockett character carry a little Detonics 45 in a black nylon ankle holster for backup, and as primary, a Smith & Wesson Model 645 45 auto or, for much of the series, an oh-so-trendy Bren Ten 10mm auto. Both were big, heavy pistols, so the Crockett character wore whichever he carried in a given season in a shoulder system. The shoulder rig *du jour* was either a Ted Blocker or a Galco, again depending on the season of production.

I spent a little time with a postal scale, and determined that a Colt Lightweight Commander pistol loaded with 185-grain jacketed hollowpoints *exactly* balanced out with two spare loaded magazines, a pair of handcuffs (I forget which set, but they may have been the old S&W Airweights made of aluminum like the Commander's frame), and finally a Spyderco Police Model knife clipped onto the harness on the opposite side. That was the rig that carried me through to recovery, at which time I went back to my old, familiar hip holsters and belt-mounted magazine pouch.

Cold Weather Carry

The shoulder holster has much to recommend it in very cold weather. By leaving one button undone, the hand can knife through the opening in the coat to grasp the pistol, even when bundled up against sub-zero weather. Living more than half a century in New Hampshire, which can become a frozen wasteland in winter, I found that when I took my overcoat off in an office or restaurant, the sport coat or suit coat beneath it generally stayed on, and the

thermostat in the given place was generally adjusted to allow for that.

Others had noticed it long before I came along. Hunters in particular learned to appreciate shoulder holsters. Part of that was that big-game hunting season generally falls in the cooler months, and part of it was that the outer garment made a perfect protector of the shoulder-holstered handgun from inclement weather in the great outdoors. When the handgun is backup to the rifle or shotgun, it also keeps the stock of the long gun from getting scratched against the handgun on the same-side hip, or the adjustable sights on the holstered 44 Magnum from being inadvertently knocked out of alignment by the butt of a long gun. Pioneering handgun hunter Al Georg, in the 1950s, did a great deal to popularize the shoulder rig among handgun hunters.

The hunter's concealed handgun can protect him from more than dangerous wild game. The following account appears in the book *Street Stoppers* by Evan Marshall and Ed Sanow, published by Paladin Press.

"While hunting bear in the northwestern United States, he carried a S&W Model 57 41 Magnum with an 8 3/8-inch barrel in a shoulder holster as backup, loaded with Winchester 170-grain JHPs. He and his hunting partner had spent a frustrating day without even seeing a bear. They had returned their rifles and related equipment to their motel room before going out to dinner.

"They were returning to their car when they were approached by a shabbily dressed individual who asked for money. The hunter gave him $5, but the man made a sarcastic remark about the bigger bills in his wallet. Ignoring him, the hunter turned toward his car when he

...and the draw smoothly flows into a classic Weaver stance.

was struck in the back. Thinking that the panhandler had hit him with his fist, he turned around to see the man holding a large knife in his hand. Realizing that he had been stabbed, he pulled the revolver from the shoulder holster and shot him twice."

The shoulder system also works very well in cold weather for uniformed police officers. When you're working a dangerous job, a second full-size fighting handgun can be a comforting thing. In a tailored uniform, with some piece of equipment already occupying every inch of space on your duty belt, it's all you can do to tuck a snub-nosed revolver into a hideout holster somewhere. But, with a jacket on, a shoulder system lets you not only utilize that unused space beneath your armpit, it lets you carry something more substantial there.

On NYPD's legendary Stakeout Unit, each officer was *required* to carry two handguns and have a long gun within reach while on that particular Job. Some used a service revolver and an off-duty snubby, but many carried two full service-size guns, and a shoulder holster was often the choice for one of them. Since they were quasi-uniformed in heavy vests stenciled POLICE in big letters on the front, convenience was a greater concern than concealment. Not all used the shoulder rig. The late Jim Cirillo, the SOU's most famous alumnus, carried one 4-inch barrel S&W Model 10 in a strong-side hip holster, and a second in a cross draw belt scabbard where he could reach it with either hand. However, Jim's frequent partner Bill Allard – probably the one guy on the squad who killed more criminals in the line of duty than Jim – was fond of the shoulder rig. He carried butt up/muzzle down, and the gun under his arm was generally either a heavy barrel 4-inch Model 10, or the Colt National Match 45 auto that he had special permission to carry on duty, and with which he killed at least three gunmen that I know of. A 38 Special revolver was generally in the holster on his right hip.

I had the chance to ride with Dave Venezian and Frank Bianculli, known on NYPD as "the Batman and Robin of Queens." Each carried one gun on the strong-side hip, and the other in a shoulder rig. They worked plainclothes, and they were able to conceal their shoulder rigs in spite of sultry heat in New York summers.

Remember the Y2K thing? We laugh about it now, but when the clocks and the computers ticked over on New Year's Eve that year, many people believed it was going to be TEOLAWAKI, the end of life as we all know it. And it wasn't just paranoid computer geeks. A few months before, I had been at a conference of the New England Chiefs of Police Association, where planning for Y2K was a major theme of the event. We were told by some *very* heavy-hitters that there was an excellent chance that the entire New England power grid would go down for an indeterminate period of time. Moreover, solid gang intelligence indicated that criminal groups in the Boston and New York metroplexes were under the assumption that a power failure would somehow magically unlock vault doors inside banks, and all the bangers would have to do would be to run stolen dump trucks through the front doors and gather up the loot. Informers also indicated that small banks in suburban and

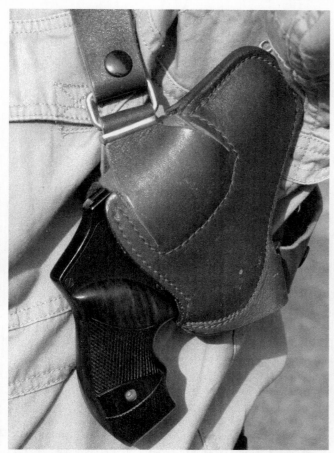

Upside-down shoulder holsters (muzzle up, butt down) work best with smaller, lighter guns, author has found. This is the old Bianchi 209, carrying an Airweight S&W J-frame 38 Special with Eagle "secret service" grips.

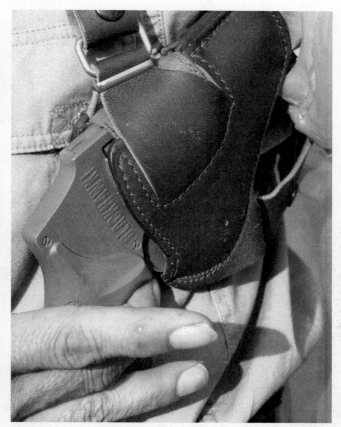

Many men have difficulty reaching far enough across their chest to get good drawing grasp on upside-down shoulder holsters. Here's Ayoob's suggestion: snag it with your middle finger…

rural areas, where "the thin blue line" was thinnest, were deemed by the gangs to be prime targets.

This was by no means just a New England perception. In New York City, generators and thirty days' supply of food were stockpiled at every precinct house. Across the nation, law enforcement and other emergency services personnel found leave cancelled. Manpower often doubled for the shift that would see "the turning of the clock."

In the small town I served then and now, two banks were located a few hundred yards from each other, and in line of sight from a major interstate highway. Given the intelligence we had been provided by unimpeachable sources, these two locations might as well have had bulls-eyes on them.

My department, like most, had its people out in force that night. We had issued M14 7.62mm NATO rifles to supplement the Ruger Mini-14s and the 12-gauge autoloading shotguns that were already permanent fixtures in each patrol vehicle. It was a typical, cold New England night, so as I and another officer stood watch over the two banks from a suitable vantage point, I had a spare pistol on under my uniform coat in a Bianchi Tuxedo shoulder rig. Since our department issue sidearm at that time was the excellent Ruger P90 45 auto, I simply kept one of those in my Safariland SSIII uniform holster and a second P90 in the Bianchi shoulder rig under my coat. My primary weapon, however, was a match-grade

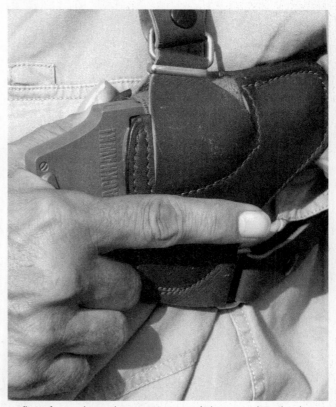

…flip it forward into drawing grasp, and *then* complete the draw. This is Blackhawk dummy version of S&W Centennial revolver, in Bianchi 209 shoulder rig.

Shoulder holsters lend themselves well to surreptitious draw. Even with transparent raincoat, folded arms hide the fact that Ayoob's shoulder holstered 38 is already *in* his gun hand and ready to draw.

M1A Springfield Armory 308 with Trijicon scope.

And, of course, the clock ticked past midnight and power *didn't* go out, and life was good. The point was, on that bitterly cold night when hard intelligence indicated we could expect very serious problems from very dangerous people who run in packs, I for one had found it comforting to be able to wear a second full-size service pistol under my uniform coat to back up the one in my security hip holster…and a shoulder holster proved to be the most convenient way to do that.

Design Features

The first selection criterion for shoulder holsters is comfort, because for well over a century, that has been the end user's biggest complaint. Narrow straps can cut cruelly into the shoulders, and will do so more in proportion to how heavy the gun and accessories suspended from those straps might be. Wide, soft harnesses that distribute the weight are critical here.

All leather (or all plastic) straps that can't stretch as you move your arms or bend your torso will not only be uncomfortable, but will tend to limit your range of movement. This is why judicious use of elastic in the harness can make or break the comfort and practicality factors. The all-elastic off-side shoulder strap of the classic Bianchi X15,

and elastic around the centerpoint of the harness on Mitch Rosen's Stylemaster holster, are reasons both designs were successful. Galco's use of strategically placed swivels in one of its harness designs was another approach to achieving the same objective.

If you're going to be wearing the shoulder rig for more than a few hours, you don't want one whose harness crosses the back of the neck. The pressure it applies will quickly cause fatigue, and could probably exacerbate existing neck injuries. A harness that describes a figure 8 turned on its side will generally be more comfortable for that reason, all other design factors being equal. This design is sometimes called "H-type," because if the holster and other gear are removed from the harness and the harness is laid out sideways, it may resemble a capital letter "H." Some others will resemble an "X".

As to gun carry position, shoulder holsters intended for concealment use will actually break down into about four types. Terminology differs from manufacturer to manufacturer.

Note orientation of muzzle of upside-down shoulder holster: subclavian artery and other vital parts are in line of the muzzle. With these, author recommends draw begin with this Kerry Najiola block, elbow high, clearing brachial artery out of the way and giving head good protection against physical blows and contact weapons. Draw is otherwise the same as with horizontal shoulder holster.

Master concealment holster designer Chic Gaylord observed that an advantage of horizontal shoulder holster is that it carries the gun already pointed at mugger or rapist who jumps you from behind. Unfortunately, it will also be pointed at *anyone else* standing behind you, and is probably the most antagonistic holster with which to practice open carry.

What I'll call here **butt up vertical carry** is the oldest configuration. The gun muzzle is pointed straight down to the ground, and the gun butt projects forward from under the armpit of the non-dominant arm. These go back to the 19th Century. The early ones were simple pouches, from which the revolver had to be lifted up and out. Later came spring-loaded designs such as the classic Heiser, which allowed the gun to be pulled down and out through the front of the rig. These were the sort worn by Eliot Ness, and accurately depicted on actor Robert Stack, who played him in the classic television series *The Untouchables*. A more effective version, the Hardy/Cooper, was named after famed gun expert Jeff Cooper, who designed it and preferred it in the 50s and part of the 60s.

Shoulder rigs of this style are still manufactured, by companies including A.E. Nelson, Bianchi, Galco, and others. They usually work best when anchored to the belt, with a leather or fabric strap that is provided for that purpose. Otherwise, the holster wants to come along with the gun when you tug it forward. With a short handgun, such as a snub-nose revolver, the belt-strap anchor doesn't seem to be needed.

These are your best bets for concealing large frame, longer barreled guns. Some books on holsters, and even some manufacturers' instructions, suggest drawing from these by ripping the handgun down through the entire open front of the spring-mouthed holster. You can do this, but the gun ends up down at belly or midriff level,

instead of up in line of sight where you can see where it's pointing. This sort of draw also requires the concealing garment to be open in front.

A faster, more efficient, and more useful draw is to grasp the butt firmly, rock the butt forward until the area of the rear sight is clear of the leather, and then simply pull *up* and out, bringing the gun across the chest. This also allows you to draw from this type of shoulder rig while wearing heavy cold weather coats. Simply leave the area at the sternum unbuttoned or unzipped. So you don't suffer pneumonia in exchange for faster draw, make sure your overcoat is cut so that the upper front will remain in position, blocking wind, even if it is unbuttoned.

Butt down vertical carry, sometimes called "upside down carry," came along circa 1930 with the Berns-Martin Lightning holster. Riding high in the armpit, it was designed for snub-nose revolvers, though I've seen them used over the years with up to four-inch barrel guns. Hugging the gun high and tight to the armpit, it proved very concealable. A rip to the front pulled the gun through the strong springs that held its split front closed, and this brought the gun naturally upward toward line of sight. It tended to work best with an open-front garment, such as an unbuttoned sport jacket.

Because the butt is toward the rear in this type of carry, the hand has farther to reach to take a drawing grasp than with any other angle of shoulder holster. A guy with a big chest and thick arms may have to catch the gun's "handle" with the middle finger, the longest digit on his hand, and pull it forward before he can complete the drawing grasp with the rest of his fingers. Another liability with this design is that the muzzle is pointed straight up toward the armpit. There are stories of guys dying when they accidentally triggered their gun while reholstering, and put a bullet through their own subclavian artery. (There is no outside pressure point for first aid hemorrhage control of a severed subclavian.)

Horizontal carry was first proven to work in the 1950s by the great concealment holster designer of that generation, Chic Gaylord in New York City, whose spirit is carried on in holsters manufactured today by Bell Charter Oak. Gaylord wrote circa 1960 that horizontal was simply the fastest of the shoulder holsters. All these years later, I have to agree with him.

As the name implies, a horizontal shoulder holster carries the gun with the butt forward and down and the barrel parallel to the ground. Good news: it's no longer pointing at your hip as in butt-up vertical carry or at your own armpit as in butt-down vertical carry. Bad news: it *is* now pointed at anyone standing directly behind you. (Gaylord felt this was a good thing, since if the mugger was directly behind you with a forearm across your throat, your gun was already pointed at his chest and all you had to do was pull the trigger and fire through the back of your coat. This theory will be lost on those standing behind you in a police squadroom with your gun muzzle pointed at *their* chests.)

This rig is fast because of all shoulder holster designs, it puts the grip-frame the closest to your reaching hand. Even if you have giant pecs and biceps, if you can scratch

WE DON'T DO IT THIS WAY ANYMORE!! This is the old-fashioned draw that got shoulder holsters banned from police academies and action shooting matches. Shooter starts facing target squarely…

…and, pausing only to slow himself down with extra movement, shooter rips gun down and out. He is now muzzle-crossing range officer behind him. This requires open front garment, and …

…swinging horizontally to his target – and having just muzzle-swept anyone to his left on the range – the shooter must now slow down at the worst possible time, or risk over-swinging past his target…

…and ends up in a cowboy-looking posture where he can't see where his gun is pointed. Did we mention that WE DON'T DO IT THIS WAY ANYMORE!?!?

your armpit you can make a quick draw from a horizontal shoulder holster. As the gun is presented, its muzzle swings neither up nor down: it's already at chest height, and all you have to do is get it 180 degrees from where it rests to where you need it pointed. It comes out and on target with the least possible movement.

One downside is that it wants a fairly small gun. I suppose there are body builders out there who can carry Colt Government Models in this fashion and conceal them. There may also be sumos who can carry even longer guns. I'm not a big guy, though, and for me a baby Glock autoloader or a 2- to 2 1/2-inch barrel revolver are about the max I can conceal before the gun muzzle starts tenting out the back of my jacket under the armpit. How big a gun you can carry in a horizontal shoulder holster will be determined directly by how deep your chest is.

45 degree butt down carry was popularized by Richard Gallagher with the previously mentioned Jackass Shoulder System, which started the Galco holster empire. Some makers offer tie-down straps that secure on a belt. This feature keeps the gun and gear from slapping against your ribs if you have to run (and believe me, that can whale on your rib cage when it happens), but it also seems to restrict range of movement a little, as it does when a butt-up vertical carry shoulder rig is secured the same way. It's up to the end-user. Most people who like this type of holster, I've noticed, don't use tie downs.

Good news: this is another shoulder holster style that generally won't have the gun muzzle pointed at some part of the wearer's body. Bad news: when the coat is off, it will now be pointing at the faces of colleagues behind you, instead of at their chests. Back in the '70s, when Dominic Napolitano was doing police sales for Heckler and Koch, he and I went on a deer hunting trip with some guys from the SLED (South Carolina Law Enforcement Division) near Edgefield. SLED SWAT used all HK guns at that time, and that was the plan for the hunt as well. Dominic and I wanted to take our Bambis with handguns, so we each had an HK P9S, Dom's in 9mm and mine in 45 ACP. Each of us was carrying our pistol in one of Gallagher's shoulder systems. It was a warm day, punctuated by a noon barbecue, and our concealing garments were off. More than one of the locals took umbrage at looking down the muzzles of our pistols when they stood in the food line behind us. I wound up parking the shoulder rig with my gear and stuffing the 45 into my waistband "Mexican style" for the rest of the lunch.

Final Thoughts on Shoulder Holsters

For a handful of people, the shoulder holster is The Answer for constant, daily wear of a concealed handgun. For some, it's just not in the cards. X- number of folks just think it's too "Hollywood." For

> When you're working a dangerous job, a second full-size fighting handgun can be a comforting thing.

most who get into concealed carry, though, there's at least one shoulder rig in the holster wardrobe, and I for one think that's a good thing.

For a majority of concealed carriers, there will be certain times when this thing just comes into its own. The back problem I mentioned, or the leg injury that has me at the moment writing this with a laptop literally in my lap, and my right leg elevated in a recliner chair. The chair's design makes it awkward for me to get at my usual hip holster. A Rosen Stylemaster double rig, perfectly balanced with a baby Glock under each armpit, keeps everything out of the way and has come in as handy as the cane.

Shoulder holsters do present safety problems that the wearer must deal with conscientiously. Because of the potential for the gun to cross the shooter's own weak side arm, and the whole body of the shooter next to him on the firing line when he draws, absolutely *scrupulous* care must be taken not to let the finger or anything else touch the trigger until you are in the very act of intentionally firing the weapon. On the range, turn your back to the target before you reholster, so the muzzle never goes uprange or points at anyone on either side of you.

One little-recognized downside of the shoulder rig is that it may be inaccessible to you if your opponent has you in a chest-crushing bearhug. If the attack comes straight on, you'll be front-to-front with the assailant, and your gun hand's reach to the weapon beneath the opposite armpit may be blocked. Access by the support hand will probably also be blocked, at least to some degree. Ed Lovette tells the following story in the pages of his excellent book from Paladin Press, *The Snubby Revolver* (second edition).

"Jim, a detective buddy of mine, and his partner go into a trailer home to serve a warrant. At the knock, the suspect opens his door and permits them to enter. But as soon as they step into the trailer a fight breaks out, and my friend reaches for his handgun – a Colt 45 Gold Cup that he carries in a shoulder holster. As his hand wraps around the butt of the weapon, the bad guy grabs him in a bear hug, effectively trapping the 45 and Jim's hand between their bodies. (Jim tells me later that his left hand is free. Had he had a snubby in his pants pocket he could have easily gotten it into action.) Fortunately, Jim's partner pulls her trusty Colt Diamondback – the 38 Special version with the 2.5-inch barrel, certainly one of the handsomest and most accurate snubbies ever – and restores order to the fracas," Brother Lovette concludes.

> For a handful of people, the shoulder holster is The Answer for constant, daily wear of a concealed handgun.

The photo sequences in this book show safe draws from all four angles of shoulder holster carry. Burn them into your program. Safety is one reason that some police departments – and most shooting academies – *forbid* shoulder holsters.

All that said, shoulder holsters do have a place.
And that place goes far beyond Hollywood.

Left-hand trouser pocket holster by
Bill Rodgers for Safariland conceals
J-frame S&W Airweight 38 with
Eagle "secret service" stocks.

POCKET CARRY

*In all kinds of weather, pocket carry makes sense.
For many, it's the ideal answer.*

People have been carrying guns in their pockets ever
since firearms became small enough to fit there.

Wild Bill Hickok carried one or more derringers in
his pockets to back up his famous pair of 36-caliber cap
'n ball Navy Colts. Wyatt Earp testified under oath *in re*
the deaths of Frank McLaury, William Clanton, and Thomas
McLaury that he began the OK Corral shootout with his
hand on the butt of a Colt Single Action Army 45 revolver
in the pocket of his overcoat. Colt's in-house gun shark
J.H. Fitzgerald made up a pair of heavy frame New Service
45 revolvers with stubbed barrels, and wore a pair of them
in leather-lined side pockets in his trousers. He made up
one of those guns for Col. Rex Applegate, who packed
one in a hip pocket when he bodyguarded Franklin D.
Roosevelt. Legendary Border Patrol gunslick Bill Jordan
was partial to a bobbed-hammer Smith & Wesson Model
37 Airweight Chief Special 38 in a hip pocket for backup
and sometimes off-duty wear. On duty or off, famed NYPD
Stakeout Squad gunfighter Jim Cirillo carried a hammer-
shrouded 38 Colt Cobra snubby in a trouser pocket.

Today, in the 21st Century, we don't have the baggy pants
of the Depression Years that allowed "Fitz" to carry a big-
frame 45 in each pocket. But, thanks to the caprices of the
fashion world, we have billowy Dockers-style trousers and

BDUs. We have light, powerful handguns only dreamt of in
Fitzgerald's time. And, perhaps most important, we have the
finest pocket holsters that have ever existed.

The Pocket Itself

In the olden days, the pocket *was* the holster. The history
of the Old West tells us that Luke Short carried his Colt
Thunderer double-action 41 in a leather-lined hip pocket,
and used that combination to outdraw and kill a gunman
deemed much more dangerous than he, "Long-Haired Jim"
Courtright. Famed lawman Dallas Stoudenmire carried a
pair of short-barrel Smith & Wesson single action, top-break
44s in special pants, whose hip pockets he had likewise
had lined with leather by an obliging tailor.

Today, the leather-lined pocket has gone the way of the
dodo bird. However, reinforced pockets designed expressly
for handguns remain. A company called Betz started the
trend to jackets with hidden, built-in holsters. A Betz coat
can carry a full-size service auto inside next to the breast.
It's drawn in a fashion similar to what you'd use with a
shoulder holster. The Royal Robbins 5.11 Tactical vest has
built-in gun pockets of similar style. Our nation's largest
sheriff's department, comprised of several thousand
uniformed deputies, orders all their uniform jackets with

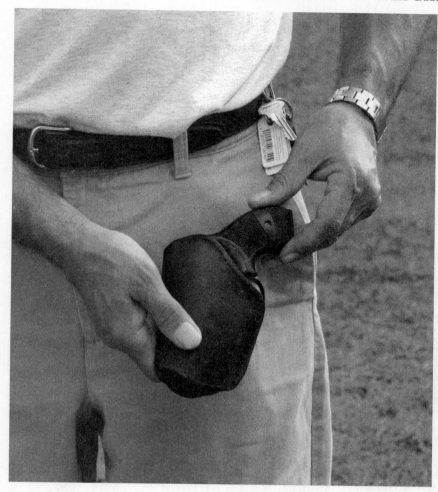

Author's preference is a lightweight J-frame 38 in front trouser pocket on non-dominant hand side, for backup, so either hand can access a weapon.

"hammerless" 357 Magnum, loaded with +P+ Hydra-Shok 38 Special ammunition.

"Civilians" have not been neglected. Blackie Collins created special jeans for pistol-packers, appropriately called Toters. Both hip pockets and both side pockets are specially reinforced for carrying handguns. Since this is the very same Blackie Collins who first became famous as a knife designer, there's also a special quick-access pocket for a tactical folder.

Pocket Holsters

Even by the time of the Old West gunfighters, it had become apparent that regular pockets by themselves weren't enough to sustain the carrying of a defensive handgun. The pistol's weight, and sometimes its sharp edges, would tear through pocket linings. A small handgun could change its orientation due to body movement through the day, and perhaps turn upside down in the pocket. The shape of the gun was likely to "print" through the fabric, betraying the "concealed" element of concealed carry.

The first pocket holsters were simply leather squares or rectangles with gun pouches sewn on, sometimes crudely. In modern times, the art and design of the pocket holster have been refined dramatically. In addition to leather, we now see them crafted of Kydex, nylon, and assorted other synthetics. Greg Kramer popularized a leather model with a flat Kydex square on the outside, which broke up the outline of the gun. With tight pants, someone might be able to see that you had something in your pocket, but they wouldn't be able to tell that it was a firearm.

a special inside pocket of this kind, cut for the J-frame S&W snub-nose 38 most of their sworn personnel carry for backup. Concealed Carry Clothiers has reinforced side pockets for small handguns in their line of vests made especially for CCW carriers.

Nor have pants pockets been neglected. For decades, the troopers of a certain state have been issued two handguns, one full size and one small. The full-size gun, of course, went in a uniform belt holster. The smaller was carried in a side trouser pocket: mandatory, no exceptions. The pants were ordered with one reinforced pocket from the uniform manufacturer. Over the years, many a trooper in that state was saved by this little pants pocket hideout. Sometimes, it happened when someone got the primary gun away and the trooper had to resort to "Plan B." Sometimes, it was just easier to approach a stopped car with the hand inconspicuously in the pocket and wrapped around the little 38. When danger threatened, this made for a lightning fast draw and return of fire. Over the years that department went from the 38 Special as a primary service revolver, to the 357 Magnum, to the 9mm auto, to their currently issued 40-caliber service automatic. The backup has stayed pretty much the same: a small-frame Smith & Wesson revolver with short barrel. The current issue is the Model 640-1

There are numerous fine pocket holsters available today. Manufacturers of same include Jerry Ahern, Lou Alessi, Gene DeSantis, Galco, Greg Kramer, Ky-Tac, Mach-2, Bob Mika, Milt Sparks, Mitch Rosen, Thad Rybka, Safariland, Uncle Mike's, and more. I've used most of the above, with good success.

Personal favorites, for my own specific needs, have come down to three. With a snub-nose J-frame revolver, I've had the best luck with the Safariland. Designed by Bill Rogers, it's made of synthetic Porvair on the inside and *faux* suede on the outside. The outer surface makes it stick to the pocket lining and yield the gun instead of coming out with it, no matter what the angle of draw; the smooth Porvair on the inside reduces friction and speeds the draw. Unfortunately, it seems to be made *only* for J-frame snubs at this writing. (Seems to wear hell out of the gun's finish, too.)

For the baby Glock, I use either the Mach-2 or the Ky-Tac. Both are made of Kydex and are so close in design and function that they're hard to tell apart. An almost curlicue flange at the top catches the upper edge of the pocket as you clear the square-shaped auto pistol, and a similar protrusion at the rear of the holster catches the bottom edge if you prefer to draw horizontally out of the pocket.

For most anything else – for instance, the neat little Kahr PM9 polymer-framed 9mm, a favorite pocket auto, or the 380 size Colt Pocket Nine – I prefer Greg Kramer's classic pocket rig. Mike Dillon, who makes a point of putting only the best of everything in his Blue Press catalog, lists the Kramer pocket holster in those pages. It's a hell of an endorsement, and when you work with a Kramer pocket rig, an understandable one.

Drawing From the Pocket

Starting with your hands well away from the gun, you'll probably find drawing from the pocket faster than from, say, an ankle holster, but it'll never be as fast as getting it out of a good hip scabbard. The reason is, your hand is surrounded (and, in tight clothing, distinctly hampered) by fabric as it makes its way to the gun.

The hand needs to be flat as it enters the pocket. Fingers should be stiff and straight, in the configuration of a martial artist's "spear hand."

Once the hand is in the pocket, middle finger and ring finger (and little finger, if the grip frame is long enough) wrap around the stocks. Keep the trigger finger stiff and straight. If the gun snags on the draw and the finger is on the trigger, there's a good chance you'll shoot yourself in the leg. The finger shouldn't enter the trigger guard until the gun is not only up and out, but on target, and not until you have made the decision to fire the weapon.

Don't let the trigger finger press tightly against the pocket holster. If you do, it will come out with the gun, rendering you unable to shoot.

With a revolver, put the thumb on the hammer or where a hammer would be. First, if you have a spur-hammer revolver, the thumb will now act as a hammer shroud and keep it from snagging on the draw. Second, and for many most important, this streamlines the shape of the drawing hand, which is why you should do it even if your revolver's

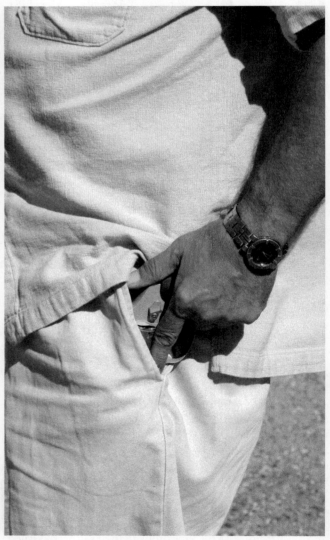

Author's preferred pocket draw technique. "Spear hand" finger configuration slides hand rapidly into pocket...

...to allow for tight pockets and spurred hammers, thumb takes this position. It dramatically reduces hand's thickness profile, thus reducing chances of a snag. It also turns the thumb into a hammer shroud for conventional-hammer revolvers...

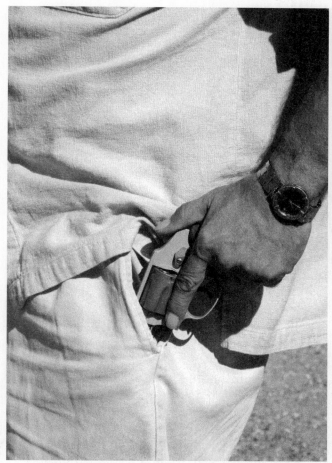

…as S&W Model 342 with LaserGrips emerges, note that trigger finger is still straight on frame, completely clear of trigger and trigger guard …

…and as gun clears the holster and begins to rock up toward threat, finger only now enters trigger guard, and *then only* if purpose of draw is to immediately fire instead of taking threat at gunpoint.

hammer is bobbed or shrouded.

A simple exercise you can do right now, even if you're reading this in an office or airport, will show you why. Put your empty hand in your side trouser pocket. Make a fist. Now try to pull the fist out. Did it snag? Well, guess what: this is the configuration your hand will be in if the thumb is curled down around a handgun's grips, and it's going to snag then, too. Now, put the hand in the pocket again. Make a fist if you want, but put the thumb up as if it was on a revolver's hammer. Do the draw again. Snaked right out of the pocket, didn't it? OK – you've got it.

This is one reason revolvers seem to be so much faster than autos when drawing from a pocket. To get the thumb up on the hammer area or the back of the slide, which is much farther back on an auto pistol than on a revolver, you have to compromise your grasp on the handgun.

You may have to tailor your draw to the type of holster you're using. If it was designed to rock to the back to escape the pocket, with the holster catching on the bottom edge of the pocket opening, you'll have to master a draw which brings the handgun out in that direction. If its "catch flange" is at the front of

> **You may have to tailor your draw to the type of holster you're using.**

the holster, it wants to catch at the top edge of the pocket. This means you draw the gun straight upward until it is well out of the pocket, then perform the same rock and lock movement you would when drawing from a hip scabbard. That is, rock the muzzle upward and lock it on the target in front of you as you bring the gun up into firing position. It's now on target if you have to fire sooner than you wanted to because the threat is closing in on you rapidly.

Most of us use the side trouser pocket for handgun carry. It's fast and secure. In the hip pocket, a gun can be uncomfortable when you sit down and is more likely to be pushed out of the pocket by pressure against the surface on which you sit. Still, some shooters prefer that location.

My friend Jim Jacobe, the ace firearms instructor from Oregon, found that the hip pocket better suited his personal range of movement. Finding no commercial pocket holster that would work from that location instead of the side pants pocket, he had a leather shop make one up to his specifications. The supple leather of that custom holster holds his S&W Model 442 very comfortably, and he's lightning fast with it.

Three of the best pants pocket holsters, in the author's opinion. Left, Ky-Tac ambidextrous with Glock 27 40. Center, right-hand Greg Kramer with 357 Glock 33. Right, left-hand Safariland pocket holster with Eagle-gripped S&W Model 442.

The Weasel in Your Pocket

Jeff Cooper and Ray Chapman taught pistolcraft. They are both big, strong men. I'm little and weak, so I concentrate on weaselcraft. In a world where action beats reaction, and where the bad guy gets to be the actor and you and I get stuck having to react, I want all the little tricks of the trade on our side that I can get.

As noted early on, getting into your pocket and withdrawing your gun can take longer than drawing from a conventional hip holster. However, when the gun is in your pocket and danger threatens, nothing says you have to start with your hands clear of your body in an IPSC "ready" position. A hand on your hip-holstered firearm might be tactically unsound, but you can slip a hand into your pocket and look perfectly casual.

The gun is now in your hand. That changes everything.

There are two basic steps to drawing a gun, access and presentation. Access is getting your hand wrapped around the blaster. That's the tough part, the fine motor skill part. Presentation is simply ripping it out of the holster and bringing it on target. That's raw gross motor skill, which is a whole lot easier – and a whole lot faster.

Back in the 2002 *Complete Book of Handguns* from Harris publications, (still available from Police Bookshelf, 800-624-9049, www.ayoob.com) I set out to test this method for speed. I began with my non-dominant left hand in my side trouser pocket, wrapped around the Crimson Trace LaserGrips of my Smith & Wesson Model 442 Airweight. I was standing as I would on patrol beside a stopped sedan, with the target in about the same position and at about the same distance as a seated driver. When the PACT timer went off, I drew and fired "from the hip," the time stopping when the 38 Special round blasted into the silhouette. Five runs took 0.76, 0.62, 0.66, 0.65, and 0.54 seconds, which averaged to 0.65 of one second. That included reaction time, which for

me on that day averaged 0.21 of one second. This means that the actual draw and fire time alone averaged 0.44 of a second.

In other words, the simple weasel trick of sneaking my hand onto the pocketed 38 before hand had given me sub-half-second draw and fire capability.

Firing Through the Pocket

For the same article, which was titled "The Savvy Fast Draw," I was able to enhance react-and-fire speed still more by using an old street trick. The same revolver was in the hand inside a jacket pocket, and already pointed at the target, which was just barely within punching distance. On the signal, the 38 was simply fired through the coat pocket.

The times recorded for five runs were 0.50, 0.46, 0.48, 0.54, and 0.49 seconds. Average time rounded off to 0.49 of one second. Taking out reaction time, the actual shooting was taking only a quarter of a second, the time it took to get the index finger off the frame and onto the trigger.

Obviously, you want to practice with a jacket that you don't plan to wear any more, since the muzzle blast will tear it apart on the first shot. Most of your practice, just for the sake of practicality, will have to be dry fire. Still, you want to do it live fire a few times to be sure that you're on target, since this is point shooting in the truest sense, with no visual index of gun on target possible. It's strictly a close range (as in, within arm's reach) proposition.

Take particular care if you are heavy through the midriff, since barrel cylinder gap gas blast from a revolver can cut through fabric and injure a protruding abdomen. It goes without saying that this technique should not be practiced live fire by pregnant women. If the garment in question is an anorak or heavy winter sweatshirt with a pocket that goes across the belly, make sure that there is enough room to get the gun muzzle pointed straight away from you before firing.

Conventional wisdom tells us that a revolver is the way to go for shooting through a pocket, since pocket lining can snag the slide or block an ejecting casing, jamming the pistol. It is also possible for a revolver with an unshrouded hammer to snag, even if the hammer spur has been bobbed off. A fold of clothing can get caught between the hammer face and the frame, causing a misfire and even jamming the wheelgun enough to prevent another shot.

Now, I hasten to add that we tried this recently at Lethal Force Institute's new CQB (Close Quarter Battle) class, at the Firearms Academy of Seattle range in Onalaska, Washinton. Three of the participants used autos for firing through coat pockets. The guns represented were the Kel-Tec P32 and the North American Arms Guardian. All three specimens went five shots for five tries without a malfunction. The shooters did notice that it was distracting to have trapped, hot casings burning their hands and wrists inside the pockets.

Do fifteen shots without a malfunction mean that it's a good idea to try to shoot an auto pistol through a coat pocket? No! Damon Runyan is credited with saying, "The race is not always to the swift, nor the battle always to the strong… but that's still the way you should bet." Something similar is going on here. The auto pistol may not *always* foul and jam after firing through clothing…but that's still the way you should bet. Consider the shooting through pockets thing to be the province of the shrouded-hammer revolver, a'la the Smith & Wesson Bodyguard or Centennial.

I've heard folks talk about clothing catching fire if a gun is fired through coat pockets. I suppose it could happen with old blackpowder guns. With modern smokeless powder ammunition, I've run students through live-fire shoot-through-pocket drills and done it a good bit myself. While you can feel a flash of heat when the gun goes off, I've never yet seen a garment catch fire. I suppose, however, that there might be some particularly flammable coat fabric out there that could prove me wrong. (*Please* don't try this after spilling gasoline on yourself at the service station pump…)

Finally, remember to shoot through only the pockets of outer garments like coats, and remember that the garment needs to fit loosely for this to work. Trying to shoot through a pants pocket, or through the pocket of a tightly fitting jacket, can lead to you shooting yourself instead of the bad guy.

Summary

Pocket carry has been proven effective since handguns became small enough to fit into pockets. For the most part, you want the gun to be in a pocket holster. Practice regularly. Remember that firing through the pocket is a special purpose emergency tactic; as a rule, you'll want to draw and visually index the weapon on target before firing. Always carry a gun that cannot go off when dropped. Guns have been known to fall out of pockets, and pants or jackets with guns still in them have been known to be taken off and tossed, landing on a hard surface.

With common sense and careful practice, a compact handgun in the pocket can be a life-saver.

Breast pocket draw, using hidden gun/wallet pocket behind breast pocket of Woolrich Elite shirt designed by Fernando Coelho, now CEO of EoTac tactical apparel. Movement pattern is like drawing from a shoulder holster; thumb is on hammer area for reasons stated elsewhere.

Chapter 14

ANKLE HOLSTERS

Gould & Goodrich ankle holster shown w/baby Glock

had the privilege of knowing the late George C. Nonte, Jr. The man knew his guns, and he had broad connections with others in the industry and in the field who knew their guns, and he funneled that knowledge into his work. In his last book – *Revolver Guide*, published posthumously by Stoeger – George told the following tale that highlights the wisdom of carrying a spare gun south of one's body's own middle border.

"Many uniformed officers consider a belly gun as much a part of their equipment as a nightstick or cuffs. And, if the truth be known, the belly gun is not always employed in the singular. An example of the plural might well be a Texas Ranger known to me, who got just a wee bit careless or unlucky one day when entering a building after a felon. Somehow the black-hat got the drop on him and relieved him of his main six-gun. Eventually an opportunity presented itself, and the Ranger whipped out his belly gun and ventilated his unfriendly assailant.

"Later he was asked somewhat jokingly, 'What would you have done if he had found your hideout gun, too?' His response was not entirely unexpected, but might be just a slight shock to those who've never had to depend upon a gun for their lives – 'Well,' he said, 'I'd probably have shot him with this one,' and slipped yet another two-inch 38 out of his boot top.'"

There's a lot of lore and wisdom in those couple of short paragraphs by the late Brother Nonte. Note that the boot top was the Ranger's choice for his snub-nose 38. It is safe to assume that horsemen prepared for trouble have been stuffing handguns down in their boot tops since the time of the earliest match-lock pistols. The spot was *there*…it was handy to a man astride a horse…and it kept belt space free for more equipment, including another handgun.

Why are ankle holsters popular today, when we're more likely to ride the family automobile (or a Police Interceptor) than something with hooves? For much the same reasons. The spot is *there*…it's handy to a seated individual…and it keeps belt space free for more equipment, including another handgun.

The rise of the ankle holster can be tracked through the history of 19th, 20th, and 21st Century America. 1934: Eugene Cunningham saw publication of his book *Triggernometry*, a study of the guns, gear, and gunfighters of the Old West. He noted that despite the movie image of big six-shooters swinging openly on hips, many Western towns prohibited the carrying of guns, and a man who wanted to be armed needed deep concealment. Said Cunningham, "The hide-outs were various. A man rammed his six-gun into the leg of his boot - just in case something came up, in which he'd want to gain what was lost in the deal by what he could do

Here's author's namesake method of drawing from ankle holster while standing…

…non-gun hand reaches down to grasp trouser leg. It's important to grasp ABOVE the knee…

on the draw."

1960: In his classic book *Handgunner's Guide,* Chic Gaylord wrote, "To be effective, the undercover holster should carry the gun in a position on the body that cannot be detected by the 'bump frisk' often employed by hoodlums or their girl fiends. Shoulder holsters and belt holsters are too easily detected by a few pseudo-amorous passes. The holster's position should also enable its wearer to reach the gun with reasonable speed."

Added Gaylord, "The best of all undercover holsters is the ankle holster. Guns the size of the Chief Special or the Detective Special are easily and effectively hidden in this manner. It is an extremely comfortable holster even after as much as eighteen straight hours of wear. You can draw a gun from this rig while seated in a car or in a tavern far faster than from any other type of holster. When seated at a table, the gun can be drawn and held at ready with no one the wiser in case of impending danger. Its ready accessibility counts heavily when you are wearing an overcoat; and when standing you can draw it nearly as fast as from a belt holster. Many a New York City police officer uses this rig while on duty in uniform. When jumped by a mob of hoodlums and knocked to the ground, he can draw his gun faster than from a belt holster. One of the advantages of this holster is that the officer can wear jeans and a skivvy shirt without

fear of being 'made.'"

1986: In the second edition of *Blue Steel and Gunleather* by John Bianchi, it is observed that ankle holsters "have grown enormously in demand in recent years. Many off-duty police carry a gun under the trouser leg, usually a small-frame, hideout piece. The handgun is well concealed in the lower body extremities, but it is not readily accessible, even from a seated position. Practice in drawing the gun with this system improves the efficiency for the draw and fire. It is recommended primarily as a second gun carry for both uniform and plainclothes situations."

At this writing, ankle holsters remain popular…and the guns carried there have gotten bigger. I can think at the moment of two state patrols who issue their troopers "baby Glock" pistols with ankle holsters, and expect them to be carried daily as backup when in uniform. One such agency issues the troopers Glock 39 pistols in caliber 45 GAP, to back up the full-size Glock 37 pistols in the same caliber that ride in their uniform holsters. That agency's issue backup holster is currently an ankle rig with thumb-break retainer by Gould & Goodrich. The other agency had been issuing 380 automatics with ankle holsters for years, but was not happy with their reliability. The department adopted Glock 27 pistols, caliber 40 S&W, and issued them with ankle rigs, the brand of which escapes me at the moment. The little

...gun hand side leg steps out wide as free hand pulls trouser leg up as high as possible. Knees flex and shooter begins to drop into deep crouch, further shortening gun hand's reach to ankle holster...

...gun hand contacts pistol, thumb breaking safety strap of Gould & Goodrich ankle rig...

...and draw of 40-caliber Glock 27 is underway. Support hand's initial task is done...

40 Glocks worked out so well that when that department's heavy 10mm Smith & Wesson service pistols were due to be replaced, the department traded them in on Glock 35 pistols with 5.3-inch barrels. The latter guns' 15-round 40 magazines will work in the G27 subcompact model, just as the full-length magazines of a G37 will work in the chopped and channeled version, the G39. In either case, a trooper whose primary Glock is snatched, inaccessible, or shot out of his hand still has another Glock in the same caliber, and two spare magazines on his duty belt, with which to continue the fight.

One reason for the rising popularity of the ankle holster can be summed up in a single word: Velcro. When I was a kid, ankle holsters were available but uncommon. One company, Legace, made one with little straps and buckles. If your ankle diameter wasn't *exactly* right for one tongue and loop combination of that set-up – and if it was uncomfortable for you to put it on one notch loose and pad the inner circumference by wearing an extra sock – it just wasn't going to work for you. Too tight restricted circulation unmercifully, and too loose was almost as painful, with the chafing that occurred as the sloppy-fitting rig bounced all over the place with every step you took, not to mention problems with concealment.

I recall seeing one ankle holster of the period – I forget the brand – that secured with lacings and grommets, like a shoe. Trouble with that was the same as with shoelaces: they could become untied. There was also the problem of a lace dangling below a trouser cuff giving away the hidden holster.

Velcro changed all that. It allowed the holster to be adjusted for pretty much perfect fit. Along about the '70s. a lot of thought went into a rig called the Milwaukee Legster. Velcro secured the regular ankle rig in the usual location, but a strap ran up from it to another Velcro'd strap that encircled the leg between the knee and the calf muscle. This gave a suspension effect that helped hold the rig in place to keep it from shifting around.

That feature was widely copied. It turned out that end users loved or hated the calf strap, with no middle ground at all. The reason, I discovered, was anatomical. The guys who liked them worked out and ran a lot, or were naturally muscular, and had bulging calves. This allowed them to secure the upper strap comfortably, without fear of it slipping down, and without having to wrap it so tightly that it interfered with circulation.

I was in the other camp. With scrawny bird-like legs, the upper strap would work its way down over the calf by the

...d shooter can now fire one-handed for all ...lient speed...

... or remain in low cover crouch with two-hand grasp...

... or, if time permits and no low cover is available anyway, rise to preferred two-hand shooting stance.

end of the day and start bunching down around the ankle if I didn't pull it up, like an old man whose garters were slipping. If I secured the upper strap tightly enough to keep that from happening, it was *so* tight, I soon felt my lower leg "going to sleep." Ankle holsters are *extremely* "individual needs intensive."

As you read the comments on ankle rigs by four masters of the topic who cover multiple generations – Cunningham, Gaylord, Nonte, and Bianchi – notice some advice they have in common. Cunningham and Gaylord make it clear that the only time it's a good idea to carry the primary gun here is when, for reasons of a tactical or lifestyle nature, you *can't* carry your primary handgun in a more accessible place. Note that Nonte and Bianchi emphasize its use for *backup* as opposed to primary handguns. Hmmm...a consensus emerges: it is not a great idea to carry the only gun you have, strapped to what is probably the part of your body that is farthest from your gun hand.

The Rationale of the Ankle Holster

Gaylord's passage above typifies why his one and only book was like pemmican: thin, but meaty and full of nutrients. In those short paragraphs, Gaylord explained the ankle rig's many advantages. It's *great* for accessibility when

seated, as he noted, and more important in our time than in Gaylord's because of mandatory seatbelt laws. A person strapped into a car seat will often have difficulty reaching a handgun in the usual location, the strong-side hip area.

When you are down on your back, with a bad guy on top of you, your body weight is no longer pressing down on the legs, and your balance is no longer dependent on having two feet solidly on the ground. Your back is bearing your weight, and now it's a piece of cake to snap your foot toward your hand and your hand toward your ankle, making for an *extremely* fast ankle holster draw.

Many years ago, I wrote an article for *Combat Handguns* magazine that extolled the virtues of the ankle holster for backup carry. It included cases like the officer in the Miami area who was caught off-guard by two vicious armed robbers who disarmed him of his duty weapon at gunpoint. They ordered him to his knees and prepared to execute him. Stalling for time, he begged, "Wait! Let me pray first." The two thugs looked at each other and laughed mockingly.

The cop had the last laugh, though. As they turned to look at each other to mock what they thought was a helpless victim, the kneeling cop reached back to his ankle and came up with a blazing Smith & Wesson Model 60. He wiped the laughter off with a 38 Special hollowpoint fired

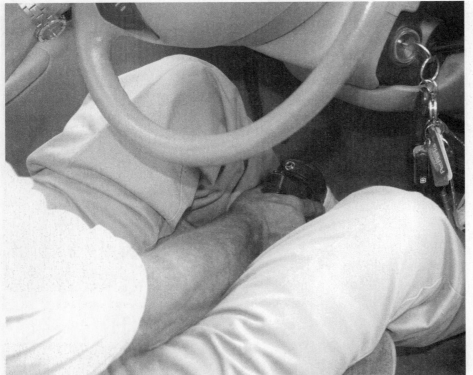

Ankle holster is ideal for seated practitioner, as here in driver's seat.

blew away several teeth, and badly lacerated his tongue. Reflexively, he jerked the 38 from the ankle holster at the same time.

The would-be cop-killer tried to bolt another shell into the chamber to finish the job.

He never made it. The cop's backup Colt was barking now, and five of the six hollowpoints he fired buried themselves into the attacker's body. The attempted murderer went down for the count before he could fire again.

The officer lost some of his sense of smell and taste, and some hearing on the left side. His face was scarred, but plastic surgery reconstructed his jaw. Last I knew, he was back to work on full duty. The ankle gun – and his alertness, and his plan – had saved his life.

Another who read that article was an African-American security professional who worked in plainclothes in a large pharmacy in upstate New York. His carry gun was a Smith & Wesson Model 10 38 Special in a shoulder holster, and after reading that particular issue of *Combat Handguns* he supplemented it with a five-shot Charter Arms Undercover snub-nose 38 Special in a Bianchi ankle holster. Part of his duties included the mission euphemistically known as "loss prevention," and the day came one winter when he spotted a large Caucasian male shoplifting African-American oriented cosmetics and hair care products. Noting the "booster's" odd choice of merchandise to steal, he followed him past the checkout counters and discreetly accosted him in the foyer of the store just before he could exit.

What the security man could not have known at the time was that he was dealing with a total whack job. The suspect was a white supremacist who tended to establish relationships with women of subnormal intellect, always choosing black women as if he was acting out some sick fantasy of being a slave-master. He kept his victims at his home in a state of virtual bondage. It was later theorized that he stole things for them because he didn't think black people were worth spending money on.

And now, a black male authority figure was about to "arrest" him. The man went nuts.

He violently attacked the security man, a slightly built fellow much smaller than himself. The fight carried out into the slushy winter street, and the powerful offender literally "ripped his arm out of the socket," causing a separation of the right shoulder that tore out the rotator cuff. His dominant arm disabled, the guard was knocked down, and in the struggle for his service revolver that followed, the Smith & Wesson went skittering out into the wet street.

The big white guy jumped up. Leaving his opponent supine and battered on the sidewalk, the supremacist ran

into each of their sneering faces.

That story and others like it apparently resonated with some of the readers. Several folks got back to me to say the article had convinced them to carry ankle guns for backup.

And two of those folks told me it had saved their lives.

One was a cop down south. He had noticed that the department issue gun/holster combination, a Smith & Wesson Model 686 in a Safariland Level III retention holster, did not allow him to draw when he was seat-belted behind the steering wheel of his cruiser. The rearward rock required to clear that particular piece of leather could not be accomplished, because the butt of his service revolver was already pressed against the rear of the seat. After reading the article, he went out and bought an ankle rig and a Colt Agent lightweight 38 Special revolver with two-inch barrel.

He got into the habit of dropping his hand to his inside lower leg and taking a drawing grasp when any stranger approached his patrol car to talk to him through the driver's window. None ever spotted the casually dropped arm, or his ready-to-draw status.

The night came when a furtive-looking man in an overcoat incongruous with the warm weather approached his parked cruiser at a rapid pace. The officer put his hand on the ankle rig. He was starting to say "Can I help you?" when the man swept the coat open and swung up a sawed-off bolt-action shotgun.

The cop's alertness had saved him. He saw it coming and he jerked his head back, almost out of the line of fire. As the sawed-off shotgun (a .410 and not a 12 gauge, thank God) went off in his face, he had pulled his head back enough to save the eyes and the brain, but the blast shattered his jaw,

Ankle draw is ideally suited to supine "downed defender." Here, unimpeded by body weight, "holster leg" begins to flex upward as gun hand begins its reach…

…moving toward each other, hand and ankle meet and draw begins…

…reciprocal movement reverses at this stage of supine ankle draw, with gun hand pulling back and holster-leg pushing forward and down to separate gun and holster…

…and holster-leg pushes itself down and clear of muzzle as practitioner prepares to fire upward in self-defense. Hardware here is "baby Glock" in 40, Gould & Goodrich ankle holster.

into the street reaching for the revolver. As he bent to pick it up he screamed, "I got your gun and you're dead meat now, Nigger!"

This turns out to be a really stupid thing to say to a black man who carries a second gun.

By the time the attacker was coming up with the six-shot S&W, the good guy already had the Charter Arms out of the ankle rig and trained on him. There was nothing left to do. He shot the assailant in the head. The bullet killed him instantly, saving the life of the security professional and perhaps, the lives of five or so witnesses the nut case would have been able to murder after he had slain the security man.

There was another case that I didn't come into until after the shooting. I was hired as an expert witness for the involved officer in the lawsuit that evolved from the justified homicide. The defendant was a California Highway Patrolman, who supplemented his standard Smith & Wesson service sidearm with a Smith & Wesson Model 36 Chiefs Special 38 snub in a Bianchi ankle holster. He pulled over a lone motorist for an open container violation after seeing him drive his pickup truck while sipping from a can of Coors Light. As he searched the truck subsequent to the stop, the driver sneaked his hand into the bed of the pickup and came up with a deadly, 28-ounce framing hammer.

He swung it at the officer, hitting him so hard he broke

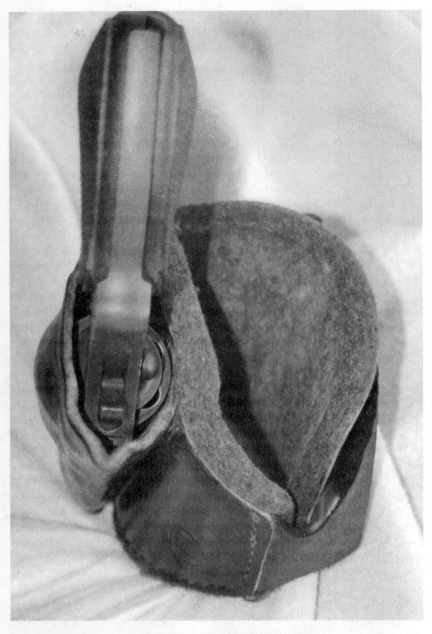

Snub-nose revolver and ankle holster are a timeless combination. This is lightweight Colt Agent 38 Spl. in ankle rig made by DeSantis for Personal Protection Systems, tightly boned for friction fit and maximum speed with silent, surreptitious draw. All-wool felt lining drinks up sweat.

his neck. As the officer staggered back, the man hammered him again, center chest, apparently trying to rupture the heart. The officer's concealed body armor, complete with steel trauma plate, saved him from death but the force of that blow knocked him backwards. As he felt himself losing his balance and about to pass out, he drew his duty gun and opened fire. Then everything went black.

The highway patrolman awoke flat on his back, and realized that his dropped gun was between him and the offender, who was on his hands and knees shaking his head like a mad bull. The offender glared at him with

a look of baleful hatred, and reached for the dropped Smith & Wesson. The state policeman realized that the bad guy could reach the gun before he could.

But fortunately, he had another.

His hand flashed to his ankle, and he came up shooting with the stubby backup gun. Five shots, five hits, and the suspect went down. This time he didn't get back up. He died in the hospital of a total of nine gunshot wounds. The highway patrolman was forced to retire as a result of his injuries. The gun in the ankle holster saved his life.

Contraindications

The ankle holster is not for everyone, and it is not for every situation. I totally agree with Nonte and Bianchi that its best role is for *backup* guns, and that it's not a good choice for carrying the primary defensive handgun. It is simply too far away from the reaching hand. It will be very difficult to reach an ankle holster while grappling with a standing man, and it's not terribly easy to draw from even while standing *still*.

Remember that article I mentioned a few paragraphs back, which convinced at least two readers to acquire the ankle holsters that wound up saving their lives? Well, another reader had what he considered a more negative experience, and wrote an angry letter to the editor that got published. I don't have it in front of me, and therefore can't quote it verbatim, but basically, it went like this:

"Ayoob and his damn ankle holsters! After I read his article I decided to start carrying my gun on my ankle. It could have got me killed!"

He continued, "There I was, walking down the street when four black guys came at me very swiftly. I tried to reach my gun. I couldn't. I bent over to get my gun and I couldn't get the pants cuff up in time! They went on past me, and..."

You caught it, huh? "They went on past me..."

You know, I don't mind folks criticizing what I write, but I wish they'd *read* it first. It would save angst on both sides.

First, I had never said that he should carry his one and only defensive firearm strapped around his ankle, about as far from his reach as a standing man can possibly get. I suggested it for *backup*, not for primary. And I still feel the same way.

Second, though, and probably much more important in this case, his inability to draw his gun probably prevented a tragedy. Alarmed by a group of young black men

> **The ankle holster is not for everyone, and it is not for every situation.**

moving rapidly toward him, he had presumed himself to be under attack. Instead of moving off mid-line of the perceived assault, he stood his ground to go for his gun… and then the young men rushed past him. Obviously, he had not been the target of anything except his own paranoia and, some would say, his own preconditioned racial prejudice. The circumstances being what they were, thank God he *didn't* get his gun out of his ankle holster "in time."

I know what he's talkin' about, though. Back in the '70s, I was in a large middle American metropolis on a hot summer day when a Colt Detective Special in an ankle holster seemed to be "enough." As I waited for the elevator at my hotel – a nice one, but on the edge of a rough part of the city – I noticed two young white guys scoping me out. I made eye contact and they both looked away, which is never a good sign.

We all got on the elevator. No attack. So far, so good, because I realized I didn't have a snowball's chance in hell of getting my hand to my ankle from a standing position if these two jumped me in those close confines. As the door opened at my floor, one said a hokey "Well, see ya later" to the other.

I got off the elevator and headed toward my room, noticing out of the corner of my eye that one of them had stepped off a moment behind me and was following me. I reached the corner of the corridor where I had to turn, and looked over my shoulder. The one behind me broke eye contact. Not good. I kept going forward, and realized he was closing the gap.

If there's anything harder to do with an ankle holster than to draw from standing with it, it's trying to draw from *running* with it. A couple of doors ahead, I saw someone else's hotel room door open, with the maid's cleaning cart just inside the doorway. As the one behind me closed the gap, I took a quick couple of steps to the door, and then a fast side-step inside, shoving the cart between me and the open door – not much cover against gunfire, but a useful short-term obstacle against contact assault. As I did so, my right hand went immediately to my left ankle. Entering the room, I'd done a

quick visual, and saw no one there.

The man following me moved jerkily, taken aback by the sudden evasive action. He tried to charge into the bedroom after me, saw me on the other side of the cart…and also saw a blue steel Colt Detective Special. His eyes widened, and he turned toward the direction whence he had come. I saw him raise his palm and move it forward down the hall, in a gesture that said, "Go back!" Then he began running down the hall.

I pulled the cart clear and stepped to the doorway. Sure enough, the guy's accomplice who'd said "See ya later" was planning to see him – and me – sooner, because he had gotten off after all and had been moving behind the first. He was now between him and the corner. The other gestured frantically, said something to him that I couldn't hear, but which made his eyes go wide. He turned and they both disappeared, sprinting toward the elevator.

I silently thanked the absent maid who had left the door open and the cart there. I snapped the Colt 38 back into the ankle holster and went on my way, making a mental note, "Lesson Learned: Ankle holsters for backup *ONLY* from now on!"

For some practitioners, the ankle rig is not the best choice even for backup. We geezers with arthritis find that a leg holster can "grate" on the ankle more than it did when we were younger. Phlebitis, varicose veins, and other circulatory problems can make the constriction of the ankle holster a bad thing. Women by and large have more delicate calves and ankles (and, fashion-wise, higher pant cuffs) than men, and I've found damn few women who like ankle rigs.

Once again, we're dealing with highly individualized needs and decisions. I also know people who've been wearing ankle holsters literally for decades and are perfectly comfortable with them.

Oh, yeah…ankle-deep mud and knee-deep snow don't go well with ankle holsters. Neither do summer shorts.

Comfort Factors

If you've ever worn a pistol at the 3 o'clock position on the belt, right on the

> What worked best for me personally was the type of ankle rig that was backed with all-wool felt.

Colt lightweight Agent 38 snub in this DeSantis holster served author as backup for many years.

STREET TIP: When wearing an ankle holster and crossing your legs, keep the foot of gun-side leg on the ground. Here, Glock 40 is not obvious…

…but here, with wrong leg crossed, ankle holstered handgun becomes glaringly apparent.

hip-bone, you've probably noticed some chafing. The stiff leather, weighted with a steel gun full of lead bullets, is pressing against a bone that has little but skin to shield it. Well, that's going on *big* time down at the old ankle bone when wearing a leg holster.

Most who've carried them for some time concur that the holster and the leg strap should be *soft* and *wide,* and that there should be some sort of *cushion* between the holster and the skin. Unless you have legs like the Incredible Hulk or are carrying a tiny mouse gun, you also probably want a carry that puts the muzzle angled back and the grip angled

forward, to minimize bulge.

That Bianchi ankle holster the New York security pro and the California Highway Patrol officer found perfectly comfortable for all-day wear just didn't work for me. John Bianchi and his design team were famous for their good quality "hard" holster leather, and they brought the concept to this ankle rig. The holster was closed at the bottom, which extended its length slightly and created a blunt edge on the bottom where the relatively heavy leather was stitched together. (The closed bottom kept snow or mud from plugging the gun barrel if the wearer stepped into same.) The back of the rig was amply lined with soft, friendly sheepskin, the purpose being comfort. For the guard and the state policeman, and for a great many other people, it worked. It was comfortable. For them.

Not for me. I loved that finely-made holster, but I just couldn't bond with it. A calf-strap might have pulled it up high enough to make it work for me, but calf straps don't work for me either, as noted earlier. This left the hard bottom edge by the gun's muzzle digging mercilessly into my ankle bone with every step. I finally had to retire the holster, and go with something else.

Another couple of makers did open bottom ankle rigs, superbly crafted of the finest leather, and backed with so much sheepskin that it felt as if I had strapped a pillow to my ankle. Comfort factor was great. Unfortunately, the cushioning was so heavy that it also *looked* as if I had strapped a pillow to my ankle. The darn things bulged too much for my legs. They didn't conceal well, and I finally had to give up on them, too.

What worked best for me personally was the type of ankle rig that was backed with all-wool felt. The felt lining just seems to soak up sweat without leaving the ankle damp, clammy, and chafed. My first such holster was made of synthetic leather by a nameless manufacturer in the early 1970s. It was a prototype that went out to several police equipment dealers. One was my old friend at Scientific Detection Devices, Dick Marple, who passed this sample along to me to "beta test." I loved it, and kept it. The company went out of business – out of the ankle holster business, anyway – and I kept that orphaned, nameless sample until the stitching started to give way many years later. It was great.

I'm partial to the Alessi ankle rig among today's crop. The Renegade holster has earned many fans: flexible, fast, silent, and *very* comfortable. Its only downside is that it wears out sooner than some high quality leather holsters. Being a cheap old guy, I've never trusted myself to throw away things that are starting to wear out. With clothing, that just keeps you off the "best-dressed" list. With defensive gear, it can get you killed. But if you have more self-discipline in that regard

than I, the Renegade may be the perfect ankle rig for you. Galco's Ankle Glove is another very popular holster, with a very well-deserved reputation for comfort and function. The Safariland has also won a lot of fans. I like the Gould & Goodrich ankle rig (I remove the modular calf strap) with thumb break that was developed for a Southern state police agency for their baby Glocks.

Clothing and Gun Considerations

Some of the fashion contraindications to ankle rigs are obvious. They won't work with shorts. They won't work with a lady's Capri or Toreador style pants. Some other contraindications are less obvious, though.

The "barrel" of the lower pant leg needs to be relatively wide, both to conceal the ankle holster and to make it readily available when you need to draw. The straight-cut leg of the pants that come with the classic American

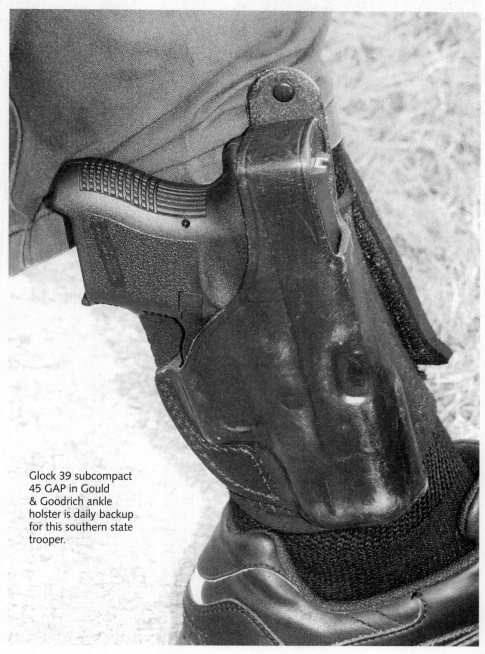

Glock 39 subcompact 45 GAP in Gould & Goodrich ankle holster is daily backup for this southern state trooper.

…only then is loaded baby Glock carefully inserted in holster, with finger off trigger…

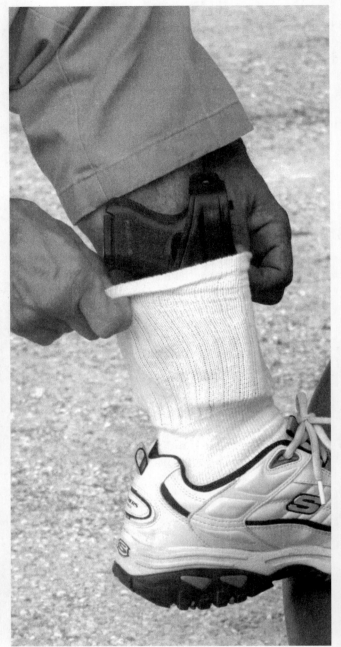

…and finally, sock is pulled up over to better camouflage the hardware. Rig is by G&G, latter tip is from the late, great Chic Gaylord.

men's "sack suit" work fine with ankle holsters, as a couple of generations of lawyers and executives who wear that "uniform" can attest. So do the pants of most Class A police uniforms.

Fatigue or "combat" uniforms may or may not work. BDU (Battle Dress Uniform) pants tend to be cut with very loose legs and cuffs. Good so far. However, if the pant legs are going to be tucked and bloused into high-top combat-style boots, there will be no place for an ankle rig. If you're going to untuck the cuffs with pants like these, that's fine. You can even wear them with boots. Gould & Goodrich is one company that offers a "boot holster" that works like an ankle rig, but is designed to go around large-circumference

combat boots, and even has grommets for the boot lacings to go through. If the pant legs are wide enough, these can work great with boots. Some concealed carry practitioners have gone to the extent of sewing additional lengths of elastic and Velcro onto regular ankle holsters so they can go around a boot.

However, if you're going to do this with BDU pants, *remove the string ties at the cuff!* Designed to keep the pant legs in place when bloused into high top boots, the string ties serve no purpose at all when the boots are inside the pant leg. However, those loose "strings" *can get caught inside the trigger guard as you are putting the pistol into the ankle rig! Your hand is likely to reflexively*

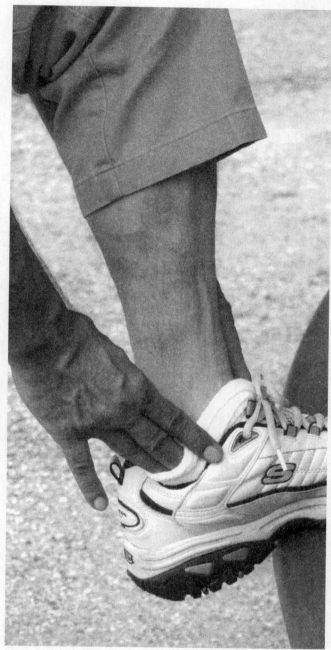

Here's how to put on an ankle holster for maximum concealment. First, roll sock down (thin white cotton sock can optionally be worn underneath if wearer is allergenic)…

…now, empty holster is strapped on snugly (tip from Richie Rosenthal, NYPD retired)…

keep pushing…and it is now pushing the trigger against the obstacle. This can lead to shooting yourself in the ankle or foot by accident! If you're going to carry this way, *remove the string ties from the cuffs of the pants!* You're doing it for the same reason we remove the string closures from warm-up jackets and windbreakers and sweatshirts when we carry guns at belt level: they can get into the trigger guard and lead to an accidental discharge.

Going to casual wear, if you're wearing an ankle holster you want your jeans or cords to have, minimum, "boot cut" cuffs. The bell-bottoms of the '70s (now back in style in some quarters and known as "flares") are even better. This gives lots of room so the pants cuff can be brought up more

quickly and smoothly, and that extra room makes it less likely that the "handle" or any other part of the gun will snag the fabric and interrupt a fast, life-saving draw. Gun guy and knife designer Blackie Collins came out with Toters jeans, expressly designed for carrying guns. They're loose in the waist for IWB, side and hip pockets are set up expressly for pocket guns and pocket holsters…and the cuffs are loose enough to work just fine with most ankle holsters.

Loosely cut pleated pants of the style popularized by Dockers are great for concealed carry. The slightly billowed legs do a great job of hiding small handguns in pocket holsters, and the loose cuffs work extremely well with ankle rigs.

If you're going to carry in an ankle holster, practice drawing and shooting that way! Here a line of Georgia State Troopers qualify with their backup mini-Glocks, all drawn from G&G ankle rigs.

You'll occasionally see pants with legs slit up a few inches from the cuffs, held closed by zippers or Velcro. I for one don't care for them. Having to open this slit adds another fine-motor movement that greatly slows the draw, and ankle holster draw is slow enough as it is. Zippers, and particularly Velcro, make a distinctive sound when opened. This blows the surreptitious draw of the kind that saved the officer's life in the Miami area incident described above. And, as we all know, zippers can stick and "jam." I wouldn't trust either of these trouser cuff designs for ankle carry.

One gun-specific piece of clothing worthy of note in this regard is the series of BDUs by Woolrich in their Elite series, and by some other makers, which have Velcro-closed cargo pockets not only at the thighs, but low at the calves. Smokers often use them for cigarette packs. A friend of mine on the Woolrich Elite beta testing team discovered that they could also carry very comfortably, at least for him, a tiny Kel-Tec P32 pistol. This particular backup gun may only be a 32 auto, but it weighs well under ten ounces – less than the famously tiny Baby Browning 25 auto – and is wafer-thin. He finds it doesn't bump against his leg, and it carries above the ankle bone. It's on the outside of the leg, not the inside, and the user has to rip open a Velcro flap to get at it. It's not my choice, but for a very small gun, it's one more option and a legitimate variation of "ankle carry."

Let me share a couple of tricks to enhance comfort with ankle holsters. I was still a kid in public school when

I read Chic Gaylord's *Handgunner's Guide* and saw his trick of pulling the outer sock up over the ankle holster. Good trick then; good trick now. When the trouser cuff comes up as you sit down, others in the restaurant or at the board meeting don't see the bottom edge of a boned and sculptured holster or, God help us, the muzzle of the gun. What they see is a bunched up, baggy sock. Might get you a warning citation from the Fashion Police, but won't draw the attention of the Gun Police.

As soon as I started packing in an ankle rig, I took advantage of Gaylord's wisdom. I discovered that depending on the type of male hosiery, the socks wear out two to four times faster than normal, or worse, depending how "fat" the package of the ankle-holstered gun may be. I learned with a handgun that had a conventional hammer spur or with adjustable sights to not let the top edge of the sock come anywhere near that point. What mid-20th century gun expert Paul B. Weston called the "Fish-Hook" effect of the hammer spur, or the sharp edge of an upraised rear sight, can catch on the top edge of the sock and snag, dangerously and perhaps even lethally stalling your draw. (Once the sock is rolled down to the proper point, I never found them to creep back up. Worn socks tend to creep down, sort of like the abdomens of guys my age.) One officer survival manual got this concept mixed up a bit, and illustrated the principle with an executive-length sock pulled entirely up over the semi-auto pistol they depicted in an ankle holster, hiding the whole gun butt and grip frame under the sock. A classic case of "people unclear on the concept."

Some folks are allergic to wool, and might otherwise have hypersensitive skin in the ankle area that makes it unworkable for them to wear an ankle holster against bare skin. In that case "neutral" or hypoallergenic white cotton socks can be worn under the ankle holster, between the rig and the skin, and the regular sock then pulled up over the ankle-holstered pistol.

I learned another useful ankle holster trick from Richie Rosenthal, an NYPD veteran who at one time worked at that department's excellent FTU (Firearms Training Unit) and went on, if memory serves, to become a chief of police in Massachusetts. Rich made the point that to get the most perfect, secure, snug fit of holster to ankle, one should leave the ankle holster *empty* to start. Put it on and adjust it until it feels just right. *Now* insert the loaded handgun, and *voila:* you have a much more secure and stable fit of the whole gun and rig. Pulling the sock up over it for added discretion

won't change anything. Thanks, Rich.

Some handguns work a *lot* better than others in ankle holsters. In one of his movies – I think it was *Kindergarten Cop,* but I'm an old guy working on memory here – the director had Arnold Schwarzenegger carrying a full-size Beretta 92 pistol in an ankle holster. Now, there are a good many cops and a good many more soldiers and Marines who have carried that pistol in an exposed duty holster, and found it a little large for even *that* application. In an *ankle holster,* there just ain't no way, even for someone Schwarzenegger's size.

A couple of other Hollywood paradigms come to mind. In one of the *Naked Gun* police spoofs, a senior detective is seen struggling desperately like Houdini trying to escape a cocoon of ropes, trying to get his revolver out of an ankle holster. Gotta laugh. That's probably just what it feels like trying to get the wrong gun out of the wrong ankle holster hidden under the wrong kind of trousers.

On the *Miami Vice* TV series, shot on location in Miami,

If ankle gun works the same as primary holster gun, all the better. Each Georgia State Patrol trooper is issued a full-size Glock 37 and subcompact Glock 39, both chambered for 45 GAP.

Ankle holster works very well from kneeling, provided that holster leg is UP and it's the OTHER leg that's in knee contact with ground.

that gun on. Not to put too fine a point on it, he actually stood and extended his arms while the aide slipped the shoulder harness on for him, like a butler helping the master slip into his dinner jacket.

More proof that in the real world, you can't walk around concealing a large auto pistol under a tightly fitted Armani suit, *or* a chunky 45 auto in an ankle rig under tight, "trim-fit" jeans. "Only in Hollywood…"

Unless you're a huge person with huge, baggy pants, you'll need a compact gun for ankle work. I know some cops who've carried Glock 19, Glock 23, Glock 30, and Glock 29 pistols in ankle holsters. They're all big guys with legs like trees. Average size people will need smaller guns.

Most small pocket autos do not thrive in ankle holster carry. The ankle rig holds the gun literally only a few inches above the ground. Every step you take is kicking up dust and dirt from the sidewalk and even mud and muck from bare ground. Anyone who has carried an ankle holster for any length of time has noticed that after just a day, protectively pulled-up socks notwithstanding, the gun is covered with a fine film of dust and grit. The longer that goes on, the more crap builds up *on* it and starts getting *into* it. I've seen the hammer-slots of shrouded revolvers, Colt snubbies with Colt or Waller hammer shrouds, and the S&W Bodyguard series and the analogous Taurus model, literally filled with "dust bunnies."

The interesting thing is, double-action revolvers always seem to work, even when they're covered with dust. Small, tightly fitted "pocket pistols" of the Walther PPK type, and virtually every 25 auto I've worked with, have such tightly fitted parts that they're prone to choking on that dust and grit once the shooting starts and the slide has to cycle. I've run across cases of ankle-holstered 380s jamming that way, from Florida to California, when the chips were down.

I can count on my fingers the small autos with "mil-spec" fitting that will survive that sort of abuse and still work. The baby Glocks, the Kahrs, and the Kel-Tecs come to mind.

It's a good idea to avoid "rubber" grips on ankle-holstered handguns. Their tacky surface will tend to bind with the inner fabric of the trouser leg, slowing or even stalling the draw.

Don Johnson as lead character carried a big autoloader (10mm Bren Ten or S&W 45, depending on the season) and a Detonics Combat Master subcompact 1911 45 in a nylon ankle holster. He also wore snug jeans or tight Armani suits. How did he conceal that hardware under that garb?

Turns out he didn't. One scriptwriter for the show was one of my graduates, and so was technical advisor Bob Hoelscher, an ace veteran of the Metro-Dade police department. I wound up visiting the set with my family while the crew was filming an episode on location in Miami. We noticed that one member of the crew seemed to have the sole, specific task of holding the shoulder-holstered duty auto and the ankle-holstered Detonics. Only when a scene required the gun to show or to come into action did Johnson actually strap

Two ankle holsters, three options. 1) use holster at top, with calf strap. 2) use same holster and lose calf strap. 3) "boot holster" at left goes *outside* patrol boot but still under trouser cuff; note grommets for boot laces. Both by G&G, shown w/baby Glocks.

Lighter is better for ankle holsters. Comfort is obviously one big reason for that statement, but a less obvious reason is security. When running, jumping, rolling on the ground or otherwise performing strenuous activity, if the ankle rig is an open top design (or if its safety strap has come undone), the heavier gun is more likely to come out of the holster "by itself." The heavier gun develops more momentum with all that bouncing. It will take proportionally more violent movement to dislodge a lighter gun. An AirLite Titanium or Scandium J-frame snub is less likely to bounce out of an unsecured ankle rig than an aluminum-framed Airweight, and the Airweight in turn will be more likely to stay in place in the same holster under the same circumstances than a still heavier, all steel version of the same revolver.

Gould & Goodrich ankle holster. Note optional, modular calf strap, and soft sheepskin lining to cushion sensitive ankle-bone.

Bottom Line

Good news is that the ankle rig can be a life-saver in terms of backup, especially if you find yourself down on your back or in a seated position when you need to draw. Bad news is it's uncomfortable, tough to reach from a standing position, and particularly demanding of certain clothing styles and of a holster style adapted to the individual wearer.

NON-TRADITIONAL CARRY METHODS

Model 640-1 S&W 357 Magnum, with Magna-Port recoil reduction treatment. Note Barami Hip-Grip, which serves revolver inside waistband without a holster.

There are certain non-traditional methods of concealed carry that are, for good or ill, in wide use. They bear discussion for that reason alone. The first point of discussion needs to be this: *every single one of them is based on convenience at the expense of serious practicality.*

One of these is so-called "Mexican carry," the gun simply shoved into the waistband without benefit of holster. The term is not pejorative. It arose long ago among gun people, in *homage* to proud Mexican men of the 19th and early 20th centuries. Beset by tyrants who stripped them of liberties,

Guardian Leather Portfolio looks like a lawyer's briefcase, but contains a hidden bullet-resistant panel…

including the right to carry guns if they were not part of the political elite, these defiant citizens chose to carry as an expression of "willful civil disobedience." They needed to be able to ditch the gun to be retrieved later if they were about to have contact with *Federales,* and since a holster could not be so quickly ditched and would be *prima facie* evidence of resistance to tyrants' law, the holster was dispensed with.

This turns out to work reasonably well with a flat-sided automatic, like the 1911 38 Super that was so popular in Mexico, the 45-caliber version having been banned as a "government-only caliber." However, the gun can come loose with strenuous activity, and can slip out when lying down for a siesta. There is no retention against a snatch, of course. It also tends to get gun oil all over the clothing.

"Improved Mexican carry," as it were, would be an attachment on the gun that keeps it from at least slipping down the pants leg. The Barami Hip Grip for revolvers and the Brown & Pharr belt clip for the 1911 serve this purpose. They'll keep the gun from sliding *down,* but won't necessarily keep it from sliding up and out. The protruding edge of a Crimson Trace LaserGrip on an auto pistol will have this same effect to some degree.

Personally, I would "go Mex" *only* for very short periods. Getting up to answer the door at 3 AM if I didn't have a holster. Putting the gun away

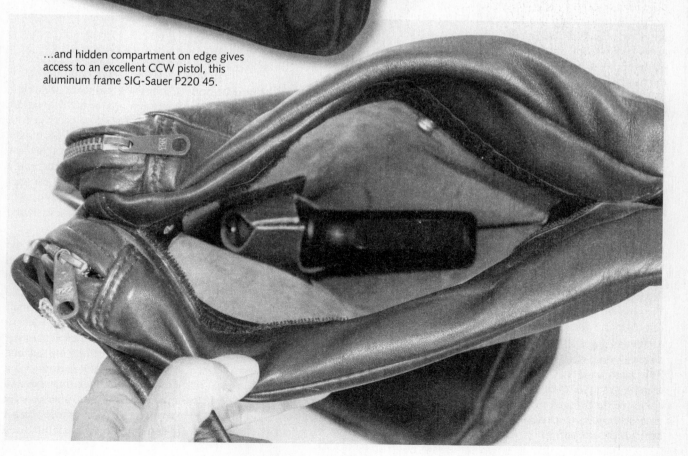

…and hidden compartment on edge gives access to an excellent CCW pistol, this aluminum frame SIG-Sauer P220 45.

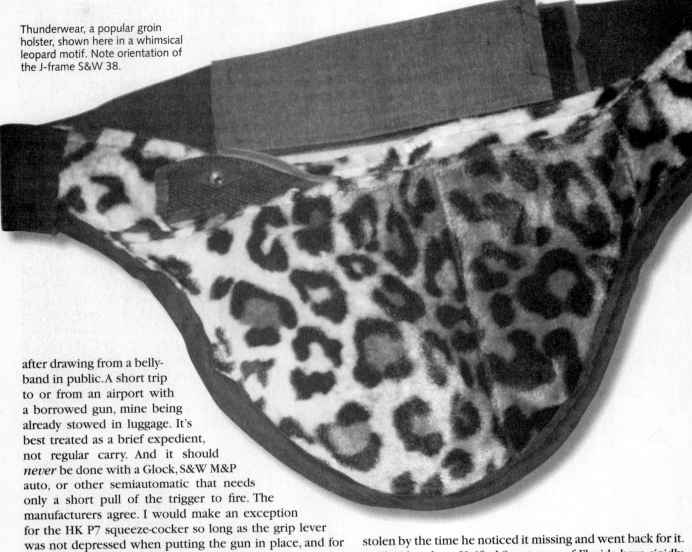

Thunderwear, a popular groin holster, shown here in a whimsical leopard motif. Note orientation of the J-frame S&W 38.

after drawing from a belly-band in public. A short trip to or from an airport with a borrowed gun, mine being already stowed in luggage. It's best treated as a brief expedient, not regular carry. And it should *never* be done with a Glock, S&W M&P auto, or other semiautomatic that needs only a short pull of the trigger to fire. The manufacturers agree. I would make an exception for the HK P7 squeeze-cocker so long as the grip lever was not depressed when putting the gun in place, and for the XD pistol if inserted with thumb on back of slide to keep the grip safety from being pressed during "holsterless holstering." Otherwise, I would stay with an auto whose manual safety was engaged, or which had a long and heavy double-action trigger pull design, or a pistol carried Israeli-style with empty chamber.

Off-Body Carry

The purse, the "man-purse," the briefcase and the short-lived "dayplanner portfolio that hides a gun" were all designed for convenience. A slowed access to the weapon was traded for greater physical comfort and wardrobe flexibility, in return for having a gun around us *somewhere*. In most situations, if safety and confidence and peace of mind are the goals, this is not a fair trade.

Purses get *snatched*. Briefcases get *stolen*. Neither is always within reach when we need what they contain. And how many times have we had to go back and get a purse or attaché case we left behind in another's home or office, or some public place? One time while in South Africa, I saw a man sentenced to prison for criminal negligence because he had left his gun purse in a restaurant, and it had been stolen by the time he noticed it missing and went back for it. In Florida, where Unified Sportsmen of Florida have rigidly kept track of all offenses involving concealed carry permit holders, the miniscule number of arrests seem to mostly involve people who forgot the gun was in their attaché case or purse when they went through a metal detector into a secured area such as airport or courthouse. When the gun is not on us to remind us of its presence, it is all too easy to forget that it is there. This can lead to huge and devastating consequences.

If you accept the trade-offs and still want this stuff, the best "gun purses" I've personally seen are the ones from Coronado and Galco. The best carry case I've seen is the Guardian Leather Portfolio, which resembles a fine lawyer's briefcase with shoulder strap, but carries a bullet-resistant panel and hidden quick-access gun pouch. It's no trick to learn to draw the handgun to a one-hand stance as the free hand sweeps the ballistic-reinforced Portfolio up against the front of your torso. Blackhawk recently introduced a similar model in plain black nylon, though you may have to find your own ballistic insert for it. I've found them useful for court…just remember to take the gun out before you hit the security checkpoint!

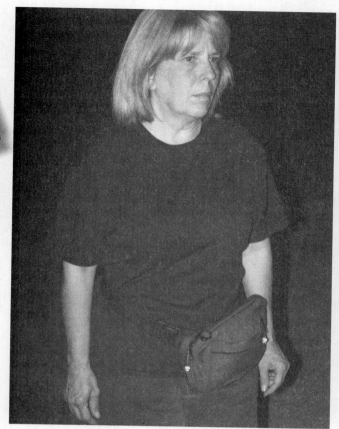

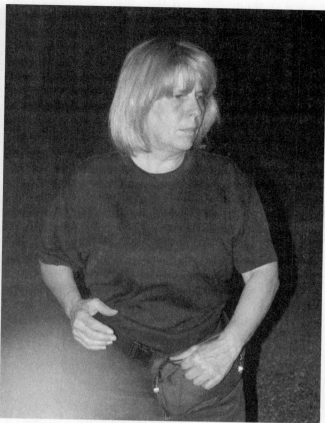

Gail Pepin, 2-time Florida/Georgia regional IDPA woman champion, demonstrates fanny pack draw with Safe Direction product…

…support hand grasps drawstring release, and gun-hand-side hip comes back to angle weapon toward threat, as right hand…

… brings up the Kahr 40 cross-draw, free hand rises into blocking position and out of way of gun muzzle…

…and comes up in classic Weaver stance, a natural posture for any type of cross draw.

Author feels its safe enough to carry XD45 "Mexican style," so long as grip safety is not depressed. He still does not recommend the practice, however.

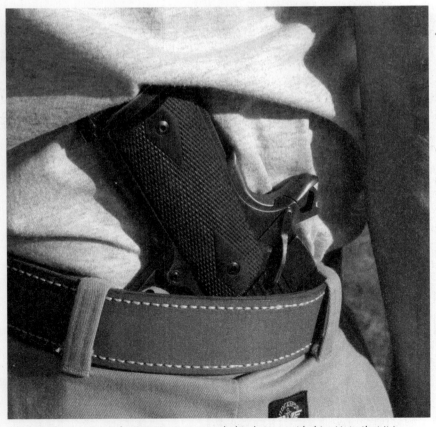

Kimber Classic 45 in "classic" Mexican carry behind strong side hip. Note that it is cocked and *locked!*

Fanny Packs

Ever since Gene DeSantis created the first firearms-specific fanny pack, the Gunny Sack, these things have been hugely popular. They can be carried off-body with the strap slung over the shoulder, but have the added advantage of securing on the body in their normal intended fashion. Gun folks like to sew Nike or Nikon labels to the front, and order them in bright pastel colors, to distract from any "gun" image. (Interestingly, joggers always ask pistol packers where to buy cool black nylon fanny packs like ours, that won't show the dirt. The grass is always greener…) The fanny pack can be easily unbuckled and left in the car when going into the post office, hospital, or other "gun-free zone."

Downsides? Thieves assume fanny packs contain wallets, so they're prime targets for theft when off your body, and even for snatching when strapped on. As with purses, having your gun in the thing the assailant is likely to grab first is not a good start to the fight. Moreover, they're slow to draw from, needing one hand to rip the thing open while the other goes for the gun, and *achingly* slow if that free hand is tied up warding off a knife-wielding opponent. Still, they're better than no gun at all. Practice, practice, practice. Centerline of the body is the best place to carry, I've found, and regular cross draw techniques are the way to draw to a fighting stance from the fanny pack. DeSantis has been making these longer than anyone else, and it shows: I've seen none better. However, I've become partial to the well-made Safe Direction from Steve Camp. Its back panel is bullet-resistant Kevlar, giving the lower abdomen some protection in a fight. More to the point, though, the whole Safe Direction line is designed to give you something to point at (the proverbial "safe direction") when routinely loading, unloading, and dry-firing handguns. Just make sure it's not strapped on your body during *these* proceedings.

Groin Holsters

Hiding below the belt and above the pubes under your pants, rigs like Thunderwear and Smart Carry resemble thin fanny packs worn between the

underwear and the trousers. I've found them uncomfortable, and particularly awkward in men's rooms. To get at the gun, the drawing hand knifes down the inside of the front of the pants, preferably aided by a support hand that pulls the front of the waistband out away from the body. Personally, I find these holsters give me the creeps, but a lot of knowledgeable people with dress codes that make their option "this or nothing" have found such groin holsters an acceptable trade-off. Thunderwear and Smart Carry are both well made, and well designed for their purpose

Bottom line? A conventional holster is generally a better bet than any of the above. However, my situation may not be your situation. The above options do sacrifice practicality for convenience, but sometimes, convenience *is* practicality.

Barami Hip-Grip has been popular for decades. Here, on petite gun shop manager Ashley Reichard, the grip is about all you can see (and a black shirt would camouflage it nicely) …

…but in fact it's a Model 640-1 S&W 357 Magnum, with Magna-Port recoil reduction treatment and an action job by her famous dad, Denny.

Chapter 16

CONCEALING LARGER HANDGUNS

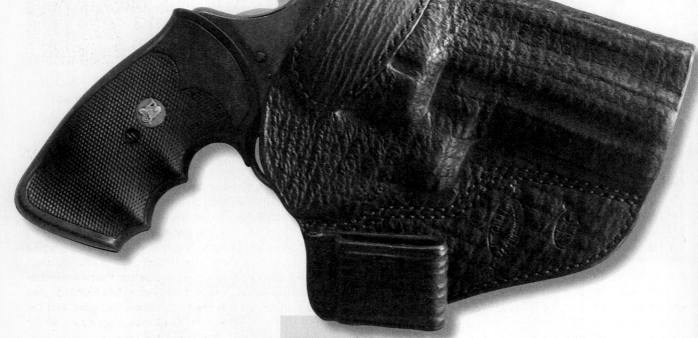

With some thought applied to holsters and wardrobe, the good guy with the larger gun can improve survival potential and save money at the same time!

Four-inch barrel 41-frame Colt Python 357 Magnum rides in Ayoob Rear Guard holster rendered in sharkskin. Securing the gun inside the waistband enhances concealment.

With more fine, powerful, very small and light handguns than ever, why would someone want to wear a full-size service pistol concealed? There are several good answers to that question.

For many, the reason is commonality of training. Let's say you're a military person

who will be issued an M9 pistol in combat, and you've cared enough about your skill at arms to purchase your own identical Beretta 92 pistol for practice. Or, you're a police officer who has been issued a full-size Beretta, Colt, Glock, HK USP, Ruger, SIG, or S&W service pistol. Your employer has not only paid for the gun and ammo and magazines, but has paid you to train with that particular gun until you can use it to the best of your ability.

Certainly, you can buy a smaller version of your duty pistol for concealment and transfer much of that skill. A Mini-Cougar from Beretta, any of several subcompact 1911s, the baby Glock, the USP Compact, or the flat little P239 from SIG or Model 4040 from S&W will share a high degree of "commonality of training" with their companion models of full size service weapons. However, if you carry the service pistol itself, you have 100 percent commonality of training with on-duty and off-duty carry since you're using the same pistol for both purposes.

Money is an issue. That chopped and channeled mini-1911, baby Glock, or whatever will cost you several hundred dollars. For well under $100, you can purchase a suitable concealment holster that lets you discreetly wear off-duty the pistol you already have for on-duty carry.

This is why the topic of the cop using the issue gun off duty versus buying his own off duty weapon can be a controversial one. There are two sides. At this point in my life, I buy and carry my own, and use the "company guns" only when working for the PD. This is because I travel a lot, and if I'm involved in a self-defense incident in another jurisdiction, I don't want a money-hungry plaintiff's lawyer thinking my use of a department gun could tie in the department, and its community's tax base, for a deep-pockets lawsuit. Having dealt with several such sharks, I'd rather keep that blood out of the water. At the same time, I remember being a young cop, not making much money, and a quality personal handgun being a significant expense that could cut into family needs. Each officer has to weigh and balance and make his or her own choice in the matter. The important thing is to carry *some* high quality handgun of adequate power off duty.

For some, the difference in performance between the small gun and the big one is dramatic. Back in the days when cops all wore revolvers, it was a four-inch gun or larger for uniform wear and typically a small-frame model with a two-inch barrel for plainclothes. Many an officer who qualified just fine with the full-size six-gun simply couldn't make the grade with the snubby; it was that much more difficult to shoot well.

There is less performance difference between the full size and subcompact police service "automatics" of today than there was between the revolvers that preceded them. Still, though, there are some advantages to the bigger guns. A friend of mine works for the FBI and was given the choice of the full-size Glock 22 or the compact Glock 23, both firing the same 40 S&W duty loads. He appreciated the greater concealability of the G23 under the suit he wears to work, but he still chose the bigger G22 for one reason: he shoots it just a little bit better than he does its little brother. If he has to pay more attention to his wardrobe and holster selection to gain absolute maximum combat shooting performance,

Top, Ruger Redhawk .44 Magnum; below, Ruger GP100 .357. The GP is a pretty big gun, and the Redhawk is relatively huge, but with the right gear the committed user can effectively carry each concealed.

he figures it's a cheap price to pay for an edge that could someday save his life.

I know what he means. I am fond of the 40-caliber Glock in both the full-size G22 configuration and the miniature G27 format. The little one, of course, is much easier to conceal. From the bench at 25 yards, the little one is actually a little bit more accurate than the big one. It'll put five 155-grain Winchester Silvertips into an inch and a half at that distance, and its big brother will seldom do better than two inches even with the load it likes best, the Black Hills EXP 165-grain JHP. But the big gun handles better when the speed and the pressure are on. The toughest qualification approved by my state, known as Course Five, comprises 36 rounds from three to twenty-five yards in time frames as fast as two shots in three seconds from the leather. In qualification mode on the B27 target, where anything inside the competition 8-ring is worth five out of five points, I can score 180 out of 180 possible with either. But when it goes to the tighter rings of competition scoring, I'll be in the 355 out of 360 range with the full-size Glock 22, but will only score around 345 with the subcompact Glock 27. Because performance edge is as important to me as it is to my FBI buddy, I, like him, am more likely to carry the Glock 22.

The full-size pistol has another performance edge: the longer barrel generates more pressure from the burning powder within, increasing muzzle velocity. This is particularly important with some rounds, like the 45 ACP, whose velocity falls off dramatically as the barrel is shortened. It can sometimes mean the difference of

Author wins Florida Sunshine Games championship using the big GP100 for Stock Service Revolver class. He wore the same gun concealed to and from the event. It's all about the right holsters and clothes. Holster is Kydex by Blade-Tech.

Concealment Holsters for Big Guns

No question about it, *inside-the-waistband* is the best place for that beast to be if you want to hide it under a minimum of clothing. The concealing garment can rise as high as the lower edge of the belt without revealing the holstered gun, and the fabric of the trousers breaks up the line of the holstered gun when you are seen in silhouette.

There is no more proven inside-the-waistband (IWB) holster than the Summer Special, created by Bruce Nelson and popularized by Milt Sparks. Both of these great holstermakers are gone now, but their work lives on. With a rough-out cut, on the theory that having the rough side of the leather toward the body stabilizes the holster and having the smooth grain side toward the gun speeds the draw, these rigs remain the choice of many gun connoisseurs today. I have several, including one for the N-frame Smith & Wesson which has concealed my 44 Magnum under an untucked bush shirt or jacket in the streets of Johannesburg and Pretoria, and in cities in Europe, without drawing undue notice nor causing undue discomfort.

However, one downside to a rough-out holster is that when you perspire heavily, it is more likely that the sweat will permeate the leather and get to the gun. This can discolor the holster and, worse, rust your finely blued sidearm brown. Milt Sparks himself tacitly recognized this problem, I think, when he encouraged his young protégé Tony Kanaley to design his Executive Companion holster. With the grain outside in the conventional manner, this model seems to protect the pistol better than rough-out designs, and with no perceptible interference with drawing speed or smoothness. The Executive Companion also rides a bit lower than its predecessor, and I for one find that it conceals a bit better as a result.

whether or not the hollow-point bullet you've fired opens up as intended.

For cops, there's another good reason to carry that full-size issue gun. If an officer is involved in a shooting, that expensive pistol can become "evidence" for a period of years until the last civil lawsuit arising from the incident is wrapped up. Even when you get it back, it may be rusty from bloodstains left *in situ* for evidentiary purposes, and its finish may have been ruined by the fingerprinting process. If the expensive gun is going to be lost to you for a period ranging from weeks to years and come back messed up, many cops' reasoning goes, let it be the department's expensive gun instead of your own. Once it is taken for evidence, unless you are indicted or something, they have to issue you a replacement anyway.

So, it may be a performance factor or an economy factor or both that brings you to the decision to use a full-size handgun for concealed carry. Whatever the reason, there are two critical areas you'll have to address in concealing a larger handgun: the holster, and the wardrobe.

Most interpretations of the IWB design have the belt loops at the same point as the gun, causing a little more bulge when the holstered gun is snapped in place. Makers such as Derry Gallagher, and Milt Sparks with the latter's Versa-Max, offer IWB holsters cut with the belt loops fore and aft of the holster body, making for more discreet carry. This also helps to stabilize the holstered gun on the belt, on a principle a bit like Pontiac's old "Wide-Track" concept. The two IWB holsters I designed each tackled that problem a bit differently. When Ted Blocker and I designed the LFI Concealment Rig for his holster company back in the '80s, we went with a Velcro tab instead of belt loops or clips. This mated with Velcro lining in the accompanying dress gun belt. The primary accessory, an IWB magazine pouch, attached the same way. This resulted in minimum bulge, with the added bonus that the wearer could adjust to the exact height and cant angle he liked, and then press the belt

L-frame Smith & Wesson, here the Model 686 in 357 Magnum tuned for maximum performance by Scott Mulkerin and including night sights. With proper holster, and acclimated tolerance of weight, this gun can be carried daily in plainclothes.

down on the Velcro to stabilize the holster solidly in place.

In the '90s, Mitch Rosen asked me to design an IWB for full-size fighting handguns. I made it with a belt loop at the rear of the holster, where it wouldn't add to gun bulge and where it would lever the gun forward in an FBI cant, preventing the common problem of the weight of the ammo in a loaded semiautomatic's butt dragging the pistol rearward to bulgingly "print" through the clothing. Because of this design feature, I called it the Rear Guard. Mitch introduced it as the Ayoob Rear Guard, or ARG. Today

he calls it the American Rear Guard.

There are so many makers of good IWB holsters on the market, that careful shopping will allow you to "mix and match" the features you seek. For instance, the well-made Galco NSA combines the rough-out design of Bruce Nelson's original Summer Special with the rear-mounted belt loop of the Ayoob Rear Guard.

A feature many like is a built-up surface toward the body, to shield the flesh from the gun and vice versa. Sweat contains salt and causes rust. Particularly on individuals with a bit of a spare tire, hard gun edges can dig into the side unmercifully. An integral shield prevents this. You can get it on Sparks leather IWBs, and on Kydex IWBs by SideArmor and other makers.

Another approach to IWB is the so-called *tuckable* holster. The first of these was Rosen's Workman, named after the original designer, Dave Workman. What makes it "tuckable" is a layer of leather in a V-shape connecting the belt loop to the holster body. Inside that deep "V" nestles the shirt-tail of a tucked in shirt. With the shirt very slightly "bloused" over the handgun, the concealed pistol disappears. Workman and Rosen recommend it primarily for

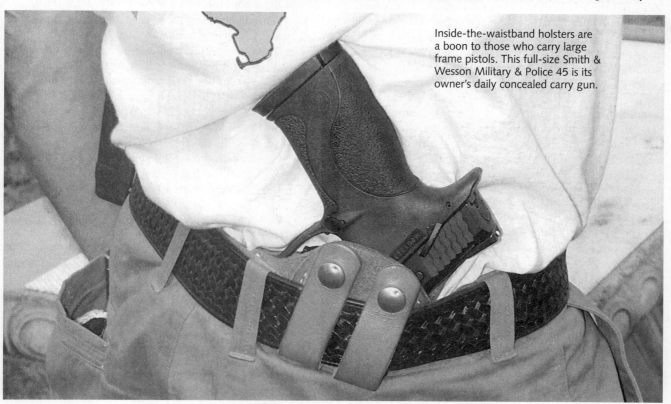

Inside-the-waistband holsters are a boon to those who carry large frame pistols. This full-size Smith & Wesson Military & Police 45 is its owner's daily concealed carry gun.

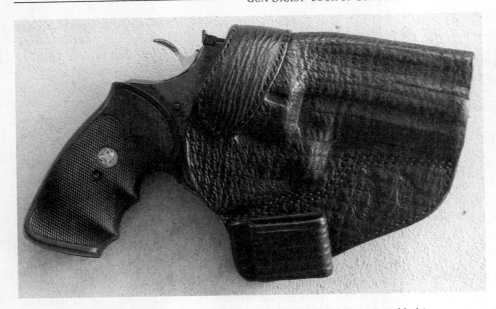

Four-inch barrel 41-frame Colt Python 357 Magnum rides in Ayoob Rear Guard holster rendered in sharkskin. Author has carried big S&W 44 Magnums concealed the same way in U.S., South Africa, and Europe. Securing the gun inside the waistband enhances concealment.

and can be a tactical problem after you have drawn your gun to hold a criminal at bay, and uniformed police are arriving who may not recognize you as a good guy with that big handgun in your fist.

My own favorite of all the many belly-bands I've used, from the original MMGR on up, is the Bianchi Ranger. Superbly made, it also doubles as a money belt and has other hidden pouches for credit cards, ID, etc.

Outside the Belt

Some people just can't bear IWBs. They've bought their pants to fit their waist, not to fit their waist circumference *and* a large-frame holstered pistol. Others have a low waist (read: small butt) and find the front end of a full-size handgun can pinch the buttocks or the back of their thigh when they sit down. Still others may have a "spare tire" that rolls over a gun inside the waistband and inhibits quick draw.

If an outside-the-belt scabbard is chosen, remember that you'll need a longer garment to keep it covered. To hold it tight to your body and minimize "print," you'll want belt attachments both fore and aft. This concept was pioneered back in the 1970s by Roy Baker with his Pancake holster. That rig is no more, but the "pancake" influence has become generic throughout this part of the holster industry.

My own favorites in this style include the Lou Alessi's CQC, designed by my friend and colleague Dave Spaulding, a long time career cop who worked a lot of narcotics and liked having a big automatic where he could reach it quickly in plain clothes. Snapping on and off the belt with sturdy fasteners, it is extremely handy and very well made. Another is the Ted Blocker DA-1 (with thumb-break safety strap) and DA-2 (open top) series. These scabbards have a ring of leather in the front belt loop. Slip it down, and the holster rides on the strong side hip with the FBI style forward tilt that many of us prefer for concealment; slip that loop upward, and the loops are now set to hold the holster vertical (neutral cant), a position favored by some tall men for strong side carry, and the best way to put the holster on the belt for a cross draw. Mike Dillon makes a nice scabbard that I like for double action, on-safe autos because the leather doesn't cover the slide-mounted safety catch, and I can get to it early in the draw. Strong Leather's Piece-Keeper is another of my favorites in this genre. It uses Roy Baker's original three-slot belt cuts to give you forward tilt, neutral cant or cross draw options, and has the added feature of a trick thumb-break safety strap which makes it act

small autos and snub revolvers, and suggest it for nothing larger than a baby Glock. However, if the body shape and the dress code allow it, a full-size 45 auto can be concealed there. Milt Sparks and Elmer MacEvoy's Leather Arsenal are two companies that make convertible IWB holsters that turn into tuckables and can hide even a Colt Government Model under a tucked dress shirt.

Of course, the most "tuckable" IWB option of all is the *belly-band*. It was designed by John Bianchi, who appeared in *Gun World* magazine with a prototype circa 1960. Before he could put it in production, a firm named MMGR in Brooklyn came out with a copy. It was an instant hit. Today, the belly-band is produced by numerous makers in numerous styles, but basically comprises a four-inch wide band of elastic with one or more gun pouches. It is designed to be worn "over the underwear but under the overwear." Carried on the strong-side hip, it is drawn from in the same fashion as a tuckable, by using the free hand to pull up the shirt in the movement known as the "Hackathorn Rip" and then making a conventional draw with the dominant hand. A small handgun on the order of a two-inch 38 can be worn to the side of the belly button for an even faster draw, but any larger handgun will tend to dig into the thigh or groin when you sit or bend.

Selling for as little as $15 for the cheapest, the belly-band is unquestionably the most economical method of carrying a large pistol hidden, and also one of the most effective. With little more than elastic around it, there is no added leather or Kydex to bulge around the gun. However, there is always a price to pay. In almost every model, it is extremely slow and awkward to reholster a drawn gun in a belly-band. This severely hampers critical drawing practice,

If you think you can conceal a big pistol inside a tight-fitting Armani wardrobe, your reality check just bounced.

as a concealable retention holster. I've often used mine to conceal my once-department issue Ruger P90 45 auto, by no means a small pistol.

Clothing Factors

If you think you can conceal a big pistol inside a tight-fitting Armani wardrobe, your reality check just bounced. For an inside-the-waistband holster or belly-band, you want about two inches more in the waist than what you'd normally wear. You wear a size 44 sport jacket in regular sleeve length? You won't be able to button it over a full-size gun in a hip holster without a giant bulge unless you go to a size 46, keeping the same sleeve length of course.

The finest belly-band or tuckable won't hide your blaster under a fishnet shirt. That's an obvious example, though; more to the point, it won't hide well under a thin fabric cotton dress shirt, no matter how finely made the garment. You want a solid weave fabric with a crisp surface. A little bit of starch won't hurt. Vertical stripes will help break up the shape of a concealed handgun under a tucked shirt of any kind.

Untucked shirts – tee shirts, polo shirts, golf shirts – will conceal a full-size combat handgun inside your waistband if they are *(a)* solid fabric, preferably of darker color or patterned; *(b)* straight cut, that is, without any taper toward the waist; and, most important, *at least one size larger than you normally wear.* This will give you the concealing fabric drape that you'll need.

Hawaiian shirts, bowling shirts, Cuban-style *guyebarra* shirts, and square-hem safari shirts are all superb for gun concealment. Just make sure you don't get them in gauzy fabrics, and make sure they're one size large…and that they fit into a wardrobe image that you're comfortable with.

Other Options

Well, let's see. There's the glove box or the desk drawer… but will you be close enough to either location to reach the gun in time when danger threatens? There's the fanny pack…but the heavier the gun, the more pressure the belt strap will put on your lumbar region, and fanny packs are slow in any case. Shoulder rigs? They only conceal under more substantial outer garments for the most part, at least with really big pistols and revolvers. Purses, attaché cases, and even day planners with hidden gun compartments are one answer. Remember, however, that with this "off-body carry" you can accidentally leave the gun in the wrong place, or have it knocked out of your hand at the opening of a surprise encounter.

Of course, there are tweed coats and photographers' vests. Hell, for that matter you can go Gothic and conceal your 50 AE Desert Eagle under a Dracula cape or a big black trenchcoat. The fact is, though, that hiding a gun under a big garment is so easy it doesn't really require you to read a book for advice. Hiding a gun big enough to fight your best with – the best you can do with a handgun, anyway – under something like a tucked in shirt or summer casual wear? *That's* a challenge.

But it's a challenge that the advice above will allow you to meet.

With a longer sight radius, a larger frame that gives the hand more to grasp, and more mass to absorb recoil, full-size service handguns are easier to shoot fast and straight than subcompacts. Here author takes First Master, Custom Defense Pistol Division, at 2007 Pennsylvania State IDPA Championships. He's wearing uniform rig, but the same gun conceals well in any of several holsters. Note that the Ruger 45 is back on target with spent casing from the first shot no more than three inches out of the ejection port.

Chapter 17

IMPROVING YOUR DRAW FROM CONCEALMENT

Here are practical tips for drawing faster and smoother from beneath concealment.

There is a lot of bad advice out there about drawing techniques.

More Americans than ever can now legally carry their handguns concealed. However, not very many of them have as much training and practice in bringing them into action from concealment as some of us would like to see. Even in law enforcement, it is common for plainclothes officers, and cops qualifying with their off duty weapons, to draw from exposed holsters when firing for the record on training days. In NRA's training programs for civilians, the shooter always starts with the pistol or revolver in low ready. If by definition the gun is carried concealed, it is an absolutely critical skill to be able to draw it swiftly, smoothly, and safely from hiding.

There is a lot of bad advice out there on drawing techniques. Some that I've seen demonstrated are nothing less than hazardous. Others are, at best, less efficient than they could be. Let's look at ways of bringing the concealed handgun to bear from the most common carry locations.

First, a few general points, geared primarily to safety.

Do your initial practice with a dummy gun or unloaded gun. It's the equivalent of a student pilot learning on a simulator before taking an actual aircraft aloft. The student should be well practiced and confident in the draw before it is attempted with a loaded gun.

*Always keep the finger completely outside the trigger guard until the gun is drawn and on target, **and the decision to fire immediately has been made!*** Strict adherence to this rule would probably do more to reduce accidental shootings than any other one thing.

Holster as carefully as you draw, with the finger outside the trigger guard and the handgun on safe or decocked. Today, most good quality holsters have covered trigger guards. This industry-wide design change has done much to reduce instances of individuals shooting themselves accidentally as they draw. However, we are seeing too many cases of people shooting themselves while holstering. If the finger is left on the trigger, the portion of the holster that covers the guard interdicts the finger and holds it against the trigger, forcing the trigger back as the holstering movement continues.

Always practice drawing with the gun in a safe direction, bringing it to bear on something that can function as a backstop should the gun accidentally discharge. This is one more "safety net for training." I recommend that those who own body armor use the vest set against a wall or on a chair for this purpose. The Better Bilt Safe Direction unit is expressly designed for this sort of thing.

Strong Side Hip, Open-Front Garment

The most popular carry position among savvy pistol-packers seems to be on the strong-side hip, concealed by an open-front upper body garment. There are many trick techniques for getting at the gun in this location, but many of them don't work if you're seated, up against the wall, or otherwise positioned where the garment can't be swung out behind the holster to clear a path for the reaching hand. I designed the following technique to solve those problems.

Let the gun hand come in and touch the torso at the centerline with all four fingertips, and then – maintaining fingertip contact with your torso – sweep the hand back to the gun. The bottom edge of the hand will not only clear the coat or vest or whatever under the adverse circumstances

described above, but will hold it back out of the way long enough to gain a grasp of the grip-frame if something happens to slow the draw.

Once your hand gets there, grasp the handgun firmly with all fingers but the index, which should be straight outside the holster. The web of the hand should be at the highest possible point on the grip frame. The thumb will at this point release the safety strap if one is in place. Keeping the elbow joint pointed to the rear (so the long bones of your arm will be in line with the direction in which you'll be applying force), clear the gun from the holster with a "rock and lock" movement that levers the muzzle up toward the target as soon as possible. Now, drive the gun forward toward the target.

Throughout the draw so far, the support hand has been at midline of the body. For a combat draw, I prefer the fingertips of the support hand to be pointed forward, which gives the arm more leverage to resist a grab by a close-range opponent. Now, as the gun is coming forward, the support hand takes its position on the firing hand. Be certain that the muzzle of the handgun is well ahead of the support hand before this part of the operation is put into effect.

You now flow into your stance of choice. A double-action auto carried on safe can be thumbed into the "fire" position anywhere during this procedure, but a cocked and locked single-action auto should remain on safe, with the thumb in position on the manual safety, until the decision to fire is made. Only when that decision is made should the trigger finger enter the guard; it should have been "in register" throughout the draw, that is, with the pad or tip of the trigger finger touching the frame above the trigger guard.

Strong-Side Hip, Closed-Front Garment

If the gun is under a buttoned or pullover shirt, a pullover sweater, an anorak or similar garment, it will be more difficult to access. All the same basic rules are in play, you just have to work a little harder.

If both hands are free, grasp the garment at its hem in front of the holster with the free hand, and jerk it upward as high toward the gun arm's shoulder as you can. You may not have enough play in the garment to get the hem that high, but if you try for the shoulder you will probably at least clear the holster area enough for a clean draw. The gun hand now draws exactly the same as it would with the holster in the same strong side position. As the gun comes clear, rock the muzzle on target. The support hand will come in from above and behind the gun, safely clear of the muzzle. This two-handed technique was popularized by my old friend Ken Hackathorn.

> The most popular carry position among savvy pistol-packers seems to be on the strong-side hip, concealed by an open-front upper body garment.

Unfortunately, you won't always have both hands free for this purpose, so of necessity you want to devote about half of your practice drawing from under closed-front garments to the following one-handed technique. Extend the gun hand's thumb toward the body and let it track up the seam of the trousers, or along the common peroneal nerve, toward the gun. This will allow the thumb to lift the garment enough to gain the proper drawing grasp. From there, the draw is the same as above, with one difference: to gain more clearance, I bend my knee slightly on the gun hand side and drop the hip, pulling the gun down and out from under any remaining fabric to prevent it from snagging.

Let me tell you how practice ingrains a technique. Early in 2005, I took a busman's holiday and attended one of my friend and colleague Chuck Taylor's excellent shooting classes as a student. When I was drawing my Glock 17 from under my open-front Royal Robbins 5.11 Concealment Vest, Chuck asked me, "Why do you bend your right knee when you draw?" I was stumped; I didn't even know I'd been doing it. It took me a day to figure out that what I was doing was born of decades of practice in drawing my off-duty gun, usually a 4-inch barrel service revolver or 5-inch barrel combat auto, from under the un-tucked polo or tee shirt that normally concealed it off duty in hot weather. The practice had – harmlessly, it turns out – transferred itself to my regular concealed draw from under an open-front garment.

Shoulder Holster/Cross Draw

Any carry in which the gun is on the side of the body opposite the dominant hand, either butt forward or suspended horizontally or upside down, is some variation of what is called a cross draw. The term "cross draw" is normally applied to a gun holstered on the belt in a butt forward position, but the popular shoulder holster is a variation of cross draw. So is the common practice of attaching a small handgun's holster to the straps on concealed body armor, carrying the gun beneath the armpit on the non-dominant side.

First, if circumstances permit, edge the non-dominant side of the body toward the target. This will minimize a close-range opponent's ability to "jam" or "stall" your draw. It will also minimize the dangerous, inefficient muzzle swing that has caused so many training courses and police departments to ban cross draw holsters.

To keep the muzzle from crossing the non-dominant arm, swing that arm up with the elbow forward and high. It is a movement similar to running your fingers through your hair. It also raises the elbow to a blocking position,

> **Any carry in which the gun is on the side of the body opposite the dominant hand, either butt forward or suspended horizontally or upside down, is some variation of what is called a cross draw.**

refined by master police trainer Kerry Najiola, which can help protect you during a close-range assault.

Reach inside the concealing garment with what a martial artist would call a "knife hand" or "spear hand," with all the fingers pointed straight toward the holster. This slims the profile of the reaching hand and allows it to get to the concealed weapon faster.

As with the straight draw, the hand contacts the gun with the web as high as possible on the back strap, middle through little fingers firmly grasping the frame, and trigger finger straight outside the holster. The thumb releases any necessary safety straps.

Now, pull the gun straight out across the midriff if drawing from the belt, or across the chest if drawing from a shoulder rig. If the body has been properly edged toward the target at the start of the draw, the muzzle should already be in the direction of the target. A straight thrust of the arm toward the target puts you into your stance. Once the muzzle is safely forward, the non-dominant hand drops down and assumes its position in support of the firing hand. Trigger and safety are manipulated as described earlier, with trigger guard kept empty until the decision to fire immediately has been made.

Pocket Holster

All but the most tightly tailored police uniform pants and suit pants will allow a small, light handgun to conceal in a side trouser pocket. So will currently fashionable "pleated pants" of the Dockers style, and cargo pants. In jeans, only a "relaxed fit" cut is likely to be practical for this sort of carry.

Always carry your pocket gun in a pocket holster! This will (*a*) keep its safety catch, if it has one, from being wiped into the "fire" position inadvertently; (*b*) keep the gun oriented properly for a quick draw; (*c*) keep the muzzle from wearing a hole through the pocket, and (*d*) keep the distinctive shape of the pistol from "printing" against the fabric and revealing the fact that you are armed. Do not allow anything else to occupy the same pocket as the gun. Ahern, Alessi, Kramer, Ky-Tac, Mach-2, Mika, Rosen, Safariland, Sparks, and Uncle Mike's are just a few of the pocket holsters that have proven popular.

The "spear hand" is once again technique of choice for beginning the draw. It slims the silhouette of the hand as much as is possible, and speeds your access to the gun. As with the techniques presented earlier, you want the web of the hand high on the grip tang, and the lower three fingers on the hand (or middle finger and ring finger, if the gun's frame is that small) to take a firm and immediate grasp. With a revolver, I put my thumb on the hammer area even if it's a "hammerless" to reduce the hand's profile and minimize chances of a snag coming out of the pocket. This often is not possible with a small auto while maintaining a firm grasp, due to the auto's different shape.

You want to be sure that the trigger finger is *outside the pocket holster.* This keeps it from entering the trigger guard prematurely. Do not press the trigger finger against the pocket holster, or it can trap the holster to the gun and cause both to be drawn together.

The angle at which you draw may be dependent on the pocket holster you've chosen and the cut of the pocket. With a square pocket, you'll have to draw straight up, and with a steeply cut "slash pocket," you may have to pull the gun rearward as you draw. Similarly, some pocket holsters are designed to catch on the pocket's lower edge and separate from the pistol, while others need to catch on the top edge. Adjust your angle of draw accordingly.

As soon as the gun is out of the pocket and completely clear, thrust it muzzle- forward straight toward the target. As before, don't allow the support hand to come in to do its job until the muzzle is safely forward and past it. Also as before, do not let the trigger finger enter the guard until the decision to fire has been made.

Ankle Holster

Remember that you need generously cut pant-legs to make this carry work. The old bell-bottoms were ideal for ankle carry, as are today's "flares." The straight-cut legs of the standard American "men's sack suit" work with it, and so do the similarly-cut legs of most police uniform trousers and BDUs. In jeans or cords, the ankle holster will generally only be compatible with "boot-cut" cuffs.

There may have been more bad drawing techniques taught with ankle holsters than with any other type of carry. Standing on one leg like a stork isn't going to work in a reactive situation. Hell, do even *storks* defend themselves this way? Though the ankle rig is extremely accessible while seated or down on your back, it's the most awkward of draws when standing. That's why I developed the following technique several years ago.

Carry the pistol on the inside of the leg opposite your gun hand, butt to the rear. The movement begins by grabbing a fistful of trouser material on the holster-side leg with your non-dominant hand and pulling it up as far as you can. This is important because once the knee bends, it will hold fabric below it taut and you'll have to push the cuff up from the bottom instead of the much easier expedient of pulling it up from the top.

As the material begins to slide up, scoot your gun hand-side leg out to the side, keeping the sole flat to the ground. Now bend deeply at the knees, trying to bring your buttocks down to about knee height. Essentially, you are sliding into

a martial artist's horse stance. With the torso bent sharply forward, the dominant hand now has plenty of reach to take its grasp of the ankle-holstered defensive handgun. The gun hand should sweep up from below, with the thumb pointed up, so it can catch any residual pants cuff material and shove it up and out of the way.

As always, make the initial hand contact with the web high on the backstrap and all fingers but the trigger finger grasping firmly, using the thumb to break the safety strap if one is present. Pull the gun up, and as soon as the muzzle clears the holster bring it up to the target. If time permits, bring your support hand into play as before. If there is time, you can stand back up into your preferred firing position, or drop to kneeling on the non-holster leg if you're behind low cover. The horse stance position, which I call the "cover crouch" or "speed crouch," is a remarkably strong firing posture, if a somewhat uncomfortable one.

Final Advice

Always stick with the safety advice given in the opening portion of this article. Remember that you'll never get so fast and so smooth that you don't need to drill on the movements: the more you train, the faster and smoother you'll get. The less you train, the rustier, slower, and clumsier you'll get. How do I know this, you ask? (Sigh.) Trust me. I know this…

Remember that safety is the overriding concern in this sort of training. You never get so good that you can drop your guard. The old adage that "familiarity breeds contempt" is absolutely true. After 23 years of accident-free training at Lethal Force Institute, we finally experienced a self-inflicted gunshot wound at a class in the summer of 2004. The student involved was an instructor herself, and quite competent. She simply went too fast, and in a "familiarity breeds contempt" moment, allowed her finger to remain on the trigger of her loaded 10mm auto as she inserted it into the holster. The resultant accidental discharge sent a 150-grain bullet down the outer edge of her leg at some 1300 feet per second. Fortunately, it was a superficial wound, but she'll be the first to tell you that it's an experience you don't want to share.

Train wisely. Train carefully. If you do, the above techniques should serve you well.

Good luck!

THE BACKUP CCW

With powerful handguns as small and light as this 13.3-ounce S&W Military & Police Model 340 357, there's little excuse NOT to carry a backup.

The backup gun is a second handgun, normally carried concealed, used as a supplement to a primary handgun that may be carried openly or concealed, depending on the circumstances. It has a long history among lawfully armed men and women. Originally a law enforcement practice, the carrying of backup has spread to ordinary American men and women who are licensed to carry loaded handguns concealed in public.

One only has to cruise the "gun boards" on the Internet to notice how many private citizens who carry are either considering the wear of a second weapon routinely, or are already committed to the practice. It has been said that in America, private citizens model their sporting rifle purchases based on what the military is using, and their defensive handgun purchases on what their police are using. The rise of the bolt-action rifle in popularity among hunters and target shooters followed the adoption of the Krag-Jorgensen in the late 19th century and the Springfield in the early 20th…semiautomatic hunting rifles such as the Remington Model 742 and Winchester Model 100 became popular among a generation of Americans who returned from fighting WWII and the Korean conflict with semiautomatic Garands…and today, the single most popular model represented in new rifle sales seems to be the AR-15, the semiautomatic version of the M-16 that has been our nation's primary military rifle since the Vietnam conflict..

Similarly, the dominance of the revolver among private citizens followed the adoption by the Texas Rangers of the Walker Colt before the middle of the 19th century. For most of the 20th century, the double-action revolver in 38 Special, followed in popularity by the same type of gun in 357 Magnum, was virtually the standard law enforcement weapon *and* the most popular home defense/concealed carry firearm among "civilians." As the police went to semiautomatics, so did the law-abiding public. At this writing, the high tech auto pistol typified by the Glock is the most common type of police duty handgun, and likewise one of the biggest sellers in the commercial handgun market.

A sweet backup gun! This Colt Pocket Nine is the size of a Walther PPK 380 and considerably lighter, yet it just put five rounds of Winchester SXT full-power 9mm into approximately two inches at 25 yards. Sadly discontinued, it is worth haunting gun shops to find second-hand.

This being the case, it is not surprising that the law officers' taste for a second handgun carried on the person, has been acquired by the armed citizens of the same population.

The Rationale of Backup

There are several good reasons to carry a second handgun for defensive purposes. None are the exclusive province of law enforcement. Let's examine them in detail.

The primary gun may be taken away. In Kentucky, an armed criminal caught a uniformed policeman off guard and took away his Smith & Wesson 10mm service pistol. The lawman was able to access his concealed Walther PPK 380, a backup gun issued to him by his department, and empty it into his attacker. The criminal died; the officer lived.

The primary gun may be unusable because it is the object of a struggle. In Ohio not long ago, a police officer found himself in a desperate battle for survival as his opponent struggled to take away his department issue Glock 22 pistol. Fortunately, the department had had the foresight to issue every officer a Glock 27, a subcompact version of the duty pistol, as backup. In the last instant before the suspect gained control of his service weapon, the officer was able to draw his backup G27 and fire a shot into his would-be murderer's head, killing the assailant and saving his own life.

The primary gun may be empty. Drawing a second, loaded weapon is often faster than reloading the first when it runs dry. In Michigan, a woman and her husband were working in the store they owned and operated together when they were hit by multiple armed robbers. The felons shot and wounded the husband early in the encounter. The wife drew a double-action revolver and shot back. Her gun ran dry, and she grabbed a second revolver with which she continued to return fire. That sustained fire allowed her to win the gunfight, saving her life and that of her husband, who survived his wounds. Their attackers were not so lucky.

The primary gun may malfunction. In the South recently, a police officer died with a jammed pistol in his hand. Witnesses said he was struggling with his choked semiautomatic when his opponent, a criminal armed with two double action revolvers, shot him to death. The officer's pistol, a popular brand famous for its reliability, had jammed part way through its 15-round magazine. The quick drawing and firing of a second weapon might have saved the officer's life.

The primary gun may be struck by an opponent's bullet and rendered inoperable. This scenario is not so far-fetched as it may sound. Law enforcement training in this country was profoundly affected by a 1986 gun battle on the edge of Miami where two FBI agents were killed and five more wounded by two heavily armed criminals who were ultimately killed at the scene. Two of the seven agents who returned fire resorted to their backup handguns during that firefight, and the agent who put the final, fatal bullets into the criminals did so with his Smith & Wesson revolver after his Remington shotgun ran out of ammo. (Bad

Sometimes it's easier, and even more efficient, to carry two small handguns of adequate power instead of one large one. Left: 20 ounce Model 640-1 above, 15 ounce Model 442 below, both J-frame 5-shots by Smith & Wesson. Right: 22 ounce all steel Kahr MK9 above, 14 ounce polymer frame MK9 below, both 7-shot 9mms.

guys also resort to backup guns. One of the two cop-killers in that encounter fired rounds from a stolen Mini-14 Ruger rifle, his own Dan Wesson 357 Magnum revolver, and his partner in crime's S&W 357 before he was finally killed.)

In that encounter, one agent's Smith & Wesson 9mm auto pistol was struck by a 223 bullet and rendered inoperable. That particular agent did not carry a backup gun, and was helpless to defend himself when the suspect with the Mini-14 walked up on him and shot him to death. Twenty years later, in April of 2006, the same phenomenon was observed in a Seattle gunfight. A city cop's Glock 22 service pistol put a 40-caliber bullet into the cylinder face of a criminal's Colt Officer's Model Match 38 Special, rendering it inoperable. In that instance, the criminal fortunately did not have a second gun, and was neutralized by police fire.

The primary gun may not be as readily accessible as the backup. In New York some years ago, an off duty cop in winter was carrying his primary handgun under two coats, and his backup Colt Detective Special snub-nose 38 in his overcoat pocket. Set upon by two armed robbers, he knew he would not be able to dig under his clothing and draw his duty weapon before being shot by the drawn gun

held to his head. On the pretext of reaching for a wallet in his overcoat pocket, he got his hand on his backup Colt, then slapped the gunman's pistol aside with his free hand as he drew and fired. His bullet went through the gunman's brain, killing him instantly; the accomplice fled, and was later taken into custody. The officer was uninjured, saved by his backup handgun.

In the Carolinas, a man with a hidden weapon approached a parked police car and opened fire at the officer through the driver's window, wounding him. Seat-belted in place, the officer was unable to reach the service handgun locked in a security holster at his hip, but *was* able to access the Colt Agent backup gun strapped to his ankle. He drew from the ankle holster and returned fire, neutralizing his assailant. He survived his wound and returned to full duty, saved by his backup gun.

The primary gun can arm only one good person at a time. With a backup gun, the user can arm a second competent "good guy or gal" who did not bring their own firearm to the emergency. In California, a police officer facing a complex problem involving armed suspects was offered assistance by a private citizen he knew to be trustworthy with firearms, but who was not licensed to be armed. He "deputized" the citizen, arming the man with the Smith & Wesson Chiefs Special snub-nose 38 the officer carried in an ankle holster. The situation came to a satisfactory conclusion.

In New York, two detectives had a reporter along in their unmarked car when they had occasion to go after a particularly dangerous armed robber they had been seeking. Knowing the reporter to be an ex-cop, one detective handed him his backup gun, a Colt Detective Special. When they made the confrontation, the suspect was facing three drawn guns. His own choice of weapons was a sawed-off double barrel shotgun. Few criminals are too stupid to realize that they can't possibly neutralize three armed good guys with a two-shot weapon without being shot himself. This one chose to surrender without violence or bloodshed, and served a long term in prison.

We've just seen no fewer than seven very good reasons why a person who has a need to carry a gun might see a need to carry two of them. Any one of those situations could face an armed citizen *or* a police officer on any given day.

"Gentlemen, Choose Your Weapons"

There are several different approaches to the selection

of backup guns. Predictable danger, wardrobe, training and familiarity already ingrained, and other situational factors will determine what might be the best approach on any given occasion.

On "heavy days" – i.e., high-risk situations – a pair of full-size fighting handguns makes sense. There is lots of historical precedent for this. On the Western Frontier, gun-wise lawmen from Wild Bill Hickok to Wyatt Earp carried a brace of sixguns. That is, a matched pair. Hickok wore twin Navy Colt .36 caliber cap-n'-ball revolvers, and allegedly "freshened" them daily by firing each charge in each chamber every morning in a short practice session, and then reloading with fresh powder, ball, and caps. Earp wore a pair of Colt Single Action Army revolvers, caliber 45 Colt.

Similar practices were seen in more modern times. On the night he and his team took down John Dillinger, FBI Agent Melvin Purvis was said to have been carrying a pair of Smith & Wesson Military & Police 38 Specials. That significantly outgunned the Colt Pocket Model 380 Dillinger was carrying, though it is believed that a 45 ACP bullet from the Colt Government Model of another agent was what actually killed FBI's "Most Wanted" fugitive that night in Chicago.

Decades later the most famous member of the NYPD

Tiny NAA mini-revolvers, 22 Magnum above and 22 Short below, are seen by author as more novelties than combat handguns because they are slow and difficult to operate due to their size, and much lacking in power. That said, Ayoob can point to several good people whose lives were saved by them, proving that little low-powered guns are better than no guns at all.

SIG P226R 16-shot 9mm, above, backed up by 5-shot 38 Special S&W Model 442, below.

Stakeout Squad, Jim Cirillo, went to work each day with essentially the same gear carried by Purvis, though by then that particular Smith & Wesson was known as the Model 10. Each of Jim's was a four-inch, with a heavy barrel on the strong-side hip and a tapered barrel version worn cross-draw as backup. Jim actually had one more backup gun on each occasion, a Colt Cobra 38 with a hammer shroud and two-inch barrel, carried in a pocket, and usually had a 14-inch barrel Ithaca 12-gauge shotgun handy to start things off.

Because most days *aren't* heavy days, a much more common paradigm has long been the full-size, serious-caliber "combat handgun" as primary weapon, with a smaller and sometimes less powerful handgun for backup. Generations of cops have used tiny 25 autos for backup. While they are better than nothing, these guns are infamous for their poor stopping power, and being very tiny, they also tend to be difficult to manipulate under stress. Long before that, it was popular for lawmen to carry a six-shooter as primary, and a two-shot derringer as secondary. The derringer, fortunately, has pretty much passed from the scene.

Today, tiny 32 autos like the Seecamp, the North American Arms Guardian, and the irresistibly slim and light Kel-Tec P32 have found their way into backup position on the bodies of

many police officers and armed citizens alike. In common with their predecessors, they are better than nothing, but they are also feeble in terms of the power they can put out. It is significant that when police departments issue backup guns, they normally look for something more powerful.

The New York City Police Department, for example, has long encouraged backup guns, but they allow only two calibers: 38 Special in a revolver, and 9mm Parabellum in a semiautomatic. This is the result of long institutional experience encompassing a great many gunfights, and it embodies common sense.

As this is written, there are at least five state police agencies that issue backup handguns to all their troopers. Two of them consider commonality important issuing Glock pistols in two sizes and the same caliber. One agency issues the standard size Glock 37 and "baby" size Glock 39, both in 45 GAP. The other issues the 5.3-inch barrel Glock 35 and the 3.6-inch barrel Glock 27, both in 40 S&W. If the primary weapon is lost, snatched away, or damaged, the trooper still has a spare pistol and two spare magazines to fight with, because the smaller Glock will take the larger Glock's magazines in the same caliber. Similarly, the G26 subcompact will accept the magazines of the compact

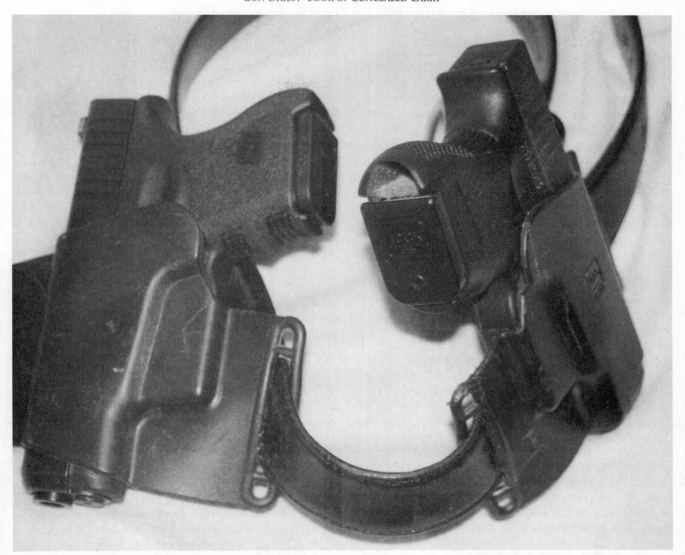

Matched pair of baby Glocks in Glock sport/combat holsters. A gun worn each side, mirror image, saves pocket space and puts one available readily to either hand. Balance on hips is perfect and natural. Author thinks of it as carrying a spare magazine with another pistol wrapped around it.

G19 or full size G17 in caliber 9x19, and the subcompact 357-caliber G33 will work with the same-caliber magazines of the compact G32 or the full size G31.

The other two state police agencies in question take a different route. One has issued the Beretta 380 for the backup role, while equipping its uniformed personnel with full size Beretta 9mm and 40 pistols over the years. With a recent switch to the Glock for duty, that department may soon be trading its 380s for baby Glocks in a more potent caliber. Another agency has issued snub-nose S&W revolvers for decades as backup, the current gun being the Model 640-1 in 357 and loaded with 38 Special +P+, complementing a SIG P226 duty weapon in 40 S&W. Within the last couple of years, a fifth state police department has bought S&W 38 Special Airweights for all troopers, in addition to their standard issue 357 SIG pistols.

Each person in the private sector must make his or her own decision. Certainly, the ability to interchange spare ammunition between the backup gun and the primary is a real "plus." For many decades, cops carried their spare 38 Special ammo loose in pouches or loops, and were encouraged to get a smaller 38 Special for backup for just this reason. Indeed, they were taught that if they carried a Colt as primary they should carry a Colt as backup, and ditto with Smith & Wesson, because the cylinders would rotate in the same direction and open the same way.

In the 1970s, revolvers still held sway in police work, but speed loaders became accepted duty gear. It was discovered that the speed loader sized to fit a K-frame Smith & Wesson service revolver would fit perfectly in a six-shot D-frame Colt backup gun. The hot set-up became a four-inch or six-inch Smith 38 or 357 in the uniform holster, and a two-inch Colt as backup gun, with the speed loaders filled with hot 38 Special ammo that could be fired from either revolver.

Today, with autoloaders so hugely popular, commonality is still a factor, but not always. Certainly, Glock interchangeability makes huge sense. Someone carrying a double-stack S&W 9mm of conventional size can carry a Kel-Tec P11 for backup, secure in the knowledge that the 14.5 ounce 9mm Kel-Tec will accept the magazines of a

Smith & Wesson 5906 or 6906 in the same caliber. If the full-size or Commander-size 1911 is chosen for primary, a subcompact such as the Colt Defender can work with full-length magazines in the same caliber in an emergency, but those longer mags can over-travel and lock up the gun when slammed into a full-size 1911 that's at slide-lock.

Many backup gun users have decided to do without ammo interchangeability in the name of convenience, concealment, or faster tactical access. Some just don't happen to have a primary gun that's magazine-compatible with a smaller one for interchangeability. For instance, this writer's department issues the Ruger P345 as a duty pistol, and this 45 auto does not have a subcompact version available. Accordingly, each officer is issued a Ruger SP101 357 Magnum snub-nose revolver for backup, and most carry a Bianchi Speed Strip with spare 357 rounds somewhere on their person while at work.

"Civilians" and police officers alike have found that while autos might be a better choice as primary weapons, revolvers may be preferable as backup because of faster access out of pockets due to their rounded grip-frames, or better resistance to dust and grit when carried in ankle holsters. Another advantage of the small revolver for backup comes in one of the applications mentioned earlier in this article, the use of the backup to arm another competent good guy or gal. You may not have time to explain to that person how your auto works or why they need to keep their weak side thumb out from behind the slide when you hand them your backup auto. However, anyone competent to wield a gun in a crisis situation will be competent to handle a double action only revolver when there is no time to explain the "manual of arms."

Where to Carry the Backup

Mirror image on the belt is how Hickok and Earp each carried their backup six-guns, with one accessible to each hand. However, neither man worried much about concealment of two full-size revolvers, and both made it a point to practice intensively firing with each hand. That is essential in this type of carry.

Strong side plus cross draw is quite popular. This is how Cirillo carried sidearms on the NYPD Stakeout Squad. The second gun in a cross-draw makes it readily accessible to the dominant hand, and also positions it where the weak hand can reach it in an emergency.

A shoulder holster is a form of cross-draw. Many cops (and armed citizens) over the years have packed their "second" in a shoulder rig. (In years past, it is believed, Earp's friend and contemporary Dr. John "Doc" Holiday wore one Colt single action on his hip and another in a primitive shoulder holster of the period. John Wesley Hardin, perhaps the deadliest gunman of the Old Frontier, fashioned a leather vest that held a pair of revolvers in semi-shoulder holster position.)

A holster strapped to a concealed ballistic vest under the weak arm is a variation of the shoulder holster draw. It is extremely popular with uniformed police, but of course,

only works if one happens to be wearing body armor. LAPD SWAT operators are issued two Kimber 1911 45 autos apiece. One is worn on a tactical thigh holster on the strong side, the other, attached to the heavy body armor in the chest area for a semi-shoulder holster type of access. This carry has also proven popular with some of our armed forces personnel in Iraq and Afghanistan at this writing.

Ankle holsters are long-time traditional favorites for backup. They are out of the way of the often already crowded gun belt. While slow to reach from a standing position, the ankle rig is ideal for a person seated behind a counter or seated behind the wheel of a car. When you are down on your back, your legs are no longer supporting your body weight and you can quickly flex your knee and snap your ankle up toward your reaching hand. The ankle holster is also fairly accessible to either hand, an important consideration in backup gun placement because there is always a likelihood of your gun hand or arm being injured and disabled in the course of a fight.

Pocket carry is extremely popular for backup guns.

Bear in mind that ankle rigs take some time to get used to. They also require full-cut pants cuffs. Police uniform pants work well with ankle holsters, as do straight-cut suit pants and cargo pants. Sports slacks and jeans will require "boot cut cuffs" if they're going to give you access to an ankle holster. This type of rig works best with smaller handguns; a compact Glock or equivalent is about the largest that most people can effectively carry in an ankle holster.

Pocket carry is extremely popular for backup guns. Tactically, it allows you to put your hand in your pocket in a "hinky" situation and already have the gun discreetly in hand if lethal danger suddenly threatens. Many backup gun users place the pocket gun on their weak side, leaving the strong hand free to carry out its trained reflex to the primary handgun. Whenever carrying in a pocket, *be sure to use a pocket holster!* This will: always hold the gun in the same position for faster access; break up the gun's outline and prevent you from being "made" as someone who is armed; speed the draw under any conditions; and prevent sharp edges on the gun (such as the front sight on a J-frame snub-nose revolver) from wearing holes in your clothing.

Off-body placement is an often ignored but sometimes practical location for backup guns. This was how the lady in the mom-and-pop store mentioned earlier accessed both the revolvers she used to gun down the armed robbers who opened fire on her and her husband. Lance Thomas, the famous Los Angeles Rolex repairman who survived multiple gunfights with armed robbers and killed several opponents, kept a loaded handgun discreetly concealed about every three feet along his side of the counter and workbench in his small shop. He was always able to grab a gun – or *another* gun, when he shot the first one empty – in time to win every single one of his gunfights. A spare handgun secreted in the map pocket of the driver's door of your car may be easier and more discreet to reach to than the primary gun in your hip scabbard or shoulder holster, when you have to draw on a carjacker or a kidnapper who is already in the car with you. While not always recommended by experts, discreet off-body placement of concealed handguns has doubtless saved the lives of multiple good people in certain situations.

The Bottom Line

Now you know why street-wise gun expert Phil Engeldrum once wrote, "If you need to carry a gun, you probably need to carry two of them."

The choices are yours. What to carry, where to carry, and whether to carry it at all.

If you do choose to go the backup gun route, remember the following.

The backup gun should be simple to operate under extreme stress. That's the only time you'll be reaching for it. That simplicity will also serve well if you must hand your backup to another person, with no time to explain how to use it.

The backup gun is literally a last resort, and therefore should be powerful enough to stop a fight. This is why most experts shy away from small-caliber handguns as backup weapons.

Because the backup gun *is* likely to be a last resort in a life-or-death situation, it must be absolutely reliable.

If you carry backup, you need to train with it. Practice getting it out and into action. Practice shooting it, particularly with the "weak" hand if you carry it on the non-dominant side. If you don't groove in the movements and techniques now, they won't be there when everything goes auto-pilot in a life-threatening crisis.

Backup handguns have saved the lives of a great many cops, and would have saved more had they been present. They can do the same for law-abiding citizens who legally carry concealed handguns to protect themselves and those within the mantle of their protection.

Georgia State Patrol issues each trooper a mated pair of Glocks in 45 GAP. Left, the service-size G37; right, the subcompact G39.

Chapter 19

OPEN CARRY:
TWO SIDES OF A COMPLICATED ISSUE

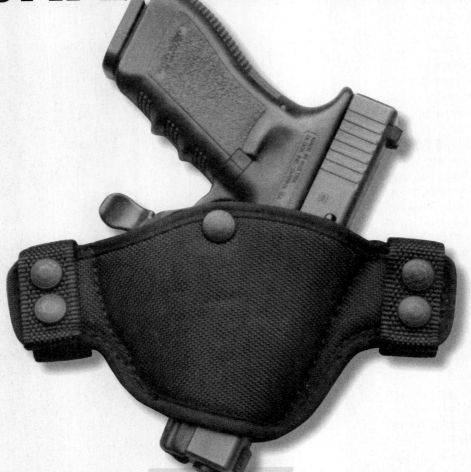

In days of old, Americans often carried handguns openly in public. Not because they were police or anything, but because *(a)* it was their right, and *(b)* in certain parts of a young frontier nation, it was expected of them.

Among those of us who are advocates for the civil rights of gun owners, there are some who think the time is ripe for a return to this concept…and there are those who not only don't feel a need to resurrect the old paradigm, but believe it might actually be counter-productive to our side of the Second

This Bianchi Evader requires middle finger of drawing hand to hit a paddle to unlock this Glock 22.

Amendment battle.

As with most intense debates, there are sound arguments on both sides of the issue.

The Pro-Open Carry Platform

The arguments in favor of private citizens carrying loaded handguns exposed to plain sight in public seem to break down as follows:

Crime deterrence. This philosophy holds that criminals who were thinking of robbing this convenience store or that bank will abort their mission when they see a gun on the hip of a citizen. On a more personal level, they argue, it will tend to deter criminals who have targeted specific individuals for crimes against the person, such as mugging or rape, in lonely places deliberately selected by the predator for being remote from police assistance.

Good public relations for gun owners. The theory advanced by advocates of open carry is that when the public gets used to seeing their neighbors and other good people carrying guns in plain sight, they'll lose their fear of firearms and become more amenable to supporting gun owners' rights.

Convenience. Particularly in warm places, it is often uncomfortable to wear a concealing garment. The plain hip holster worn exposed is simply more comfortable and convenient than a belly-band, a shoulder rig, or an inside the waistband holster, before you even consider the potential discomfort of an additional piece of clothing to hide a gun.

The exercise of rights. This argument comes with a powerful sound bite: "A right that is not exercised will wither away."

The Concealed-Rather-Than-Open Carry Platform

These arguments come, not from anti-gun groups or other opponents of civil rights, but from armed American citizens who are neither uniformed security professionals

The importance of "dressing to the gun" in open carry. In ordinary indoor lighting, author does not readily appear to be armed…

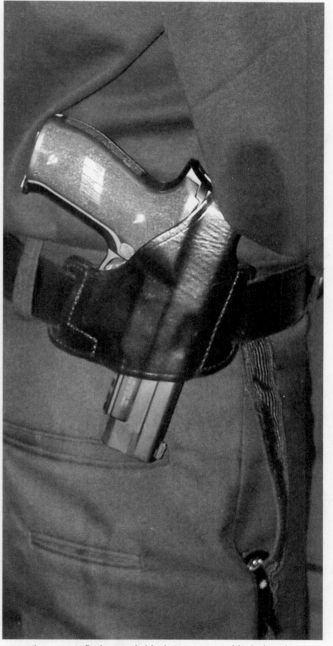

…until camera's flash reveals black SIG P226 in black thumb-break Blocker holster/belt set, normally somewhat camouflaged against dark gray pants and black shirt.

nor police officers, but simply don't like the idea of carrying their guns out in the open before the eyes of the general public.

Open carry invites disarming. Those who prefer to carry their guns concealed point to all the police officers who have been killed with their own weapons. They prefer to keep their guns hidden on their person, where only they know where they are.

Open carry sacrifices the advantage of surprise. Concealed carry advocates point out that the decades-old archives of the Armed Citizen columns in the National Rifle Association's *American Rifleman* magazine show countless cases of armed citizens who only won their armed encounters because they were able to draw from concealment and take their criminal opponents by surprise, an advantage that would have been lost if the assailants could have seen beforehand that they were armed.

Open carry makes enemies for the pro-gun movement, instead of friends. The vast majority of the American public does not carry guns openly on city streets and do not see others that they know to be law-abiding private citizens do so. Therefore, says this argument, they are frightened when they observe guns worn openly by people not readily identified as those they are "socialized" to seeing armed, such as armed guards and police officers, and are therefore frightened when they see ordinary folks with guns on their hips.

Open carry advocates are just show-offs crying for attention. This is probably the least effective argument for concealed as opposed to open carry.

Personal Experiences

For those of us who go armed, open versus concealed carry is an intensely personal issue. It is only fair to the reader that they know the personal experiences of anyone addressing that issue, since such personal experiences can create preconditioned bias or prejudice. Any opinion must be seen in the light of the person doing the opining.

This writer has been carrying concealed since the age of 12. In a time and place where a permit was only required to carry a *concealed and loaded handgun in public,* and in which the chief of police of the city in question had told my father and me that it was perfectly legal for my young self to carry loaded and concealed

inside our family-owned place of business so long as I didn't step out on the sidewalk so armed, it gave me an early start on the concept. I have "open-carried" as a sworn, part-time police officer for thirty-some years, which doesn't really count except for the "deterrence" argument on one side and the "exposed to disarming attempts" argument on the other, but have also open-carried in plainclothes from Arizona to North Carolina on city streets.

And, in those capacities, I have seen things that support both sides.

In Arizona, a friend and I were in a convenience store between Prescott and Paulden on the way to Gunsite Training Center. My friend came from a state that then had no provision for private citizens to carry a handgun in any fashion, and was luxuriating in his ability under Arizona law to carry his custom Colt 45 auto in an exposed holster. I was a few steps away when I saw a man walk in, do a double take when he spotted the gun, and deliver a "target stare" to the loaded pistol. Almost in exaggerated pantomime, he mugged an expression of outrage and pointed at the pistol, making eye contact with others in the store that indicated his outrage. And then, that man moved in behind my friend, reaching out for the holstered pistol.

I stepped between them, glaring at the interloper. He stopped, looked at me, obviously decided that whatever was going to happen wasn't worth it, and walked away with

Most folks in this pastry shop won't spot the fact that one is wearing a gun openly, its black finish blending in with black LFI Concealment Rig and black clothing.

an angry look on his face. I don't *think* he was going to try to shoot anyone with my friend's gun, but he was obviously going to grab it and do some show-off thing, which could have led to a struggle for a loaded gun in a crowded convenience store, with an obviously high potential for tragedy. Score one for the case against wearing an exposed handgun in public.

Yet, in North Carolina, I had an exposed pistol on my hip when I walked out of a store and saw a very aggressive panhandler approach an apparently unarmed and unprepared citizen, who fled on foot. The panhandler then turned toward me, walking toward me rapidly with a hostile expression on his face. I turned to face him in an interview stance…and he saw the weapon on my hip.

It stopped him in his tracks, without a word or a touch from me. He looked back and forth between my eyes and my sidearm, then shook his head and made a gesture that said he didn't want to fight, and turned around and walked away. Score one for the deterrent effect claimed by the advocates of open carry.

Been there, experienced both sides, and realize that each side as some solid points. Now, with that out of the way, let's look at the issue argument by argument.

Analyzing the Arguments Over Open Carry

Crime deterrence? There's no doubt in my mind that openly carried firearms have prevented crime. The trouble is, whether you're talking capital punishment or open carry, deterrence is something that is impossible to empirically measure and quantify. All we have is anecdotal evidence. The Virginia Citizens' Defense League (VCDL) is an extremely effective gun owners' civil rights group, and has taken the promotion of open carry (legal in their state) as one of their causes to promote. One of their members was recently in a bank, openly wearing a pistol, when he observed a man acting suspiciously like a robber. The man saw the VCDL member's pistol; his eyes widened; and he backed off and left. Bank employees later confirmed the armed citizen's

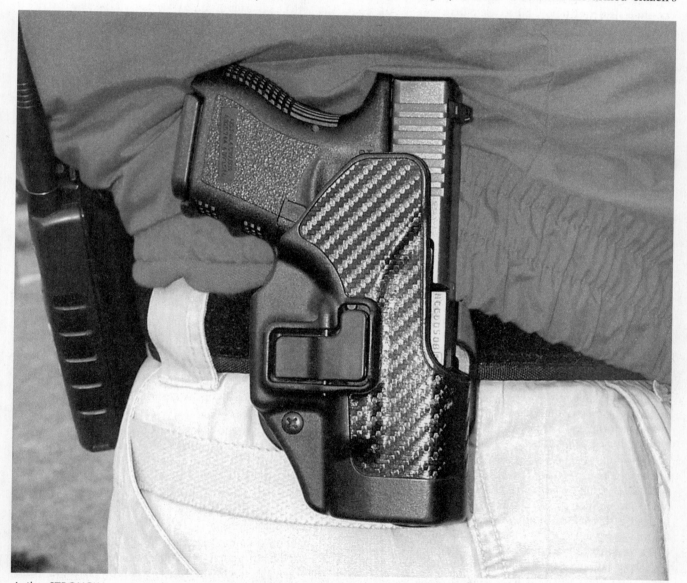

Author STRONGLY recommends some type of security holster to those who feel they must practice open carry. This carbon fiber Blackhawk SERPA with proprietary trigger-finger lock release mechanism is carried by a state police trainer in casual clothes. Pistol is baby Glock.

impression that the man was definitely about to attempt a bank robbery, and was scared off by the sight of a good guy with a gun. No arrest was sought since the man had made no overt act, but I for one am comfortable scoring that as a point for the pro-open carry argument.

What about the vulnerability to disarming attempts? The concealed weapon is no guarantee against gun snatches: many plainclothes officers have been disarmed of their concealed weapons. The "out of sight/out of mind" thing works both ways, and those whose weapons are exposed can at least hopefully be presumed to be more alert to disarming attempts. Any fight that degenerates into a wrestling match can find the opponent's arms going around the good guy's body, feeling his gun, and attempting to snatch it from under the concealing garments.

That said, though, the long history of police being disarmed and murdered with their own guns shows that a definite danger comes with carrying an exposed handgun. Advocates of open carry cry, often stridently, "Show me a case where it was a private citizen instead of a cop who was disarmed because the criminal could see his open-carried gun!"

OK.

I'll show you two.

Both occurred in Indiana, to gun shop owners who carried handguns openly exposed in hip holsters. In the first case, the criminal pretended to be a customer and asked the shop owner for an item on a counter behind him. When the shopkeeper turned to reach for the product, the suspect ripped the dealer's Colt 45 auto from its open-top scabbard, and tried to shoot him with it. Fortunately, the Gold Cup Colt was on-safe, and efforts to pull the trigger failed. The owner was able to grab a second gun and open fire, driving the assailant off.

In the second instance, gunmen entered the store with weapons drawn and took the owner, off-guard, at gunpoint. They may well have "cased" the place before and already known that he was armed. They took his HK P7 out of the holster. Attempting to shoot him with his own gun, they failed because the one with the P7 didn't know how to operate its unique squeeze-cocking lever. This bought the shop owner time to grab a hidden 357 Magnum. Final score: two dead bad guys, one live good guy, but no points at all for the open carry deterrence argument and two strong cases in point against letting the other guy see beforehand that you have a gun, and letting him see where it is.

Are some open-carry advocates really just show-offs crying out for attention? "Look at me, look at me, I'm ba-a-ad?" Well, I think a *few* of them are, and you only have to read some of their posts on this or that Internet gun forum to realize that it's true. However, I think it's *only* a few. I know a lot of folks from VCDL, for example, and I honestly don't think that's what's motivating them. As noted earlier, the "show-off" accusation is probably the argument against open carry that carries the least weight.

Where the "show-off" element comes in most heavily, I personally believe, is in the negative behavior that open

carry brings out in certain strangers who observe it. Remember the guy in the Arizona convenience store? He saw, I suspect, a man who held a power he didn't have, and felt an atavistic (and really stupid) need to show that he was bigger and stronger than the man with the gun. On an Internet forum, a practitioner of open carry told of the time he was having an ice cream in a restaurant with a lady when a belligerent stranger went ballistic (no pun intended). The man started screaming, "What the (expletive deleted) are you carrying that (expletive deleted) gun for in here?!?" The incident ended without physical harm to anyone, but that sort of thing does not exactly promote pro-gun feelings among the general public.

What about the "exercise of rights" argument? It is indeed persuasive to say that something unexercised will atrophy. However, the argument does not necessarily stand the twin tests of history and logic, at least insofar as open carry.

The state of New Hampshire has had "shall-issue" concealed carry licensing since the first quarter of the 20th century. It has also had open carry legal on the books the whole time. In more than half a century of living in that state, I only *once* saw a man walking on city streets with an open-carried handgun and no police badge clipped to the belt alongside it. Guys in hunter's garb with hunting licenses clipped to their shirts, and a Ruger Super Blackhawk or Smith & Wesson Model 29 hunting revolver strapped to their belts, in a rural diner during the pre-dawn hours during deer season? Sure…

and no one looked twice. But that was a totally different thing. They were literally "in costume," readily identified as someone with both a right and a good reason to have a gun on. But, say, a Glock worn openly in a large bookstore in the state's most populous city? One fellow did so – one of my graduates, actually, who respectfully disagreed with my comments in class about "discretion" – and found himself grabbed and thrown "into the position" by uniformed police officers responding to a frightened citizen's desperate 9-1-1 call that amounted to "man with a gun, there now!" He raised a ruckus about being treated so when merely "exercising his rights," and fortunately was not arrested for disturbing the peace (a genuine possibility under the prevailing law). It's still safe to say that the incident didn't win any new friends for the gun rights movement.

With almost no one exercising their right to carry concealed in NH, the right still exists. So do a huge number of concealed carry permits, in the hands of residents and non-residents who exercise that privilege constantly, and who keep their handguns discreetly concealed when out and about in public. Therefore, I have to question the "rights unexercised will wither away" argument, as strong as it sounds on the surface.

I will make one suggestion, though. I have lost count of the number of people who practice open carry who say that when asked why they do so will reply, "Because I can!"

I will most strongly suggest, *throw away that particular argument!*

> There's no doubt in my mind that openly carried firearms have prevented crime.

"Because I can" is an answer that carries a very negative connotation. Any cop can tell you of the drunk wife-beaters who, when asked "Why did you do that?" as the handcuffs went on, sneered back, "Because I can!" Any parent who has ever upbraided a young bully who was pushing around a smaller child and asked him why he did it can remember hearing, "Because I can!" Those are near-universal human experiences. When *you* are asked by someone who has had such an experience, "Why do you carry that gun like that?" and you reply "Because I can," you will almost certainly be perceived as the same sort of bullying dirt-bag they previously heard utter the same words to defiantly attempt to excuse inexcusable behavior.

May I submit that you would be far better off to say, "I am an advocate of gun owners' civil rights, and as a good citizen I carry this to remind other people that they have the right to protect themselves to the same degree," or words to that effect. Some open carry advocates, including some members of VCDL, even carry cards with such messages to hand out to people who ask. If you are going to open carry, I don't think that's a bad idea at all, so long as the wording of the explanation is neutral. Hint: don't let the message include the word "sheeple" to describe anyone who *doesn't* carry a loaded gun in plain sight in public.

Winning Hearts and Minds

One point where the open carry folks butt heads directly with the concealed carry folks is the issue of making friends for the Second Amendment among members of the public who are sitting on the fence in terms of gun issues. In an adult lifetime of active advocacy for "gun rights" causes, I have met many former fence-sitters, and even some "antis," who came over to our side of the debate because they were influenced in a positive way by someone in their life whom they respected and whom, they found out to their surprise, carried a gun for personal protection. However, I have not yet met even one person who changed their opinion to our side of the issue because they saw that person carrying a loaded gun exposed in a place open to the general public.

On the other hand, we've seen whole communities frightened by ostentatious displays of people carrying guns in what those observers perceived to be a "show of force." Remember the Black Panthers, marching armed in California? It's safe to say that this action won no converts to the rights of African-Americans from previously uncommitted citizens and voters. It is probably safe to say that the same will be true insofar as an arguably "ostentatious" display of what much of the public sees as only "the power to kill"?

The weak fear the strong. The helpless fear the armed. Fear breeds hatred. Think about it: fear is the key ingredient to hate. That which we call hate, absent fear, would be merely contempt. One benchmark of our lives, of our empowerment, is when we realize that those we once hated we merely hold in contempt. Many of those people out there in the vast public aren't where you are yet. They still fear armed people they don't see wearing the badges they've come to associate with the guns that society told them will protect them.

When fear equals hate, oppressed minorities such as, oh,

Author's favorite exposed-in-the-station plainclothes holster for his then-department issue Ruger P90 45 was this Strong Piece-Keeper. Baker-like triple "pancake" slots allowed optional carry angles…

gun owners probably should not be creating fear among those who may one day vote in a referendum to determine whether or not they will be allowed to even *own* handguns. Such referenda have gone to the polls in California and Massachusetts during the lifetimes of many of us. The potential for open carry to create fear that in turn creates hatred should not be discounted.

Many, many decades ago there was an arbiter of etiquette named Beatrice Tanner Campbell. She was the "Miss Manners" of her day. She wrote a classic line: "I don't care where people make love, so long as they don't do it in the street and frighten the horses."

The wisdom holds true. Think about it for a moment. When we are out and about in public carrying a loaded gun, we literally *are* "doing it in the street."

It follows that we have an obligation to "not frighten the horses."

Insofar as the issue of "winning hearts and minds," it's hard to look at things realistically and not come down on the side that says flaunting guns in public among strangers may not be the best way to "win friends and influence people."

Bottom Line

Elsewhere in this publication, you'll read about security holsters suitable for daily carry that make good sense for anyone who carries a gun openly in public. Such holsters have long since become the rule more than the exception among the cops and uniformed security personnel who have carried exposed handguns in public for lo, these many years, and we would be foolish to discount the wisdom they have learned so hard at the cost of so much preventable pain and death. Open carry can be done, *in jurisdictions where it is expressly legal,* of course. We just need to ask ourselves whether, in the balance of competing harms and needs, the practice does not pass the point of diminishing returns.

Suppose one is in a jurisdiction where it *not* possible to legally carry concealed, but *is* legal to carry a loaded, *exposed* handgun?

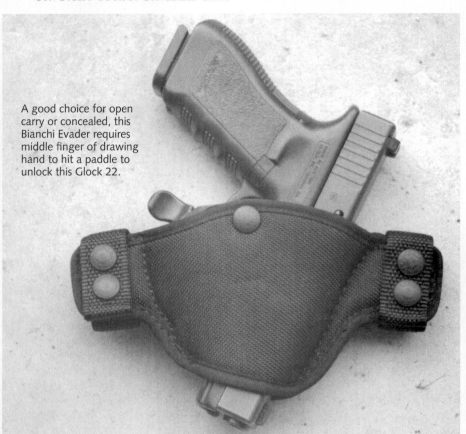

A good choice for open carry or concealed, this Bianchi Evader requires middle finger of drawing hand to hit a paddle to unlock this Glock 22.

…and the proprietary Piece-Keeper thumb snap required two separate movements to release.

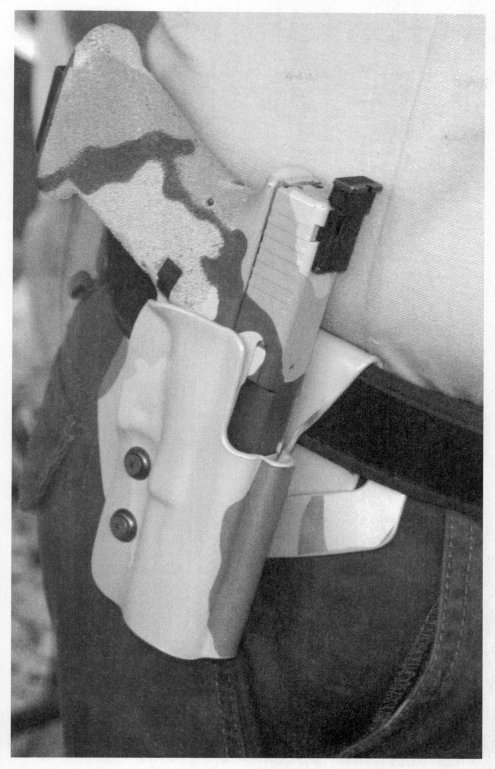

Camo-finished Glock in camo holster. With camo pants and shirt, author wonders, what would be both legal and practical interpretations of "concealment"?

I can only say, "been there, done that." I can remember when North Carolina issued carry permits only to residents, and had no provision for non-resident permits, but did allow open carry. When I was in NC at that time, my choice was to be able to protect myself with an openly carried handgun, and risk upsetting some people, or to go unarmed.

I chose open carry. I never regretted that decision. I was amazed at how many people never even noticed that I was carrying a full-size 357 Magnum revolver or 9mm or 40- or 45-caliber semiautomatic pistol. (No, I *won't* use the word "sheeple" … I won't … I *won't* …) But, the fact is, I almost certainly did alarm or upset a very few people.

I would not have bothered those folks if there was no reason to carry exposed. But there *was* a reason, and under those circumstances – carry your gun openly, or go unarmed – my assessment of the doctrine of competing harms told me to carry my gun openly, and I did.

Things are different now. I drove through North Carolina last week. For some time, NC has had reciprocity with Florida, and my Florida concealed carry permit authorized me to keep my 9mm SIG discreetly concealed under my photographer's vest and my Smith & Wesson Airweight 38 just as discreetly concealed in my trouser pocket. And no one was startled or alarmed. "No 'sheeple' were frightened in the course of the trip."

And that, it seemed to me, was the best of all worlds.

But it's just one guy's opinion. Each of us has to make our own decision on the complicated issue of open carry versus concealed carry. Let me leave you, though, with a final thought: if we have made the decision to responsibly carry loaded guns to protect ourselves and those who count on us to keep them safe, we are not enemies on this matter. We are allies in agreement on a fundamental issue of human rights, and are merely debating the fine points.

MAKING OPEN CARRY SAFER

If you choose to carry an exposed handgun in public where the law allows, can you "keep yourself safe" even more safely? This writer says you can, and shows you how.

A number of jurisdictions allow law-abiding private citizens to carry loaded handguns, *exposed,* in public. This chapter will focus on two specific elements of open carry, which have been called into discussion by those in the gun owners' rights movement who think carrying concealed is a better idea.

Those two particular elements are *discretion,* and *handgun security* against snatch attempts. By discretion, we mean a method of carry that, while exposing the gun, does not call attention to it. You don't want to "frighten the horses." You don't necessarily want any criminal in sight to realize that if he blindsides you with an ambush from behind, your firearm is his for the taking. Unless you're a show-off screaming silently for attention, you want as few people as possible to notice the exposed handgun.

Handgun security against snatch attempts is something cops came to terms with long ago. Any officer will tell you, "In any conflict where someone is within arm's reach of you, they have a gun within their arm's reach: *your* gun." Since open carry allows a present or potential antagonist to see that you do have that gun, you want it to be held in something that will not yield it up to the first clutching hand.

Discreet Appearance

I learned early that "protective coloring" extends to the visibly armed citizen as surely as it does to the beasts of the forests, the denizens of the sea, and the fowl of the air. For polar bears, protective coloration is "white on white." The reflective surfaces of metal are such that a chrome-plated, pearl-handled gun may actually be *more* conspicuous against a white shirt with white slacks. However, a matte black gun and holster almost disappear against black clothing.

Some years ago, in North Carolina, I arrived to teach a deadly force class and was told that, cop or not – even though I was officially on police business and teaching in a police academy setting – I could not carry concealed as an out-of-state policeman unless I was extraditing a felon. I asked about non-resident carry permits or permit reciprocity: no dice. I asked if there were any avenues at all. "Sure," said one indigenous cop, "just carry it exposed in the holster. We have 'open carry' here."

I do not care for the "frighten the horses" effect of open carry. However, I also do not care to be unarmed and, therefore, all but helpless against the armed. Suddenly, open carry was looking more attractive. In fact, I took to it like a duck to water. (Well, maybe like a reluctant duck that didn't like water very much.)

The handgun I was carrying that week was a blue steel Colt Python 357 Magnum revolver, with black Pachmayr grips. I wore it most of the time in an inside-the-waistband holster I had designed for Mitch Rosen, the Ayoob Rear Guard (ARG). Even with most of the mass of the weapon obscured from view by the inside-the-waistband design, the weapon was clearly visible against the royal blue trainers' shirt generally worn by my school's staff.

While on that trip, I had to do a film for a trial that showed how rapidly a certain suspect could have disarmed and shot the officer who had been forced to kill him to keep that from happening. On the day of the filming, I happened to be wearing a black polo shirt and black BDU pants. A photographer was taking stills while the cinematographer was shooting the video.

Later, in court, I had occasion to closely examine not only the videotape, but also the giant blow-ups of the stills that were introduced as evidence. A couple of people in the courtroom told me that they'd hadn't realized that I was armed, even though the big 41-framed revolver was toward the cameras and in plain sight. I asked a few other folks, showing them the pictures, and most when subsequently asked hadn't noticed that I was wearing the big six-gun.

Hmmm…interesting.

I thereafter made it a point to bring black or very dark gray gun, holster,

Not the right way to do it. In coffee shop, author is standing with back to customers, point-and-shoot SIG 9mm in unsecured open-top holster, arms folded. Open to a gun snatch? Ya think?

shirts, and trousers whenever it looked as if I would have to "open carry." The gorgeous, high polish Royal Blue of the Python had not reflected enough to show up in the pictures or the video, but that was only because the ARG holster hadn't exposed much of its sideplate. Later experience with flat black Glock pistols, and a Kimber with a flat gray/black finish that resembles Parkerizing, showed me that these finishes blended beautifully with black holsters and belts, and black clothing.

The holstered guns were still in plain sight. They could be spotted by someone looking for them. But they did not draw the eye.

One evening I found myself stopping on the way home from the range at a supermarket that must have had a hundred people in it. I was open-carrying the dark Kimber 45 cocked and locked in a black basketweave Gordon Davis thumb-break holster on a matching Bianchi dress gun belt, with black polo and black BDUs. The old "one of a hundred people will notice" prediction absolutely came true. The only person who showed indication of having spotted the big military auto pistol was a little girl, and that was probably because she was only a couple of feet away from me in the aisle, and her height put her at eye level to the gun.

I saw the little tyke's eyes widen in alarm, and watched as she urgently grabbed her dad's sleeve and began tugging. When he looked down, she wordlessly but vigorously pointed at the 45. I had made a point to wear my police badge clipped in front of the scabbard, and her dad spotted it at the same time he saw the pistol.

"Aw, it's OK, honey," I heard him tell her gently. "He's a *po*-lice."

So far, so good. There are some dads out there who might be macho enough to feel a need to impress their kids if those kids were alarmed by what the father perceived as an ostentatious display of a deadly weapon. In this case, there was no problem. And the lesson is, black gun in black holster against black clothing draws very little attention from those who *aren't* at eye level with the handgun.

As noted earlier, an inside the-waistband holster buries much of the gun in the lower body's clothing. The gun is still exposed *per se,* and therefore still openly carried. In a jurisdiction where the given person is legal to carry openly but not concealed, that's an important distinction to bear in mind.

In theory, one could resort to genuine camouflage. Several manufacturers have produced pistols and revolvers with camouflage finishes, including recognized patterns such as Woodland. I've often wondered about getting one of those, and a matching camo set of belt and fabric holster, and wearing it outside pants and shirt in the same camo pattern. Would it conceal as well as black on black on black on black? Probably. Maybe better.

Open carrying in a Starbucks, Ayoob keeps his gun side toward the counter, a reasonably secure posture.

I haven't tried it yet. The reason is, while a camouflage thing is going with the black on black, the color black is not considered camouflage per se. A regular camouflage pattern most certainly would be. One definition of "camouflage" is "concealment." If a camo gun was openly carried in a camo holster against camo clothing, all matching, could a creative anti-gun prosecutor convince a grand jury to indict for concealed carry, if the latter was against the law in that time and place? Almost certainly.

Now, whether that case would be decided against the armed citizen at trial would be something else again. It would make a fascinating test case. Since my mother did not raise me to be a test case, I've never undertaken the experiment to find out. If y'all want to do so, feel free, and let me know in care of the publisher how it worked for you. However, neither the publisher nor I will take any responsibility for what happens. And, yes, my tongue is *slightly* in my cheek as I write this...

The Security Factor

Will criminals attack an obviously armed person just to get his gun? Sure. It has happened. I know a guy who was a young cop out West who was walking foot patrol when the lights suddenly went out. He groggily regained consciousness to discover that he had a massive headache and an empty holster. A two-by-four was lying nearby. The department determined that an unknown, never-caught malefactor had come up behind the officer stealthily, smashed him in the back of the head with a board, and taken his custom Smith & Wesson and sauntered away from the cop's unconscious form. The officer recovered from the blow, and his assailant did not choose to execute him as he lay helpless. He was lucky. And he knows it.

More recently – this past winter, as I write this in the

"Out of Sight, Out of Mind": A Two-Way Street

Concealed carry advocates are often heard to say, "Concealed means concealed! If they don't know it's there, they can't grab it away from you!"

I'm afraid it isn't quite so simple.

First, *the assailant may know where your concealed gun is before the assault begins.* This can come about in any of several ways.

Perhaps the assailant *knows you carry a gun, and even knows where you carry it.* This in turn can come from several directions. The attacker could be an estranged former significant other. He could be the disgruntled former employee you had to fire, and he hates you for it and wants revenge. He might be your son-in-law, whom you found out was abusing your daughter and who has seen you with a gun and wants to hurt *you* to punish *her.*

Perhaps the attacker is a stranger, who didn't decide to attack you until your concealed handgun inadvertently became exposed, and he saw it. In many areas, a $500 handgun is worth $1,000 on the black market. Guns and prescription drugs are about the only two things crooks can steal from you and re-sell for more than their intrinsic value, instead of fencing for dimes on the dollars. Did you or a friend ever unintentionally expose a concealed handgun to one another? If that happens in front of the wrong person, you could be targeted in a disarming attempt.

And perhaps the gun becomes visible or palpable in the course of a fight that has not yet reached deadly force proportions. Watch armed men in plainclothes punching or grabbing each other, and you'll see coats sweeping back, shirts being pulled loose, pants cuffs coming up…things that will expose hip holsters, shoulder holsters, and ankle holsters. A common wrestling maneuver in a streetfight is to grab the other man around the waist with your arms. If the antagonist does that to you, he'll almost certainly feel your holstered gun, and now the struggle for your weapon is on.

There is also the absolute fact that in concealed handgun carry, *"out of sight, out of mind" goes in both directions.* That is, the person who is perhaps falsely confident that no one will spot his gun, is less motivated to be alert to a grab for that gun.

I guess what I'm saying here is that, concealed *or* open carry, recognizing beforehand that you might experience a gun-snatch attempt is a wise thing. It follows that it is equally wise to plan ahead to defeat that attempted gun grab.

Proven Retention Strategies

Handgun retention is the corollary science to handgun disarming, and it encompasses both a hardware side and a software side. Let's look at the hardware first.

Security holsters have been available for some time that will ride on a conventional dress gun belt and don't require a police officer's or security guard's big, heavy utility

"Gosh, look at the tall buildings." At a friend's request, Ayoob open carries in Phoenix area. SIG-Sauer pistol is at right hip. Black clothing, belt and holster make black gun less conspicuous. Note that forearm remains near pistol to forestall snatch attempt.

summer of 2007 – a perpetrator in New York City decided the best way to pay off his debts was to commit a string of robberies, and he determined he'd need a gun for that. Where to get a gun? He came up behind a uniformed rookie cop and smashed him in the head with a baseball bat. When the cop fell to the pavement, his attacker beat him about the head some more with the bat, then managed to get his 16-shot 9mm out of the duty holster. The suspect was captured shortly thereafter by other officers, and he confessed, which is how we know not only what he did, but why. The officer was seriously injured and possibly permanently impaired when last heard from.

So, yes, there have indeed been cases of people who attacked those visibly carrying guns for no other purpose than to get the guns. In is not an everyday thing, but it is something to worry about. The private citizen around other people unknown to him, with an exposed gun clearly visible, runs the same risk.

Unless you're a show-off screaming silently for attention, you want as few people as possible to notice the exposed handgun.

belt. The most popular of the breed these days seems to be the Blackhawk SERPA. This synthetic rig has a discreet trigger-finger panel that is biomechanically natural for the wearer's draw angle, but not for the hand of an unauthorized person coming in on it from an angle other than straight above...and your own gun arm and shoulder are blocking his access to that particular angle. I know a lot of cops are now wearing the SERPA when they do open carry in plainclothes on investigative duties, or in the not-readily-recognizable permutations of the various "administrative uniforms."

Strong Holster Company has long made their Piece-Keeper, which uses a special thumb-break design to require a double release movement before the draw can begin. Bianchi has a wide line of holsters with "level two" retention. Safariland has produced a whole series of holsters with hidden releases, or niche locks that require the gun to be pulled in a certain specific direction before it will come out. All have great promise for low-profile open carry, and for that matter, these holsters are concealable.

I would strongly recommend a thumb-break safety strap as a bare minimum of security for anyone openly carrying a loaded handgun in public.

Mechanical safeties are another good thing in these circumstances. History has shown us again and again – with cops, armed citizens, and security professionals alike – that when a bad guy gets a gun away from a good guy and tries to shoot him with it, he often takes several seconds to figure out how to make the gun work. Those seconds have often been the difference between life and death.

Are these hardware fixes desirable even for those trained in handgun retention? Yes. When my older daughter briefly open-carried in Arizona, she had an on-safe Beretta 92 in a Strong Piece-Keeper holster, and appreciated the peace of mind that combination gave her. (She also quickly grew tired of people staring at her, pointing, and mouthing "The little girl has a gun!") My kids learned handgun retention early – this daughter was the youngest instructor ever certified to teach the Lindell Handgun Retention System by the National Law Enforcement Training Center – but remember the cops I mentioned earlier who were cold-cocked before they had a chance to defend their guns. For situations like that, hardware that is "proprietary to the user" can be a lifesaver.

The *software* fix is every bit as important. When I first discovered I had to carry open or not at all in North Carolina, I was carrying a point-and-pull revolver in an open top holster. I was damn glad that I was an instructor of long standing in Lindell weapon retention. The same was true more recently, when I posed for some photos walking around the greater Phoenix area open-carrying a rig I had intended to carry concealed: a point-and-shoot SIG P226 in an open top LFI Concealment Rig by Ted Blocker. Since the gun-grab may come after you've already drawn and off-safed, being able to successfully grapple with the grabber and peel him off the gun is an essential skill in any case.

Bottom Line

Some carry openly to make a statement about gun

Safariland 0701 is an excellent, and concealable, security holster. It works on a similar principle to same company's famous SS-III snatch resistant duty holster...

...and delivers "Level II security," meaning it requires two movements before this Glock 17 can start out of the holster.

owners' civil rights. I can sympathize with that. Some few do so to make a spectacle of themselves. No sympathy here. Either will experience the word "make" in another context: they will be "made" as someone carrying a deadly weapon in public.

The more the gun can "hide in plain sight" through discreet selection of the color of gun finish, stocks, holster, and surrounding clothing, the less trouble the exposed handgun will cause instead of quell.

The more difficult the gun is for an unauthorized user to get out of its holster, and the more difficult it is for an unauthorized person who gains control of it to activate, the better. These are not just political correctness issues. When you look at the number of people who have been killed with their own or their partners' weapons in the history of law enforcement and professional security, you can see just how significant the risk is that we are talking about. Only a fool would ignore it.

Open carry may not be this writer's choice, but for many of our brothers and sisters, it is the only legal way they can be armed in public to protect themselves and their loved ones. Whether or not we choose to exercise it, we want to keep the right of open carry. The above advice is offered in the hope of doing so with maximum safety for ourselves and others.

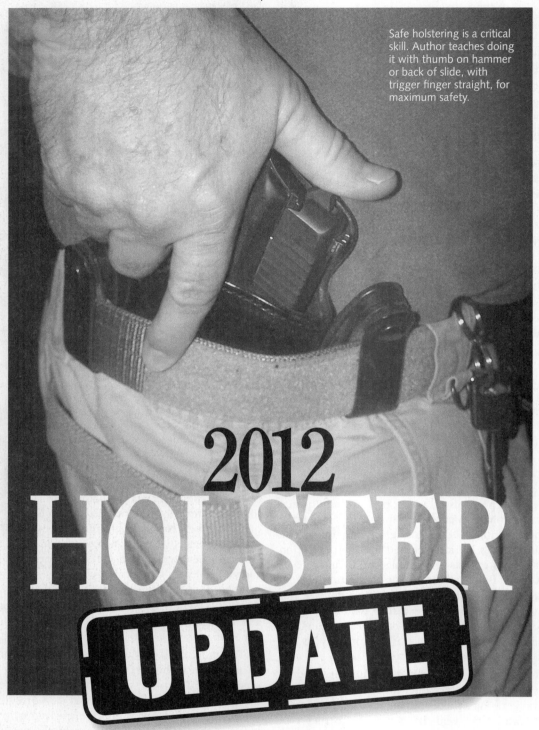

Safe holstering is a critical skill. Author teaches doing it with thumb on hammer or back of slide, with trigger finger straight, for maximum safety.

2012 HOLSTER UPDATE

Holster making has always been a cottage industry, with many small leathermakers producing excellent products, often at home, whether full or part time. That trend accelerated dramatically with the coming of Kydex holsters, which are much easier to build on small scale. There are so many craftsmen producing these right now that I can't possibly touch on all of them, and it would fill the book if I could. So, apologies to anyone not mentioned: it isn't because I think their work is crap or anything, it's simply because I wasn't able to test all their goods.

Hybrid Holsters

Hybrid holsters have become hugely popular in the last few years. One such is Mark Craighead's Crossbreed brand, so popular the brand has become almost a generic term for this sort of rig. As the name implies, the hybrids comprise a mating of leather with Kydex or polymer. The portion that encompasses the gun on the outside is made of the hard synthetic, while the leather is used to form a broad backing between wearer and holster, separating and protecting

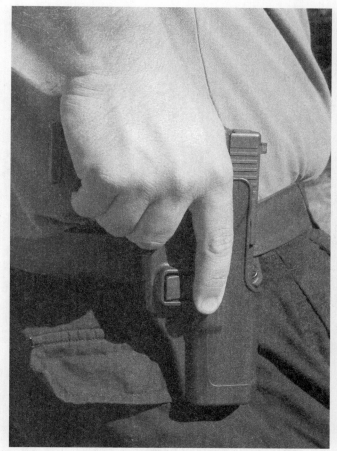

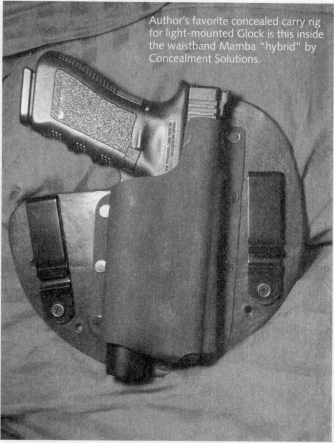

Author's favorite concealed carry rig for light-mounted Glock is this inside the waistband Mamba "hybrid" by Concealment Solutions.

Accidents have happened with the SERPA trigger-finger-release paddle when finger hit trigger prematurely. Author advises, *release the paddle with fingerprint of straight finger as shown here, not with fingertip!*

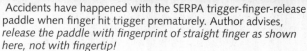

one from the other. I use that phrase advisedly: the "shield" protects the gun from the user's sweat, since these are often carried under a shirt directly against bare skin, and at the same time protects the skin from being abraded by sharp edges on the firearm.

Several companies make hybrids that are also "tuckable," meaning they can be effectively concealed beneath a tucked-in shirt. Comp-Tac produces a popular model in this vein, the Minotaur MTAC.

The backing material varies. Crossbreed offers both horsehide and cowhide, explaining, "Horsehide is a denser and lighter-grained flesh than cowhide. This results in it being more moisture resistant. Customers in very humid climates or who tend to sweat heavily find this to be a useful option, as horsehide tolerates dampness better. Horsehide is only available in natural finish, as its moisture resistance can also cause it to not take dye well. Additionally, the natural finish is very attractive on Horsehide."

It is possible to eliminate leather entirely from the picture. N82 – phonetically, Nate Squared, since the company was founded by two guys named Nate who consider their partnership more than the sum of their parts – makes a very comfortable hybrid holster whose backing is a cushioned synthetic.

The concept of leather or other material between the

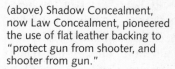

(above) Shadow Concealment, now Law Concealment, pioneered the use of flat leather backing to "protect gun from shooter, and shooter from gun."

(right) This Crossbreed holster with Glock 23 has "combat cut" to keep leather from overlapping back of grip.

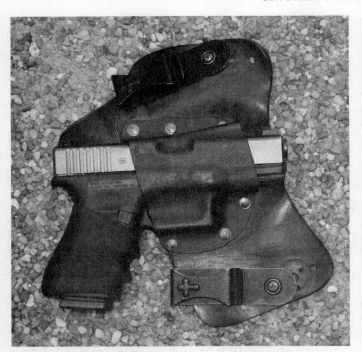

A Crossbreed holster for a Glock 23, seen from outside…

…and from wearer's side.

gun and the wearer is not new. It goes back at least to the Shadow Concealment holster of years ago, now produced as the LAW Concealment holster. The good news and the bad news existed then, and remain for this type of holster.

The good news is that the shield does indeed protect the wearer from the sharp-edged gun, and the gun from the sweaty wearer. The bad news is that the side of the pistol's grip area is pressed tight against the leather shield, and the fingers have to dig between the two to gain a drawing grasp. This very definitely slows down the draw.

Honest holster-makers recognize this, and give their customers some options. At Crossbreed, the option is the Combat Grip. The company explains, "The Combat Grip is where we trim away some of the leather from the holster backer. This allows a firmer grasp on the gun during the draw stroke. This modification does sacrifice a little bit of comfort but does increase the draw speed. This is an extra cost option because this cut is made to follow the contour of the slide/grip of the individual firearm and varies from one gun to another. Approximately 20% of our customers like this option, the others either have no preference or feel it sacrifices too much comfort."

Raven Concealment is another brand of hybrid, and perhaps best known for combining the concept with not only bare pistols, but those with lights attached. The brand has earned a strong following.

Jason Christensen at Concealment Solutions also makes a hybrid with the option of a light on the gun, the Mamba holster. I find its synthetic backing slows me down less than leather, and for that reason it's my current choice for concealed carry of a full-size Glock with SureFire light attached.

One thing to consider with the backing design on these hybrid holsters is body shape. If there's a spare tire around

Author is fond of this snap-on/snap-off holster for full size Glock, hand-crafted by Cerisse Wilson of Soteria Leather.

your middle, the good news will be that the hybrid's backing will be particularly comfortable. The bad news is that the pressure of the flesh will tend, over time, to roll the material over the back of the slide. On the models where the entire grip-frame is shielded by the backer, it may eventually start rolling over the backstrap of the grip frame itself. This won't just slow the draw, it can stall it or cause a "fatal fumble" when you need the pistol most. A minimal backing will be more important for those with this type of body shape.

This N82 holster uses cushioned synthetic material for complete backing, creating a total shield between gun and wearer. Pistol is one of the author's Glock 30s.

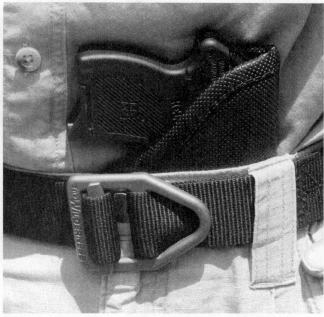

Slim Beretta Nano 9mm carries comfortably at centerline inside the waistband with Remora holster.

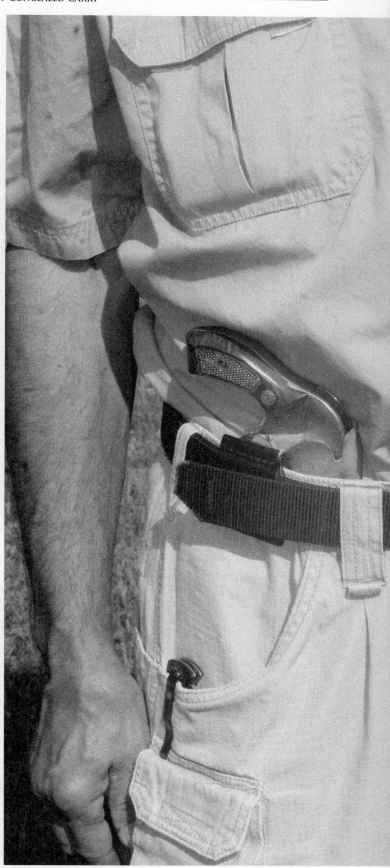

Recommended by such famous instructors as "Southnarc," Todd Louis Green, and Gabe Suarez, "appendix carry" is seeing an upsurge in popularity today. Here's a Bobby Mac IWB holster carrying S&W Bodyguard Airweight .38 in that position.

Crossbreed holster with body shield, here with
full size S&W M&P 9mm.

Women's Holsters

More attention has been paid to women's holsters in the
last few years, due to the welcome surge in females availing
themselves of the armed lifestyle. "Bra holsters" used to
be a novelty item that tended to be designed by men and
bought by men for women who never wore them because
they rarely worked. Recently, Lisa Looper came out with the
Flashbang, which carries a small handgun with the barrel
parallel to the ground and beneath and between the breasts.
The cover garment is pulled upward with the free hand, as
the gun hand takes a firing grasp on the pistol and snaps it
down and out of the holster and toward the threat. If she
has to fire, the sequence is "flash" the assailant, and "bang,"
hence the Flashbang's appropriate name. Not shaped to test
it myself, I've relied on gun-wise women who've tried it to

(right) For good looks, you can't beat leather, and author found this rig very comfortable, concealable, and fast. Outside is sharkskin...

(bottom right) ...and this is the facing side. Holster by Andrews Custom Leather for Wilson Combat, here holding author's S&W 1911 .45.

(below) This Kydex rig from Devin Wulle at White Dog Holsters rides tight enough for good concealment, is fast enough to win IDPA matches. Pistol is S&W M&P.

New and useful: Lisa Looper's "Flashbang," which author considers to be the first viable "bra holster."

give me their opinions and, to my surprise, two out of three liked it very much. One found the little Ruger LCP .380 she tried it with would occasionally hang up. I'm not in a position to know whether that was a problem with the bra or the holster. There are lots of satisfied female customers out there for it, though, and Lisa also has come up with a belt holster shaped for women, which she calls The Sophia. I think Flashbang holsters are here to stay.

Ms. Looper's Sophia holster is leather – the old ways have not yet yielded entirely to Kydex. Among other things, leather gives a more quiet draw than Kydex when surreptitiousness might be the key to survival – and I've had good luck with another female holster-maker's artistry in leather, Cerisse Wilson of Soteria Leather. She made a very nice rig for my Glock 17, conveniently quick-on/quick-off in the Alessi CQC style which I believe was first designed by my friend and colleague Dave Spaulding, and handsome enough that I wore the Soteria holster during the making of a recent training film.

A male Kydex craftsman, Devin Wulle at White Dog Holsters, makes some very nice "just for women" custom designs. My girlfriend, a state and regional IDPA champion, uses White Dog for daily concealed carry with her Springfield XD(m), and is extremely happy with it. The White Dog holsters for men have made a lot of friends, too. I have one for a Smith M&P auto which carries very comfortably, is very fast, and conceals very well.

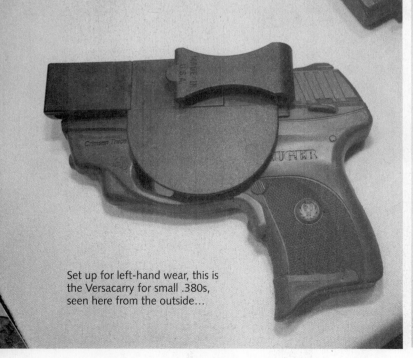

Set up for left-hand wear, this is the Versacarry for small .380s, seen here from the outside…

…from the wearer's side…

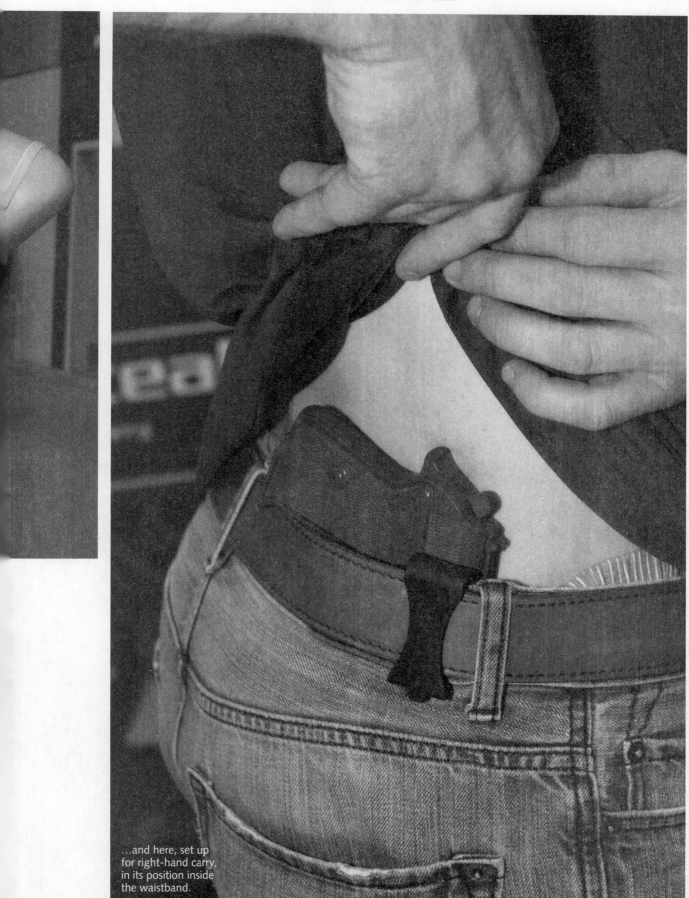

...and here, set up for right-hand carry, in its position inside the waistband.

Remora Holsters

A new concept since the first edition of this book is the Remora holster. Alan Bogden was starting his research on this product about the time the first edition came out. Using a tacky synthetic substance, the Remora is a pouch that can serve as a very effective pocket holster, but is designed to carry the handgun primarily inside the waistband. As advertised, it uses no clip or other belt attachment. I've carried guns ranging from little "slim-nine" 9mm autos to the Glock 30 in .45 with appropriately-sized Remoras, and found them to stay in place yet still be quick to draw from.

Nothing is perfect, but Bogden tries to please his customers. Some of them wanted a shield; he came out with a version that had one. My own big complaint was that the standard model collapsed upon the draw and made reholstering difficult; he came out with one that had a reinforced mouth, which allowed tactical one-handed reholstering.

One thing I discovered (don't ask me how I discovered it) was that when you pull your pants down for whatever reason, the holster and gun fall, since they are not directly attached to the belt or pants. Solution: remember to hold the gun and holster when you drop your drawers. Having worn the Remora crossdraw behind the hip, at centerline, and in the appendix position, I've been happy with it and found it a very useful, moderately priced addition to the concealed carry holster wardrobe. It may be named after a suckerfish for its tenacity in staying in place, but this Remora definitely doesn't suck.

Remora holster, here with .45 caliber Glock 30.

The Remora can also serve as a pocket holster.

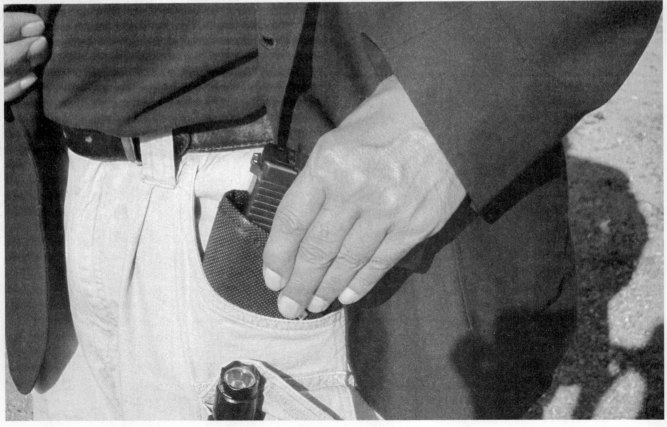

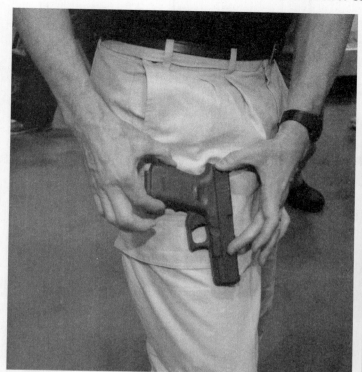

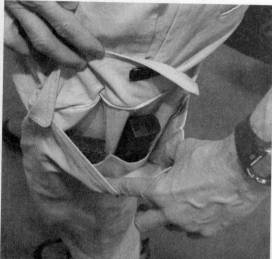

(left) Here's how the pistol lies inside CCW Breakaway pants, slightly forward of the trouser seam, allowing concealment of full size auto pistol.

(below) Accessory carrier for spare magazines, flashlight, etc. is available for CCW Breakaway pants.

(bottom) Here's the Breakaway feature in action on CCW Breakaway pants.

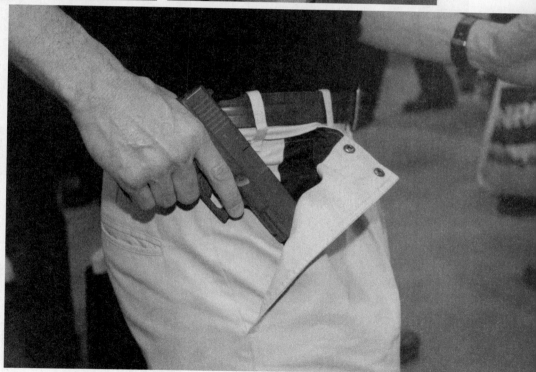

Breakaway Pants

New since the first edition are the CCW Breakaway Pants of Jay and Georgann French. Cut to resemble casual slacks of the Dockers breed, these have snaps around the pocket which when pulled, clear away a large part of the outer trouser leg to reveal a full size handgun such as a Glock 22 or a 1911 Government Model. The draw is sort of a combination of pocket draw and thigh holster draw, with the gun riding a little more forward than in either usual pocket or thigh carry. I know multiple concealed carry professionals who swear by this new concept already. CCW Breakaways are clearly catching on.

Versacarry

Another popular new design is the Versacarry, an ingenious little contraption of metal and plastic that carries the gun inside the waistband, surrounded by neither leather nor synthetic, but instead held in place by a rod that extends upward through the barrel. Attachments shield the triggerguard area for safety. Good news: this minimalist design does away with a layer of holster material and feels very much like just the gun in the waistband, with only the width of a belt clip added. So long as the bore diameter is the same, you can use the same Versacarry to hold your long auto pistol or your short one. (Revolver models are not offered at this writing, but may be available by the time you read this.) Bad news: the manufacturer recommends that the holster be removed and the gun inserted, rather than reholstering in the normal fashion after the gun has been drawn, and further advises, "Do not carry any semi-auto firearm in a cocked and locked condition, or with a live round (in the chamber)." For some of us concealed carriers, that's a deal breaker.

I didn't list websites for the above, because I've found those sometimes change over time. A Google search for "Versacarry holster," "White Dog holsters," etc. should get you where you need to go.

WARDROBE FACTORS

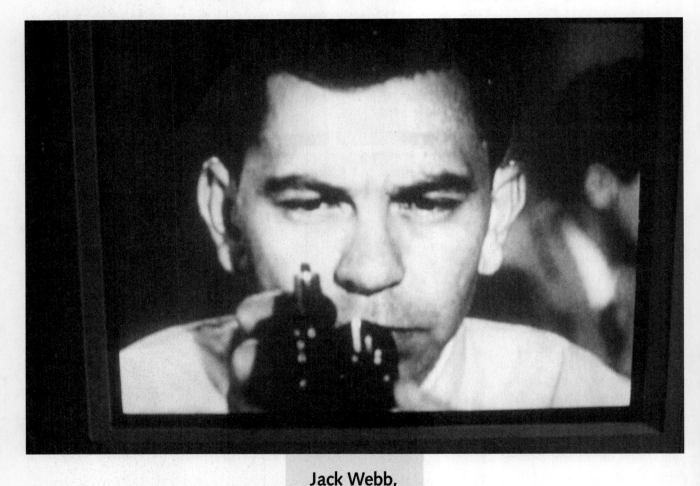

Jack Webb, shown here checking his Colt Detective Special on an old Dragnet, set more fashion trends for CCW people than he probably ever knew.

The clothing you wear is obviously going to be critical to discretion and comfort when you are carrying a concealed weapon. It's all a little more subtle than "big coats hide more hardware easier than small coats."

First, it's a given that "concealed means concealed." If only 5 percent of the gun is exposed, does that mean it's 95 percent concealed? No, it means that if someone can see that you're carrying a gun, even if only a small portion of the gun – or the gun's distinctive outline – is visible, the gun is 100 percent "exposed" and 0 percent concealed.

Here are a few random tips from 47 years of carrying a concealed handgun…

Jackets

Learn from LAPD. I hate to keep invoking Hollywood, but get some of the old videos of Jack Webb's *Dragnet* series. You'll note that most of the time, he's wearing black slacks and a tweed sport coat. In the old days of poorly dyed holsters, black dye would wear off the leather and stain the trousers. It didn't show up on black cloth. The solid "hang" of relatively heavy tweed tended not to outline a holstered handgun, and its patterned appearance tended to break up "printing" outlines of a gun beneath the fabric. We see a similar effect with untucked Hawaiian print shirts, checkered garments, etc. Unlike a typical shirt, a tweed or corduroy sport coat has enough substance to its material to often mask the strapping of a shoulder rig's harness, too.

With more casual jackets, something like a plaid hunter's coat works great. The black and red checks catch the eye, and divert attention from gun-shaped bulges.

You don't need James Bond's or Mike Hammer's tailor to conceal your firearm.

Simply get the suitcoat or sport coat slightly larger, i.e, size 44 if you normally wear a size 42. You will get just enough more "drape" to cover a good-size fighting pistol. You will appear to have gained a few pounds through the torso, but won't look like a little boy wearing his daddy's clothing. *This is true of any gun-concealing outer garment, not just sport jackets or suit coats.*

Leave the front of the suit coat or sport coat unfastened as much as possible. This will give a natural, concealing drape to the garment, and will allow the fastest access. With the garment closed in front, you'll have to open it (or pull it up, difficult if not impossible in a garment whose hem falls as low as a sport coat's). If the garment is fastened, fabric is pulled tightly over the gun and tends to outline it, in addition to the slower draw.

Outside pockets of sport jackets and suit coats are a lousy choice for pocket guns. They tend to bulge and sag obviously. Inside breast pockets are a little better, but they will constantly be bumping against your chest and will probably work best in that location with pocket holsters.

Depending on your generation and locale, the term "windbreaker" can describe two different garments. The short "Eisenhower" jacket and the

Author, (left, his Glock invisible in belly-band under tucked shirt), chats with Scott Jordan at SHOT Show about the Scott-E-Vest.

Scott Jordan demonstrates his hi-tech windbreaker. It looks ordinary…

...until you discover the myriad of built-in pockets for electronic whiz-bangs, many sized just right for guns and related gear, all discreetly hidden from view...

heavier "bomber jacket" are less than ideal choices for gun concealment because they are generally cut to stop at the waist or just below, which increases the chance of a hip holster becoming exposed. These styles also tend to have elastic bottom hems, which are contraindicated if you have a gun on or in your belt because the elastic feature pulls the fabric in on the gun and outlines it rather than hiding it.

Nylon jackets of the style known in some places as "warmup jackets" are better, because being "hip length" garments their bottom edges fall much lower, affording better gun concealment.

With any jacket that can close top to bottom, you want to make sure that the bottom portion can be unfastened while the top part remains closed. On a chilly day, when comfort (and sometimes, avoidance of pneumonia!) demands that the chest be covered, you want to be able to get the area below the stomach to clear so you can reach a gun at your strong side hip. If the coat is zipper front, you want two-way zipper design that can let you unzip the

...and even a solar panel that folds down in back, for "green" techno-pistol-packers!

belly part beforehand so you get at that hip holster. If the garment is button front, all the better; button over the chest, but leave everything from the lower edge of the rib cage down unbuttoned.

Nylon windbreakers tend to be "straight cut" and therefore have a straight-down natural drape that conceals large handguns very well. *Caution:* Many such windbreakers will have a drawstring at the bottom. *Remove it!* The loose end of the drawstring can find its way into the trigger guard as you re-holster, setting the stage for an accidental discharge! Don't just tie a knot in the end. Don't just shorten it. *Remove the drawstring!*

Photographer's Vests

Later in this chapter, we'll discuss garments specifically designed for concealing guns. Right now, let's touch on the common fisherman's vest or photographer's vest.

These hit the pistol-packer's fashion mainstream in the 1980s. Light and comfortable depending on material and cut, they give more freedom of movement for things like fist-fighting or shooting from an Isosceles stance than any regular jacket, since they generally don't bind at the shoulders when the arms extend.

Watch out for many of the true lightweight vests, which have mesh on the back and sides for comfort. The gun and holster can become visible through the mesh. They're probably not ideal for shoulder holsters, either, since the harness straps can become visible at the armhole of any sleeveless vest. I only know one top gun guy who ever wears a shoulder holster with just a vest, and with a badge

The tighter your clothes fit, the more snug to the body you need to carry the gun. This is author's full-size SIG P226, in IWB LFI Concealment Rig.

Size of gun vis-à-vis type of clothing help dictate holster choice. Pistol is full-size Dave Lauck 1911 45 with light rail. Holster options are, from left: Kydex OWB for looser-fitting outer garments; Leather Arsenal Quad Concealment with ITB capability for tighter fitting clothes; and Secret Squirrel IWB for when clothing is even "lighter and tighter."

last vest-wearing good guy is shot on sight by the Storm Troopers with ray guns, the princess is captured.

But that "happened long, long ago, on a planet far, far away…"

Vests, like other garments, should be purchased at least one size large, and side vents are to be avoided. Make sure they go down far enough to conceal a hip holstered gun: a surprising number of these, especially the cheap ones, are cut to waist length rather than hip-length.

Shirts

Tucked-in shirts, such as dress shirts, should not be tightly tapered and form-fitting if you're carrying a gun. Even if your gun is concealed by an outer garment instead of a holster, a too-tight shirt can bind the upper body and restrict your range of movement if you're fighting for your life … and if you don't see yourself ever fighting for your life, why do you carry a gun in

and ID card in one pocket, he's not particularly concerned about concealment anyway.

There is a very popular belief in the "gun culture" that because so many of our kind wear these vests, they have become a mark of the gun carrier. Some call them "shoot me first" vests.

I dunno about that. I've been wearing them for more than twenty years, and never had that sort of problem. I've seen them worn (and sold!) in airports. The many pockets and high comfort factor make them great "traveling vests." You'll see them all over the place at Disney World and other "gun-free zones."

I've never heard of a documented case of a "shot him first" case in which a good guy was shot by surprise by a bad guy who "made him" as such. The only such case I've ever seen was fictional.

Remember the first Star Wars movie? Princess Leia and her bodyguards, who are wearing a uniform that includes a vest that looks remarkably like the ones under discussion, are fighting a losing battle against the Storm Troopers of the evil Empire led by Darth Vader. When the

Floral print sport shirts, if they aren't too loud for your taste, are great for concealing guns.

the first place?

If the tucked-in shirt is going to conceal a handgun in a Kramer undershirt, a belly-band, or a "tuckable" holster, it needs to be loose fitting and kind of "blousy" at the appropriate areas, i.e., the shoulder/armpit region if the gun is there, or at the waist if the gun is at belt level. You want an *opaque* shirt, such as an Oxford fabric. Pinstripes will help break up the outline.

If you carry in a belly-band or tuckable, one of the fastest locations is front cross-draw. Without pulling the shirt loose, you can knife the hand right in there with the movement martial artists call a "spear hand." This generally means leaving the second button above the belt unfastened. A necktie will generally cover this minor breach of style etiquette and let you off with only a warning from the Fashion Police. If you're serious about it, sew that button to the outside and secure that part of the shirtfront opening with a bit of Velcro. However, be advised that the ripping sound will alert people, and may prevent a surreptitious draw or low-profile hand-on-gun state of readiness.

If you decide to carry under an *un-tucked* shirt, concealed carry life just got a whole lot easier for you. Again, whether the shirt is tee or polo or button-front style, get it about one size larger than normal. This is partly to give you more concealing "drape" at the beltline, and partly to give the hem of the garment more range of movement to come up when you have to clear it out of the way to make the draw. A fabric with some stretch to it is a bonus; you want to be able to pull it up high enough to clear the gun. Not just above the butt of the holstered pistol, but high enough for the gun to come up and out and on target without being impeded.

Floral print sport shirts, if they aren't too loud for your taste, are great for concealing guns. Their patterns break up the underlying outlines. Mike Venturino and Roy Huntington at *American Handgunner* magazine have, almost jokingly, raised the profile of this sort of garment among serious CCW folks.

If the untucked shirt has a button front, you want the area of the lowest button to be unfastened. Some such shirts come that way: the Woolrich Elite line offers one. The ancient but still popular *guyebarra* shirt comes that way, perhaps a heritage from a culture where it was common for men to carry pistols in their waistbands. Old style American bowling shirts can still be had that are cut in the same way, with a straight bottom and a generous drape, and sometimes without the lower button and buttonhole in the usual place. Intended to allow range of bending and arm movement for bowling, they turn out to be great for pistol-packing.

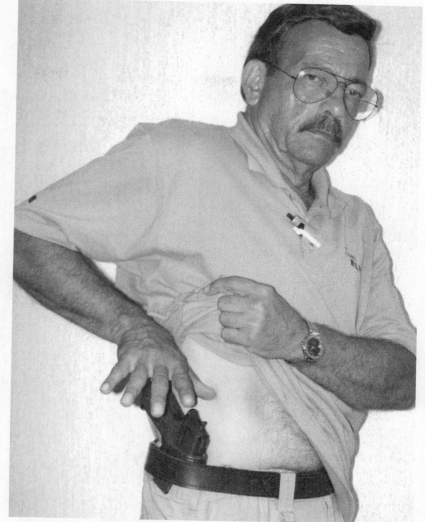

A polo shirt one size large gives enough drape to cover full-size SIG duty pistol in IWB holster, here an LFI Concealment Rig inside a Safariland Velcro belt. Clothing is by Woolrich Elite, on whose factory competition shooting squad, Team Elite, Ayoob shot in 2007.

Pants

If you're carrying inside the waistband, get the trousers two inches larger in the waistband than your actual waist measurement. As discussed elsewhere in this book, doing this adds greatly to your comfort. It also "keeps you honest" by encouraging you to always wear your gun, if only to keep your pants from feeling as if they're about to fall down.

When buying any sort of pants, make sure the belt loops are "gun compatible."

The loops need to be large enough to allow a substantial gun belt, and in appropriate positions to allow the holster to ride exactly where you want it. You'll want the dress gun belt to be a minimum of an inch and a half wide, and loops that will take an inch and three-quarter belt are a plus.

With any sort of belt holster, make sure the belt is wide enough, and fastened snugly enough. Otherwise, the holster will sag downward and the gun butt will tilt outward, severely compromising discreet concealment.

If you're going to carry inside the waistband, make sure there's room for you and the gun and holster, and perhaps a spare magazine pouch, too. As a rule of thumb, you want the pants two inches wider in the waist than you would normally wear them without a gun in your waistband.

No matter what the men's fashion magazines may say, side vent suit coats and sport coats are permanently "out of style" for those who carry in hip holsters. The gun butt will work its way through the vent and expose itself. A middle of the back holster will do the same with a center vent.

Black pants stain less. Again, flash back to those *Dragnet* reruns and notice how often Jack Webb's "Sergeant Friday" is wearing black pants. In the old days, poorly dyed leather "bled" its coloring onto clothing, especially when people got hot and sweaty. Gun oil can drain out from the muzzle end and stain the garment. Black shows it less.

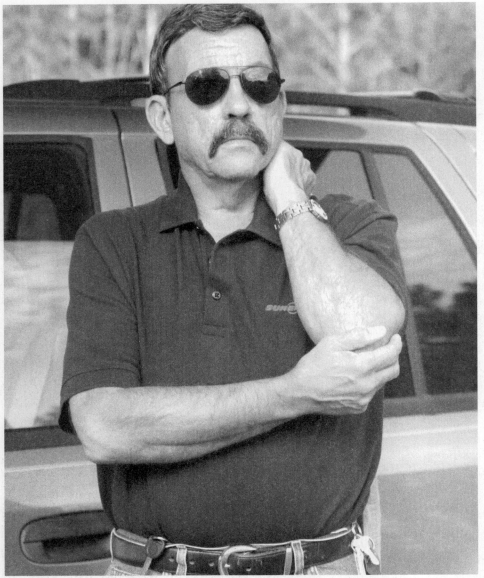

Weapon placement helps you interface with clothing options. Full size Beretta 92 and spare magazine are invisible behind author's hips, but to conceal from sides and rear, he'll need to don that vest he's holding over his shoulder.

replacement pockets made of a heavy fabric called "cotton drill," designed for uniform and work pants. Good quality BDUs (cargo pants) will have these already. You don't need to sew in the canvas and leather pockets that were "custom gun wear" for the gunfighters of long ago. When you are looking at the pants at the clothing store, insert your hand into the front pants pocket with the fingers extended, until the fingertips hit bottom on the pocket. The opening of the pocket should now be up just a little past your wrist. If they pass this test, they're deep enough to properly conceal a snub-nose revolver or a small autoloader in a pocket holster without any of the gun showing.

Pleated casual dress pants of the style popularized by Dockers are "in" at this writing. They drape enough in the thighs that they're ideal for pocket carry, and the cuffs seem to be amenable to ankle holsters as well.

In conventional brands, Carhartt and Wrangler have very strong adherents. The latter company makes "work casual" pants with leather-reinforced pockets that work beautifully with tactical folding knives designed like Sal Glesser's pioneering Spyderco Clipit. Some gun owners prefer not to purchase Dockers or Levis on the grounds that the manufacturers are anti-gun. If that's the case, any designs they have that you like are almost certainly replicated in someone else's product line.

Gun-Specific Clothing

On the October day in 1881 when the Earp faction met the Clantons near the OK Corral, Wyatt Earp put his long-barrel Colt revolver in his coat pocket with his hand on it. It helped him to be among the first to get his weapon into action at the historic "Gunfight at the OK Corral." The mackinaw-style denim coat had just arrived, on special order. Earp had specified an extra-deep, heavy pocket that could discreetly contain a large revolver.

John Wesley Hardin, believed by some to have been the deadliest gunfighter of the Old Frontier, liked to wear a vest he had designed (and possibly made) himself. It had leather gun pockets rib-cage-high on either side, with revolver butts facing forward. It was not a concealment vest; rather, he concealed the vest and the twin revolvers under a coat.

Today's holsters may not "bleed" (the good ones, anyway), but they can still seep gun oil. A big concern is the skeletal Yaqui Slide design. If you've been shooting, each time the gun goes into the holster, carbon on the barrel or slide can transfer onto the trouser fabric. Since that stuff is black, it'll show up less on black pants.

If you might be wearing an ankle holster, you want straight leg cuffs at the very least, and no tapered leg or pegged bottom styles. In jeans or cords, "boot cut" is the minimum that will give you access, and "flared cuffs" are better. Standard American cut men's suit pants and police uniform pants will have the proper cut, and BDU/"cargo" pants also generally have cuffs of sufficiently generous size and shape to work well with an ankle holster.

The pockets of the trousers want to be deep, and made of strong material. A seamstress or clothing store can access

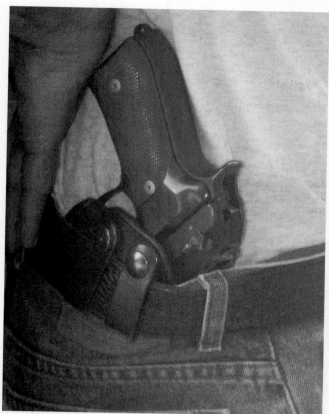

By angling Milt Sparks IWB holster to put butt of Beretta 92G pointing distinctly upward, wearer makes it easier for clothing to cover the pistol discreetly.

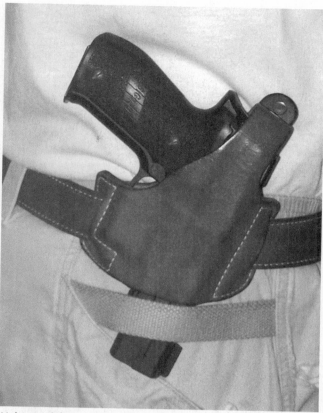

Holster stabilizer strap on 5.11's hugely and deservedly popular BDUs, seen here applied to thumb-break belt-slide by Ted Blocker that holds SIG P226R.

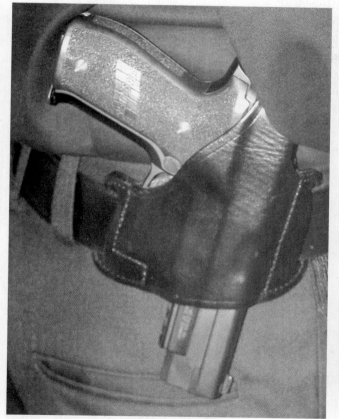

A caution with belt-slide holsters: if gun is covered with carbon from a long session at the range, some of the black crud may wipe off onto your pants.

CCW-ers often carry tactical folding knives with pocket clips as well. These Wrangler jeans have special leather-reinforced pockets for just such practices. Most regular pants quickly get frayed at this spot from the knife clips.

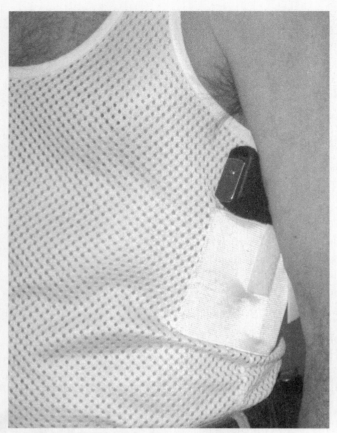

Yes, CCW people have their own special underwear. This undershirt by Greg Kramer, the Confidante, has holster pocket for small handgun sewn in under each armpit. This one holds 9mm Kahr PM9 lightweight subcompact for shoulder holster-like draw through concealing dress shirt.

Yes, clothing expressly designed for gun concealment goes back a long way. Today, it's a small but fascinating cottage industry…and, apparently, a growing one.

Concealed Carry Clothiers has an excellent line that includes models with pockets lined with a semi-stiff synthetic, to hold a small handgun. My favorite in the line is the Tropical, which feels as close as you're going to get to wearing no outer garment at all. This line also offers vests that aren't festooned with pockets, which is much more to some folks tastes than the "tactical" look of a many-pocketed vest.

5.11, with their line formerly known as Royal Robbins, really kicked off the tactical vest market. Their vests are expressly designed for carrying heavy equipment such as radios, guns, and spare ammunition. (For ordinary folks, the elasticized vertical pouches at the rear are perfect for holding water bottles.) The only flaw I can find with them (since they offered a lighter one than their original, which was too heavy for warm weather wear) is that the snap-flap on the inside, designed to hold a gun-carrying system, can catch on the butt of a handgun carried in a belt holster, and slow the draw. If that's a problem, just cut it away and you're good to go. They pioneered the front thigh level pockets that are great for spare magazines and cell phones, and they're no longer on the wrong side. I'm not sold on the band over the rear pocket that's supposed to help stabilize a holster, but they popularized the brilliant concept of deep hip pockets with a diagonal slash that lets the hand get past the holster and into that pocket for one's handkerchief or whatever.

EoTac is captained by firearms/ammo industry veteran

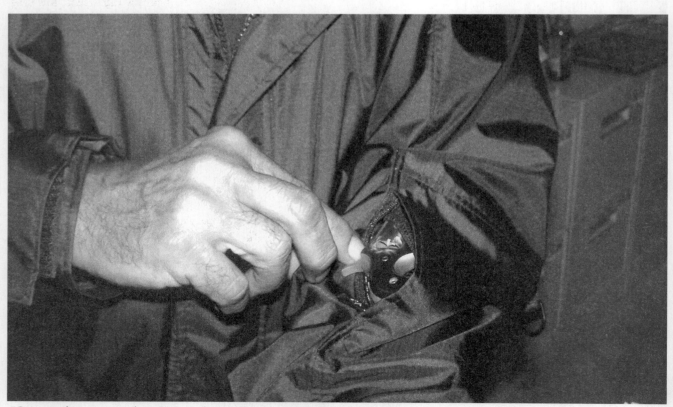

"Got something up your sleeve?" Actually, yes. If you'll look carefully, the tiny sleeve pocket on Scott-E jacket…

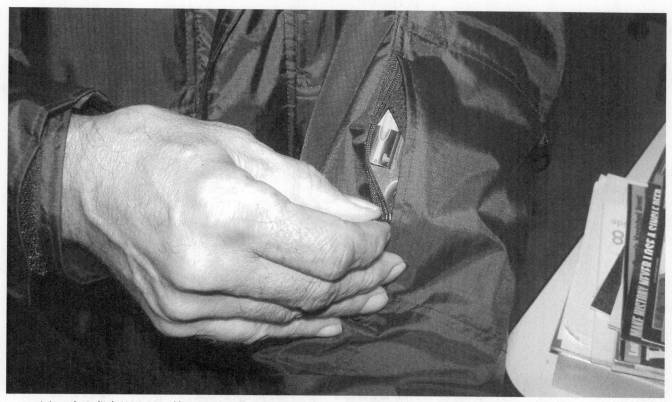

… contains a last-ditch NAA 22-caliber mini-revolver.

Fernando Coelho, who brought in a top beta-testing team of real world professionals to help with design. The result is a superb line of pants, shirts, and trousers for those who go armed. The pants can be had in BDU style (one version of which has tiny outer pockets at ankle level, which Velcro shut and can more or less comfortably carry a Kel-Tec 32), or in a Docker's style casual dress pant. Elastic judiciously applied at the waist helps allow for IWB holsters, and the belt loops are well placed. I've found Coelho's weatherproofing superior, with rainwater beading up on the outer surface of the fabric, but with no discomfort that we normally associate with "non-breathing" waterproof clothing. The shirts are comfortable, heavy duty, and sport useful hidden pockets. The casual dress shirt, mentioned above, has a Velcro attachment at the bottom of its buttoned front and just the right amount of clearance for drawing from a hip holster.

If jeans are more to your taste, Blackie Collins designed a neat pair. They're called Toters. Each front pocket is actually two pockets, and reinforced for carrying guns therein. The waist is generously cut for IWB holsters, and the cuffs are just right for ankle rigs. I've worn out two pair, not because they aren't sturdy, but because I found myself wearing them that much. They come with knife pockets, too; Blackie Collins is first and foremost a knife designer.

> **Dang…we've got our own boutique wear for pistol packers. The CCW culture has come a long way!**

SIG-Tac has a very good series of "designer gun wear," too. If you carry a long barrel pistol on the hip, the SIG-Tac vest is a great way to go: it's longer than most, and therefore gives such a combination the best possible "coverage."

Scott-E-Vest makes a high-speed, low-drag, way-cool series of garments that he designed originally for "techies." There are pockets for the PDA, the iPod, the cell phone, you name it…tubes for electronics and hidden radios and BlueTooths…and even a fold-out solar back panel that gathers energy for your batteries. While not designed expressly for pistol packers, this line has ingenious hidden pockets that folks in the CCW lifestyle can make use of. Inventor Scott Jordan has some high quality chino-style dress slacks with double hidden pockets similar to the Toters, but in higher style. Magnetic closures hold the "secret pocket" shut, while the parallel pocket beneath it is conventionally open. Material is excellent, and the pocket lining works fine with small handguns in pocket holsters. One of his jackets even comes with a hidden sleeve pouch that's just the right size for an NAA mini-revolver.

Blackhawk also has a new line of tactical wear. I haven't had a chance to work with it much, but it's promising, and the company certainly has both the financial and the human resources to run with the best in the business on this kind of stuff.

Dang…we've got our own boutique wear for pistol packers. The CCW culture has come a *long* way!

IDPA:
HOW IT HELPS THE CONCEALED CARRY PRACTITIONER

In IDPA, you get a chance to watch the best in action, and try to beat them. Here the legendary Jerry Miculek draws his S&W 45 revolver in a blur as he bolts from seated start position en route to winning 2006 IDPA National Championships, Enhanced Service Revolver division.

Founded in 1996, the International Defensive Pistol Association (IDPA) was created so those who carried conventional, concealed handguns would have a venue for testing their skills in deploying them. Its founders were all distinguished alumni of the International Practical Shooting Confederation (IPSC) and members in good standing of that organization's arm in the United States, the U.S. Practical Shooting Association (USPSA).

Forgive all of that alphabet soup, but it helps to know the background. The late, great Jeff Cooper laid the groundwork for IPSC with the open gunfight simulation competition he and his colleagues pioneered in California in the mid-1950s, and Jeff was the prime mover

As in real life, IDPA sometimes gives you targets that are "down but not out." Ken Ortbach "finishes the fight" with flame blooming from his S&W Model 686 4-inch .357 as he wins the 2007 Pennsylvania State Championship, Stock Service Revolver division.

You won't find props this elaborate on your backyard range. At 2006 Nationals, Terri Strayer shoots around an overturned automobile.

Automobiles figure in street gunfights, so they figure in IDPA. Author moves out of path of car as he fires at "armed occupant," using his department-issue Ruger 45 and Safariland security holster, and then…

… in another stage, has to fire from inside the car outward. Note flying glass as 45 slugs smash through rear window. Photos taken at 2007 Pennsylvania State Championships.

In this stage at the 2007 Florida State Championship, Jon Strayer has to fire from elaborately constructed "rocking boat." Weapon is S&W 625 45 ACP, backed with moon clips and Blade-Tech holster. Jon won ESR Champion title.

in the creation of IPSC some twenty years later. IPSC started with "street guns" in "street holsters," but because rules were left open to encourage innovation, competitive enthusiasm took over. Soon the gun it took to win a match was a huge pistol with a widened magazine chute big enough to be a flower-pot, an optical sight on top, exotic recoil compensation devices that might blind the shooter if fired from a retention position in real world self-defense, and a pure speed holster so huge it would take Count Dracula's Cape to conceal it.

USPSA eventually caught onto that, and now has competition categories that allow ordinary stock firearms to compete effectively, though concealment is still not required. However, IDPA struck a responsive chord when founded by Bill Wilson and a board that included street-smart Walt Rauch, renowned combat handgun expert Ken Hackathorn, and some other knowledgeable authorities. It remains one of the most popular and fastest-growing handgun games in the country today.

IDPA In Context

IDPA's founders and directors are clear on their purpose. *IDPA is a sport and a skill test, not a training course!* Certainly, you can learn from it. But, really, any skill test should be a learning experience.

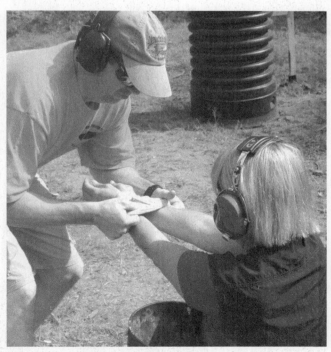

In real life, access to guns has saved captives of criminals. Here, range officer binds hands of FL/GA Regional Woman IDPA Champion Gail Pepin with heavy elastic…

In IDPA as in real life, one hand is often encumbered. Norm Ambrozy fires his S&W M&P 9mm one-handed while maintaining control of "attaché case with priceless contents" with other hand, at 2007 Florida State Championships.

...and she awaits start signal with gun at bottom of bucket at 2007 New England Regional Championships ...

...and on signal, retrieves her 9mm Glock 34 and engages her "armed captors" with her hands still literally bound.

Like real life, IDPA forces you to shoot from less than ideal positions. Here former national champ Tom Yost has to take one foot completely off the ground to get a shot at his last "opponent" at New England Regional Championships, 2007.

Understand that you are not necessarily there to be the next national champion. Those titles have been held by some of the greatest combat handgunners in history: Ernest Langdon, Rob Leatham, Jerry Miculek, Dave Sevigny, Scott Warren, and more. As in most competitions, the majority of entrants are going for a personal goal. Perhaps a personal best, perhaps a trophy in their particular class.

Shooting classifications start at Unclassified and go through Novice, Marksman, Sharpshooter, and Expert, all the way up to Master. While IDPA's shooting *classifications* are performance-driven, the organization's shooting *categories* are determined by the type of gun used. It was understood at the beginning that it would not be a level playing field if Competitor A used a 6-shot revolver against Competitor B with an 18-shot Glock 17 on an 18-shot course of fire, even if both contestants were identical in skill. Because IDPA was created during the period of the onerous Clinton Crime Bill that banned manufacture and sale to civilians of magazines of greater than ten-round capacity, this was established as the uppermost limit for auto pistols. That rule remains in force, not to endorse the Clinton concept by any means, but simply to maintain the level playing field that is essential in any sport.

There were once four handgun categories, and for the

IDPA often has night stages. Here, light beam and gun flame combine as author shoots a darkness stage, defending his New England Regional Stock Service Revolver Champion title in 2007. He lost to Jerry Biggs.

Movement is life in a gunfight, and is required in IDPA. Here, safely holding Glock 34, teenager Randi Rogers sprints toward her next target and the National Woman's Champion title of 2007. Randi, shooting under the monicker "Holy Terror," beat all male contestants at a recent national Cowboy Action Shooting championship.

last few years IDPA has had five, and arguably a sixth. Those categories are as follows, and they pretty much cover anything you're likely to be using in self-defense in the real world.

Stock Service Pistol (SSP). This is the most popular category in the game by far, and has been since IDPA's inception. It encompasses double action semiautomatics of the traditional style, double action only autos, and the Safe Action Glock, which is the single most popular brand in the

category. Calibers may be 9mm Parabellum and up.

Custom Defense Pistol (CDP). This is the home of the classic Cooper gun, the single action, cocked and locked 45 auto. Maximum magazine capacity allowed is eight rounds. A minimum power floor of performance is required that is roughly equivalent to 45 ACP hardball. Shooters with single stack, double-action 45 autos often compete against the single actions in CDP because in SSP, an eleven-shot stage may require them to reload but not the contestant with an

Like real life, IDPA can get complicated. Here, author jumps off-line from no-shoot target and reaches for GP100 in Blade-tech holster as two radio-controlled, knife-armed targets, visible at right, begin to race forward, ducking sideways on curving rails, at 2006 National Championships.

11-shot pistol.

Enhanced Service Pistol (ESP). This category is for single action auto pistols, caliber 9mm and larger. Originally intended for the classic Browning Hi-Power, it tends to be dominated by 9mm, 38 Super, and 40 S&W guns in the 1911 format. It is also the home of the popular Springfield Armory XD, determined by BATF to be a single-action semiautomatic. No more than 10 rounds per magazine, and no more than 11 rounds in the gun to start.

Stock Service Revolver (SSR). Minimum 38 Special caliber, maximum four-inch barrel length, and firing a rimmed cartridge inserted with speedloaders instead of moon clips. A review of such electronic gun boards as www. smith-wessonforum.com show that an amazing number of people carry four-inch service revolvers concealed daily for

self-defense, and more keep them as home defense guns. This is the place to test skill with them. It generally takes a +P 38 load to make the power factor, a minimum figure of 125,000 when velocity is multiplied by bullet weight, the same power floor as in SSP and ESP. The revolver cannot be loaded with more than six rounds at any time.

Enhanced Service Revolver (ESR). When SSR encompassed any six-gun 38-caliber and up, the Smith & Wesson Model 625 revolver kicked butt. That was because it could fire round nose 45 ACP ammo in moon clips, which went into the gun faster than any speedloader could insert rimmed cartridges. Once again, the goal was to level the playing field: these moon clip guns were moved into their own category, ESR. The 625 is *still* the gun to beat there.

Earlier, I said there was arguably a sixth category. That

Shooting on the move is a staple of IDPA, demonstrated here by gunwriter and competitive shooter Chris Christian with S&W M&P at Florida State Championships.

arguable category is Back-Up Gun (BUG). There are *side matches* for these guns, most notably at the National Championships where last year Smith & Wesson provided the Model 640-1 snub-nosed J-frame revolvers that were used in the competition. I shoot IDPA in a lot of places, though, and only one venue has regular BUG stages, and those are usually factored out of the main competition.

A pity, because the two-inch 38 revolver and the small pocket-size auto pistol, the guns that the BUG concept were built around, are perhaps the most popular carry guns out there, yet are not truly represented in mainstream IDPA competition. I for one would like to see it come into its own as a full-fledged gun competition category awarded the same respect as the big autos and revolvers are in IDPA.

What You Get

There's a modest entry fee to join IDPA, and for your first match you don't have to even be a member. After that, a typical local match fee with go about $15 or $20 at this writing. For that, you get to shoot four or six or so live-fire "scenarios" that have been set up elaborately with props. The targets often are "clothed" in tee shirts or similar garb, just as your opponent would likely be in real life. There are cover points that range from automobiles (sometimes fake, sometimes actual cars) to barricades that represent vertical building corners, doors you have to maneuver through, and the whole nine yards. Let your imagination run free: the match designers do. At the last national championship, there was one stage in which an automobile was turned over on its side as part of the scenario.

You might have dummies you have to drag out of the line of fire, and large dolls representing babies you are required to not only carry to safety, but shield with your own body as you do so. You may start pushing a lawn mower, serving food at a barbecue, or burping a "baby" you have to carefully set down before you engage the threat. (If you "spike" the baby like a football, you get the dreaded twenty-second Failure To Do Right penalty added to your time. When I was match director one year for the Mid-Winter Regional IDPA Championship at Smith & Wesson Academy's fine facility in Massachusetts, I had to uphold a range officer's penalty on a contestant who used the "baby" as a human shield between him and the bad guy targets. Sorry, fella, that just ain't the spirit of the defensive handgun game...)

There are moving targets. Pop-up targets. "Gravity turners" that may only expose themselves for a fraction of a second. Steel knockdowns and cardboard silhouettes alike. Because having to shoot vicious animals is a very real scenario for both armed citizens and cops, the cardboard silhouette targets will occasionally be turned over on their sides to represent vicious dogs, or a wolf pack. A friend of mine won the Wisconsin IDPA Championship shooting matches like that, and when he was on patrol one day and had to shoot a wolf that was menacing a group of little girls, he was able to achieve 100-percent hit potential with his department-issue Beretta 92 and kill the beast before fangs reached flesh. He got a commendation out of the deal. He'll tell you that, yes, IDPA is "job-related."

It would cost you a fortune in time and money to set all those scenarios up for yourself. Fifteen or twenty bucks to have someone set it up for you, and time you and score you as you go through? That, brothers and sisters, is a *helluva* deal. Look at some of the props we had to work with at the 2007 Pennsylvania

State Championship hosted by the Ontelaunee Sportsmen's Club, where some of the photos illustrating this article were taken.

The Concealed Weapon Factor

Most IDPA stages will start with the gun concealed. This is one of its most important benefits to the CCW shooter. Where is your gun likely to be when a deadly fight starts if you're not a cop, soldier, or security professional? Why, under a concealing garment. IDPA, *and IDPA alone among the major, established handgun sports,* requires you to begin with your hands away from your body, and *actually get the clothing out of the way and draw the damn thing from concealment!*

Now, this doesn't happen 100 percent of the time, but it's good for maybe 90 percent. In the Classifier shoot (about which more later) that IDPA rules require every member to shoot once a year, no concealment is worn. This is because the range safety officers are assessing pure skill, and they know they'll have a lot of new shooters, and for safety reasons they want to see what the hands are doing when the draw of a loaded handgun is underway. In matches, there will also be stages where the shooter starts (as is often the case in real life) with the gun in a drawer, an attaché case, a backpack, or lying on the ground. In one memorable match, there was a stage where the gun was in a lock box, and the shooter was given the punch-in combination just before the start signal sounded.

I've also been at some matches where brutally hot weather caused the match sponsors to forego the concealment requirement in the name of shooter safety: their concern was heatstroke. That was the case in a match I recently shot at the Central Florida Rifle & Pistol Club in Orlando, FL, where the thermometer was at 97 degrees, the humidity was close to max, and the "heat index" was well over a hundred.

One other exception is that those who carry openly at work (uniformed cops and soldiers, for instance) are allowed to forego the concealment requirement. However, the holster must be suitable for uniform wear and worn with all safety/security devices fastened, and if it's on a police duty belt, there better be handcuffs in the belt pouches. Having shot this way with my department issue double action .45 and Safariland level II security holster, I can tell you that it gives one no competitive advantage over an open-top speed holster concealed under a photographer's vest.

The Use of Cover Factor

History shows us that when bad tactics get good guys killed in gunfights, the failure to use available cover is usually the single biggest of the fatal errors. In IDPA, you are required to have at least half of your upper body behind "cover" if such replicated cover is available on that stage, and your whole lower body behind it as well.

One direction in which competitive shooting went wrong insofar as being a positive learning experience for those who took handguns into harm's way, was in emphasizing speed of shot placement over use of cover. In the real world, as any firefight survivor can tell you, the bullets are going in both directions. The goal is not to shoot the bad guy; the goal is not to get shot. Shooting the bad guy is merely one of your options in achieving the goal of survival.

The emphasis on use of cover in IDPA is, to this reviewer's mind, one of the strongest aspects of the game as far as its value to the person who carries a gun "for real." I was certified as an IDPA Safety Officer several years ago under Mike Briggs, and recently audited another such class by Florida's IDPA go-to guy, Lance Biddle. Both emphasized the importance of staying true to the core concepts of IDPA by assessing penalties on shooters who exposed themselves to what in real life would be incoming fire, unnecessarily.

IDPA rewards speed, accuracy, and smoothness. Laura Torres-Reyes, MD displays all three as range officer holds the timer at '07 New England Regional Championships. Pistol is 9mm Glock 34.

It was good to see. It shows me that, then and now, IDPA is about *Defensive* Shooting more than it's about Defensive *Shooting.*

Real World Factors

The timer is digitally ticking away the seconds. A bunch of people are watching you. Is there stress? *Oh,* yeah! Not necessarily the full-blown fight or flight response that occurs in the true near death experience of the kind you carry a gun to ward off, but yes, there can be big-time stress.

At another fast-paced match of another nature (the first Bianchi Cup in 1979), I found myself on the same relay with a famous big city cop who had survived a number of deadly shootouts. As we walked side-by-side from one stage to another, he said, "(Expletive deleted), I've never felt stress like this in any of my (expletive deleted) gunfights!"

I asked him, "Why do you think that is?"

He replied, rapidly (and, I think, from the heart) "Because there wasn't all this (expletive deleted) time to build up to it, and there weren't all these (expletive deleted) people watching you!"

No, it's not the same as getting shot at and knowing that life can end for you in the next instant. But, ya know what? It *does* condition you to ignore extraneous things and focus on the tasks you need to accomplish right now. History tells us that men and women who focus on such tasks in such terribly dangerous moments are the ones who are most likely to accomplish those tasks, and to survive the threat to their life.

At about fifteen or twenty bucks a dose at local IDPA matches, that's *awfully* cheap for "preventive medicine" that conditions you to function when your hands are shaking, your tongue is stuck to the roof of your mouth, and you're so deep in alligators that you can't remember that

your original intention was to drain the swamp, *and there is a loaded gun in your hand that you must fire **safely**, swiftly, and accurately!*

The Awkwardness of the Real World

One thing I appreciate about IDPA is that it recognizes that while we all love to shoot from our strongest position so we perform well and look good, the real world has an unfortunate way of catching us off guard in awkward positions. IDPA course designers like to start you and me off in such awkward positions. "It's a good thing."

In just the last few months of IDPA shooting, I've had to do the following.

"Shoot through a window from the front seat of the car." I remember the falling glass coming into my field of view as the Ruger 45 came back on target for the next shot. That would be pretty expensive to replicate in my back yard. At the Pennsylvania State IDPA Championships, it came with a moderate entry fee for ten separate stages.

"Draw the gun from this or that odd place." It could happen. My review of the gunfights of Lance Thomas, perhaps the most accomplished Armed Citizen Gunfighter of the 20th Century, didn't show any that started with him making a classic draw from a holster "on Main Street in Dodge City at high noon." In every case, he grabbed one of the several guns he had secreted in tactical locations in his watch shop, to shoot the many armed robbers he put down.

"Grab the gun and shoot while on your back/on your belly/on your knees." Been there, done that in IDPA. It's a real good idea for your brain to be able to say "Been there, done that" when you find yourself in such a position and about to die if you don't get a gun into action and shoot back, right now.

"Expose only what needs to be exposed to aim and fire." The great combat pistol champ Ray Chapman pioneered the concept of coming up on the ball of the opposite foot just enough to get you to where "you can shoot him with impunity, but he'll have a tough time shooting you." This works on the street, and it works – not altogether coincidentally – in IDPA.

"How much do I need the rest of that ammo?" Several shots have been fired. Like most people in actual gunfights, you lost count when it went past three or four. Do you speedload your pistol and leave the few live rounds in the magazine on the ground, or do you take a little extra time to retain that partial magazine before you snap in a fresh one, in case you need those last few rounds as the fight goes on?

"Speed reload" versus "tactical reload" versus "reload with retention" is an argument that can go all night between trained professionals looking at the issue from different, but equally relevant, sides. After having to debate this issue more than any other with its members, IDPA has gone to "any IDPA-approved reload technique" for most matches, and this has cut the Gordian knot. However, the 90-shot Classifier course covers both "tac loads" and "emergency (slide-lock) reloads," as well as shooting while moving forward and

IDPA doesn't address only man-to-man conflict. Here, at '07 PA state shoot, the target array is a "dog pack attack," with knife-armed humanoid target on a swinger at far left.

back, multiple targets, head-shot failure-drills, shooting from both tall vertical and low horizontal cover, and left-hand-only, right-hand-only, *and* two-handed shooting. It is one of the most challenging and comprehensive skill tests you will find.

Specialty Categories

IDPA has categories for high individuals of certain categories: high female, high cop, high soldier, high geezer, etc. These are determined from among *all five gun categories combined,* so you would be wise if you are shooting to win one of these particular awards to use a gun that holds 11 rounds, which puts you in SSP or ESP. There are enough occasional 10- and 11-round stages that guns which have to be reloaded before that many shots are fired will put you at the "have to climb uphill" end of the playing field. Several years ago, I managed to win the Senior Championship at the Mid-Winter Nationals at Smith & Wesson Academy, which were directed by Ken Hackathorn at the time. I did it with an Al Greco-tuned S&W Model 625 45 ACP revolver. But the lesson to learn is, that in all these years, that's the *only* time I've been able to do that with a 6-shot revolver against 9- and 11-shot autos against a highly skilled field. I just had one of those perfect days when everything seemed to go right for me. That is *never* guaranteed. Not at the range, and not on the street.

Don't let anyone else be the role model as to what you'll shoot. Determine your goals, and shoot with the best gun for the job. Personally, I'm a full-time use of force instructor and a part-time cop, and since my students come in with all the different gun types, I shoot with them all. My personal favorite is Stock Service Revolver category. I like the challenge: it's kind of like shooting a single shot or a muzzle-loader during regular deer season. Of course, it also makes it more likely that I'll win the particular gun category, since way more folks shoot autos than revolvers, so there are fewer competitors to beat.

If I was a full-time cop, I would shoot mostly with my duty gun and duty holster, and one time out of every three or four, with my off-duty gun and leather. And if you're an armed citizen getting into this to fine-tune the skills you'll use once the potentially deadly encounter truly comes down to shooting, your smartest course of action is to use the guns you actually carry on the street, the guns you actually keep at home to ward off home invaders.

> **Determine your goals, and shoot with the best gun for the job.**

"You pays your money, and you takes your choice." If you are there to test *your* skill with the handgun *you* are most likely to be using when you have to fire to defend your life or the lives of other innocent people, then *you* decide what you will compete with.

Personally, I'm geared more to training than to competition, and I've found IDPA to be the most useful competitive venue available to me for testing and analyzing the relevant skills. To see if it will be the same for you, check out the organization at www.idpa.com, where you will find references to IDPA-affiliated groups reasonably near you.

Good luck. Keep it all in perspective. And, stay safe!

IDPA is "the concealed carry competition sport." David Sevigny, shown here winning the 2006 National Championship with G34, began IDPA shooting to sharpen his skill with the smaller Glock pistol he was licensed to carry concealed.

FINAL ADVICE

This small-frame S&W 357 was used by the young woman who carries it to ward off two assailants, with no blood shed on either side. Concealed carry was a practice she learned from her mom and dad, and it saved her.

Whether I'm finishing a book or finishing a class, there's a voice in the back of my mind yelling, "Dammit, there wasn't time to cover it all!" I suppose I'll be thinking the same thing on my deathbed. Hell, I suppose we'll *all* be thinking that on our deathbeds.

This is a life study. I've written several books and literally thousands of articles on this, and *still* haven't covered it all. For instance, this book touched little on defensive shooting techniques and skills. For that I'd recommend *The Gun Digest Book of Combat Handgunnery, 6th Edition*, from Krause. In the book you're holding, there wasn't space to go into the different gun platforms in detail, but *The Gun Digest Book of ...* series covers that nicely. My old friend, colleague, and fellow shooting competitor Patrick Sweeney did a great job covering the 1911, the Glock, and the Smith & Wesson line to name three, and I did the Beretta and SIG books. If you own the given brand or are thinking of acquiring it, you'll find the appropriate book from that series useful.

Almost half a century of carrying a loaded, concealed handgun has taught me a few things. Let me say adieu with a final sharing of discoveries.

■ **Never take safety for granted.** You and yours will constantly be in the presence of a loaded, lethal weapon. Kinda like driving a car. Familiarity absolutely does breed contempt. Never lower your guard or your level of care, and think like an engineer: put multiple safety procedures in place, and follow them religiously.

■ **Live in a state of relaxed alertness.** The late, great Col. Jeff Cooper called this Condition Yellow. At any given moment, you know what's going on around you, who's near you, and where you are. He said that a well-adjusted man or woman should be able to spend their entire waking life in Yellow with no adverse psychological effects. I've found it's even better than that. It makes you a people-watcher. You see the good, life-affirming things around you that you were missing before.

Ayoob testifies on behalf of shall-issue concealed carry legislation at a State House. If we don't fight for our rights, he warns, we'll lose them.

■ **Stay current with the topic.** Read the periodicals, particularly *American Handgunner* and *Combat Handguns*. Take classes. There are more good firearms/self-defense training programs available today than ever. We're talking about skills that degrade easily if not refreshed. Don't limit those classes to guns and combat. Adult ed courses in body language, deviant human behavior, and criminology can be rich mines of useful self-defense knowledge.

■ **Commit to always carrying.** If we knew when we were going to need a gun, we'd change our plans and go somewhere safer. Danger comes from out of nowhere and doesn't limit itself to "bad areas." Mass murders take place at good schools, upscale malls, and family restaurants in nice neighborhoods. The only way to make sure the gun will always be there when you need it is to always carry it. Go online to www.handgunlaw.us and commit to getting all the permits you can. The more places you can legally carry, the safer you'll be.

■ **Be prepared, in your heart and mind, to use deadly force if necessary.** It's a long search of the soul, but a critically important one. If you don't know for certain that you can kill a violent attacker if you have to, you're likely to hesitate at the worst possible time, and he'll kill you and

yours instead. Ironically, because predators have a finely tuned sense of what is and is not prey, that commitment seems to transmit. Thus, an irony: the person prepared to kill is less likely to have to do so. The great majority of situations in which armed citizens drew down on criminal suspects have ended with no bloodshed, because the predators sensed they were about to die and either surrendered or fled. They won't surrender or flee if they sense hesitation on the part of their opponent. In LFI classes, I explain the worst of the aftermath and how to deal with it, so the student can get that out of the way and be prepared to act instantly if the moment ever comes. If you haven't sorted it out beforehand, the fight will happen too fast for you to come to terms with the cosmic act of ending another human life.

■ **Fight to keep your rights and privileges.** There are those in this society who work in a tireless, well-funded, concerted effort to deprive you and your children of the right to self-protection. You have a genuine duty to "you and yours" to fight that. Whether or not you appreciate the National Rifle Association, join and support the NRA: they literally coined the term "armed citizen," and they are the strongest voice for those citizens' rights in Washington. Personally, I have served for many years on the board of trustees of the Second Amendment Foundation, and do what I can to support the highly effective grassroots gun-owners' groups at the state level. This is about civil rights. It's about human rights. The great authority on the common law, Lord Blackstone, said "Self-defense is the highest of all human rights." Work hard to keep it, because powerful forces don't want you and your descendants to have it.

■ **Maintain a logical perspective.** I don't know if you in particular are going to need what's in these pages. I do know that some of you are. My paternal grandfather came to these shores in the year 1896, and in every generation since, at least one member of my linear family has been saved from death or great bodily harm by the ability to produce a loaded handgun when attacked on the street. And even if that never happens to you, your commitment to concealed carry will have bought you a lifetime of peace of mind, and there's no dollar price to put on something that precious.

I'm out of time. You're not. Continue your learning in this life study. Share it with others. Fight to keep your rights and privileges.

Good luck. Stay safe, and keep your loved ones safe.

– Massad Ayoob, December 2007

KEY PRINCIPLES

It is wise for the individual who lawfully carries a concealed handgun in public to keep a few things foremost in mind.

Know the laws governing concealed carry *where you are at any given time,* and follow them religiously. "Gun crimes" committed by those licensed to carry are extremely rare, but of those that occur, a huge percentage involve people who simply "forgot they were armed" when they entered an area where the practice was legally forbidden.

Concealed means concealed. Yes, I know it's a trite and hackneyed phrase, but it carries a lot of truth. Our society is such, like it or not, that the presence of an obviously lethal weapon in the hands of someone not readily identifiable as an "official protector" frighten people. Someday, if you haven't already, you'll buy a newspaper or a candy bar from a convenience store clerk who was terrorized by an armed robber who menacingly drew his coat back to reveal a weapon. If you accidentally do the same, can you blame her for her predictable reaction? The results won't be good for either of you.

Keep it quiet. The fewer people who know you carry a gun, the better. You don't want to be caught up in the middle of an armed robbery where the multiple offenders with drawn guns hold all the cards, and have a terrified victim look at you and scream, "My God, you've got a gun, *do* something!"

The potential for false accusations is endless. You don't want an employee you fired for incompetence to vengefully go to the police and swear out a complaint saying, "And then my boss pulled out a snub-nose .38 from inside his shirt and pointed it between my eyes!" When the police come and find you carrying that kind of gun in just that place, you're behind the eight-ball. I've seen a false accusation of aggravated assault leveled at a man solely because another motorist, in a state of road rage, spotted the NRA decal on his car, correctly assumed he would have a gun with him, and told the police falsely that the good guy had pointed a gun at him without provocation. It took that good man about fifty grand in non-refundable legal fees and costs to win an acquittal on the felony charges.

Don't carry a "CCW" badge. Sold in great numbers to well-meaning CCW permit-holders, these are seen by police and prosecutors (and the general public and the jury pool) as "fake badges." At best you look like a wanna-be trying to play cop. At worst, you fit the profile of criminals from home invaders to child molesters who impersonate a police officer in the course of heinous offenses. That's not a profile you ever want to fit.

Avoid trouble more than ever. Under the "higher standard of care" principle, the armed private citizen is seen as having a particular duty to avoid conflicts – shouting matches, upraised middle fingers, curses – and is expected to de-escalate rather than "keep the ball rolling," let alone offering provocation.

Gain familiarity and competence with your weapon and carry system. A life or death situation is no time for fumbling. Practice with empty or dummy guns to gain smooth speed of draw from concealment. Some supervised live fire speed work (training, or an IDPA competition) will boost both confidence and competence with your concealed handgun. Train and practice as frequently as you can, to make the mechanics of drawing (and, if necessary, firing) as much second nature as possible.

Prepare for the totality of the circumstances. Make sure that those most likely to be with you if an armed encounter takes place know what to do. Always have a plan in case you have to remove your weapon and secure it, which can arise from anything from an unexpected trip to the Courthouse for routine paperwork, to an auto accident in which you had to be transported to a hospital by ambulance.

Be vigilant about gun safety. Familiarity breeds contempt. Put layer after layer of safety into your daily handling and carrying practices. Remember Jeff Cooper's Four Rules. (1) All guns are always (considered) loaded. (2) Never point the gun at anything you are not prepared to see destroyed. (3) Never touch the trigger until the gun is on target and you are in the act of intentionally firing. (4) Always be certain of your target and what is behind it. Remember that the responsibility to keep your weapon out of incompetent and/or unauthorized hands falls solely upon *you.*

Remember why you carry. The gun is there to protect your loved ones, and to keep you alive to return to them. Just as its presence is a constant reminder of your responsibilities, let the presence of that deadly weapon also be a constant reminder of the importance of the loved ones in your life. Consciously or subconsciously, this recognition is one reason that those who carry guns seem to be among not only the most responsible people in this society, but the most caring and compassionate.

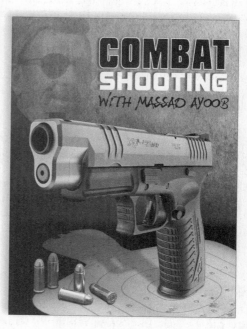
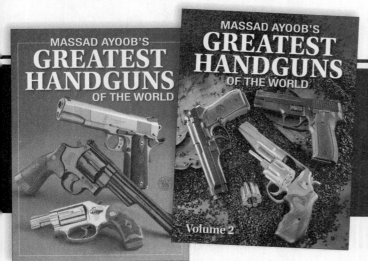